12-5-61

NEW MEXICO BIRDS

TOTAL AREA OF STATE: 121,666 SQUARE MILES

REPRESENTATIVE BREEDING BIRDS SHOWN ON FACING PAGE

13,160

HUDSONIAN - ARCTIC—ALPINE ZONE

AREA: Approximately 159 square miles.

AVERAGE ANNUAL PRECIPITATION: 26 to 32 inches, including 20 to 25 feet of snow.

AVERAGE (MEAN) TEMPERATURE: 26.9° F.

TREES: Dwarf Spruce, Foxtail Pine, Willow.
  Treeless above 12,000 feet elevation.

CHARACTERISTIC BIRDS: White-crowned Sparrow, Gray-crowned Rosy Finch, Water Pipit.

11,500

CANADIAN ZONE

AREA: Approximately 2,500 square miles.

AVERAGE ANNUAL PRECIPITATION: 22 to 28 inches.

AVERAGE (MEAN) TEMPERATURE: 35.7° F.

TREES: Alder, Aspen, Fir, Spruce.

CHARACTERISTIC BIRDS: Gray-headed Junco, Olive-sided Flycatcher, Golden-crowned Kinglet.

8,500

TRANSITION ZONE

AREA: Approximately 10,500 square miles.

AVERAGE ANNUAL PRECIPITATION: 19 to 23 inches.

AVERAGE (MEAN) TEMPERATURE: 42.8° F.

TREES: Douglas Fir, Juniper, Oaks, Yellow Pine.

CHARACTERISTIC BIRDS: Hermit Thrush, Mountain Bluebirds, Audubon's Warbler.

7,400

UPPER SONORAN ZONE

AREA: Approximately 90,000 square miles.

AVERAGE ANNUAL PRECIPITATION: 15 to 19 inches.

AVERAGE (MEAN) TEMPERATURE: 52.7° F.

TREES: Cottonwood, Juniper, Pinyon, Scrub Oak.

CHARACTERISTIC BIRDS: Horned Lark, Painted Redstart, Canyon Wren.

4,200

LOWER SONORAN ZONE

AREA: Approximately 18,400 square miles.

AVERAGE ANNUAL PRECIPITATION: 8 to 12 inches.

AVERAGE (MEAN) TEMPERATURE: 61.6° F.

TREES AND SHRUBS: Cactus, Catclaw, Cottonwood, Creosote Bush, Mesquite, Squaw Bush.

CHARACTERISTIC BIRDS: Blue-gray Gnatcatcher, Black-throated Sparrow, Bridled Titmouse.

2,850

NEW MEXICO'S LIFE ZONES

I

REPRESENTATIVE BREEDING BIRDS OF NEW MEXICO'S LIFE ZONES

II

THE ROADRUNNER — NEW MEXICO'S STATE BIRD

NEW MEXICO BIRDS

AND WHERE TO FIND THEM

BY

J. Stokley Ligon

THE UNIVERSITY OF NEW MEXICO PRESS

IN COOPERATION WITH

THE NEW MEXICO DEPARTMENT OF GAME & FISH

MANUFACTURED IN THE UNITED STATES OF AMERICA

BY THE UNIVERSITY OF NEW MEXICO PRINTING PLANT, ALBUQUERQUE, NEW MEXICO

COLOR PLATES PRINTED BY RAND AVERY - GORDON TAYLOR, INC., BOSTON, MASS.

Library of Congress Catalog Card Number 61-10050

First Edition

DEDICATED WITH AFFECTION
TO MY WIFE, ROSE

PREFACE

THE AUTHORSHIP of bird books which are regional or national in scope generally is attributed to an individual. In reality such contributions are the fruits of an author's intensive field work over a long period of time, supplemented by the findings of many qualified observers. This book is no exception to the general rule. Wild birds are elusive creatures. The normal life of an ornithologist, regardless of how ambitious or proficient he may be in the field, is not long enough to permit him to learn all there is to know about all birds he wishes to feature.

The national interest in birds and bird watching is reflected in the great number of ornithologists the past two decades have produced. The author is indebted not only to many contemporary ornithologists but also to some now deceased, among them Dr. Albert K. Fisher, Dr. Edward W. Nelson, Maj. Allan Brooks, Vernon and Florence Merriam Bailey, Maj. Edward A. Goldman, and Ralph T. Kellogg. It is with a deep feeling of gratitude that he acknowledges the aid and inspiration he received through association with these eminent naturalists who continued to blaze the way for those who were to follow.

For proposing the publication of another state bird book to replace the monumental work by Florence Merriam Bailey, a Department of Game and Fish sponsored publication (1928), long out of print, credit is due the late Roy E. Carey, former Game Commissioner, and Elliott S. Barker, long-time State Game Warden. The proposal was approved July 10, 1950, by the State Game Commission, as sponsors of the project, with Angus Evans, chairman, and Russell Edgar, Jr., George Eager, Paul Wright, and Carey, as members. Succeeding Game Commissioners Judge C. M. Botts, chairman, Clyde Hill, Henry E. Brown, and George Turner, as members, with Homer C. Pickens, director of the Department, unanimously supported the plan.

Inasmuch as the author's voluminous bird records and general information dating back to 1908, on birds occurring in the state were incorporated in the Bailey *Birds of New Mexico*, the Game Commission assigned him the task of conducting such field work as was deemed necessary to determine the status of the state birds since its publication in 1928. For this initial service he was employed on a part-time basis. In addition to conducting, intermittently, intensive field investigations, considerable time was devoted to the intricate details leading to the preparation of the manuscript, such as incorporating notes and records of observers from all parts of the state. The time devoted to the writing of the manuscript, and to the endless details, such as making arrangements with the artists for the color work, supplying them with information and specimens indicating background desired; compiling data from observers, endless correspondence with observers pertaining to bird notes and records, et cetera, was donated to the project—the author received no remuneration for these tasks, preferring that this contribution be reflected in a reasonable sale price which will make the book available to all who want or need it.

For supplying important notes and records over an extended period on birds throughout the state, the author is most grateful to Mr. Jens K. Jensen, Mr. Raymond Fleetwood, Col. Vester Montgomery, Maj. James E. Sikes, Mr. Adolph Krehbiel, Mr. W. W. Cook, Mr. Harry Williams, Mrs. Lena McBee, and Miss Mary Belle Keefer. For notes on rare birds thanks are due Edgar Kincaid, Larry Merovka, Carey Bennett, John Campbell, Dr. Allan Phillips, and Dale A. Zimmerman.

The personnel of the Department of Game and Fish, including Levon Lee, Wayne Bohl, James W. Peckumn, James McClellan, E. M. Lang, Elmo Traylor, among others, contributed valuable notes and records from time to time.

Dr. Edward F. Castetter, Dr. W. W. Hill, Mr. John N. Durrie, and Dr. James S. Findley, of the University of New Mexico, are thanked for their helpful suggestions and continued interest in the progress of this book. Mr. Roland Dickey, Mr. J. Robert Feynn and Mr. Blair Boyd, of the University of New Mexico Press, worked with this volume during its editorial and publishing stages.

The author acknowledges with gratitude and appreciation the able assistance rendered by Dr. Ira Gabrielson in reading the draft of the manuscript, making corrections and many helpful suggestions, and again examining the manuscript in final form. Thanks are due Dr. Frederick C. Lincoln for reading portions of the manuscript and making suggestions and corrections particularly pertaining to scientific and vernacular names in accordance with the revised *A. O. U. Check-list* (Fifth Edition) , which had not been published at the time the manuscript was being prepared; Dr. E. R. Kalmbach for his many suggestions pertaining to the art work, and for reading the manuscript critically; Mr. W. L. McAtee for biographical data on pioneer ornithologists and for information on the naming (vernacular) of many birds; Dr. R. W. Schloemer and Dr. C. F. Von Eschen of the U.S. Weather Bureau for climatological data pertaining to life zones; the U.S.

Forest Service for preparing maps of the National Forests, and the U.S. Fish and Wildlife Service for supplying photographs and drawings; and John C. Gatlin, Regional Director of the Service, for cooperation in various ways.

The author expresses his sincere appreciation and gratitude to Mrs. Gladys Day Jackson for her abiding interest, her many helpful suggestions, and for her painstaking efforts in typing and retyping the manuscript. More than to any other, the author is indebted to his wife Rose for condensation of material, attention to major and minor details and for her constant encouragement and devotion. Without her aid this book probably never would have reached library shelves.

J. Stokley Ligon

Carlsbad, New Mexico

CONTENTS

COLOR PLATES

*Original owned by the New Mexico Department of Game and Fish, Santa Fe.

ILLUSTRATIONS

NEW MEXICO BIRDS

AND WHERE TO FIND THEM

INTRODUCTION

IN THE PREPARATION of material for *New Mexico Birds and Where to Find Them*, the constant aim of the author has been to provide a simplified and practical guide which will serve the greatest number in the observation and study of birds. In conceding to the popular concept of and trends in bird study and observation, some departure from the usual order followed in publications of this nature was necessary. The more simplified approach, it is felt, lends greater appeal to bird studies for those still outside the realm of their magic. With few exceptions, subspecies have been disregarded, since they are frequently recognized on slight differences which often lead to confusion on the part of the beginner in his field observations. Species —resident or migrant—which nest in the state are, in the main, given preferential treatment. The contents of this book are based on the author's studies and observations over a period of several decades, and on information obtained from many bird observers who have graciously made their records available to him. Though dealing primarily with the birds of New Mexico, much of this contribution is applicable to the Southwest in general.

The chapters on bird watching, it is hoped, will be helpful to the birding public in knowing where to find the birds, and will encourage the vast potential audience of friends of the birds to become participants in this interesting and important field in natural history.

Three hundred ninety-nine species, including thirty-four "strays," based upon the *American Ornithologists' Union Check-list* (Fifth Edition) have been recorded in the state. Of this number 247 are known to nest in the state, while 152 migrants enter the state, but are not known to nest here. Of the nesting species, 82 may be regarded as resident, with more-or-less fixed habitat; 77 are semiresident, but may be observed within the state throughout the year; while 91 species known to nest in New Mexico are absent during the severe part of the winter. For ready reference, the names of all birds known to nest in the state are preceded by a paragraph mark (¶).

The most opportune and pleasant time for bird observation and study is during the nesting season when birds are very active and most males are conspicuous in their breeding plumage. Many birds which nest in the state are present at this time of the year only, and winter migrants by then are out of the way. Absence of winter migrants, however, does not entirely remove the possibility of confusion in the case of smaller species or groups which nest in the state, such as Flycatchers, Sparrows, Warblers, and Vireos. But the beginner need not be dismayed by these problem species. The identification of these by sight alone tests the ability of even the more advanced ornithologist. As a general rule, the larger birds (for the most part limited in numbers of species in a family or group) are more easily identified. The smaller and shyer species are usually reluctant to leave concealing cover. Then, too, many of them live for the most part in the upper branches of the taller and denser forest trees. It is the identification of these that requires time and infinite patience. Yet it is the rare, the usually retiring birds that are of consuming interest, challenging the ability and determination of the observer.

Names of birds, both common and scientific, and order of listing throughout the main text, conform to the Fifth Edition of *Check-list of North American Birds*, prepared by a Committee of the American Ornithologists' Union (A.O.U.). However, in instances of changes of well established common names, the former name follows the new designation in parentheses. Listing of birds, except in a very few explained instances, is confined to recognized species as recorded in the *Check-List*. Bird lists of the Tributary Flyways and Bird Watching chapters, however, are not in strict accord with the *Check-List* since these were prepared before the revised *Check-List* was available.

NEW MEXICO
HISTORY, TOPOGRAPHY, CLIMATE

NEW MEXICO, fittingly proclaimed "The Land of Enchantment," is the fifth largest state in the nation, with an area of 121,666 square miles. Its turbulent and colorful history began in 1540 with the Spanish Conquistadores seeking the mythical Cities of Cibola. Santa Fe was founded in 1610 and, with the famed Santa Fe Trail, has long symbolized the magic West. Through a bloodless conquest, the area became a Territorial possession of the United States in 1846, and in 1912 New Mexico became the forty-seventh State of the Union.

Elevations in the state range from 2,850 feet, where the Pecos River enters Texas below Carlsbad, to 13,160 feet at the summit of Wheeler Peak, the average mean elevation being approximately 5,700 feet. (See *Life Zones.*) The seasonal range of temperatures and precipitation varies widely in respect to elevation, thus creating habitats of many types for a great variety of resident birds, although a majority, particularly song and insectivorous kinds, are summer dwellers only.

The topography of the state is dominated by two major north-south watercourses —the Rio Grande and the Pecos—and by two rather well-defined mountain ranges paralleling the Rio Grande, one on each side. The Rio Grande bisects the state from the Colorado line to the Texas line at El Paso. The Pecos River rises in the Sangre de Cristo Range, about 75 miles airline from the New Mexico–Colorado border, and flows south, passing out of the state below Carlsbad to form a junction with the Rio Grande far down in western Texas. While most of the country west of the Pecos is broken and mountainous, the portion lying eastward to the Texas line is predominantly high plains–mesa terrain type. The lateral river drainage systems consist of the Canadian in the eastern and the Dry Cimarron in the northeastern sections of the state. The San Juan, Zuñi, San Francisco, and Gila Rivers, west of the Continental Divide, constitute a portion of the Pacific watershed. The Sangre de Cristo Range, lying in the northern part, constitutes the dominant mountainous mass of the state.

The mountains are repositories for a good portion of the state's natural resources, such as water, timber, and minerals. The national forests in the higher regions, approximating 13,280 square miles, provide the principal public playgrounds of the state. Much of the higher mountainous country is characterized by a rather rigorous winter climate, but the southern section is favored by one of the most equable, sunny winter climates to be found in the nation. Hence the bird student may pursue his interests while participating in winter sports in the northern region or as he basks in the sunshine of the southern section.

ELEVATIONS OF REPRESENTATIVE
TOWNS AND CITIES IN NEW MEXICO

Alamogordo	4,335'
Albuquerque	4,950'
Carlsbad	3,100'
Chama	7,860'
Clayton	5,050'
Cloudcroft	8,650'
Deming	4,335'
Farmington	5,300'
Gallup	6,500'
Las Cruces	3,900'
Las Vegas	6,435'
Lordsburg	4,245'
Los Alamos	7,330'
Portales	4,010'
Raton	6,660'
Roswell	3,600'
Santa Fe	7,000'
Silver City	5,900'
Taos	6,950'
Tucumcari	4,085'

FOREST TRAIL, GILA NATIONAL FOREST
Photograph by the Author

LIFE ZONES

LIFE ZONES are of interest to the bird student because of the many different species of resident and summer resident birds which are intimately adjusted to natural conditions of each zone. The life zone concept is based on both latitude and altitude and therefore climate, a combination which creates a phenomenon of profound interest. This combination is basic in the ecology that governs the existing distribution of flora and fauna indigenous to the various regions. Geological features, temperature, and precipitation determine zonal boundaries. Six of the seven life zones of the nation occur in New Mexico: Lower Sonoran, Upper Sonoran, Transition, Canadian, Hudsonian, and Arctic-Alpine. They range in elevation from less than 3,000 feet (Lower Sonoran) in the southern part of the state, to timber line and higher (Arctic-Alpine) in the northern

section. Only the Tropical Zone is not present in the state.

Dr. C. Hart Merriam (1855-1942), one of America's most able naturalists and first chief of the U.S. Biological Survey, predecessor of the present Fish and Wildlife Service, was the first to advance and define the life zone concept. In his treatise *Results of the Biological Survey of the San Francisco Mountain Region and Desert of the Little Colorado in Arizona* (1890), he graphically records his conclusions—that forms of life are peculiar to given altitudinal areas or zones, hence the designation of a region or zone by the presence of flora and fauna not found in others.

Since temperatures on north canyon and mountain slopes differ from those on south and southwest exposures, life zones do not run on arbitrary contours. North and northeast slopes where the sun's rays are less intense are more shaded and cooler, hence the zones dip down, while on the south and southwest where the more direct heat from the sun dries the surface, the zonal elevation rises proportionately. Because of radical variation in elevations, the Rocky Mountain region provides a vivid example of zonal characteristics within limited distance in contrast to such zones at sea level which extend from the tropics to the arctic.

One of the remarkable aspects of life zones in New Mexico is the fact that some species of birds and plants common to the Arctic are at home on the miniature skyline islets of the Sangre de Cristo Range. Hypothetically, if the area of Carlsbad (elevation about 3,000 feet) were projected on contour northward, the climate and representative bird and plant life common to the summit of Wheeler, Truchas and other peaks of the Sangre de Cristo Range would be encountered far to the north in Canada, and many of the resident and summer resident birds found in the state would not be present.

The variation in climate of the different zones results in a long bird-nesting season in the state. By following springtime northward and upward, the bird observer starting about the International Boundary in late April with the desert species of the Lower Sonoran Zone can, by progressively stairstepping the different zones, arrive in the northern part of the state at or above timber line in early July to hear the breeding song of White-crowned Sparrows, Rosy Finches, or the trill of a soaring Pipit, or perhaps, as a fitting climax, observe a pair of Ptarmigan with their downy young.

HAROLD BUGBEE. *Courtesy of*
The Globe-News Publishing Co., Amarillo.

PIONEER ORNITHOLOGISTS WHO CONDUCTED EXTENSIVE FIELD WORK IN THE SOUTHWEST

THE FOLLOWING biographical notes touch briefly on the ornithological activities of a few of the pioneers who, with the exception of Spencer Baird, conducted extensive field work in the Southwest. While Baird did not actually participate in such field work, it was under his influence and guidance as Secretary of the Smithsonian Institution that so many eminent ornithologists developed within a short time while attached to the U.S. Army Medical Corps or to exploratory expeditions in the Southwest. For a full account of ornithologists connected with the military forces in the Southwest see *Ornithologists of the U.S. Army Medical Corps,* by Edgar Erskine Hume. Accompanying photographs are for the most part from the Deane Collection in the Library of Congress. Asterisk following name indicates attachment to the U.S. Army Medical Corps.

SPENCER FULLERTON BAIRD (1825-87). Professor Baird, one of the greatest and most influential naturalists of all time, served as Assistant Secretary and also as Secretary of the Smithsonian Institution from 1850 to 1887. He was graduated from Dickinson College, Pennsylvania, at the age of 17, and "the next year made an ornithological excursion through the mountains of Pennsylvania Counties, walking, according to one of his biographers, '400 miles in 21 days.'" (Encyclopaedia Britannica). After he met the renowned John James Audubon (1785-1851) in 1838, his interest in ornithology was greatly intensified. Audubon gave him a portion of his own bird collection. According to Dr. Elliott Coues, "He exerted an influence perhaps stronger and more widely felt than that of any of his predecessors, Audubon's and Wilson's not excepted, and marked an epoch in the history of American ornithology."

SPENCER FULLERTON BAIRD

SAMUEL WASHINGTON WOODHOUSE* (1821-1904), Assistant Surgeon, U.S. Army. He and Dr. Thomas Henry were among the first to collect and report on birds in the Southwest. Dr. Woodhouse served under Lt. Lorenzo Sitgreaves in Western Texas and New Mexico, 1850-51. This expedition covered the Rio Grande Valley from El Paso, Texas, to Santa Fe, thence west to Inscription Rock and the Zuñi River Valley. He collected many birds, and described some new to science. He was bitten on the hand by a rattlesnake while in the Zuñi River country, and wounded in the leg by an Indian's arrow.

SAMUEL WASHINGTON WOODHOUSE

THOMAS CHARLTON HENRY* (1825-77), Surgeon and Lieutenant-Colonel, U.S. Army. Stationed at various points in New Mexico, including Forts Fillmore, Webster, and Thorn, during the years 1852-55. According to the records, his monthly pay was $81.83. His bird collecting—and there

THOMAS CHARLTON HENRY
Portraits courtesy of the Library of Congress

seems to have been a great deal of it—was confined largely to New Mexico. In a letter written by him and published in the *Philadelphia Inquirer*, September 21, 1853, Dr. Henry states about New Mexico: "This is a curious and unique country —New Mexico, full of hostile Indians . . . and lizards, tarantulas, and flies in profusion." Quoting him further: "The plains swarm with antelope; the hills with deer and 'grizzlies'; the rivers with swans, ducks and wild geese; while among the timber generally, are to be found many curious birds, peculiar to the country, some specimens of which are yet undescribed." (*Ornithologists of the U.S. Army Medical Corps*, pp. 208-09). Dr. Henry was also bitten by a rattlesnake, the effects of which, however, were less serious than was the case with Dr. Woodhouse.

DEWITT CLINTON PETERS* (1829-76), Surgeon and Lieutenant-Colonel, U.S. Army. His principal ornithological work was conducted about Fort Union and Fort Massachusetts, 1854-56, and about Fort Union in 1867. Dr. Peters is well known as the author of *A History of Kit Carson* and was a personal friend of the famous

scout. He retired from the Army in 1875 because of an illness contracted while in the service, and died in New York in 1876.

CALEB BURWELL KENNERLY* (1829-61), Surgeon, U.S. Army. Dr. Kennerly was highly regarded by Baird, who personally aided him to get started on his ornithological career. Dr. Kennerly was with Lieutenant Ives in 1853 on his expedition from San Antonio to El Paso, Texas, thence up the Rio Grande to Albuquerque. From all accounts, this proved to be a most trying experience for the men. In spite of adversities Dr. Kennerly managed to make extensive bird observations and collections en route. At Albuquerque, his party joined that of Lieutenant Whipple, which was surveying the route for a prospective railroad to the Pacific. From Albuquerque the expedition proceeded west to Inscription Rock and down the Zuñi River into Arizona, Dr. Kennerly continuing his intensive bird work. Old reports on Army expeditions and surveys devote considerable space to Dr. Kennerly and his work, although he was only 32 years of age when he met a tragic death in a shipwreck off the west coast of Mexico.

DEWITT CLINTON PETERS

CALEB BURWELL KENNERLY

CHARLES EMIL BENDIRE (1836-97), Major, U.S. Army. While Major Bendire developed into an enthusiastic ornithologist, his major interest was in eggs—oölogy. He became actively interested in birds and eggs while he was stationed at Camp (Cantonment) Burgwyn, New Mexico. While there, and at Forts Bowie, Lowell, and Whipple, Arizona, 1872-73, he did a great deal of egg collecting. In 1883, at the request of Baird, he became Honorary Curator of Oölogy at the National Museum, and he began to show his ability as a writer on the subject of birds and eggs. He is best known for his superb, two-volume *Life Histories of North American Birds* (the forerunner of the *Bent's Life History* series). This work is outstanding in the excellent color reproductions of eggs. Major Bendire gave his personal collection of about 8,000 eggs to the U.S. National Museum. He was one of the founders of the American Ornithologists' Union. He died February 4, 1897, at the age of 61, and was buried with military honors in the National Cemetery at Arlington, Virginia.

ELLIOTT COUES* (1842-99), Surgeon, U.S. Army. One of the greatest ornithologists of all time, and a prolific writer on the subject. Much of the field work that formed the basis for his *Birds of the Colorado Valley* (Government Printing Office, 1876) was conducted in 1864-65, in the Zuñi River country of New Mexico, and about Fort Whipple near Prescott and other points in Arizona. His two-volume *Key to North American Birds* is a monument to his genius and literary skill. While Audubon popularized and dramatized ornithology, Coues unified and stabilized it as a science of the highest order. He was a founder of the American Ornithologists' Union. Dr. Coues evidently had a profound attachment for the Southwest. Although a sick man, he returned the year before he died as if to recapture the magic of some of the scenes of his earlier field experiences, spending some time in Santa Fe. He returned to Washington where he died on Christmas day, 1899, at the age of 57.

CHARLES EMIL BENDIRE
Portraits courtesy of the Library of Congress

ELLIOTT COUES
Courtesy of the Smithsonian Institution

HENRY WETHERBEE HENSHAW (1850-1930). Mr. Henshaw's principal ornithological field work in the Southwest—and there was much of it—for the most part was conducted while he was serving with the U.S. Geographical and Geological Explorations and Surveys west of the One-Hundredth Meridian. He observed and collected birds during 1873-74 in the northern part of the state, in the Rio Grande Valley about Albuquerque, and around Old Fort Wingate. He was the first ornithologist of note to explore the rugged upper Gila River country in its primitive state. Apparently he featured observing and recording birds during the time he was attached to exploring expeditions, rather than collecting. From July 18 to October 28, 1883, he was with Dr. E. W. Nelson (who later became the third Chief of the U.S. Bureau of Biological Survey) in the upper Pecos country east of Santa Fe, where according to the records, they did considerable collecting. [See Auk II, pp. 326-33 (1885), and III, pp. 73-80 (1886).] Mr. Henshaw was the second Chief of the Biological Survey from 1910 to 1916.

EDGAR ALEXANDER MEARNS* (1856-1916), Lieutenant-Colonel, U.S. Army. While Dr. Mearns may not have qualified as a "born" ornithologist, he was nonetheless a great naturalist. The dearth of literature by him would indicate that he preferred field work and the collecting of nature specimens of all kinds to writing or that because of these time-consuming activities, he had little time in his early life to devote to writing. His first assignment in the Southwest took him to Fort Verde (Camp Verde), Arizona, in 1884, where he was attached to General Crook's Command for four years. His field work in New Mexico was limited largely to his assignment as medical officer and naturalist, with the United States–Mexican Boundary Survey Commission, 1892-93, an assignment that was ornithologically important. The Survey extended from El Paso to the Pacific, and Dr. Mearns was favored by ample time for observation and collecting of rare birds, including many that occur only along the International Boundary, in both New Mexico and Arizona; some of which were first records for

HENRY WETHERBEE HENSHAW
U.S. Fish & Wildlife Service

EDGAR ALEXANDER MEARNS
Courtesy of the Library of Congress

these states. It is doubtful whether any other naturalist ever did more intensive collecting of natural history specimens over so long a period. Dr. Mearns served in the Philippines, 1903-07. In 1908 he was selected by President Theodore Roosevelt as naturalist on the Roosevelt Expedition to Africa. He died on November 1, 1916, at the age of 60, at Walter Reed General Hospital, Washington. A tablet set in a ledge on Plummers Island, in the Potomac River above Washington, a rallying place for naturalists, marks the spot where his ashes were scattered.

FLORENCE MERRIAM BAILEY (1863-1948). Although not a contemporary of the pioneer ornithologists who did field work in the Southwest, Mrs. Florence Merriam Bailey warrants the title of greatest American woman ornithologist. Mrs. Bailey and her husband, Vernon Bailey (1864-1942), as an inseparable team, did a vast amount of intensive field work over a period of several decades in the Southwest, and particularly in New Mexico. Author of Hand-book of Birds of the Western United States, Birds of New Mexico, and many other contributions on Western and Southwestern ornithology, Mrs. Bailey was awarded the Brewster Medal of the American Ornithologists' Union in 1921. In 1923, an honorary LL.D. was conferred upon her by the University of New Mexico. In all her field work she was aided by her husband, who for years was Chief Naturalist of the U.S. Bureau of Biological Survey, predecessor of the U.S. Fish and Wildlife Service. Among Mr. Bailey's contributions on New Mexico are Life Zones and Crop Zones of New Mexico (which includes the principal birds of the different life zones of the state), one of the Fauna Series of the Biological Survey; Animal Life of the Carlsbad Caverns (including birds about the Caverns and adjoining Guadalupe Mountains); and Mammals of New Mexico, another of the Fauna Series. Mrs. Bailey died in Washington, D.C., September 22, 1948, at the age of 85, six years after the passing of her husband.

FLORENCE MERRIAM BAILEY
Courtesy of the Library of Congress

To the adventurous pioneers who helped make ornithological history in the Southwest, New Mexico, the hub of this magic land, had no less appeal, even under adverse conditions than has this favored section of the nation to the bird student of today. On October 15, 1860, Baird wrote William Wallace Anderson, who was connected with the Pacific Railroad Surveys, and was one of his faithful bird reporters: "I really don't see how we can get along without you at Burgwyn [New Mexico]. It is certainly the greatest center of rare birds in the United States." The fact that many distinguished themselves in the field of ornithology under the brilliant and inspirational leadership of Baird while they were attached to the U.S. Army Medical Corps as surgeons, or to exploratory expeditions in the West and Southwest indicates that opportunity and association, rather than just an inherent love for birds, were factors in the development of these ornithologists.

The historic notes on their activities and the difficulties encountered by these adventurous pioneers in carrying on field work, and their timely accomplishments in classifying and naming many species of birds during the period from about 1850 to 1875, were edifying and inspiring to those who were to follow. Baird, Coues, Bendire, Henshaw, and their colleagues were to ornithology in the Southwest what Emerson, Longfellow, Whittier, and Thoreau were to early New England literature. Those who blazed the wilderness trails of conquest and thrilled to the virgin field of ornithology awaiting exploration, earned the recognition that time bestowed upon them.

The bird student traveling in comfort and with ease in high-powered automobiles over smooth state and federal highways cannot fully appreciate the hardships endured by the pioneers who explored the ornithological fields of the West and Southwest a hundred years ago. Modes of travel—over poor or imaginary roads with ponderous wagons drawn by horses or mules at best, often by plodding ox teams —and the intermittent marching and field work were a physical strain and debilitating to all who participated. Fever, smallpox and cholera were not uncommon. The camps and forts afforded shelter, some comforts, and safety; but such establishments in proportion to the vast uncharted spaces were few and far between, and only the more fortunate had the benefits of them. Exposure to the elements and to danger of warring Indians was more often the lot of those who braved the trail and wilderness life. It is significant that the life span of five of the six Army Medical Corps surgeons herein featured was approximately 49 years.

ORNITHOLOGICAL LITERATURE OF THE SOUTHWEST

NEW MEXICO has the distinction of having the earliest recorded notes on birds of any state in the Union. Historians attached to Coronado's Expedition into the Southwest, in 1540-42, made reference to birds observed about the Indian Pueblos in the upper Rio Grande Valley. Mention is made of Cranes, Wild Geese, Quail, and Starlings (no doubt Blackbirds). After Coronado's time, little information was recorded about birds until the arrival of pioneer American ornithologists, who recorded much new and vital information during the latter half of the nineteenth century. Some important records date prior to 1850, but these notes are more or less fragmentary. The period from about 1850 to 1890 marks the first planned ornithological field work in this region. Those who followed these pioneers lacked the virgin field of operations enjoyed by their predecessors, but they, too, did a vast amount of field work and filled in gaps with intricate detail to round out the whole.

Findings, as result of this pioneer field work and that of many later ornithologists, constitute a liberal portion of *Birds of New Mexico*, by Florence Merriam Bailey. This monumental work, in its more than 800 pages, contains a wealth of ornithological history about the state, and is replete with descriptions of birds, and their nests and eggs, covering the period up to 1928. Long out of print, it remains a reference work. The author, who contributed much time and many records to the Bailey book, has drawn freely from its pages, particularly descriptions of birds and nests and eggs, since these descriptions were based largely on field notes of the former U.S. Biological Survey field force, as well as on the vast collections of the U.S. National Museum. Considerable reliance has also been placed on the author's bird and egg collection. Mrs. Bailey is also author of *Handbook of Birds of the Western United States* (Revised in 1917), which for many years served as a popular field guide for the Southwest, including New Mexico.

The only bird list of the state prior to 1928 was one prepared by Fanny Ford (Mrs. Arthur Sloan) and published in 1911 in Report Number 1, *The Natural Resources Survey of the Conservation and Natural Resources Commission of New Mexico*. Produced as a preliminary list of birds of the state, it included 314 species and subspecies, and recorded important observations. Many of the recordings, however, are merely credited to the A.O.U. distributional lists.

Although more regional in scope, Roger Tory Peterson's *Western Bird Guide* and the Audubon publications are also applicable in a general way to each of the Western states, and are very popular with the birding public. The most recent contribution to New Mexico bird literature may be found in *Guide to Bird Finding West of the Mississippi*, by Olin Sewall Pettingill. This publication covers each of the twenty-two states west of the Mississippi. Among many other publications on Southwestern birds, a splendid source of information is the files of ornithological magazines in public and private libraries. These include the *Auk*, dating back to 1886, one of the oldest, and the voice of the American Ornithologists' Union; the *Condor*, featuring Western birds; the *Wilson Bulletin*, and the *Audubon Magazine*.

CLASSIFICATION AND IDENTIFICATION OF BIRDS

ORNITHOLOGY, of Greek derivation— *ornithos*, "bird"; *logos*, "discourse", is the science or knowledge of birds pertaining to physical structure and distinguishing characteristics. Oölogy is the branch of ornithology treating of bird eggs. Thus, ornithology and oölogy are inseparable in the more intensive study of birds in their relation to the land and to man.

Many bird students, particularly beginners, are interested primarily in learning to identify birds by their common, or vernacular, names, and regard with a mixed feeling of awe and trepidation the translation of their scientific names which are, nevertheless, essential in accurate classification. In spite of the Latin and/or Greek origin of the scientific designation, its translation can become a fascinating detail in the study of birds. As an example of what a translation of the scientific term may reveal, and how helpful it is in accurate designation: The scientific term for the White-necked Raven, which ordinarily displays no white, is *Corvus cryptoleucus*. *Corvus* denotes the family relationship, while *crypto* means "hidden," and *leucus*, "white." The translation implies "hidden white," which in this instance applies to the bases of the neck feathers which are white but exposed only when they are agitated by wind or when the bird voluntarily raises its neck feathers. (See Plate XXI.)

The bird student today rarely has opportunity to examine a bird in hand. His identification must be made by sight in the field or from specimens in museums. Familiarity with the topography of a bird is essential. Acquaintance with the rudiments of classification adds interest to the study of birds and facilitates identification. Birds are grouped according to orders, families, and genera. The order is the broadest of the groupings; the family expresses a closer relationship; families are divided into genera, and genera into species, the latter denoting the individual bird. Each group as, for example, the Loons, the Grebes, the Herons, and Bitterns, the Ducks, Geese, and Swans, etc., is identified by features which distinguish it from members of other groups. Knowledge of these distinguishing features enables the observer more quickly to catalog a bird as to group, thereby facilitating identification through the process of elimination.

Familiarity with the individual characteristics, as color of plumage, flight, notes, and songs, simplifies the identification and classification of a bird. When all bird values are assessed, it is perhaps their vocal magnetism and that ethereal quality of the melodic voices of songsters that sharpen one's appreciation of the essential part which birds play in a well-organized and well-conducted society. With the exception of the Mockingbird, which accurately imitates the notes of many species, songs of no two species are exactly alike. Hence, the attentive observer with the trained ear can identify his subjects by their notes or song even though the performer is invisible, as the Chat by its raucous note issuing from dense cover, the Horned Lark by its joyous song beyond vision in the heav-

enly blue, or the Bittern by the "pumping" emanating from some cattail marsh. In some cases, song is the most dependable means of identification, even though the singer is in plain sight. The Eastern and the Western Meadowlarks are typical examples. Where the ranges of the two birds overlap, they are practically indistinguishable by sight alone, yet their songs are entirely unalike. The Western has a vibrant and more raucous, broken song; the Eastern has a soft, flowing song of the most pleasing quality.

In the case of non-breeding species which migrate into and through New Mexico, life zones are less respected. Routes of least resistance, as the Eastern High Plains, Pecos and Rio Grande Valleys, constitute the most attractive flyways and wintering grounds for these species, and since they are usually more or less concentrated during migration, identification of many is simplified. Such migrants are entirely independent of breeding birds and without conflict with summer residents.

Although the annual turnover in bird populations adds to the problems of identification, the phenomenon of migration is an abiding wonder in wild bird conduct. Quite certain it is that these cruisers of the flyways have homing instincts not known to man.

In the identification of such migrants, as water, marsh, and shore birds, the beginner is favored by the fact that most summer-dwelling species—which might cause confusion in identification—have left the state by the time the migrants from the north arrive. Likewise, the departure of these travelers to the north usually precedes the spring arrival of those species which breed locally. Species of waterfowl which migrate into and through New Mexico are so well described and illustrated through photographs and colored plates in many excellent regional and national publications, only brief de-

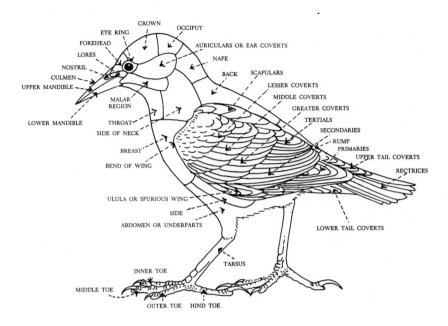

CROWN
EYE RING
OCCIPUT
FOREHEAD
AURICULARS OR EAR COVERTS
LORES
NAPE
NOSTRIL
BACK
SCAPULARS
CULMEN
LESSER COVERTS
UPPER MANDIBLE
MIDDLE COVERTS
GREATER COVERTS
MALAR
REGION
TERTIALS
LOWER MANDIBLE
THROAT
SECONDARIES
SIDE OF NECK
RUMP
PRIMARIES
BREAST
UPPER TAIL COVERTS
BEND OF WING
RECTRICES
ULULA OR SPURIOUS WING
SIDE
ABDOMEN OR UNDERPARTS
LOWER TAIL COVERTS
TARSUS
INNER TOE
MIDDLE TOE
OUTER TOE HIND TOE

EXTERNAL TOPOGRAPHY OF MEADOWLARK
E. R. Kalmbach

scriptions of most of these are given herein. More detailed accounts of these and other non-nesting species are to be found in *Audubon Water Bird Guide*, Kortright's *Ducks, Geese and Swans of North America*, and similar publications.

ECONOMIC AND ESTHETIC VALUES OF BIRDS

PUBLIC INTEREST in the economic and esthetic values of birds has only recently begun to manifest itself fully in the Southwest, and particularly in New Mexico. This long overdue appreciation is most timely in view of the fact that intensified land use and abuse are often disastrous to birds unless means are employed to safeguard their welfare. The many years of missionary work carried on by such organizations as the National Audubon Society, the U.S. Fish and Wildlife Service and its predecessor, the Biological Survey, state bird organizations, state game departments, and by the many individuals who devoted their lives to the defense of birds and their protection, are at last bearing fruit. Excessive grazing by livestock and periodic drought, resulting in loss of essential food and ground cover, seriously affect upland game birds, while the resultant curtailment of stream flows into water impoundments, and the drying of marsh lands likewise have an adverse effect on water, marsh and shore birds. Fortunately, the U.S. Fish and Wildlife Service and the State Game Department have saved some key areas in time, and created others for such birds. Fortunately, too, most of the wooded and forested mountainous country is in public ownership—national forests, parks, and monuments—where it is reasonable to assume that representative species of song and insectivorous birds are fairly secure in perpetuity. Aside from their esthetic appeal, birds in normal population, or in concentration where their food is most plentiful, constitute the most effective and most economical means of check and control of many kinds of insects and other pests. The value of such service defies calculation. Without the controlling influence of birds the enormous damage by these insects in defoliating native vegetation, destroying extensive segments of valuable timber, and in taking heavy toll of man's earnings from the soil, would unquestionably be many times greater. Virtually all species of land- and forest-dwelling birds almost constantly search for and destroy eggs, larvae, and adults of such pests.

The food of most birds, at least seasonally, includes some kinds of destructive insect life. Therefore, when the birds are scarce or absent, insects are more in evidence. Bark-probing species, such as the Nuthatches, Creepers, and Woodpeckers, avidly and repeatedly go over the bole and limbs of trees from top to bottom, prying into every hole and cranny for eggs and elusive larvae. The Warblers, Kinglets, Vireos and Titmice search leaves, needles, and buds for crawling and flying insects that infest them, and for egg cases to obtain their rich larval content. Robins, Bluebirds, Wrens, Flickers, and Thrashers, with ears attuned to under-surface clues, detect the faintest crunching sound or surface movement of hidden worms or grubs in lawn, garden, or forest, which they skillfully unearth. The total number of destructive pests taken by these protectors of forest, range and cropland, particularly when feeding their young, is vast in proportion to the size of the bird. The Flycatcher on some prominent perch waiting patiently to sally out to pluck moths or other flying pests, or the Nighthawks and Swallows, at times in vast numbers, cruising the airways as harvesters of all manner of insects, are Nature's means of insect control. The question arises: are control measures by the use of lethal sprays on agricultural crops and forests as effective, and how disastrous are such sprays to these birds? This question gives rise to another

depressing reminder—how man's conquest of space will eventually affect avian travelers of the airways. The Quails and native Sparrows in numbers are no less an asset to farmers and to the land in general in their control of insect pests and through consumption of seeds of noxious plants, while the wild turkey, where permitted to live in numbers, literally turns the forest floor of leaves and needles upside down, searching out and consuming hordes of potential forest pests. In the words of that eminent conservationist and wildlife authority, Horace M. Albright, "Insect pests are no less a peril to forest conservation than is fire." And as yet, insects are more difficult of control by man.

As if working in organized shifts in their quest for secreted, crawling, and flying enemies of the products of the land, by the time the diurnal harvesters have gone to roost for the night, the nocturnal foragers, such as the Owls, Nighthawks and Poor-wills are present, in season, to continue the harvest of the fecund pests that are inactive by day.

Even the persecuted birds of prey are, for the most part, highly beneficial. Unfortunately, the large Hawks, which are almost wholly beneficial, have been willfully and shamefully slaughtered. The general conception seems to be that the larger the Hawk, the greater the damage it commits. With the exception of the little Sparrow Hawk, the reverse is true. It is the smaller, shy, streamlined species, as the Cooper's and the Sharp-shinned Hawks, which are the destructive ones. To the uninformed, the very name "Hawk" is synonymous with depredation, and every Hawk, regardless of species, in the past has been regarded as a bad, or "chicken," Hawk. The smaller, harmful ones, because of their elusiveness, are rarely killed and remain in almost, if not quite, normal abundance, whereas the large rabbit-, rodent- and grasshopper-feeding species are progressively becoming scarcer. Meanwhile, an alarming upturn in population of all species of forage- and seed-destroying rodents continues, thereby creating one of the most serious control problems involving the land today.

So valuable and important are migratory insectivorous birds that the Governments of the United States and Canada long ago entered into a treaty wherein such birds are given complete protection in both countries. In upholding the Migratory Bird Treaty Act, the United States Supreme Court did so with one of the most brilliant, convincing eulogies ever accorded wild birds:

Here a national interest of very nearly the first magnitude is involved. It can be protected only by national action in concert with that of another power. The subject matter is only transitorily within the State and has no permanent habitat therein. But for the treaty and the statute there soon might be no birds for any powers to deal with. We see nothing in the Constitution that compels the Government to sit by while a food supply is cut off and the protectors of our forests and our crops are destroyed. It is not sufficient to rely upon the States. The reliance is vain, and were it otherwise, the question is whether the United States is forbidden to act. We are of the opinion that the treaty and statute must be upheld.

Virtually all song and insectivorous species, whether wholly or partially migratory, are protected under both State and Federal laws.

FAMILY LIFE OF BIRDS

THE FAMILY LIFE of birds, particularly at the time of nesting and raising young, is comparable in some respects to that of a well ordered society. Most birds of aerial classification—song and insectivorous kinds, and bird of prey—usually are monogamous, pairing for the breeding season. There is evidence that a few, as the Ravens and the Eagles, mate for the duration of the normal life of a pair. This supposition of lifetime mating is supported by the fact that many pairs return to the same nesting place year after year. This does not preclude the possibility of the surviving mate acquiring another should one of the pair meet disaster. More intensive research, however, is necessary in order to determine this point.

At mating time birds are most active and aggressive. They woo, entice, and beguile in courtship antics ranging from modest exhibition to pretentious parade and, when occasion demands, engage in deadly combat to thwart the advances of other males. Once united for a season, most monogamous birds apparently remain constant and faithfully share nesting duties and take part in caring for and defending their young, some even to the point of sacrificing life in the attempt.

It is interesting to note that there are one or more species of birds adapted to every type of climate or environment, be it desert, plain, mountain, forest, stream or lake. But intensified occupation of the land by man and the resultant altering of normal functions of water, soil, and its vegetative products have imperiled the welfare of some species. Unfortunately, the most desirable species, usually the smaller and frailer birds, are the most seriously affected by habitat impairment. Others, the Quails for example, are not physically constituted for seeking greener fields, since their flight endurance is limited, and regardless of how seriously depleted their habitat, they must endure what comes or, if fortunate, rely on handouts from sympathetic hands.

Although many changes in the landscape have proved detrimental to birds, there are isolated cases where new environments are equal or superior to the original.

An unusual example of the creation of habitat suitable for both summer- and winter-dwelling birds is the replacement, in the past few decades, of salt grass by the exotic tamarisk along the banks and over floodlands of the Pecos River. A like transition has occurred to a considerable extent in the Rio Grande Valley. On the McMillan and Avalon Lake deltas along the Pecos in Eddy County, thousands of acres of these plants, many reaching tree proportions, provide favorable nesting environment for a variety of song birds and, in addition one of the most heavily utilized breeding retreats for Mourning Doves to be found in the state.

Some birds are always ready at nesting time to take advantage of man's ingenuity. Many of the concrete bridges along the highways of the Southwest are utilized at nesting time by throngs of Cliff Swallows which in former years were only passing migrants. The Domestic Pigeon, or Rock Dove, is also finding such structures to its liking, while many species, as Barn and Cliff Swallows, Phoebes, and some of the Wrens take advantage of various types of buildings for nesting places.

BIRD SONGS

BIRDS have an advantage over mammals in their esthetic appeal as songsters, and over humans in that they do not have to learn the "language." Their vocalism—be it a twitter, chirp, far-carrying call, or co-ordinated song—has a definite significance which is understood by all of a kind. It is amazing how even very young birds can distinguish between their parents' notes— those alerting them to danger and those signifying "all is well." Young wild Turkeys, Quails, Grouse, Ducks and shore birds, among others, will either "freeze" or scurry to cover when the parent bird flashes the warning notes, and remain hidden until a faint "all is well" announcement

brings them to life. The vocal endowment, which plays a major role in self-preservation, is especially well defined among those species which dwell for the most part on the ground and thus are the prey of many enemies.

In the spring and early summer, the outpouring of song by such talented singers as the Thrushes and Thrashers may be expressions of joy over a well-favored habitat. If essential habitat requirements are lacking, songs of joy (if such they be) may be less frequent or entirely absent. The song may be inspired self-enjoyment by the singer, but more likely it is a tribute to his silent mate, somewhere within radius of the chosen nesting retreat. The most noted and persistent songsters are found among the tree, or arboreal, dwellers, those that are active on wing and are much of the time separated, indicating that notes and songs are important means of contact, not only on nesting grounds but in migration as well. Since practically all birds are most vocal just before and during nesting time, it may be assumed that such expressions during this period also serve as a warning to other males of their kind that a given area has been pre-empted.

Some authors endeavor, with limited success, to record bird songs; in the main, such notes and songs defy the printed page. Certain notes, such as "Bobwhite," "Killdeer," and "Poorwill" are exceptions, but these can scarcely be classed as songs. Bird songs are mechanically recorded, however, and this method of reproduction is destined to become both a means of entertainment and an aid in identification of birds.

Although the full meaning of bird songs is difficult to interpret, nature provides few or no other vocal renditions more pleasing or inspiring to the appreciative and trained human ear than that of gifted songsters of the avian family. New Mexico has been favored with such masters of song. The Mockingbird, Sage Thrasher,

Hermit Thrush, Robin, Bluebird, Horned Lark, and the various Buntings, Orioles, Meadowlarks, all rate high as songsters.

THE BIRD, NEST, AND EGG

MOST SPECIES of birds throughout their lives are vulnerable to violent end from many sources. This is especially true of song and insectivorous birds which are not physically constituted to defend themselves. The stronger, more aggressive kinds —birds of prey and those which are comparatively free from attack by predators— escape many of the dangers which constantly beset those less capable of self-defense. It is significant, however, that species which are most subject to violent ends are cleverly endowed by nature with compensating means for sustaining normal populations, so long as man's adverse influences are not involved. That those that are constantly threatened are able to sustain anything like normal numbers is a credit to their remarkable skill in evading or outwitting their enemies.

Nest construction, egg clutches, and shape and color patterns of eggs are almost as varied as are species of birds. Some nests, such as those of the Verdin, Bush-tit, Oriole, Cliff Swallow, and Dipper, are masterpieces of construction. Other species, such as Doves and Cuckoos, build scant platforms of twigs and straw that barely hold the eggs. Some, like the Goat-sucker group, make no pretense at nest building, laying their eggs on bare ground. The consistency with which the various species follow, not only the ancestral pattern in construction, but type and location of nesting site as well, is a source of wonderment.

The number of eggs normally laid is generally a fair indicator of the mortality rate of the species. A good example is that of Quail, Turkeys, and Waterfowl, which have numerous enemies and likewise lay large clutches. Some of the frailer species, like the Bush-tits and Kinglets, also lay large clutches—a means seemingly necessary to sustain their numbers. Doves and other kinds which are also subject to predation, seem to be exceptions to this rule. They lay small clutches, but the young develop rapidly, and two or more broods are usually raised in a season. Other exceptions are the Nuthatches and Chickadees, which nest in sheltered positions, as hollows in trees or Woodpecker holes. These birds lay large clutches, although it is the adult birds which more often fall prey to Sharp-shinned and Pigeon Hawks, and to snakes. Eagles and most large non-game birds which have few natural enemies, as a rule, lay small clutches and raise but one brood annually.

Jays are no doubt one of the more serious enemies of the smaller nesting birds since they are semi-predaceous by nature and occupy the same type of habitat at nesting time. The Hummingbird, although the midget of the feathered kingdom, seems to be less subject to nesting tragedies than are many other small birds. Its dashing flight and pugnacious nature enable it to defend nest and young. Two eggs are the usual number and one brood, if successful, is the rule with Hummingbirds.

ATTRACTING AND HOLDING BIRDS

THE most effective means of attracting and holding desirable species of birds is to remove, so far as possible, the causes for fear, and to provide, especially in times of need, preferred kinds of food and suitable escape cover. In winter, when food is scarce or lacking, most species are likely to seek out places where their wants or needs have been provided by sympathetic hands. In arid sections, such as characterize much of New Mexico, food is enticing to birds, not only in winter but during periods of drought when natural foods are scarce or absent.

As a rule, when wintering birds come to man in numbers for sustaining food it is because of lack of natural supply. The prolonged drought which terminated in 1957 brought about such a condition over much of the Southwest. During September and early October, 1956, there was an unusual concentration of Clay-colored Sparrows, attracted by seeds of weeds on a plot of irrigated ground on the author's farm near Carlsbad. Shortly after the drought ended in 1957, and there was widespread rank vegetation, none of the birds were about at migrating time. Also during the winter of 1956-57, more than a hundred White-crowned Sparrows were present at the farm, living in and about the game bird flyways where there was a constant food supply. The following winter, when there was sufficient natural food for them, no more than a half dozen stayed about the place at one time.

Another example of bird dependence on habitation of man in the arid Southwest is that of the Scaled and Gambel's Quail. When natural food is scarce, these Quails congregate about ranches. Where protected they become tame and feed about corrals or barnyards with Chickens.

It is in the spring, and at nesting time, when such desirable species as Kingbirds, Goldfinches, Orioles, Mockingbirds, and Grosbeaks are at their best in beauty, in action, and in song. They can be induced to become intimate neighbors in yards, gardens, or fields by the planting of trees and shrubs, the principal attractions where natural tree growth is lacking.

The growing of trees where previously there were none has been a direct benefit to arboreal-dwelling species. The plains country east of the Pecos River is a good example of desirable, created habitat for such species as the handsome Scissor-tailed Flycatcher, the Bullock Oriole, the

Kingbird, and Pyrrhuloxia. Species that congregate in large flocks during fall migration, such as Redwinged Blackbirds, Cowbirds, Lark Buntings, House Finches, and English or House Sparrows, may at times do some damage to field head crops, and especially when the fields are few and far between. Such damage, however, can often be attributed to impairment of natural bird habitat as result of excessive grazing by livestock. On the other hand, these same species that temporarily depredate constitute a very potent factor in the destruction of insects about such fields.

Fortunately, when most summer-dwelling songsters depart for the South, migrants from the North come in to animate what too often would otherwise be a drab and lifeless scene for the bird enthusiast. Providing feeding stations and water basins for these distinguished winter guests who too frequently find insufficient natural food and water to sustain them, is one of the principal means of attracting and holding them. However, when bird feeding is begun it should be continued, otherwise those that have become reliant on such aid might suffer without it.

BIRD ENEMIES

SO LONG AS favorable habitat conditions—cover and food—exist, most birds thrive despite their many enemies. But when their habitat is disrupted as result of man's use and abuse of land, adversities most often overtake them.

Storms at nesting time often take a heavy toll, particularly of the most beneficial kinds—the song and insectivorous birds. Frequently during periods of incubation, the eggs and young are destroyed by wind, hail, floods or fire. Added to these perils is the great array of skulking, creeping, crawling, and flying enemies of both the young and adults. That such birds manage to survive and reproduce attests their alertness and skill in avoiding these perils. When vegetative cover is normal, depredation of birds is far less serious than when the land surface is barren and scourged by dust bowls. Indirectly, many so-called predatory birds have a beneficial influence in that they help control rodents, particularly rats and mice, which eat and store the seeds of plants on which many birds are dependent, especially in winter. Here again the sad plight of birds often can be attributed to habitat impairment rather than to depredation.

Birds that confine their breeding to life zones with a higher rate of precipitation, i.e., zones characterized by woodlands and forests, and those that nest in brushy valleys and along timbered watercourses are much less vulnerable at nesting time because they have better concealing cover and a more dependable source of food than birds that range in the more arid sections. Were it not for their persistence in nesting and efforts to raise their young, many species inhabiting inhospitable places would have little chance of survival. The life span—at least for some small birds —is known to be fairly short, three years or less. Under normal conditions, sustained populations of most larger species are favored by rather long life expectancy. Two male Mockingbirds secured as nestlings by the W. T. Shermans, of Silver City, are now more than 18 years of age. The Gordon Whites, of Las Cruces, had a male Bullock's Oriole, acquired as a cripple, age when taken unknown, which died (1956) 17 years later. It is only reasonable to assume that with the infirmities of age, without the protective care they received, they would not have survived to such advanced age.

Mortality among song and insectivorous birds, even under most favorable conditions, is always greatest from the time fledglings leave the nest until they are sufficiently developed and equipped to shift for themselves. During this period the mortality rate may run dangerously high among some of the more delicate species with exacting food requirements. This loss fortunately is somewhat offset by the persistence on the part of most species to renest, and by the lower mortality rate among such birds as the Bluebirds, Nuthatches, Chickadees, Martins, and House Wrens, that nest in hollow trees and holes excavated by Flickers and Woodpeckers, where the eggs and young are comparatively safe. Snakes—particularly the bullsnake and coachwhip (prairie racer)—are serious enemies of small and medium-sized birds which nest both on and above ground in the foothills, valleys, and plains. The skill displayed by a prairie racer in locating and robbing nests of Orioles, Finches, and Flycatchers, even those high in the tallest trees, is amazing, but no more so than the lightning speed with which it can ascend a tree trunk and conceal itself in the upper branches. Even so, it is surprising how a bird sentinel, always conveniently on duty, unfailingly spots the enemy and gives the alarm. Soon all his neighbors are alerted and join in a chattering, scolding chorus. With the departure of the culprit, all defenders soon disperse. Mockingbirds in particular are adept at spotting enemies, and with unmitigated boldness attack the intruder, be it snake, Roadrunner, cat, or dog. Near dwellings, in gardens, orchards, or fields, house cats rate high as enemies of adult and young birds alike, but because of their status as household pets they are among the most difficult of enemies to combat.

EDUCATION IN BIRD PROTECTION

LOCAL and regional bird clubs, such as are sponsored by the Audubon Society and by various other nature organizations, are direct means of getting both young people and adults actively interested in birds and their protection. The State Game Department also is an important and appropriate agency for encouraging and sponsoring bird clubs through its own facilities and in cooperation with educational institutions, game protective associations, and particularly Boy and Girl Scout units. Bird clubs, through effective teamwork, can be of much help in semidesert areas, especially during periods of drought when natural food for birds is often scant or lacking. Providing supplemental feed and water is the usual means to this end. Such aids not only induce more birds to remain in winter, but are a direct means of increasing and sustaining their numbers.

One reason for the fall migration of many birds from the state is lack or absence of winter food. Growing of food-producing and cover shrubs induces Robins, Thrushes, Finches, Waxwings, Bluebirds, Mockingbirds, and many others, to remain.

Effective artificial aid to nesting birds has been clearly demonstrated by Mr. Jens Jensen, an enthusiastic and accurate bird observer, who has induced many beneficial birds to nest in the juniper-pinyon wooded valleys and ridges about Santa Fe. Over a period of years Mr. Jensen placed suitable nesting boxes where natural cavities were all but absent. Such species as Bluebirds, Chickadees, Ash-throated Flycatchers, Wrens, Titmice, and some of the small Owls freely utilize the improvised nest facilities which he placed at their disposal. Without such aid, these breeders would have had to move on in their quest for suitable nesting places.

Boy Scout leaders may well feature conservation programs that will help members to appraise and appreciate the various types of terrain—river, valley, plains, desert, mountain or forest—and the birdlife adjusted to the different types, thereby widening the range of the Scouts' interests in outdoor activities. The making and placing of nesting boxes are especially adaptable to Boy Scout activities and could be made a major project of a conservation program. Many ways and means of implementing projects which will benefit birds while broadening the knowledge of the participants await the attention of informed Scout and bird club leaders. Highways and improved roads, and rapid means of transportation make accessible practically every type of bird habitat in the state. Scout, school, and church encampments in mountains and forests provide rare opportunities for great numbers to observe and study birds under most favorable conditions.

DESCRIPTIONS

LOONS
Family: GAVIIDAE

LOONS are large web-footed swimming and diving birds. Almost the size of a Goose, they have long, Duck-shaped bodies, with legs set far back. They have short necks and stout, sharp-pointed bills. Loons have astonishing diving ability. Wetmore advised the author that Loons have been taken on baited lines and in set nets at around 200 feet below the surface, and that "their average dive appears to be of about one minute's duration with extension when necessary up to three minutes." Since the Loon does not nest in the state, its weird breeding cry, reminiscent of the howling of a wolf, is not heard here. The Common Loon is the dominant species in the state. The Arctic, which is somewhat smaller, was recorded about fifty years ago. There is also one record for the Red-throated Loon (see Stray Birds).

COMMON LOON

Gavia immer

28—36" long. Color pattern of sexes alike.

As its name implies, this is the most common of the Loons in interior America. There are few old records of the bird for the state. As the result of creation of more large bodies of water for irrigation, Loons are more in evidence during migration, and some remain throughout the winter. George Willett observed two on Elephant Butte Lake, December 8, 1916. Elmo Traylor has one record for Conchas Lake. The author saw one on the City Lake at Carlsbad, March 6, 1951. R. C. Brummett, of the Carlsbad Irrigation District, reported seeing three on Lake McMillan, December 20, 1955. It is reported as "transient visitor, occasional," at both Bitter Lake and Bosque del Apache Refuges. A. J. Krehbiel reported seeing two on Clayton Lake, near Clayton, November 18, 1956. There are no nesting records for the state. *Adults in winter:* As seen in the state—Crown and nape brownish gray; other upperparts almost black, usually with some evidence of the black and white crisscross effect of summer plumage. Throat and underparts white; bill about 3 inches long, sharply pointed.

GREBES
Family: *PODICIPEDIDAE*

THESE lobe-footed expert divers are easily distinguished from Ducks by rudimentary tails and pointed bills of variable lengths. In many respects Grebes are unique and their conduct, especially at nesting time, is a source of interest and amusement. An endearing family trait is that of parent birds carrying the young on their backs apparently in order to rest them, or as a means of quick exit in the face of danger. Grebes are decidedly aquatic, and much prefer swimming and diving to flying. Once in the air, however, they fly swiftly. They swim with head erect, seeming to float and wheel along effortlessly, but usually dive at the slightest provocation, emerging some distance away. Their diving proclivity serves them well, both in eluding enemies and in obtaining food. Except in migration flights, they are rarely seen out of water. On land their movements are awkward, bordering on the grotesque. Of the four species of Grebes (not including the Red-necked—see Stray Birds)—the Horned, Eared, Western, and Pied-billed—that occur in New Mexico, only the Eared and Pied-billed are known to breed within its borders. Unfortunately there are so few suitable breeding places for this group in the Southwest that opportunities to observe them at nesting time are limited.

HORNED GREBE
Podiceps auritus
13½" long. Color pattern of sexes alike.

In size, and in winter or summer plumage, the Horned and the Eared Grebe are similar. The winter head markings of either the Horned or Eared bear little resemblance to their breeding adornments. The "horns" of the Horned Grebe, in summer, are more pronounced and much lighter in color than are the "ears" of the Eared Grebe. Crown, hind-neck, and throat glossy black; breast and underparts white. *Horned, winter:* Upperparts grayish black; underparts white. *Eared, winter:* Upperparts grayish brown; underparts white.

DISTRIBUTION. The comparatively few migration records of the Horned Grebe, in New Mexico, should not be regarded as evidence of its apparent rarity. The few authentic records of its occurrence may be attributed to difficulty in distinguishing it from the Eared Grebe. The Horned is listed "rare fall migrant" at Bosque del Apache Refuge. It was included in the 1955 Christmas Count of Bitter Lake Refuge. Krehbiel included it in his 1956 migration records. "Less common from the Great Lakes to southern Texas and New Mexico" (*A.O.U. Check-list*).

EARED GREBE
Podiceps caspicus
12—14" long. Color pattern of sexes alike.

The Eared, one of the smaller Grebes, usually occurs during migration in small groups in close association, when it may be seen on ponds or lakes serenely floating about with carefree abandon, but always ready to submerge at the slightest disturbance. *Adults, summer:* Prominent black crest; head and neck black; ear tufts buff; back and wings blackish; sides, chestnut; lower breast and underparts white. *Adults, winter:* Upperparts grayish brown; underparts white.

DISTRIBUTION. Summer distribution in New Mexico is limited because of the scarcity of suitable nesting places, such as ponds or lakes with permanent shorelines.

EARED GREBE ON NEST. *W. F. Kubichek, U.S. Fish & Wildlife Service.*

Such bodies of water are largely limited to the higher sections of the northern part of the state. Most of the Eared Grebes leave the state for the winter.

NESTING. Preferred nesting waters of the Eared Grebe are the larger lakes with aquatic vegetation, such as rushes, adjacent to expanses of open and deeper water, where they feed. Burford Lake, Rio Arriba County, is the principal Eared Grebe nesting lake in the state, so long as water remains at constant level. The value of this lake for the Grebes is vested both in elevation—approximately 7,500 feet, and size—about 2,000 surface acres. Here on one occasion, in mid-July, the author counted 250 nests in a single colony. These nests were floating in two to three feet of water. On a return visit a short time later another colony, containing 200 or more nests, with others under construction, was found some distance from the one previously located. At the time the lake was at maximum level. The many irrigation reservoirs of the state, although serving as resting places for such birds, do not as a rule provide suitable nesting habitat because of the radical fluctuation in shoreline, and also because they lack protective vegetation as result of water withdrawal for irrigation. Burford Lake is not subject to such withdrawal, although prolonged drought seriously affects the water level. Upon leaving the nest, Eared Grebes usually cover their eggs with trash. The precocial young are soon at home in the water. The fluffy little balls, about the size of a Bantam chick, floating on the water while the parent birds glean food for them below the surface, present an amusing spectacle. *Nest:* A floating mass of water-soaked vegetation. *Eggs:* 3 to 5; dull white.

WESTERN GREBE
Aechmophorus occidentalis
22—29" long. Color pattern of sexes essentially alike.

The Western, also referred to as the "Swan" Grebe, is the largest of the

Grebes. Before the passage of the Migratory Bird Treaty Act in 1920, these Grebes were ruthlessly slaughtered for the beautiful silky white breast and neck feathers, in great demand by the millinery trade. *Adults:* Crown and back of neck black; back brownish gray; underparts white; inner web of wing quills more or less white; neck long and slender; light-yellow bill. The female is somewhat smaller than the male.

DISTRIBUTION. The Western Grebe is a rather rare migrant in the state. It may be looked for on such large bodies of water as Elephant Butte and Conchas Lakes. It is recorded as "winter visitor, unusual" at both the Bosque del Apache and Bitter Lake Refuges. The author has a beautiful study skin of a Western Grebe, taken on Elephant Butte Lake, April 2, 1935.

(PIED-BILLED GREBE
Podilymbus podiceps

12—15″ long. Color pattern of sexes alike.

The Pied-billed is easily distinguished from the other three Grebes that occur in the state. It does not have a crest. Its bill is thick and rounded, whereas the Horned and Eared have slender and pointed bills. It is much smaller than the Western. The Pied-billed is usually seen singly or in pairs. It is even more skillful at diving than its relatives. When alarmed, it all but vanishes from view by keeping its body submerged with only the bill above water. It is usually absent from the state in winter. *Adult summer plumage:* Crown and neck grayish black; broad black throat patch; side of head and neck brownish gray; upperparts brownish black; underparts ashy white; bill thick, rounded bluish white, encircled with black band. *Winter:* Adults and young darker, throat patch white; bill dullish yellow without band.

DISTRIBUTION. Occurrence of the Pied-billed Grebe during the nesting period is governed by the availability of suitable breeding places such as ponds and lakes with permanent shorelines where rushes and other aquatic vegetation grow in the water. At this season it is more common in the northern part of the state, particularly on Burford Lake, Black Lake, or other high-altitude bodies of water. During migration the species is apt to be seen wherever there are ponds or larger bodies of water. Drainage of ponds and sloughs, particularly in the lower Rio Grande and Pecos Valleys, has destroyed many former nesting places.

NESTING. Unlike the Eared Grebe, the Pied-billed does not colonize at nesting time. The young are precocial, and are at home in the water shortly after hatching. The author came suddenly upon a nest on Burford Lake which contained eight eggs and three chicks just out of the shell. One chick wiggled off the nest, swam away, and was soon lost to sight in the nearby cover. Like the Eared Grebe, the Pied-billed transports its young on its back when occasion demands a quick getaway. *Nest:* A floating pad, constructed of decaying vegetable matter anchored to reeds or rushes, usually in two or three feet of water. It is generally better concealed than that of the Eared. *Eggs:* 5 or more; dull white, and usually nest-stained.

PIED-BILLED GREBE, FEMALE WITH YOUNG
E. R. Kalmbach, courtesy of Rose Ligon

PELICANS
Family: PELECANIDAE

PELICANS are among the largest of American birds, with wingspread up to 9 feet, and weighing from 15 to 17 pounds. With its conspicuous gular pouch swinging from the long bill accentuated by its short legs, the Pelican is truly an oddity among birds. Of the two species indigenous to the United States, the Brown and the White, only the latter has been recorded in New Mexico.

WHITE PELICAN
Pelecanus erythrorhynchos

54—66" long. Color pattern of sexes alike.

Breeding plumage: White with straw color on breast and wing coverts; primaries black; gular pouch varying from yellow to deep orange; bill yellow, 11 to 15 inches long; feet and legs yellow. *Adults in postnuptial plumage:* Back of head gray; bill, legs and feet yellow. *Young in first winter:* White; top of head and wing coverts brownish gray.

DISTRIBUTION. This spectacular large white bird, with black outer wing feathers, may frequently be observed on the large bodies of water in the state. During fall migration, Pelicans sometimes appear in conspicuous white rafts far out on lakes. On August 10, 1951, the author observed approximately 75 resting in three groups on Lake Avalon. A few others that appeared to be summer residents were seen in June on Lake McMillan. For the Roswell area, Col. Vester Montgomery states: "common in April-May; here sometimes July to November." Recorded as "transient visitor, common" at Bosque del Apache Refuge. So far as is known, the Pelican does not nest in the state, although it may ultimately do so if suitable breeding conditions develop at one or more of the large reservoirs, especially should islands be created through sedimentation or additional water impoundments.

WHITE PELICAN AND YOUNG. *W. F. Kubichek, U.S. Fish & Wildlife Service.*

CORMORANTS
Family: PHALACROCORACIDAE

DOUBLE-CRESTED CORMORANT
R. J. Sim, U.S. Fish & Wildlife Service

CORMORANTS are expert swimmers and divers, and although, like the Coots, they require a running start on the water to enable them to get into the air, once on the wing they fly rapidly, usually in wide circles. They seem to be incapable of sustaining their weight in the air when their speed is altered. At a large rookery at the north end of Bosque del Apache Refuge, one of the birds was observed lighting on a dead limb of a nesting tree. The limb gave way and the bird splashed into the water 25 feet below. Out of water, Cormorants are ungainly and are readily recognized by their Penguinlike attitude when at rest.

❮ DOUBLE-CRESTED CORMORANT
Phalacrocorax auritus

24—30″ long. Color pattern of sexes alike.

This Cormorant has a large black body and long neck; long slender bill hooked at tip; legs short; tail somewhat long and rounded. *Nuptial plumage:* Black plumes on both sides of head, often mixed with white, throat patch orange. *Adults in post-nuptial plumage:* Black except back feathers slate, edged in black.

The Double-crested, also formerly known as the Mexican Cormorant, is the only species of this group which occurs in the state. Formerly it was known only as a rare migrant. However, with the impoundment of large bodies of water in reclamation projects, favorable breeding conditions have been created, and today the species is a regular breeder, although radical changes in water levels often have a direct bearing on its nesting sites. The food of Cormorants consists largely of fish, mostly rough or undesirable species, such as carp and suckers. The birds spend much of their time sitting, Vulturelike, on snags or dead trees over water, on dikes, or on floating logs, adjacent to their feeding grounds.

DISTRIBUTION. The Double-crested, the only one of the three species native to the West and the Far West, may be seen, in migration, on the larger bodies of water or main streams. In summer its distribution is confined almost entirely to the larger water impoundments, such as Bitter Lake and Bosque del Apache Refuges.

NESTING. The Double-crested Cormorant nests rather commonly on the Rio Grande, particularly on the Elephant Butte Reservoir delta and Bosque del Apache Refuge. It probably eventually will be found nesting at other water impoundments where there are "rough" fish. On Bosque del Apache Refuge, May 20, 1951, many of the birds had nests under construction, while some had clutches of fresh eggs. The nests, several to a tree, were 25 to 30 feet up in half-dead cottonwoods that stood in three or four feet of water. The rookery spread over an acre or more of the marsh, and both Cormorants and Common Egrets were nesting in association and in apparent amity. *Nests:* Scantily made of cottonwood limbs and twigs, lined with a few strips of soft inner bark of the cottonwood. *Eggs:* 4 or 5, bluish white, with chalky surface.

HERONS AND BITTERNS
Family: ARDEIDAE

THE Herons and Bitterns comprise a group of long-legged, long-necked wading birds with sharp-pointed bills which serve them in spearing their prey in water. In flight they are readily distinguished by the position of the head and neck which are drawn back to the shoulder. Birds in this group vary in size from the Least Bittern, which measures 12 to 14 inches in length, to the Great Blue Heron, which may be more than 50 inches in length. This family includes the beautiful Egrets with their highly ornamental seasonal nuptial plumes. Prior to 1920, the Common and Snowy Egrets were rarely recorded in the state. Today both of these nest in the Rio Grande and Pecos Valleys. Just how long they will continue to do so depends on how long lakes and marshes, with trees and aquatic vegetation, will survive drainage. But for the Migratory Bird Treaty Act between the U.S. and Canada, and the efforts of bird protective organizations, the Egrets probably would have been exterminated.

(GREAT BLUE HERON
Ardea herodias

45″ long, average. Color pattern of sexes alike.

This Heron stands about four feet tall. Neck and legs very long; bill slender and pointed. *Adults in breeding plumage:* Head mostly white, black line over eye, and crest—consisting of two long black slender feathers—on back of head; throat white; neck grayish brown; whitish shoulder plumes; long plumelike feathers on breast; back bluish gray; sides blackish; underparts streaked with white; tail bluish black. *Adults in winter plumage:* Lack crest. *Young in juvenile plumage:* Lack all lengthened feathers.

The Great Blue Heron, one of the most dignified and wary birds to be found in the state, should not be confused with the Sandhill Crane, since in habit it is entirely different. In continued flight the head is drawn back to the shoulders, whereas that of the Sandhill Crane is outstretched. It does not congregate in numbers as do the Sandhill Cranes. Great Blue Herons are usually seen singly or in groups of two or three, except during nesting time, when they generally colonize. This patient sentinel may be seen standing along streams or in shallow water of lakes, waiting for its prey. The name Fish Crane, commonly applied to it, is a misnomer, since its food consists of a great variety of aquatic life. The fish on which these Herons feed are largely undesirable, such as carp and suckers, usually the dominant species where the birds feed. Snakes, water dogs, crayfish, snails, worms, and small rodents are consumed. They are especially fond of water snakes which are destructive to small fish. In the heat of summer when many waterways contain little water, Great Blue Herons are often on hand to partake of the fish and other landlocked aquatic life, thus serving as scavengers.

DISTRIBUTION. Great Blue Herons in New Mexico are only semi-migratory. Although they usually are absent from the northern part in winter, some do remain in the southern area. They are less apt to be in evidence in January and February. In spring, summer, and fall they occur statewide where water and suitable food are available. Altitude seems to have little bearing on their presence. Formerly, before drainage and irrigation reservoirs altered their environment, these Herons nested in some localities which are no longer suitable. On the other hand, newly-created lakes and reservoirs have tended to offset the loss of former breeding places. Periods of continued drought have adverse effect on them as summer residents.

NESTING. The author has observed small rookeries between Roswell and Fort Sumner (Crane Canyon); in the Burford Lake area; in the Rio Grande Valley, between Elephant Butte Reservoir and Socorro; and more especially in the cottonwoods on the Gila River, from Redrock to the hot springs at the junction of the East and Middle Forks. In New Mexico, nests are usually placed on the terminal branches of the tallest cottonwoods. In other sections of the country nests are found on rocks or on the ground, but such places appear not to be utilized here. *Nests:* A dozen or more may be placed in a single tree; scantily made of sticks, sparingly lined with strips of cottonwood bark. *Eggs:* 4 to 6; greenish blue.

GREAT BLUE HERON
L. A. Fuertes, U.S. Fish & Wildlife Service

(GREEN HERON
Butorides virescens

15—22″ long. Color pattern of sexes alike.

The Latin designation, *virescens*, "growing green," is descriptive of this, the smallest of the Heron family. The Green Heron is not an uncommon summer resident in the state, but because of its shyness and nature of feeding mainly very early in the morning and at dusk, it is not as readily observed as are the other Herons. *Adults:* Crown and crest greenish black; neck chestnut; back with long gray feathers or plumes, glossed with green; wing coverts green margined with buff, tail dark glossy green; underparts brownish ash. Legs deep orange. *Immature:* Similar; underparts streaked with brown; back without plumes; crest, less conspicuous.

DISTRIBUTION. The range of this little Heron is confined almost wholly to the southern half of the state, where it may be seen about marshes and lakes bordered by willows, tamarisk, rushes and similar vegetation. It occurs also about streams where there is sluggish or still water with banks of overhanging trees, bushes, or cane, the tamarisk-bordered Pecos River being a good example. Montgomery records it as "somewhat common April to October" in the Roswell area. Recorded "summer resident, common" at Bosque del Apache Refuge.

NESTING. The author has found the Green Heron nesting in the Pecos Valley, along the tamarisk-willow lined banks of lakes near Carlsbad. On August 3, 1949, he located a nest containing a single fresh egg, in the rank rushes growing in three feet of water in Wade Lake, above Lake McMillan delta. In this area they were nesting in association with Snowy Egrets and Black-crowned Night Herons. "They nest regularly in the Rio Grande Valley about Las Cruces" (Williams). Since Green Herons may be seen where suitable habitat occurs, as at Washington Ranch, 30 miles southwest of Carlsbad; at Bitter Lake Refuge; and at San Simon Marshes in Hidalgo County, it is quite obvious that they breed more commonly than the sight records indicate. An unusual nesting site was that used for two successive years in the top branch of a tall Chinese elm in the Miers Johnson yard near City Lake, in Carlsbad. *Nest:* In bushes or trees near water, or among rushes in water, made of dry twigs and sticks. *Eggs:* Usually 4 or 5; pale green.

❨ COMMON (AMERICAN) EGRET
Casmerodius albus

38–41″ long. Color pattern of sexes alike. (Pl. III)

The Common Egret is a white Heron with long, pointed yellow bill; legs and feet black. During the breeding season the head is adorned with white plumes. *Post-nuptial plumage:* Plumes lacking; otherwise the same. Egrets are not difficult to identify since they are the only medium-sized white marsh birds indigenous to the Southwest. Two of these white Herons—Common and Snowy—occur in the state. The Common is easily distinguished by its larger size and by the yellow bill and black legs and black feet; the Snowy has a black bill, black legs, and yellow feet.

DISTRIBUTION. The Common, like the Snowy, is migratory. During the warmer months it is most common in the Rio Grande Valley, but it is a summer resident in the Pecos Valley also. Until recent years there were no records of the Common Egret in the state. Complete protection under the Migratory Bird Treaty Act gave it a new lease on life with the result that it has increased and greatly extended its summer range. The Common Egret is listed as "summer resident, common" at both the Bosque del Apache and Bitter Lake Refuges. "Recorded May 1, 1955, at Alcalde, near Española" (Hawkins).

NESTING. The Common and the Snowy Egrets are often found nesting in association. Nests may be placed either in rushes or small trees in, or surrounded by, water. In August 1949, at Wade Lake in the McMillan Reservoir delta, nests were found on dry mats of rank rushes in three to four feet of water. In a dozen or more nests there were well-developed young. At Bosque del Apache Refuge, the Common Egret and the Double-crested Cormorant occupied the same rookery, nesting in half-dead cottonwoods and willows standing in two to three feet of water. On May 20, 1951, many nests were still being built while others contained fresh eggs. *Nests:* In trees, are constructed of twigs and small dead branches; those placed on matted beds of rushes are made of blades of the rushes. *Eggs:* 4 or 5; pale blue.

❨ SNOWY EGRET
Leucophoyx thula

20–27″ long. Color pattern of sexes alike. (Pl. III)

The plumage of the Snowy Egret is entirely white; bill and legs black; feet yellow. During the breeding season, back of head and lower back adorned by recurved plumes.

Bent's appraisal of this marsh dweller probably expresses the sentiments of almost anyone who has seen the Snowy Egret adorned in its magnificent nuptial plumes: "This beautiful little heron, one of nature's daintiest and most exquisite creatures, is the most charming of all of our marsh birds." Considerably smaller than the Common Egret, it is readily identified.

In former years, when the fashion of trimming women's hats with "aigrette" plumes was at its height, the demand for these nuptial plumes was enormous, and hunters ruthlessly slaughtered the Egrets. Plumes were at their best when the young were in the nests, so young were left to starve when parent birds were shot. Finally, defenders of our migratory birds succeeded in having these and other valuable species given complete protection under the Migratory Bird Treaty Act. Without this law, these beautiful white Herons probably could not have survived.

DISTRIBUTION. During migration, the Snowy Egret may be seen almost any place in the state where there is water, particularly about sloughs and in marshy places. As is true of some other species, Snowy Egrets have the distinction of migrating northward from the known breeding range and remaining during the summer as non-breeders. Even young of the year are known to follow this pattern, spending the late summer and fall well north of where they were raised, and returning south late in the fall.

NESTING. In recent years the Snowy Egret has become a regular nesting bird, in both the Pecos and Rio Grande Valleys. Its progressive increase indicates that its nesting range may be further extended provided suitable breeding environment is available. Nesting of the Snowy Egret first came under the author's observation on May 4, 1933, when he and the late Allan Brooks (1869–1946), one of the world's foremost bird artists and ornithologists of his time, located a rookery of 20 pairs in a cattail-willow slough on the west side of the Rio Grande, four miles southwest of Las Cruces. The nests were all in willow bushes in two feet of water. Since that time there has been a marked increase in numbers entering the state annually. However, such nesting seems to be irregular as well as unpredictable. In 1954, an estimated 200 pairs were nesting in two rookeries at Bosque del Apache Refuge. In 1955, a few Common—but no Snowy— Egrets nested at this refuge. On August 3, 1949, approximately 75 pairs of Snowy Egrets were nesting in the rank rushes in the southeast corner of Wade Lake, just north of Lake McMillan delta. The next year some birds were observed in the area, but no occupied rookery was located. In August 1955, after high water had flooded the low land above the delta, approximately 100 Snowy Egrets were observed, probably nesting; however, no rookery was located. Nest: Usually on beds of rushes or cattails, above water, but also in low willows or cottonwoods surrounded by water; made of blades of rushes, or, if in bushes or trees, a frail structure of dry sticks and twigs. Eggs: 3 to 5; pale bluish green.

(BLACK-CROWNED NIGHT HERON
Nycticorax nycticorax

23–26" long. Color pattern of sexes alike.

The Black-crowned Night Heron is a short, plump, and almost tailless bird of marshlands, stream borders, and lake shores. At nesting time it is especially distinctive with its two or three long, white nuptial plumes extending from crown down the back. Adults: Crown and back black with bluish or greenish gloss, in sharp contrast to white of forehead, neck, and underparts. Bill, black; legs and feet, yellowish; neck and legs, short. Its common name as well as the scientific term nycticorax, "the night raven," may lead one to believe that it is entirely nocturnal. Although most active at night, it may be seen during the day perched, or slowly wheeling about in flight, watching for aquatic life, or in company with others of its kind resting in trees until sunset, when it flies to nearby feeding grounds. During spring and fall migrations, Night Herons are most vocal at night with their loud Ravenlike "quawk."

DISTRIBUTION. In summer, the Black-crowned Night Heron is one of the most widely distributed and most common of

BLACK-CROWNED NIGHT HERON
R. J. Sim, U.S. Fish & Wildlife Service

the marsh birds in the state. Sloughs, ponds and lakes constitute its principal feeding places.

NESTING. Adapting itself to both tree and marsh nesting, the Black-crowned is a more common breeder than are most marsh birds. It nests commonly in the Pecos Valley on Lake McMillan delta, and at Bitter Lake. Here, and in the Rio Grande Valley (Las Cruces and Bosque del Apache Refuge), it was found nesting in close association with the Snowy Egret. Farther to the north it nests commonly in the Albuquerque area, as well as at Burford and other lakes on the Jicarilla Apache Indian Reservation in northern New Mexico. Altitude seems to have little bearing on its choice, so long as water and aquatic vegetation, and a supply of food are available. Black-crowned Night Herons, in New Mexico, usually nest in small colonies, or in association with other species of similar habits, such as the Snowy Egret. *Nests:* In trees, or on mats of rushes or cattails. *Eggs:* 3 to 5; bluish green.

⟨ LEAST BITTERN
Ixobrychus exilis
12—14″ long. Color pattern of sexes different.

The Least Bittern (Latin, *exilis*, "slight," "small"), as implied, is the smallest of the Heron family. Its restricted range and shyness make it difficult for anyone but the most persistent observer to see, as it escapes noiselessly and swiftly by climbing over and through the cattails or brush. When suddenly flushed from its marsh cover, it flies laboriously, with legs dangling, for a short distance, drops down abruptly, Rail-like, remaining motionless in a concealing pose, like that of its larger relative, the American Bittern, or dodges about in concealing cover. Once down, it is very clever at concealment. *Adult male:* Crown black, slightly crested; back of neck brown; upperparts glossy greenish black; buff patch on wing; throat white; underparts buff; bill pale yellow; legs greenish yellow. *Adult female:* Back mainly brown with buff stripe on each side; underparts striped with brownish. *Young in juvenile plumage:* Similar to female, but feathers of back and shoulders tipped with buff.

DISTRIBUTION. The Least Bittern is most common in the Rio Grande Valley, from El Paso to Albuquerque. However, it occurs sparingly in the Pecos Valley as far north as Roswell and the Bitter Lake Refuge, and also in the San Simon Marshes, Hidalgo County. The author recorded it at Wade Lake, above the Lake McMillan delta, August 3, 1949. Some are present in the southern part of the state throughout the winter. Its soft cooing notes can be a clue to its presence.

NESTING. Many former breeding marshes of the Least Bittern have been eliminated as result of drainage. Bosque del Apache Refuge is one of the few remaining nesting places. On May 20, 1954, breeding pairs were located there. Formerly the Least Bittern nested in marshes at Truth or Consequences, where buildings are now situated. *Nest:* Usually in rushes or similar aquatic vegetation, or in bushes over water. *Eggs:* 4 to 6; greenish white.

(AMERICAN BITTERN
Botaurus lentiginosus

24—34″ long. Color pattern of sexes alike.

In some respects the American Bittern is a most unusual American bird. Its ability to assume a pose of all but complete effacement through statuesque simulation of its surroundings is remarkable. Its brownish color, long, snakelike neck, head, and bill are striking features in its "obliterative" pose. *Adults:* Upperparts brown, streaked and mottled with buff; wing tips black; throat white, sides of neck with wide, velvety black streak. Underparts yellowish, coarsely striped with white. Bill large, 2½ to 3 inches long; tail short. *Young:* Like adults, but without black on sides of neck.

The protective attitudes assumed by the Bittern set it apart from all other marsh birds. To avoid detection it stands, stiff and erect, among cattails or other marsh cover, bill pointed upward, and so well does it succeed in simulating its surroundings in coloration and pose that only the keenest observer will distinguish it from a snag or dry plant blades. No less deceptive are the vocal strains of this Bittern, emanating from the depth of some marsh. Its guttural tones, suggesting the sound of an old-fashioned wooden pump, from which it gets the name "Thunder Pumper," are not always recognized as the voice of this shy marsh dweller. Its vocal performance, especially during the summer, more often attests its presence than does a rare glimpse of this pantomime artist.

DISTRIBUTION. The distribution of the American Bittern, like that of other marsh birds, is limited in New Mexico by the scarcity of suitable marshes for dwelling places and nesting. Suitable retreats are now restricted more than ever as a result of drainage and marshland reclamation activities. About 15 were noted by the author in the thick willows at San Simon Marshes, Hidalgo County, May 9, 1920. It is more in evidence during spring and fall migration than at breeding time. It is usually out of the state by November first, returning in mid-April.

NESTING. There are but few nesting records of this Bittern in the state. It nests in rushes on the McMillan Reservoir delta (Wade Lake), and in similar places along the Rio Grande. It nests also within Bosque del Apache Refuge. Its fascinating "pumping" notes were heard at Burford Lake in early June, indicating that the birds were nesting, since these are breeding notes. *Nest:* Usually in marshes, made of sticks and coarse grasses. *Eggs:* 5 to 7; brownish drab.

STORKS AND WOOD IBISES
Family: CICONIIDAE

THE ONLY representative of this family in America, the Wood Ibis, is really a Stork. It is a relative of one of the best-known large birds of Europe. The large size, long legs, featherless head, heavy, decurved bill, and contrasting black wing and tail feathers distinguish it from the true American Ibises, and from any other American bird.

WOOD IBIS
Mycteria americana
34–45″ long. Color pattern of sexes alike.

So distinctive in appearance is the Wood Ibis, or American Stork, there is little possibility of confusing it with other large white birds. This large white tropical species, with dark bare head, big, long bill, tip decurved, and black wing tips and tail feathers, is unusual in that it is here a wanderer far from its established home. Until late years there was but one record of its occurrence in New Mexico. More recently, however, it has been seen frequently. On June 26, 1952, Homer C. Pickens observed one on Palomas Creek, southwest of Truth or Consequences. On June 24, 1952, one was recorded at the Bosque del Apache Refuge; on July 14, three, and on July 26, four more were recorded at this Refuge, all by Raymond Fleetwood. These and other observations indicate that the birds are becoming more common in the Southwest, due probably to more rigid protection in the Gulf states and the increasing number of water impoundments. The number of recent records may also be due in part to there now being a greater number of observers in the state. Judging by its frequent occurrence, this Ibis may ultimately be found nesting at the Bosque del Apache Refuge and elsewhere in the state. The young may be distinguished from the adults by the grayish-brown coarse hairlike feathers of head and neck.

1192066

IBISES
Family: THRESKIORNITHIDAE

THESE lakeshore- and marsh-dwelling birds, in attitude, size, long legs, and long decurved bills somewhat resemble Long-billed Curlews. They usually occur in flocks, and fly with the neck outstretched. Of the four representatives of this family which occur in the United States—Glossy, White-faced, White, and Scarlet—only the White-faced has been placed on record in New Mexico.

WHITE-FACED IBIS
Plegadis chihi
23″ long. Color pattern of sexes alike.

This Ibis is a migrant species occurring practically statewide, but up to the present time there is no record of its nesting here. It is a beautiful bronze-reddish bird, appearing almost black at a distance. Wings and tail are iridescent purple and green. In size and general appearance it strikingly resembles the Long-billed Curlew, even to the long, decurved bill. The white markings on front of head and around base of bill, which have given the bird its common name, are key distinguishing features. White-faced Ibises are usually observed in rather compact groups of six to many times that number, rarely as high as 6,000 feet elevation. On April 25, 1937, 35 were observed on the San Simon Marshes in Hidalgo County, and on several occasions they have been observed in the Playas Valley, Hidalgo County. They also occur quite regularly about Deming. Montgomery reports them "occasional, April, May, July and September," in the Roswell area. They are recorded as "transient visitor, common" at Bosque del Apache Refuge. The White-faced Ibis may ultimately be found to breed there.

E. R. Kalmbach

WATERFOWL HEAD PROFILES
LEFT: WHITE-FRONTED GOOSE, WHISTLING SWAN, BLUE GOOSE
RIGHT: WHITE-WINGED SCOTERS, RING-NECKED DUCKS, WOOD DUCKS
E. R. Kalmbach, courtesy N.M. Dept. of Game & Fish

SWANS, GEESE AND DUCKS
Family: ANATIDAE

ANATIDAE are represented in New Mexico by seven distinct subfamilies: the *Cygninae* or Swans, the *Anserinae* or Geese, the *Dendrocygninae* or Tree Ducks, the *Anatinae* or Fresh Water or River and Pond Ducks, the *Aythyinae* or Diving Ducks, the *Oxyurinae* or Ruddy and Masked Ducks, and the *Merginae* or Mergansers. Variation in size, physical features, contrasting color in plumage, and nature of living in the open render the identification of members of this large family less difficult than is true of land species that rely on concealing cover for protection. The majority of them are also subject to annual hunting which provides opportunity for close observation and identification.

SWANS

The large size of the Swan, and the immaculate white plumage, are sufficient clues for identification. Only the Whistling Swan now occurs in the state. In the remote past, however, the Trumpeter was recorded in New Mexico and in Colorado. Now, through cooperation between the Canadian Government and our own, the Trumpeter seems to have been rescued from extermination, and it is possible that in time it will be observed in the Southwest.

WHISTLING SWAN
Olor columbianus

About 55″ long; wingspread 7′. Color pattern of sexes alike.

The Whistling Swan can be distinguished from other large white birds by its great size, the immaculate white plumage, yellow stripe from eye to base of bill, its outstretched long neck (in flight), and the absence of black in wing tips. Young: Brownish in color.

DISTRIBUTION. Although this bird may occasionally be observed in migration, winging its way to or from its northern nesting grounds, or resting on lakes or the larger reservoirs, it is regarded as of uncommon occurrence. Krehbiel regards it as "uncommon transient" about Clayton. "From December 12, 1953 into 1954, one stayed at Bitter Lake, usually with or near Snow Geese" (Montgomery). It is listed as "winter visitor, unusual" at Bosque del Apache Refuge. "On December 16, 1955, five were observed on Lake McMillan" (Brummett). The large, shallow Playas Lake, in southern Hidalgo County, frequently is used by the migrating Swans as a resting place. However, this lake may have little or no water during periods of drought. It is quite probable that many swans pass high over the state without stopping. Seventeen of the birds spent the winter of 1955-56 on some lakes in the La Cueva area, north of Las Vegas, the largest number yet recorded. Swans, like airplanes, require a considerable "runway" in order to become wingborne. In Hidalgo County, Jim McClellan and Paul Gordon observed that in the absence of a larger body of water, a Whistling Swan had alighted on a small livestock watering tank. Upon approaching the scene the men noted the grounded bird's repeated attempts to take wing, which because of lack of space and the abrupt banks about the water's edge, proved futile. The bird was captured, and after some difficulty, taken to the top of the windmill tower and freed, whereupon it readily took wing.

GEESE

The Canada, or common, Goose is well known to most bird observers. The White-fronted, the Snow, and the Blue are less familiar, the White-fronted being of very rare occurrence in New Mexico. According to old records, Geese formerly visited the state in great numbers during migration, particularly along the Rio Grande. The Canada, so far as the records disclose, is the only wild goose ever to be found nesting in the state, and this single record dates back a hundred years. If there were suitable and ample winter feeding grounds, these birds would no doubt winter in greater numbers in the Southwest.

CANADA GOOSE
Branta canadensis

35—43″ long. Color pattern of sexes alike.

The difference between the common Canada Goose and any of the subspecies that might be seen in New Mexico is in size rather than in characteristic markings, the Canada being larger. *Adults:* Head and neck black, with broad white throat band extending up across cheeks; body brown or brownish gray with lighter tips to feathers; rump and tail black; upper- and under-tail coverts white; bill, legs and feet black.

DISTRIBUTION. The Canada is present throughout the state during spring and fall migration. A considerable number of these Geese usually spend the winter from Albuquerque south; fewer in the Pecos Valley. They also winter in the lake-grain-field sections of the northeast counties (Colfax, San Miguel, Mora and Harding) and to some extent in the farming districts of the eastern high plains, when the many lake basins there contain water. The numerous large storage reservoirs serve as resting places, but otherwise are of little benefit to Geese or most other waterfowl since they do not produce suitable food. On November 26, 1950, there were approximately 2,000 Canada Geese at Bosque del Apache Refuge. They were observed in December and January at La Joya, and near Albuquerque along the Rio Grande. On December 21, 1953, 220 were noted at Bitter Lake Refuge.

NESTING. The only records of the Canada Goose nesting in New Mexico are those by Henry, 1853-55, on the Rio Grande near Fort Thorn, not far from the present town of Hatch. Under favorable conditions these Geese may again be found breeding in the state.

WHITE-FRONTED GOOSE
Anser albifrons

26—30″ long. Color pattern of sexes alike.

The White-fronted Goose is smaller than the common Canada, being nearer the Snow Goose in size. *Adults:* Forehead white; head, neck, and body brownish gray; upper-tail coverts mainly white; breast and underparts dark gray banded by black. Bill varying from pink to orange, nail whitish; feet yellow or orange. The Latin, Anser—"a goose," albifrons—albus, "white," frons, "forehead," refers to the white on front of the head. This Goose is of rare occurrence in the state, according to the few authentic records. Until recently, there was but one record—by Henry at Fort Thorn in 1854. Other early records seem to be without supporting evidence. Recently it has been recorded more frequently, probably because of a greater number of observers. It is listed as "winter visitor, rare" at Bosque del Apache Refuge and at Bitter Lake Refuge as an "uncommon winter resident." On July 23, 1954, Larry Merovka, of the Game Management Branch, U.S. Fish and Wildlife Service, Albuquerque, wrote: "I killed a White-fronted Goose on October 16, 1940, at Contreras Lake about 55 miles south of Albuquerque and I have no personal knowledge of any other being killed in this State. The one I killed was a lone bird." Thus the only authentic records for the species apply to the Pecos and the Rio Grande flyways.

SNOW GOOSE
Chen hyperborea
24–30" long. Color pattern of sexes alike.

The adult Snow Goose is a pure white bird except for black wing tips. The young, in fall plumage, are not snow-white, yet are light enough in color to be easily distinguished. Though smaller than the typical honker, it possesses most of the Canada characteristics including the familiar honking note. Sportsmen, however, do not regard the Snow Goose as highly as they do the Canada. The Snow Goose nests in the far north, but in migration it is common in New Mexico and some may be noted wintering in the southern half of the state. Normally, Snow Geese arrive in late October and do not leave until early spring. There is one record of their presence as late as May 16 when 14 were noted at Bosque del Apache Refuge.

DISTRIBUTION. Although the Snow Goose may be observed almost any place in the state during migration, it is most common in the Pecos Valley. On November 8, 1953, about 12 miles north of Carlsbad, more than a hundred Snow Geese were observed flying low in a long, wavy line, all the while engaged in continuous exchange of Goose gabbling as if the members were seeking a feeding ground as they moved southward. "On October 22, 1951, 40 were seen on North Lake, about 30 miles northwest of Magdalena" (Lang). "On November 26, 1950, 100 Snows and 2,000 Canadas were noted on the Bosque Refuge" (Fleetwood). On December 16, 1953, the author observed about 250 on Avalon Lake north of Carlsbad. Cottonwood Valley, northwest of Artesia, where alfalfa and grain fields provide suitable feeding grounds and where some farmers give them special attention, is usually occupied by great numbers of Snow Geese in winter. Local conditions—water and available food—will aid materially in attracting and holding this bird seasonally in the state.

BLUE GOOSE
Chen caerulescens
28" long, average. Color pattern of sexes alike.

The Blue, a medium-sized Goose, is rather rare in the state. The principal distinguishing features of the adults are the white head and neck and dark body; plumelike wing coverts; pinkish bills, and pink legs. Under-feather pattern may vary from gray or almost white to very dark in some individuals. It is sometimes seen in association with Snow Geese. State records are confined to the two main north-south state flyways—the Rio Grande and Pecos Valleys. It is listed as a winter visitor at Bitter Lake Refuge and as an unusual winter resident at Bosque del Apache Refuge. According to Larry Merovka, of the U.S. Fish and Wildlife Service, an authority on waterfowl in the Southwest, the Blue Goose is more common than the White-fronted. In the central Pecos Valley, "one occasionally in October, November, December, and March" (Montgomery). This interesting species merits the close attention of bird watchers.

WATERFOWL HEAD PROFILES
Left: Red-breasted Merganser, American Goldeneye, Canvasback
Center: Hooded Merganser, Lesser Scaup
Right: American Merganser, Bufflehead, Redhead
E. R. Kalmbach, courtesy of N.M. Dept. of Game & Fish

WATERFOWL HEAD PROFILES
LEFT: CINNAMON TEAL, AMERICAN WIDGEON, SHOVELER, MEXICAN DUCK
CENTER: GREEN-WINGED TEAL, CANADA GOOSE
RIGHT: BLUE-WINGED TEAL, GADWALL, PINTAIL, MALLARD
E. R. Kalmbach, courtesy of N.M. Dept. of Game & Fish

DUCKS

Waterfowl pose one of the most difficult problems confronting wildlife administrators in the arid Southwest, particularly pertaining to Ducks in the Rio Grande and Pecos Valleys and on the high plains to the eastward. Drainage of marshlands, ponds, and lakes, and curtailment of stream flow as result of water impoundment, all in the interest of agriculture along the two rivers, have seriously restricted suitable feeding and nesting places for the birds. The arid climate, with the resultant scarcity of and demand for water, aggravates the situation. Heavy concentrations of Ducks in migration, or in winter, such as now occur regularly, may be deceptive in that they may be construed as an over-all population abundance rather than as the result of lack of suitable nesting and feeding places elsewhere, thus prohibiting orderly widespread distribution such as occurred under more primitive conditions. Excessive numbers of the birds on limited areas for continued periods, often result in serious complaint of damage to agricultural crops. Since Ducks and other waterfowl are public property, it is incumbent on federal and state officials to provide suitable feeding and breeding environment for them in the ever-increasing competition for use of surface water.

The U. S. Fish and Wildlife Service has acquired and developed two key waterfowl areas: Bosque del Apache in the Middle Rio Grande Valley, and Bitter Lake in the Pecos Valley. These two refuges constitute the principal remaining feeding and nesting grounds for water, marsh, and shore birds on the two main flyways in the state. The State Game Department also has acquired suitable areas which will be of great benefit to waterfowl. The future security of even these sanctuary areas, however, depends upon ability to hold water concessions in times of extended drought.

Burford Lake, lying in the lap of the Continental Divide, is potentially the most important waterfowl breeding ground in the northern mountainous section of the state. This lake is located on federally-owned lands, and its administration takes the welfare of wildfowl into account, although during periods of prolonged drought the water gets too low to provide requirements of the breeding birds. From 1952 to 1956 the lake was practically dry. There are many smaller high-altitude lakes in northern New Mexico where some Ducks nest. These lakes could be greatly improved, particularly those in the national forests, by permanently protecting shorelines and adjacent meadows and slopes against livestock devastation. Protection against livestock would likewise benefit rainy-season lakes of the eastern side of the state where many Mallards, Teals, and Shovelers formerly found suitable nesting environment. The San Simon Marshes in southwestern New Mexico (Hidalgo County) formerly were important breeding and wintering grounds for Ducks and marsh birds and, under proper management, still have possibilities. Lakes on top of the Chuska Mountains, north of Gallup on the Navajo Indian Reservation, would provide nesting environment for many Ducks if livestock grazing were curtailed.

The many irrigation reservoirs are of minor benefit to Ducks except to such fish-eating species as Mergansers. For others, they are useful principally as resting resorts. The water level is usually too erratic to provide food and nesting requirements. On reservoirs or impoundments where water enters through deltas which remain fairly constant, some feeding-nesting environments may be found.

Generally speaking, the more common Ducks are better known than birds of other groups because their size, and the nature of their habits and habitats permit comparatively close observation.

Of the 23 species of Ducks that occur in the state, 14 are known to nest. As time passes, more thorough field work and habitat development may result in additions to the nesting list.

Since New Mexico is far removed from salt water, few marine Ducks enter the state; thus the study of this big family is simplified. One of the desires of the more advanced bird observer is that of seeing such rarities. Some of the species that are listed, such as the Tree Duck, Wood Duck, and Hooded Merganser, are so rare as to provide a thrill for those fortunate enough to observe one.

An interesting phase in the life cycle of the Ducks (also of Geese and Swans) is the annual summer molt, at which time, because of loss of flight feathers, the birds are unable to fly. During this flightless period, which fortunately is rather brief, the birds are dependent for survival upon permanent water and available food and cover. The uninformed, seeing such flightless birds flapping and quacking as they seek cover, may erroneously regard them as young, not able to fly.

Space does not permit a detailed account of the various molt and seasonal plumage changes, or plumages of immature birds. However, these are fully and accurately recorded in several excellent publications, among them *Ducks, Geese and Swans of North America*, by F. H. Kortright, and *Life Histories of North American Wild Fowl*, by A. C. Bent.

TREE DUCKS

The Tree Ducks comprise two species: the Black-bellied and the Fulvous. They are largely tropical species and their distribution in the United States is confined for the most part adjacent to the Gulf Coast of Texas and Louisiana, and to southern California. Their occurrence is rare elsewhere. However, the Fulvous occurs occasionally in west Texas, southern Arizona, and southern New Mexico.

FULVOUS TREE DUCK
Dendrocygna bicolor

20—21″ long. Color pattern of sexes similar.

The Fulvous Tree Duck is a long-legged bird, so unlike other Ducks in general appearance as to cause no confusion in identification. In flight, the slow wingbeats, and legs extending out past end of tail, are distinguishing characteristics. *Adults:* Head, neck, and underparts largely buffy or cinnamon, darker on crown; back and wings blackish, feathers of middle back broadly tipped with tawny; upper- and lower-tail coverts and stripes along sides creamy white; black streak on back of neck.

DISTRIBUTION. The Fulvous Tree Duck has been recorded in the Rio Grande Valley, from Las Cruces southward. For the El Paso area, Lena McBee advises, "Our two records are for Zaragoza, and Ascarate Lakes. One specimen taken is in T.W.C. [Texas Western College] Museum here."

Levon Lee, of the State Game Department, on April 6, 1949, saw two Tree Ducks standing on a log in the Rio Grande, three miles northwest of Las Cruces, and on the following Sunday, R. A. Nichols, of New Mexico State University, saw two bunches, totaling about 24, near Mesilla Dam. Dr. Nichols, who spent many years in Costa Rica, is quite familiar with the Tree Duck.

NESTING. It may be assumed that if the Fulvous Tree Duck continues to occur in the El Paso—Las Cruces section, ultimately it will be found nesting provided suitable nesting places are available. Since the bird is shy and most active by night, it could readily escape being seen even when nesting. This Duck is unique in the great number of eggs it lays, often 20 or more. If suitable nesting boxes were provided where the birds are known to occur, it is possible such boxes might serve as an inducement to nesting. The Fulvous Tree Duck nests both in hollows of trees and on the ground in marshes or near ponds.

RIVER and POND DUCKS

Ducks of this group that occur in New Mexico are the Mallard, Mexican, Gadwall, Pintail, Green-winged Teal, Blue-winged Teal, Cinnamon Teal, American Widgeon (Baldpate), Shoveler, and Wood Duck. All except the Wood Duck are known to nest in the wild here. These surface-feeding Ducks frequent any pond, lake, marsh, or stream available to them. The group includes the most desirable table Ducks, and they are therefore most popular among sportsmen.

The State Game Department has acquired or created marshes and lakes—among them, La Joya in the central Rio Grande Valley, Salt and Charette Lakes near Wagon Mound, Jackson Lake near Farmington, Clayton Lake, and Fenton Lake in the Jemez Mountains, that have considerable value for resting and feeding, and as potential nesting grounds, for surface-feeding Ducks. Such areas are yet to be fully protected and developed. Other lakes and ponds are being acquired, some primarily as fishing waters but these, too, are of benefit to waterfowl. Formerly, during periods of normal rainfall, great numbers of Ducks, as well as shore birds, nested about the many lakes of the prairie and plains country along the eastern side of the state, but these are now largely nonproductive for waterfowl because of devastation of shorelines by livestock. Here also are opportunities for the State Game Department to restore many breeding places by acquiring lands and water, or by obtaining concessions from landowners.

(MALLARD
Anas platyrhynchos

20—26″ long. Color pattern of sexes different.

The wild Mallard, or Green-head, is so similar to the domestic Mallard, and the drake so different from other wild Ducks, it is easily identified. The green head, broad yellow bill, white neck band, and ruddy breast of the adult male are distinctive identification marks. Prevailing color of the female is brown and buffy. In a group of mixed species, the female may be confused with female Pintail or Gadwall. As with the other similar females, one of the best clues to identification on sight is the presence of the male.

The common Mallard is a Duck of worldwide distribution, and is a favorite among sportsmen. More tolerant of man's occupation of its habitat than most Ducks, it submits readily to domestication. For this reason it is widely propagated, thus helping to meet the ever-increasing demand for this fine table bird.

DISTRIBUTION. Because of its adaptability to virtually all climates, the Mallard is widely distributed at all seasons. In migration and in winter it is one of the most abundant Ducks in New Mexico, particularly in the Rio Grande and Pecos Valleys. Wherever there are rainy-season lakes on the high plains of the eastern section of the state, Mallards will be present. The author has found them wintering as high as 7,000 feet elevation (headwaters, Gila River), where their numbers and constant movement kept the center of the V + T Lake open when the remainder of the lake was frozen. They fed along the running water of the river below the lake, but seemed to prefer to spend idle time and the nights on the lake, probably as a precaution against disturbance by prowling enemies. Altitude and rigors of winter do not appear to influence distribution when food and open water are available.

NESTING. The Mallard prefers grassy meadows or marshes for nesting, but is so adaptable and hardy that it will reside and reproduce in areas most other Ducks would not utilize. On the White Mountain tableland in Arizona, the author found a Mallard nesting in bunchgrass under a small yellow pine in a dense forest at least three-fourths of a mile from Big Lake. This bird was nesting at such distance from the nearest water because sheep had destroyed almost all suitable nesting cover on the shores and meadows around the lake. In the absence of more suitable nesting environment in the Rio Grande Valley, near Las Cruces and Albuquerque, this Duck utilizes many drainage canals with aquatic vegetation, and weed- and brush-covered banks. They nest in numbers at Burford Lake and other mountain lakes. At La Jara Lake, eight miles south of Dulce (7,500 feet) five broods, totaling 40 young, were noted by Fleetwood and the author July 14, 1951. Many nest at Bosque del Apache and Bitter Lake Refuges. *Nests:* In grass, or among bushes, made of grass, fully lined with down from the female. *Eggs:* 6 to 10; greenish in color.

([MEXICAN (NEW MEXICAN) DUCK

Anas díazi

21—22″ long. Color pattern of sexes essentially alike.

The Mexican (New Mexican) Duck is one of the most difficult of the Ducks to identify on sight alone, especially when among other Ducks. Fortunately, it is usually seen only with its kind. *Adults:* In general appearance both males and females are very much like dark female common Mallards. Forehead and top of head black streaked with pinkish buff; sides of head and neck pinkish streaked with black; breast black, margined and mottled with cinnamon to buffy on lower underparts; back, rump and upper- and lower-tail coverts black and buffy; speculum dark bluish-violet; bill greenish; legs and feet orange. In fall it is darker. Plumage coloration may vary somewhat as result of hybridization with the common Mallard.

DISTRIBUTION. The summer range of the Mexican Duck is confined largely to the southwestern part of the state, the Rio Grande Valley north to Albuquerque, and sparingly beyond. It occurs uncommonly also in the Pecos Valley north to Bitter Lake Refuge. Specimens of so-called Black Ducks were taken by pioneer ornithologists in the Southwest, but uncertainty as to identification prevailed until about 1915, when a series of specimens obtained by Wharton Huber resulted in his classifying it as a new species, and he named it the New Mexican or Díazi Duck, for Sr. Agustín Díaz, director of the Mexican Geographical and Exploring Commission, 1886. In past years the Mexican Duck was fairly common, in summer, over its restricted range, but it became progressively less in evidence until it is now regarded as rare. On April 25, 1937, the author recorded 30 of these Ducks at the San Simon Marshes in southwestern New Mexico, and on June 8, a dozen or more were seen in Picacho Bosque three miles west of Las Cruces. The renowned bird artist, Allan Brooks, was elated upon collecting a pair of these Ducks in May 1925. While traveling down the Rio Grande Valley, accompanied by the author, and hoping for just such good fortune, Brooks spied a pair of the Ducks in a small pond by the roadside. He took both with the same shot, and that evening made them into beautiful study skins. Records of observations on this Duck at Bosque del Apache Refuge show that in 1946 there were 250 at the Refuge. In spring, 1947, the population was estimated at 100, a decrease of 60 percent. Their numbers continued to decline until November 5, 1956, when Raymond Fleetwood, biologist at the refuge, wrote: "The birds are seldom seen. November 1, four were seen." It is listed as "unusual" at Bitter Lake Refuge. Most Mexican Ducks are usually out of the state before the hunting season. However, there may be heavy hunting in northern Mexico, where most of them doubtless winter. Draining of marshes and destruction of other former nesting places, plus human disturbance have also had adverse effects.

NESTING. The Mexican Duck formerly nested commonly in the Rio Grande Valley and the southwestern section of the state (San Simon Marshes). The first authentic nesting record was that by the author at Burford Lake, July 1913, while he was recording breeding birds of the state. The female and set of eggs were taken and sent to the Biological Survey, U.S. Fish and Wildlife Service. Harry C. Oberholser, ornithologist of the Survey, was at a loss to classify the bird. The identification therefore remained a mystery until about 1915, when this Duck was described and classified by Huber as a new species, the "New Mexican Duck." Later, field work disclosed the fact that the Duck was uncommon at Burford Lake. On June 6, 1935, approximately 12 pairs were found nesting at the San Simon Marshes, in Hidalgo County, where one Duck with a brood of young about a week old, and two broods, one-fourth grown, were also noted. "Adult with 7 young was seen at Radium Hot Springs [north of Las Cruces], May 25, 1947" (Nick Short, as reported by Lena McBee). In May 1947, an estimated 200 young were recorded at Bosque del Apache Refuge. In 1948, 32 young were noted, and in 1949, 5 broods. On November 5, 1956, Raymond Fleetwood wrote the author: "We saw one brood of 6 New Mexican Ducks this year." Wayne H. Bohl, of the Game Department, states: "On June 25, 1955, I saw a female New Mexican Duck with a brood of 5 or 6 young, in the San Simon Marshes."

The most exhaustive study of the Mexican Duck in New Mexico yet made was that by Alton A. Lindsey, in 1944-45 ("Nesting of the New Mexican Duck," The Auk, Vol. 63, No. 4, 1946). While Lindsey found few Mexican Ducks nesting at Bosque del Apache Refuge, he states, of the San Simon Marshes: "Obviously such a marsh is a highly unusual feature of this arid country, and the New Mexican Duck nests in greater concentration here than any other known breeding locality." Of the four nests under Lindsey's observation in 1944 and 1945, incubation of none of the eggs was successfully concluded. Such failures sustain opinion as to the growing scarcity of the species. Its present status emphasizes the urgency in giving the species all possible consideration at both the San Simon Marshes and Bosque del Apache Refuge, if this Duck is to be saved. Nest: One found by the author at Burford Lake was in rank rushes, above shallow water, a few feet from shore; made of dry blades of rushes and water-soaked grasses. Eggs: (Burford nest) 5; white with a greenish blue cast.

(GADWALL
Anas strepera
18—21" long. Color pattern of sexes similar.

The Gadwall is a medium-sized Duck, gray ash-brown above waterline. Adult male: Head and neck pale brown usually speckled with black, darkest on top of head; throat brownish gray; back and sides with wavy transverse bars of black, brown and white; breast feathers with scaled effect; wing patches white and reddish brown with black band; upper- and undertail coverts black; underparts dull white; legs and feet orange. Adult female and young: Brown, streaked and spotted, wing patches similar to those of male, but restricted; underparts white, spotted in summer; legs and feet pale yellow.

DISTRIBUTION. The Gadwall, particularly in migration, is one of the common

Ducks of the state, and many winter here. Like the Mallard, the Gadwall is so adaptable that it may be seen wherever there are lakes, ponds or marshes. It is listed as "permanent resident" at both Bosque del Apache and Bitter Lake Refuges.

NESTING. The Gadwall nests sparingly in the Rio Grande Valley, and commonly about high altitude lakes in the northern section of the state. On August 10, 1913, the author found broods two-thirds grown, at Burford Lake. "In June 1918 about 60 pairs were breeding at Lake Burford" (Wetmore). *Nest:* On dry ground, usually near water, in grass or other vegetative cover; made of grass and lined with dark-colored breast down. *Eggs:* 8 to 12; pale buff.

⟮ PINTAIL
Anas acuta

Male, 26—30"; female, 21—24" long. Color pattern of sexes different.

Adult Male: Neck long, head cinnamon-brown; breast and under-neck feathers white, white extending forward on each side of head terminating as a point in the brown head markings; fore-back and sides gray, finely striped; long, middle tail feathers black, long scapulars striped with velvety black and gray; speculum coppery or violet, bordered front by brown, back by black and white bars. *Adult female:* Brown, blackish on top of head, sides of head and entire neck buffy brown and streaked, throat lighter; upperparts and sides with dark U-shaped marks and white borders; speculum brown, partly iridescent. The male escort is a dependable clue to her identity.

DISTRIBUTION. Migrants begin to enter the northern part of the state by late August. Soon thereafter they may be seen wherever there are marshes, ponds, or lakes, even about small livestock watering tanks. They constitute a good portion of the sportsman's seasonal bag of Ducks,

and yet their over-all numbers seem to be well sustained. An example of the heavy concentrations of Pintails is that of Bosque del Apache Refuge where, on October 25, 1955, an estimated 13,000 were present.

NESTING. Prior to 1958 the only nesting record of the Pintail is that of a parent and a brood of 5 at Bosque del Apache in 1947. William S. Huey, of the State Game Department, advises that he saw several broods of Pintail Ducks on various lakes on the Jicarilla Apache Indian Reservation during the 1958 nesting season. *Nest:* On dry ground, sometimes far from water, in grass, weeds, small bushes; made of grass and weed stems, and lined with breast down from the bird. *Eggs:* 5 to 12; pale olive-green or olive-buff.

⟮ GREEN-WINGED TEAL
Anas carolinensis

12—15" long. Weight: Less than 1 lb. Color pattern of sexes different. (Pl. IV)

The Green-winged Teal is the smallest and daintiest of the Ducks that occur in the state. *Adult male:* Head brown with metallic, green patch from eye back to crest; upperparts, including tail, dark brown; wing with bright green speculum (violet at certain angles), bordered by buffy brown and black; outer scapulars widely edged with black; breast pinkish brown dotted with black; underparts: white. *Adult female:* Dark brown above; breast and flanks lighter; usually identified by diminutive size and iridescent speculum similar to that of male. This little Duck is generally regarded as one of the most beautiful of the inland Ducks, a distinction it shares with the Wood Duck.

DISTRIBUTION. In migration the Green-winged Teal is widely distributed in the state. No pond, lake, or stream seems to be too high or too low in elevation for it and, in keeping with its bantam size, no body of water too small. It is one of the first migrants, arriving in late August. Although the main southbound flight clears the state by early November, some remain throughout the winter, being seen along drainage ditches (Rio Grande Valley) where aquatic food is available and the water does not freeze. In the spring, Green-winged Teals are among the earliest to start north.

NESTING. There are two nesting records of the Green-winged Teal for Bosque del Apache Refuge: six broods totaling 30 young, and four broods with 20 young. However, the northern mountain lakes seem to be preferred as breeding places, particularly those in Carson National Forest north and northeast of Canjilon, where broods of young have been observed in July by the author. *Nest:* Near water in aquatic vegetation or among willow or other bushes; made of grass and lined with down. *Eggs:* 8 to 12; buffy white.

(BLUE-WINGED TEAL
Anas discors

14—16″ long. Color pattern of sexes different.

The Blue-winged Teal is one of the common small Ducks occurring in New Mexico. The most dependable distinguishing marks of the adult male are the conspicuous white crescent in front of the eye and the large blue patch adjoining the green speculum framed in white. Head and neck dark gray, becoming black on top of head; upperparts dark brown; underparts chestnut brown dappled with black; wing lining mostly white; bill bluish black; legs and toes yellow. *Adult female:* Upperparts dark brown; feathers edged with buffy; eye streak dusky; sides of head and neck heavily speckled; wing similar to that of male but speculum less conspicuous; throat white; rest of underparts grayish brown.

DISTRIBUTION. The Blue-winged Teal,

like the Mallard, is widely distributed, both during migration and as a nesting summer-dweller. It is an early fall migrant and although some remain throughout the winter, the main flight is usually out of the state by early November. However, in early October 1954, approximately 7,000 were recorded at Bosque del Apache Refuge, "the largest number ever checked there."

NESTING. This Teal nests throughout the state, taking advantage even of temporary ponds, as well as marshes, lakes, streams, and drainage canals. Formerly it nested commonly about rainy-season lakes throughout the eastern section of the state and in the Texas Panhandle, but because of shoreline devastation by livestock, suitable nesting cover is now rarely present about such lakes. It nests either near or at some distance from water, but prefers grassy meadows. In the absence of such preferred nesting cover, this Teal will take advantage of the shelter of brush cover, rushes, or other water grasses. *Nests:* Usually made of grass, lined with down from the bird. *Eggs:* 6 to 12, creamy buff.

(CINNAMON TEAL
Anas cyanoptera

15—17″ long. Color pattern of sexes different. (Pl. V)

The male Cinnamon Teal is easily identified in its cinnamon or reddish brown attire and light blue wing patch. The small brown female accompanying the conspicuous male can, as a rule, be regarded as of the same species. Like other Teals, the Cinnamon prefers its own kind in association, hence it is not apt to be confused with other Ducks. *Adult male in breeding plumage:* Crown and chin black, rest of head, neck and underparts cinnamon brown; fore-back brownish black with U-shaped bars and edgings of chestnut; lower back and rump greenish brown, feathers edged with paler; upper-tail coverts and tail brown or black; wing with large light blue patch in front of white bar and metallic green or blackish speculum; wing linings white and dull brown; under-tail coverts black; iris orange; bill black. *Adult female*: Like the female Blue-winged Teal but head and chin more speckled and with cinnamon brown and U-shaped markings on breast; legs and feet greenish. *Young in juvenile plumage*: Similar to adult female but streaked below.

DISTRIBUTION. The Cinnamon Teal, although not as common or widespread in the state as the Blue-winged, is indigenous to the western half, being most common in the Rio Grande Valley, much rarer in the Pecos. It is listed as "transient visitor, uncommon" at Bitter Lake Refuge. The author noted a pair at Dexter on April 9, 1953. The Cinnamon prefers ponds, small lakes, marshes, and drainage canals rather than the large streams and irrigation reservoirs. By late September, the birds usually have departed, returning to the state in late March or early April.

NESTING. The Cinnamon Teal nests throughout the western half of the state, when and where water and accompanying water and shore vegetation are in keeping with its needs. As with other ducks which nest here, drainage, particularly in the Rio Grande Valley, has seriously curtailed nesting environment. The author has found the species nesting at San Simon Marshes, Hidalgo County; Patterson Lake, west end of the San Augustin Plains, Catron County; and at Burford and La Jara Lakes, Jicarilla Apache Indian Reservation. "It nests also in Bosque del Apache Refuge" (Fleetwood), and at Colfax County Lakes (Springer). Nests may be located on islands or in salt or marsh grass near water. They are well made of grass and lined with down. *Eggs*: 6 to 12; creamy white or pale buff.

❲ AMERICAN WIDGEON
(BALDPATE)

Mareca americana

18—22" long. Color pattern of sexes different.

The American Widgeon (Baldpate) is one of the common migratory and wintering Ducks in the state. *Adult male*: Among the most easily identified of the Ducks—white along top of head, encircled from the eye backward by a conspicuous wide green band, rest of head and neck finely mottled or spotted; back mainly brown, marked with black; wing with large white patch, and metallic green joined by velvety black of speculum; chest and sides reddish maroon; underparts white; white flank patch sharply contrasting with black under-tail coverts; bill grayish blue with black tip. *Adult female*: Head and neck thickly spotted; upperparts grayish brown barred with yellowish brown; wing as in male but chiefly brown above; speculum dull black, occasionally with a small patch of metallic green; underparts white; sides and flanks deep reddish brown.

DISTRIBUTION. The American Widgeon is among the most widely distributed wintering Ducks in the state, but is most common in fall and in early spring just before the final movement northward. These Ducks are often seen in rafts of hundreds, with no other species among them. Lake Van, a mile east of Dexter, is a preferred place for spring concentrations. This three-acre, permanent lake is privately owned. On February 11, 1953, it was almost covered with an estimated 2,000 of these Ducks, all seemingly impatient to be on their way to their northern breeding grounds. These exclusive spring concentrations are common, particularly in the Pecos Valley.

NESTING. There seems to be no early record of the American Widgeon nesting in New Mexico. In July 1913, the author observed them at Burford and other lakes on the Jicarilla Apache Indian Reservation, but no nests were found. In June 1918, Wetmore reported: "Two pairs of Baldpates [American Widgeon] were apparently nesting, and single males were occasionally seen at Lake Burford." "An adult with young was seen at Black Lake [Colfax County] Aug. 11, 1942" (Lena McBee). The several recent nesting records of the species at Bosque del Apache Refuge indicate that it breeds there rather commonly; as many as 6 broods in a season having been observed there. Nest: Usually on dry ground, often some distance from water, generally concealed in grass, weeds or bushes; made of dry grass and weed stems, lined with light gray down from the bird's body. Eggs: 7 to 12, deep cream to buffy white.

(SHOVELER
Spatula clypeata

17—21" long. Color pattern of sexes different.

The Shoveler, or Spoonbill, is one of the most common of the puddle- or surface-feeding Ducks in the state. The Latin spatula, "spoon" and clypeata, "shield," pertain to shape of bill. It is long and shovel-like, and serves this Duck well for skimming the surface of water for small plant and animal life. The exceptionally long, wide bill is diagnostic. Head of the adult male is metallic green; body a conspicuous mixture of white and black; tail feathers edged with black; wings with blue patch and green speculum; breast white; lower underparts maroon. Adult female: Head and upperparts brown; feathers edged with buffy and those of back irregularly barred or mottled; wing like male but duller, speculum with less green and with two white bars; breast spotted.

DISTRIBUTION. Shovelers are statewide in distribution, and they often congregate in considerable numbers. It is not prob-

able that the winter dwellers and the summer residents are the same birds, but the species is present over much of the state, both in summer and winter.

NESTING. The Shoveler formerly nested far more commonly in the state than it does at present. Drainage, reservoir impoundments, and livestock devastation of lake shorelines, meadows, and marshlands have resulted in seriously curtailing suitable nesting environment. This is especially true of rainy-season lakes of the high plains in eastern New Mexico and adjacent parts of Texas. The Middle Rio Grande Valley (Bosque del Apache Refuge), Burford Lake, and other mountain lakes in the northern part of the state constitute the principal nesting grounds under present conditions. Like the Mallard, the Shoveler seems to prefer rank meadow grass near water for nesting, or in emergencies it may nest at some distance from water. Nest: A depression in the ground, lined with grass or weeds and down. Eggs: 6 to 14; pale olive buff to greenish gray; like those of Mallards and Pintails but smaller.

WOOD DUCK
Aix sponsa

17—20" long. Color pattern of sexes different.

In beauty, charm, and dignity, the Wood Duck has few equals. "It is one of nature's most perfect creations" (Henshaw). The scientific name, Aix (Greek), indicates that it is a water bird, and sponsa (Latin), "betrothed," as if in wedding dress. Adult male: Head and long, droopy crest purple and green, streaked with white; throat white; back, dark iridescent; chest, rich cinnamon spotted with white; underparts mostly white. Adult female: Head dull grayish brown, glossed with green on crest and crown; sides of head and throat white; back glossy grayish brown; underparts white.

DISTRIBUTION. The Wood Duck is uncommon in New Mexico, although records from widely separated areas date back 75 years or more. Recently it has been recorded more frequently, probably because of more observers. "Shot one over decoys in the Pecos River East of Dexter in late October 1948" (Montgomery). "One seen April 24, 1954 on Perico Creek, 6 miles West of Clayton" (Krehbiel). Most records are for Bosque del Apache Refuge. The following observations, supplied by Raymond Fleetwood, Refuge biologist, from the official reports: "October and November 1950, 4; January and September 1951, 2; January, October and November 1952, 7; October, November and December 1953, 12; July 1954, 1." He states in a letter (November 5, 1956), "We do not have any records for 1955 or 1956." There are no nesting records for the state.

DIVING DUCKS

The Diving, or "Bay," Ducks consist of those species which as a rule inhabit the larger bodies of water and obtain their food mostly by diving for it, although, like surface-feeding Ducks, they resort to marshes and meadows for nesting. They have large feet with broad webs, hence are expert swimmers and divers.

(REDHEAD
Aythya americana
17–22″ long. Color pattern of sexes different.

The Redhead, a favorite with sportsmen, is a medium-sized Duck, almost as large as the Mallard. *Adult male:* Head and upper neck red; lower neck and breast black; body gray above waterline; underparts white; bill blue. It may at times be confused with the Canvasback although the male Canvasback is much lighter in color. *Adult female:* Upperparts and breast dark grayish brown; grayish buff or whitish around base of bill; underparts white; bill blue.

DISTRIBUTION. Although not so numerous as some of the other Ducks, the Redhead is widely distributed in New Mexico both in migration and in winter. "They were fairly common on the Burford Lakes when visited the last of September 1904, and since when shot at they repeatedly refused to fly, diving and swimming away perhaps, but not taking wing, it looked as if they had bred there, and that the young and molting birds were not in condition to fly" (Bailey). In July 1913, Redheads were the most numerous of the larger Ducks at Burford Lake. The Redhead is listed as "winter resident, common" at Bosque del Apache and Bitter Lake Refuges.

NESTING. Nesting is confined almost wholly to the higher mountain lakes of the northern part of the state. The author found Redheads nesting at Burford Lake in 1913 and 1916. On June 13, 1918, Wetmore located 50 pairs and a nest containing 14 eggs. Where the lake shores were heavily grazed, these Ducks resorted to the steep hill slopes, placing their nests in the scrub undergrowth. *Eggs:* 10 to 14; buff or creamy buff, larger than those of the Mallard.

RING-NECKED DUCK
Aythya collaris
16–18″ long. Color pattern of sexes different.

The Ring-necked Duck often is referred to as Ring-billed Duck. *Adult male:* Foreparts, upperparts, and under-tail coverts mainly black, with white triangular chin patch and inconspicuous chestnut collar; black of head glossed with green and purple; speculum gray; underparts white; sides gray, vermiculated, separated from breast by white, upward-pointing patch; iris yellow; bill dark gray with white bands at base and bordering tip; legs and feet dark. *Adult female:* Face white around bill; upperparts dull brown, sides of head grayish brown, with whitish streak back of eye; speculum gray; chest and sides brown; underparts white; iris brown; eye ring white; bill black with indistinct light crossbar near tip.

DISTRIBUTION. The Ring-necked Duck generally is regarded as uncommon in the state, although listed as "winter visitor, common" at both Bosque del Apache and Bitter Lake Refuges. It evidently is more common than formerly since some older publications refer to it as "very rare in New Mexico." There seem to be no nesting records for the state.

CANVASBACK
Aythya valisineria

20—24" long. Color pattern of sexes similar.

With most sportsmen, the Canvasback ranks highest of the Ducks as a table bird. *Adult male:* Readily identified by the rufous brown of head and neck; blackish breast, and speckled, whitish upperparts. Its long wedge-shaped bill, almost in straight line from top of head to point, is also a distinguishing feature. *Female:* In size and shape, similar to the male, with foreparts reddish brown; back and sides grayish brown with wavy white barring.

DISTRIBUTION. The Canvasback is a fairly common Duck throughout the state during migration, and winter records are numerous. Heavy concentrations are sometimes noted on the larger bodies of water. In December 1916, George Willett recorded 300 to 400 Canvasbacks on the Carlsbad Reservoir (Avalon Lake). It also occurs in considerable numbers on Burford Lake during migration. "Winter resident, occasional summer resident, at Bosque del Apache Refuge" (Fleetwood). It is recorded as "winter visitor, common," at Bitter Lake Refuge.

NESTING. Wetmore noted three pairs of Canvasbacks which "were apparently nesting" in June 1918 at Burford Lake. It is recorded as a breeder at Bosque del Apache, the only place it has been found nesting in the state. Evidence indicates that additional nesting records will be established in time. *Nest:* In aquatic vegetation over water, or in rank grass, on land; made of tules or grasses, lined with gray down. *Eggs:* 8 or 9; grayish olive.

GREATER SCAUP
Aythya marila

18—20" long. Color pattern of sexes similar.

Adult male: Head, neck, and foreparts black, head glossed with green, back and shoulders gray; underparts white; upper- and under-tail coverts black; bill bluish with black nail. *Adult female:* Back and breast rusty grayish brown; lower underparts white; base of bill encircled with white; bill dull blue or grayish. Bills of both sexes short and flat at end. White striping on wings is only evidence of speculum.

DISTRIBUTION. The Greater Scaup seems to be of rare occurrence in the state. While reported from different sections, definite records are few. "November 27 and 28, 1916, both the American [Greater] and Lesser Scaup were observed on Elephant Butte Lake" (Willett). It is listed as "rare transient" by the El Paso Bird Club for the El Paso area. A. J. Krehbiel records it as "accidental transient" in the Clayton section.

LESSER SCAUP
Aythya affinis

15—17" long. Color pattern of sexes similar.

The Lesser Scaup, so named to distinguish it from its close relative, the Greater Scaup, is also known to hunters as the

Bluebill. It is smaller than the Greater Scaup, and has a purple glossy head, whereas the Greater has a green head. *Adult male:* Foreparts black, head glossed with purple, back and shoulders gray with wavy black and white lines; underparts white; speculum white; bill bluish with black tip. In midwinter, black parts are duller and there is little or no evidence of white on back. *Female and young:* Brown instead of black as in male; yellowish brown on breast; underparts white.

DISTRIBUTION. The Lesser Scaup is common in migration, and many spend the winter here. It is most numerous along the two main state flyways, the Rio Grande and Pecos Valleys.

The author observed with much amusement the feeding conduct of a small assembly of Lesser Scaups on the Rio Grande, below Elephant Butte Dam. The river was full at the time and the water was running rather swiftly. The Ducks would drift with the current until they reached a desired point, then take wing and fly back upstream two or three hundred yards and repeat the downward drift, all the while intent on garnering their meals. The attraction in that particular segment of the river was not determined.

NESTING. There are breeding records for the Bosque del Apache Refuge where young have been observed. Summer records for Burford Lake indicate that the species nests there; however, no nests were found. Careful observation should result in other breeding records. *Nest:* Usually in a marsh, or perhaps on dry land, near water; of grass and weed stems, lined with down. *Eggs:* 6 to 10; dark olive or buff.

COMMON (AMERICAN) GOLDENEYE
Bucephala clangula

18—23″ long. Color pattern of sexes different.

The Common (American) Goldeneye is often referred to as "Whistler" because of the whistling sound made by the wings when the bird is in flight. *Adult male:* Head buffy, with green or violet reflections, and rounded white spot at base of bill; lower neck encircled by white; back black; wing with large white patch; breast and underparts white. *Adult female:* Head, buffy or snuff brown without white spot at base of bill; collar white or gray, incomplete; body mainly grayish except for black rump and white lower underparts; bill dusky.

DISTRIBUTION. The Common Goldeneye is a comparatively rare winter visitor to the state, but occurs both in the Rio Grande and Pecos Valleys. It is listed as "rare winter resident" at Bosque del Apache Refuge. "Ten seen January 31, 1953, 1 mile above Velarde (near Espanola)" (Mrs. P. R. Snider). George Willett recorded it on Elephant Butte Lake, November 23 to December 9, 1916. "On the Rio Grande near Albuquerque a few, generally single birds, occur in December and January" (Leopold). It breeds far north of New Mexico.

BUFFLEHEAD
Bucephala albeola

12—15″ long. Color pattern of sexes different.

This spirited little diver, one of the smallest Ducks, often referred to as "Butterball," is generally more admired for beauty than valued as game. It is reputed to be able to duck under water before a load of shot strikes. Although probably not that quick, it has the faculty of dropping out of sight at the least provocation, and swimming long distances under water. Apparently this species prefers its own kind as it is seldom observed with other Ducks. The bantam size and contrasting green, black, and white plumage of the Bufflehead are dependable identification features. *Adult male:* Bill short and pointed; body plump; head rich purple with broad white patch or hood from below eye extending around top of head. Neck and underparts white; back black. *Adult female:* Similar in size; plumage gray above; white below; head dark with white splash back of eye.

DISTRIBUTION. Bufflehead Ducks, while not an abundant species, are widely distributed during migration and some winter in the state, particularly along the Rio Grande and Pecos Rivers. A few may be seen on the Pecos about Carlsbad throughout the winter. It is listed as "winter resident, common" at both Bosque del Apache and Bitter Lake Refuges. There are no nesting records for the state.

WHITE-WINGED SCOTER
Melanitta deglandi

20—23" long. Color pattern of sexes similar.

The White-winged, largest of the three American Scoters, is an almost solid black Duck with white wing patch, and black knob at base of upper section of bill. *Adult male:* White arch under eye, curving backward. *Adult female:* Similar in appearance, but a uniform brown.

HEAD PROFILES: RUDDY DUCKS
E. R. Kalmbach, courtesy of J. S. Ligon

DISTRIBUTION. This Duck is rare in New Mexico, since its range is largely confined to seacoasts and large bodies of water far north of New Mexico. One was taken on Duck Creek, 30 miles northwest of Silver City, November 10, 1921, by R. T. Kellogg. "One was observed October 10, 1954 on Bitter Lake Refuge" (Montgomery). "One was taken by a hunter near Santa Rosa in November 1955" (Carey Bennett). One was observed on Elephant Butte Lake, October 11, 1956, by Charles Hayes and Don Krieble, U.S. Fish and Wildlife Service game agents.

([RUDDY DUCK
Oxyura jamaicensis

14—17" long. Color pattern of sexes different. (Pl. VI)

The dense, bristly plumage, broad, short bill, short, thick neck, and stiff, pointed spiny tail, generally held upright, and the fact that it does not molt into eclipse in late summer, set the Ruddy apart from all other Ducks. As the name implies, the adult male is a ruddy or reddish color; it has a black cap, white cheeks, and blue bill. The color pattern of the female Ruddy is somewhat similar except that she is more brownish. Ruddy Ducks usually occur by themselves, a further identification clue. During the nesting season the male displays his charms in various ways. As if unable to restrain his appeal for attention, he paddles and noisily treads the water for some distance, terminating the performance by patting his breast with his conspicuous blue bill. As with the dainty little Bufflehead, the highest value of the Ruddy is its esthetic appeal.

DISTRIBUTION. The Ruddy Duck, strictly a North American species, seems to have little regard for climate or altitude in summer. It is widely distributed during migration. On October 20, 1956, Wayne Bohl and the author estimated no less than 2,000 Ruddy Ducks in a great raft on Lake

McMillan, near the dam. Apparently the congregation was of the one species only, although a raft of about 200 Coots was observed nearby. The Ruddy is listed as "winter resident, common" at both Bosque del Apache and Bitter Lake Refuges.

NESTING. The nesting of the Ruddy Duck is confined almost entirely to the high mountain lakes in the northern section of the state. The author has found it nesting in greatest numbers at Burford Lake, La Jara Lake, and other lakes within the Jicarilla Apache Indian Reservation. In 1916, he estimated there were 200 confined largely to one section of Burford Lake. In 1918, Wetmore estimated there were 55 pairs breeding at this lake. The Ruddy is regarded as probably the only wild Duck that raises two broods in a season, and the male has the rare distinction, among Ducks, of assisting with the care of the young. *Nest:* Bulky structure, made of water grasses. *Eggs:* 6 to 10; grayish or buffy white; astonishingly large for size of the bird.

MERGANSERS

Mergansers are crested, diving Ducks with long, slender bodies, and slender, serrated bills, which have given them the name "Saw-bill." Their bills are well adapted for seizing and holding their slippery quarry. They are experts at pursuing and catching fish and can swallow surprisingly large ones. Fortunately, they consume large quantities of so-called rough fish that are of little value for human consumption. All three species—Hooded, Common (American), and Red-breasted—occur in New Mexico.

HOODED MERGANSER
Lophodytes cucullatus
17—19″ long. Color pattern of sexes different.

The Hooded Merganser is named from the white, black-rimmed, fan-shaped crest of the male. The bill is narrow, rounded, and serrated. *Adult male:* Head, neck, and back are black, with black and white barring on wings (folded); rump, tail, breast and underparts white. *Adult female:* Crest unlike that of the male—bushy, more of a cinnamon color and without white mottlings; underparts white.

DISTRIBUTION. This Merganser is an uncommon winter visitor to the state. A pair was taken by Kellogg near Silver City on November 29, 1919. "It is a rare winter resident at the Bosque del Apache Refuge" (Fleetwood). On December 18, 1954, Larry Merovka, of the U.S. Fish and Wildlife Service, killed a female Hooded Merganser on the Rio Grande near Belen. He writes: "First one I have ever seen in New Mexico." It is recorded as "winter visitor, occasional," at Bitter Lake Refuge and "winter visitor, unusual," at Bosque del Apache Refuge.

NESTING. There is one old record of a female with young being observed on the Upper Pecos River, but this record is now regarded as questionable. *Nest:* In hollows of trees, sometimes in nesting boxes, rarely on the ground. Lined with grass, leaves, and down. *Eggs:* 8 to 10; white, usually nest stained.

([COMMON (AMERICAN) MERGANSER
Mergus merganser
25—27″ long. Color pattern of sexes similar.

The Common (American) Merganser is a handsome, streamlined Duck, but is in disrepute with sportsmen because of its fish-eating nature, although the "rough" or undesirable kinds are included in its diet. *Adult male:* Head black, glossed with green; neck, breast, and entire underparts white or pale salmon; forepart of back black; hindpart and tail gray; wing mostly white, with one black bar; bill, legs and feet red. *Adult female:* Head and long, pointed crest, tawny or reddish brown; upperparts gray, speculum white, crossed by a dusky bar; chin white, separated from white patch on throat by brown collar, neck grayish; underparts creamy or buffy; bill red, feet orange.

DISTRIBUTION. The Common Merganser is a rather frequent winter resident in New Mexico, where it generally inhabits larger bodies of water, such as big irrigation impoundments. These Mergansers have been found most abundant on Elephant Butte Reservoir, where large numbers spend the winters. Because of heavy concentrations here, control measures are at times necessary to curtail depredations on edible fish. They are listed as "winter visitor, common," at Bitter Lake Refuge. "Twelve were observed on the Rio Grande above Pilar, February 25, 1953" (Hawkins).

NESTING. All nesting records of the Common Merganser in the state are fairly recent. "In July 1951, adult and three young were seen on the Chama River below El Vado Lake" (Montgomery). Under date of June 22, 1955, Carey Bennett, of the U.S. Fish and Wildlife Service, wrote: "On May 17 I observed what is probably a new record for breeding of the [Common] Merganser. A hen with a brood of approximately 15 ducklings in the downy stage was on a beaver pond located on the Middle Fork of the Gila River, approximately 2½ miles above its confluence with the West Fork; elevation less than 6,000 feet." Other nestings have been reported but not verified. *Nest:* Usually in

hollows of trees or in stumps, but sometimes on the ground; lined with twigs, moss, leaves, grass, and down. *Eggs:* 6 to 10, creamy white or buff.

RED-BREASTED MERGANSER
Mergus serrator

20—25″ long. Color pattern of sexes different.

Adult male: Head with double-pointed black crest, glossed with green; neck collar white; forepart of back black, middle and hindpart gray with white and dusky waving; tail gray; wings, when closed, appear largely white, crossed by two black bars; brown band of chest spotted with black; underparts mainly white; bill, legs and feet red. The male is a rather highly colored and conspicuous Duck, somewhat smaller than its relative, the Common Merganser. *Adult female:* Head and crest light brown or cinnamon; upperparts ashy brown, feathers with dark centers; speculum white, with two black bars; bill, legs and feet dull red.

DISTRIBUTION. The Red-breasted Merganser is a rather rare migrant and winter resident in the state. Like the American, it inhabits larger bodies of water, such as Elephant Butte and Conchas Reservoirs. It is recorded as "winter visitor, unusual" at both Bosque del Apache and Bitter Lake Refuges. "It is uncommon in the state. When numbers of the American [Common] were being shot on Elephant Butte Lake, several of the Red-breasted were killed" (Larry Merovka). No nesting records of this species for the state.

AMERICAN VULTURES
Family: CATHARTIDAE

VULTURES are large, dark or black birds, easily distinguishable by their bare heads and wide wingspread. The group consists of the Turkey Vulture, Black Vulture, and the California Condor. The last-named is rare, and confined to a limited mountainous area in central-western California. The Turkey Vulture alone is indigenous to New Mexico. Although the Black Vulture occurs in southern Arizona, and western Texas (Presidio County), there is as yet no authentic record for the state.

([TURKEY VULTURE
Cathartes aura

26—32″ long. Color pattern of sexes alike.

The Turkey Vulture, or Buzzard, has a bare red head, long deep beak, wide wingspread, and uniformly blackish body. Vultures are frequently seen at rest in trees and on posts, or on rock ledges sunning their backs in a unique manner—with outstretched wings—particularly during the early morning or following showers; sailing about in wide circles; or beating back and forth on wing with little apparent effort. Numbers of them gracefully wheeling about usually indicate the presence of food in the form of a dead animal. These carrion-eaters serve man as destroyers of decaying bodies and refuse which are breeding places for flies. Although there is widespread belief that they locate their food through smell, this is unfounded, as exhaustive experiments indicate. Their keen vision while in flight serves them well in locating a meal, as does the presence or conduct of crows and ravens, as well as coyotes and other mammals. The mammals, with a keen sense of smell, unwittingly serve as pilots to prospective feasts.

DISTRIBUTION. Turkey Vultures usually arrive in the southern part of the state—Carlsbad and Las Cruces—in early March. In the spring or fall, when the birds are migrating, concentrations of considerable numbers occur, particularly where suitable roosting trees are found. The greatest evening concentrations were those recorded by Bailey as occurring about the Carlsbad Caverns, where, at one time, he estimated there were 200 or more strung along the rimrocks which border Walnut Canyon. Turkey Vultures are usually out of the state by mid-October.

NESTING. Nests usually are placed under overhanging ledges, in caves, or in openings among slide rocks on mountain or canyon slopes, often making them difficult to locate. However, nests or young have been observed in various parts of the state: "near Vaughn May 25" (E. F. Pope); "white downy young were in nest in Walnut Canyon near Carlsbad Caverns in late April" (Bailey); "nest near Santa Fe, May 28" (Jensen); "nest under rimrock of Eagle Creek near Alto" (George Hightower). On August 28 the author saw young able to fly only short distances in South Diamond Canyon, southwest of Chloride, at 7,500 feet. These nesting records were given the author by Jensen: "May 19, 1929, 2 eggs under slide rocks east of Cerrillos; May 18, 1930, 2 eggs same place; May 26, 1933, 2 eggs under boulder near same place." *Eggs:* Usually 2; greenish white, spotted with brown or lavender, especially about the larger end; laid on the barren shelter floor.

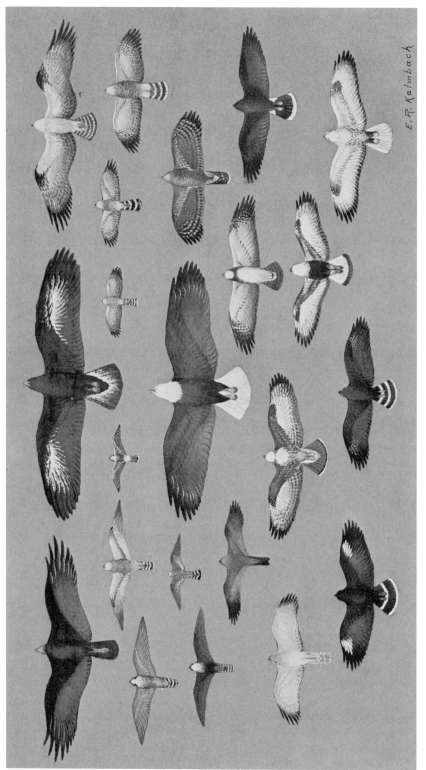

VULTURE, HAWKS AND HARRIERS

Top: Turkey Vulture, Golden Eagle, Osprey

Row 2: Peregrine Falcon, Prairie Falcon, Sparrow Hawk, Sharp-shinned Hawk, Cooper's Hawk, Gray Hawk

Row 3: Aplomado Falcon, Pigeon Hawk, Bald Eagle, Goshawk. Row 4: Mississippi Kite, Swainson's Hawk, Harris' Hawk

Row 5: Marsh Hawk, Red-tailed Hawk, Rough-legged Hawk. Bottom: Black Hawk, Zone-tailed Hawk, Ferruginous Hawk

E. R. Kalmbach, N.M. Dept. of Game & Fish

HAWKS and HARRIERS
Family: ACCIPITRIDAE

THIS FAMILY is represented in the state by the beautiful streamlined Kite whose long wings serve it well in its graceful and seemingly tireless flight; the swift-flying Accipiters with short, rounded wings and long tails—generally regarded as bird Hawks; the slow-flying Buteos, or Buzzard Hawks, with broad wings and broad, rounded tails, commonly seen soaring or "floating" high in the air; and the largest and most powerful of American birds of prey, the Eagles—the Golden, appearing almost black in flight, and the Bald with white head, neck, and tail. And, finally, the Marsh Hawk, the only Harrier native to North America. Marsh Hawks usually are seen beating about over marsh, meadow, or prairie. The brownish or bluish gray plumage and the long tail with conspicuous white patch are distinctive. The Falcons, though members of the family *Falconidae*, are because of affinity generally referred to as Hawks.

In their varied plumages the Hawks are not always easily identified by sight alone. Plumage of the young may differ sharply from that of adults, and some individuals occur in dark or melanistic phase. Such variations may be very confusing. Furthermore, females of most species of Hawks are larger than the males. Of the many species of Hawks (including Falcons) occurring in New Mexico, all but five—Mississippi Kite, Red-shouldered Hawk, Broad-winged Hawk, Rough-legged Hawk, and the Pigeon Hawk—are known to nest within its borders.

MISSISSIPPI KITE
Ictinia misisippiensis

14″ long. Color pattern of sexes essentially alike.

The Mississippi Kite, a bird of treetops and the air, is among the most graceful on wing as it circles and soars seemingly with the greatest of ease. Rarely seen on the ground, it takes most of its food—principally insects, largely cicadas and grasshoppers—in flight. Its beauty, inoffensiveness, and charming ways apparently endear it to man, as it has not suffered the persecution that have most other birds of prey. *Adults:* Head pearl gray; back bluish slate; neck and underparts bluish gray; tail black without bands, rather wide and square at end.

DISTRIBUTION. It is significant to note that there were no New Mexico records of the occurrence of the Mississippi Kite prior to 1955. Several records since that time indicate that this handsome species is entering the state in increasing numbers. John M. Campbell, of New Haven, Connecticut, who has spent considerable time in New Mexico recording birds, advises the author that he saw a lone Mississippi Kite, May 13, 1955, in the upper Animas Valley, about four miles east of Cloverdale.

In September 1955, R. C. Brummett reported seeing several about a large cottonwood grove a few miles south of Carlsbad. Mrs. Lena McBee and Miss Mary Belle Keefer observed Mississippi Kites about El Paso, including adjacent New Mexico, July 31, and August 1 and 24, 1956. "On August 6, 1957, five, two of which were immature, perched in one tree, at the Boy Scout Camp [about four miles above El Paso]" (Lena McBee). On July 9, 1957, Mrs. McBee and Mrs. McClintock observed two feeding over an irrigated field near Canutillo, in New Mexico. Mrs. McBee states: "Roy Fisk and Al Smith, members of the Audubon Society of El Paso, saw the Kites (2) May 19, 1958. One was carrying a stick. We have seen this pair (and we think at least another pair) all summer, but detected no further sign of nesting." "One was seen May 25, 1957, by Cook and Krehbiel, near Perico Creek, 3 miles west of Clayton" (Krehbiel). "I had a good observation of a Mississippi Kite June 26 [1958] about 7 miles northwest of Roswell" (Montgomery). Fleetwood observed one at Bosque del Apache Refuge, May 21, 1958.

NESTING. The several summer records of the Mississippi Kite in the El Paso area of both Texas and New Mexico strongly indicate that the birds nest in the state. However, in the absence of a definite record, it is not herein given nesting status. There is little doubt that this Kite will soon be added to the state breeding list, particularly in the Rio Grande and Pecos Valleys, and possibly along the Canadian River, in the vicinity of Tucumcari. Nests should be looked for in cottonwood trees 25 to 40 feet above ground. However, in the Vernon, Texas, area Mississippi Kites nest in mesquite trees, 8 to 10 feet from the ground. *Nest:* Made of small sticks and twigs, usually lined with plucked green leaves. *Eggs:* Normally 2, sometimes 3; plain white or bluish white.

ACCIPITERS OR SHORT-WINGED HAWKS

THIS GROUP includes three species of shy, dashing, undercover Hawks: the Goshawk, most powerful and destructive of the three, the Sharp-shinned, and the Cooper's. The Goshawk feeds principally on birds, but fortunately it is not common. At times, it also feeds on the rock squirrels and other rodents. The Sharp-shinned and the Cooper's prey on practically all species of small- to medium-size birds, but they have some redeeming traits. They seek out the places where their prey is most abundant, particularly in the ranks of fall migrations of which they are a part. It is then that they may be an asset as a controlling influence on concentrations of House or English Sparrows, Starlings, Blackbirds, or even of Lark Buntings or House Finches which often do serious damage to unharvested crops such as maize, particularly in the eastern high plains and the irrigated sections of the Pecos and Rio Grande Valleys. The influence, good or bad, which these Hawks exert depends largely upon the population status of their prey.

⟨ GOSHAWK
Accipiter gentilis
20—26″ long. Color pattern of sexes alike.

The beautiful, streamlined Goshawk, indigenous to the high forested mountains of the state, is the largest and most powerful of the Accipiters. *Adults:* Wings short, tail 10 to 13 inches long; general color mottled, bluish gray; upperparts dark bluish gray, top of head blackish, and white stripe over eye; wings barred; underparts whitish, covered with finely crosslined grayish markings, overlaid with broken lines of blackish penciling; front part of upper half of legs feathered; feet yellow; iris red in male, brownish orange in female. The Goshawk is almost always seen in heavy forests of the higher mountains where no other large Hawk, except the Red-tailed, is apt to occur—a fact which aids in identification.

DISTRIBUTION. This Hawk, usually referred to as the Western Goshawk, may be looked for in any of the heavily forested mountains of the state above 7,000 feet, rarely at lower altitudes. The author has three beautiful study skins which were taken in December 1926 at a lodge in upper Eagle Creek about six miles northwest of Alto, where they persisted in preying on chickens. He also has records of Goshawks in the Sacramento Mountains, August 15, 1951, when two (probably a pair) had caught a large chicken at the Velmer Lane home in James Canyon, six miles west of Mayhill. One of these was killed, and later identified. On October 15, 1953, another was seen in Walker Canyon about eight miles northwest of Mayhill. There are records for the Sandia Mountains east of Albuquerque, the Sangre de Cristo Range, the Mogollons, the Black Range, and the San Juan Mountains. While Goshawks are widespread, they are nowhere common. They are most numerous in northern New Mexico, where they prey on the Blue Grouse and Abert's squirrel. This Hawk apparently is resident or semi-resident where found.

NESTING. Authentic nesting records of the Goshawk are few for the state. The author obtained convincing evidence that a pair was nesting on Blue Mountain, San Mateo Range, about 50 miles southwest of Magdalena, although the nest was not located. Since the birds are usually shy, live in dense timber and nest high above ground, their nests are most difficult to find even though the birds become noisy, screaming and chattering whenever nests with young are approached. On July 15, 1935, the author examined a nest located by forest ranger Ed C. Groesbeak about five miles northeast of Canjilon. The author accompanied Fred Merkle, the Carson National Forest supervisor, and the ranger to the nest location. The nest tree was a tall aspen growing in a canyon among conifers, at about 7,000 feet. The nest was 50 feet from the ground. The adult birds chattered about in the treetops and in flight overhead. Finally the male was killed. It was necessary to fell the tree in order to examine the nest. Two well-feathered young were killed. The nest was a bulky structure of sticks and lined with dried Douglas fir and aspen twigs that had been plucked green. The nest had been used previously. Apparently Red-shafted Flickers constituted a major portion of the food brought to the young.

SHARP-SHINNED HAWK
Accipiter striatus

Male, 10—11″; female, 12—13″ long. Color pattern of sexes similar.

The small, swift-flying Sharp-shinned Hawk often is referred to as Little Blue Darter. The female, considerably larger than the adult male, is almost the size of an adult male Cooper's Hawk. Other than in size, the Sharp-shinned and Cooper's are much alike in appearance and conduct. They fly with several rapid beats of wings, followed by sailing. The Sharp-shinned has a small head. *Adults:* upperparts bluish gray; tail with three or four blackish bands and narrow white tip; underparts heavily crossbarred or spotted with dusky spots; legs and feet yellow or greenish; iris varying with age from yellow to red. The Sharp-shinned, like the Cooper's, is a bird Hawk and seems to have little difficulty dashing through or around brush or other cover close to the ground to surprise its prey, which includes a great variety of small birds. At the author's game farm near Carlsbad, one spent the winter and lived almost entirely on the House Sparrows, hence was a welcome visitor.

DISTRIBUTION. In fall and winter the Sharp-shinned Hawks are rather common and statewide in distribution. In summer they are found sparingly in forested mountains throughout the state, more commonly in the northern section. Their fall migration movements parallel rather closely the southward movement of small birds, which constitute a large part of their food.

NESTING. Sharp-shinned Hawks have been observed by the author in summer in various mountainous sections over the state, even in the Animas Mountains near the New Mexico–Mexico boundary (May 9), but the only nesting records are for the Sangre de Cristo Range near Santa Fe. Lack of records should not be taken as evidence that they do not nest elsewhere, for their favorite breeding retreats are in the high-altitude coniferous forests far removed from most observers. These nesting records are from Jensen in the Sangre de Cristo Range, east and northeast of Santa Fe: "June 2, 1928, nest, 8 feet up in small Douglas fir, upper Santa Fe Canyon, four fresh eggs; June 9, 1929, nest in same tree, about 2 feet below the old one, contained three eggs. In late July 1936, a nest found in upper Little Tesuque Canyon, northeast of Santa Fe, contained five well-incubated eggs." *Nests:* In conifers, usually Douglas firs. *Eggs:* 4 or 5; highly colored, greenish or grayish base, spotted and blotched with brown.

⟨ COOPER'S HAWK
Accipiter cooperii
Male, 14–17"; female, 18–20" long. Color pattern of sexes similar.

The Cooper's is a larger counterpart of the Sharp-shinned. It is named for Samuel Graham Cooper (1830–1902), U.S. Army Surgeon, author *Land Birds* (1870), and other works, particularly on the ornithology of California. *Adult male:* Wings, short and rounded; top of head blackish, in contrast to bluish gray of back; underparts barred crosswise with rufous on white ground color; tail long for size of bird; eyes reddish. *Adult female:* Without bluish gray of males; brown above; underparts streaked with reddish brown. Young similar to adult female.

The Cooper's Hawk, or Blue Darter, is in bad repute with sportsmen and bird lovers alike. It aptly may be called the Quail Hawk since, in the Southwest at least, it seeks out and preys on Quail whenever and wherever they are available. The Cooper's is not usually numerous. It is so shy and retiring that comparatively few are killed. Many of the larger, beneficial Hawks are persecuted becaused of depredations of the Cooper's. Farmers, ranchers, and sportsmen can learn to recognize this Hawk and should refrain from killing beneficial species because of the Cooper's depredations. In appearance and habits, the Cooper's is entirely different from the large, soaring Hawks and there is little likelihood of confusion.

DISTRIBUTION. In fall and winter the Cooper's Hawk occurs statewide, even over the eastern high plains. It relies on brush cover or hedgerows for concealment. Where such chosen cover is frequented by Quail and Doves, one or two of the Hawks may spend considerable time preying on them and on smaller birds at such places. Elsewhere, in the absence of Quail, they feed on a variety of birds, Flickers apparently being a favored food, probably because they are comparatively easy prey. Among the oaks of a canyon in the foothills of the San Mateo Mountains, the author shot one that had just killed a Screech Owl. They also prey on the various Jays, for which they should not be too harshly condemned. In summer, restricted numbers are confined to the forested mountains and timbered canyons and watercourses, even to the extreme southern border of the state.

NESTING. The Cooper's Hawk nests rather commonly throughout the state, where there are suitable nesting trees. Fresh eggs usually are found in early May (Chloride area). On June 28, 1916, the author found a nest containing half-feathered young, 35 miles northeast of Grants. On May 18, 1955, another with 4 fresh eggs was examined at Cloverdale Grove, near the Mexican boundary. *Nests:* Usually 20 to 30 feet above ground, made of sticks and lined with bark or leaves. Sometimes nests of other raptors are repaired and used. *Eggs:* 4 or 5; pale bluish white.

BUTEOS

The Hawks of the Buteo group are characterized by broad wings, wide tails, and slow-flying and soaring movements. Those native to New Mexico are the Red-tailed, Broad-winged, Swainson's, Zone-tailed, Rough-legged, Ferruginous, Gray (Mexican Goshawk), Harris', and Black (Mexican)—the Broad-winged and the Gray being the rarest of the group. For the most part, they inhabit open lands and timbered valleys. The Buteos are regarded by conservationists as the most beneficial of the Hawks.

No other group of birds has a higher economic or esthetic value than the Buteo Hawks, yet none has been so thoughtlessly and ruthlessly destroyed. Their natural and preferred food consists of rabbits, rats, mice, ground squirrels, grasshoppers, and other pests highly destructive to rangeland forage and agricultural crops. When Hawks and Owls, and other rabbit- and rodent-preying species are reduced in numbers, as is now the case, their prey increases proportionately. Although all of the Buteos have been decimated, the Ferruginous, American Rough-legged, and the Red-tailed, among the larger species, have borne the brunt of man's folly. The Swainson's, being wholly migratory and usually out of the state before fall when Hawk shooting is rampant, have been less seriously affected.

The unrestrained killing of beneficial species of Hawks and Owls has been indirectly disastrous to the welfare of upland game and other desirable birds. With the decimation of such birds of prey, rodent populations often reach a saturation point, particularly in the sandhill terrain where these pests consume plants and seeds so essential in season to the birds. Whatever grass and weed seeds mature are mostly eaten or cached by rodents. Thus little winter food remains for Quail and other beneficial seed-eating birds in winter, and little seed for re-seeding the denuded ground. This is an alarming situation on arid lands where under the most favorable conditions soil-binding ground cover and palatable forage are scant. Far better would it have been for the land, its vegetative cover and its bird inhabitants, had all Hawks—except when and where damage actually occurred—been legally protected a hundred years ago. Damage resulting from questionable species is infinitesimal compared to the benefits rendered by the valuable Buteo Hawks.

Concentrations of Quail and other birds about ranches, farms, and even urban communities—a common occurrence—is evidence of lack of natural food formerly available to them. Thus those guilty of shooting the large Hawks, as well as Owls, are indirectly contributing to the scarcity of food for the birds they seek to preserve.

The tragic fate of the Buteo Hawks in the Southwest became increasingly evident with the growing occupation of the land. The resultant improved roads were soon paralleled by fence and telephone lines, the posts and poles of which became tempting resting places for the big Hawks, particularly in the plains and sandhill areas. The Hawks thus exposed became tempting targets for hunters. Unfortunately, the beneficial Hawks have too long been the victims. Very few of the shy, swift-flying, bird-preying Hawks are killed. There is need for killing birds of prey when and where their control is justified. On the other hand, local depredation does not justify indiscriminate destruction.

The erroneous designation "Big Chicken Hawk," as applied to big Hawks since pioneer times, has been a factor in the continued destruction of these friends of man. Buteo Hawks in the Southwest rarely occur where there are domestic fowls, with the rare exception of the Harris' Hawk. Distribution of this species is so limited that depredation is nominal. The indiscriminate killing of beneficial

Hawks in the light of present knowledge of their economic value is not in keeping with sound conservation policies. Enlightenment as to the value of the large beneficial Hawks should create a more favorable public sentiment for their protection.

(RED-TAILED HAWK
Buteo jamaicensis

19—23″ long. Color pattern of sexes alike.

Adults: Varying from light color to almost black. *Light phase:* Upper parts dark brown, marked with lighter brown and whitish; tail bright reddish brown with a black subterminal band and sometimes additional bars; underparts white or buffy. *Dark phase:* Uniform sooty brown except for rufous tail. Intermediate phase: reddish brown on underparts with wash of same as upperparts; many gradations of

Young Red-tailed Hawk
Photograph by Kathryn Morris

these three plumages are also found. Bill brown; legs and feet yellow. *Young:* Dark brown, heavily spotted on lower underparts; tail grayish to yellow brown, crossed by eight to ten blackish bands. Red-tailed Hawks are most likely to be confused with the Swainson's. However, the Swainson's Hawks are usually out of the state in the fall when Red-tails are most numerous. Those in the dark plumage are most confusing, but even in this plumage the tail is usually rufous.

Although the Red-tailed occasionally takes poultry or game birds, it is generally regarded by those who know the Hawks as far more beneficial than harmful. According to the food chart of the various Hawks prepared by the National Audubon Society, more than 75 percent of its food consists of gophers, rats, mice, ground squirrels, grasshoppers and rabbits. In the sparsely settled sections of the state, its economic value may be even higher than elsewhere. In the forested mountainous areas, these Hawks feed on rock squirrels which are destructive to bird eggs, and on gophers. When after gophers this Hawk selects a perch in the dense cover of a tree adjacent to a hillside or meadow infested with these rodents. When one opens a surface hole and ventures out, as they often do to gather grass or leaves for nest-making, the Hawk, by a straight dash from its perch, snatches its unsuspecting prey. Snakes also seem to be a preferred food, and large grasshoppers at times make up a good percentage of the diet of young Red-tails which are just starting to forage for themselves.

DISTRIBUTION. In New Mexico, Red-tailed Hawks are the most widely distributed of the Buteo group. Although they are more numerous in winter than summer, they are found statewide even in summer. Altitude seems to have little bearing on their presence, so long as trees are available to them.

NESTING. In the lower altitudes in the

southern section of New Mexico, Red-tails usually start nesting in mid-March; in the higher mountainous areas, somewhat later. *Nests:* Rather bulky, made of sticks and lined with roots and bark. They may be on rock ledges, in tall yuccas of the Southwest section, or in cottonwood, ash, and other trees that grow along watercourses or in canyons. In high mountainous country, nests are usually placed in pines or on rimrock ledges. The same nests, with some repairs, are generally used year after year. *Eggs:* 2 or 3; bluish white; usually 2 of a set of 3 will be blotched with brown, while the third, probably the last laid, will be almost or wholly without markings.

BROAD-WINGED HAWK
Buteo platypterus
14—17″ long. Color pattern of sexes alike.

This handsome little Buteo deserves full protection. *Adults:* Upperparts dark brown, wing quills and tail blackish, tail narrowly tipped with white and with two to four broad grayish bands; underparts brown barred with rufous. The normal plumage of the Broad-winged and the Swainson's is similar, but the Broad-winged Hawk is much smaller.

DISTRIBUTION. The Broad-winged seems to be the rarest of the Buteos in New Mexico. However, it may have occurred in the eastern part of the state in the past, during migration, without being recorded, because of lack of competent observers. On October 3, 1954, the author collected a beautiful male in the rare dark or melanistic plumage, 40 miles south of Portales. Its gizzard was crammed with grasshoppers. There are no nesting records for the state.

⟨ SWAINSON'S HAWK
Buteo swainsoni
19—20″ long. Color pattern of sexes similar.

The Swainson's is a handsome, medium-sized Hawk of the more open valleys, mesas and plains. It is named in honor of William Swainson (1789-1855), a leading British ornithologist, co-author with John Richardson of the *Fauna Boreali Americana*, 1831. *Adult male in normal plumage:* Upperparts almost uniformly dark brown; tail crossed by 9 or 10 blackish bands; throat and underparts white, contrasting sharply with reddish brown, or rufous, chest band. *Adult female:* Like male but chest patch grayish brown rather than rufous. Legs and feet rich yellow. *Dark phase, both sexes:* Sooty brown. "Every possible gradation occurs between these dark and light phases." *Young in juvenile plumage:* Upperparts blackish brown, varied with buffy or yellowish brown; head, neck, and underparts buff or fawn color; head and neck streaked; underparts usually more or less marked with blackish.

DISTRIBUTION. In summer Swainson's Hawks are the most common of the larger Buteo Hawks, ranging from the Mexican boundary into Canada. In the state their principal habitat is open or semi-wooded country up to 6,000 feet, rarely higher except in migration when they may occur up to 9,000 feet or higher. However, they shun heavy forests of the mountains. Populations remain rather consistently high, since they have a vast breeding range, are migratory, and most of them have left the state before the usual hunting seasons, when other Buteos are targets. Swainson's, an adornment to the wide open spaces, are almost wholly beneficial. During migration great concentrations often occur where they find heavy grasshopper infestations. Formerly such concentrations often numbered 1,000 or more. Large concentrations still occur, but it is not often that such vast numbers are seen. On one occasion in the fall of 1909 the author observed more than 500 Swainson's in the arid Jornada del Muerto Valley where they were feeding on large, wingless grasshoppers. In early May 1918, he and R. T. Kellogg of Silver City, encountered a concentration of about 400 of the Hawks in San Luis Pass on the Mexican boundary, Hidalgo County, where they were also feeding on the hordes of grasshoppers. On September 12, 1954, Allen E. Anderson, of the State Game Department, observed about 150 of the birds eight miles east of Carrizozo. Their value as destroyers of insect pests of rangeland forage and agricultural crops is not fully realized. Their prey consists of rats, mice, ground squirrels, large grasshoppers, and even snakes. On the ranch of Jack McCombs southwest of Carlsbad, a Swainson's Hawk, whose unusual conduct indicated that it was in the act of killing something, attracted Mr. McCombs' attention. He watched the Hawk for a short time as it flapped about, obviously in contact with some intended prey. When it settled down, he rode nearer to investigate, whereupon the Hawk moved away a short distance, hesitated, fell over and was soon dead. The bird had killed its prey—a rattlesnake—but in turn it too was the victim.

On June 12, 1951, 10 Swainson's Hawks were observed flying over and behind two tractors which were being used to break new, sandy land in southern Roosevelt County. It was quite evident that they were catching mice and kangaroo rats which were being exposed by the big plows. No greater aid could have been given the farmers, because hordes of rodents in that locality often were responsible for poor stands of grain crops as result of their scratching out the planted seed.

Some early bird publications list the Swainson's Hawk as wintering in the state, even as far north as Colorado. However, there seem to be few, if any, authentic midwinter records to sustain such statements. Such cases may have been errors in identification. Swainson's are usually out of the state by late October, returning about the first of April.

NESTING. Since Swainson's usually nest in open country where trees are scarce, they may choose "tree" yuccas, Spanish bayonet, cottonwood, hackberry, native chinaberry (soapberry), mesquite, or any other tree, small or large. In the mesquite brush country east of the Pecos River, nests are often no more than four to six feet above ground. Occasionally nests are placed on sand dunes. On May 14, 1934, a nest was found on a dune in the deep Mescalero Sandhills, about 40 miles east of Roswell. Nests: Rather bulky structures, made of sticks and twigs, lined with bark, grass, or hair. Eggs: 2 or 3; creamy or bluish white. If 3, 2 may be rather heavily spotted with brown on large end, while 1 may have little or no such marking.

(ZONE-TAILED HAWK
Buteo albonotatus
18½—21″ long. Color pattern of sexes alike.

The Zone-tailed is a handsome, streamlined, black Hawk of the Buteo group. *Adults:* Bill horn-colored at base, blackish at tip; iris dark brown; tail black with two or more white zones. It has a rather rapid wingbeat and soars gracefully.

DISTRIBUTION. The Zone-tailed is rather rare in the state. However, its shyness and habit of frequenting the large cottonwoods of stream and canyon, and coniferous forests of the high mountain country of its summer habitat render it difficult of sight identification, unless observed where nesting. Its summer range extends from the Arizona line eastward to the Guadalupe and Capitan Mountains, and north to Mills, Harding County; upper Mimbres and Gila Rivers, and Reserve. The Zone-tailed Hawk has survived best in the Silver City and Capitan Mountain sections. It is absent from the state in winter, returning in early April. Preferred food seems to be the small tree- and ground-dwelling lizards common to its range.

NESTING. There are nesting records for the Zone-tailed Hawk throughout its New Mexico range. A nest containing eggs was recorded by Frank Stephens, May 28, 1876, in the canyon of the Gila River about 20 miles from the Arizona line. The author recorded a nest with young, 10 miles northwest of Silver City, and others for the southwest slope of the White Mountains; upper Cedar Creek near Ruidoso; Bonita Creek, near Hondo; east point of the Capitan Mountains; and Turkey Creek, Guadalupe Mountains. The birds were observed in the cottonwood bosques along the Rio Grande, south of San Antonio, under conditions that indicated nesting. On July 9, 1956, Elmo Traylor of the State Game Department, found a pair with young in nest in Mills Canyon, a few miles northwest of Roy. The Hawks nested at the same place in 1957, when Traylor secured the adult female for identification. Traylor, Krehbiel, and others who saw the birds at their nesting place pronounced them "Black Hawks" [Mexican]. Since the two species are so very similar, this sight error is not surprising. This record is of special interest since the location is about 175 miles north of the most northerly previously known breeding location, the Capitan Mountains. However, it does not preclude the possibility of its nesting in the intervening, rugged wooded country.

The securing of a Zone-tailed Hawk egg proved to be an exciting experience for Maj. Charles E. Bendire, an account of which appears in his *Life Histories of North American Birds*. At the time of the incident, 1877, the Major was in command of a cavalry post which had been established in southern Arizona to protect the settlers from the Apache Indians. One day while scouting from the post, he spied a Zone-tailed Hawk nest. He climbed the nesting tree, and as he was removing the single egg, he glanced down, and saw what he had not been able to observe from the ground—"several Apache Indians crouched down on the side of a little canyon. They were evidently watching me, their heads being raised just to a level with the top of the canyon." As the safest means of transporting the treasured egg, he placed it in his mouth—"and rather an uncomfortable large mouthful it was"—and leisurely descended the tree so as to disarm the suspicions of the onlookers; mounted his horse, and lost no time reaching camp where, he concludes, he "found it no easy matter to remove the egg from my mouth without injury—my jaws ached for some time afterward."

NESTING. In New Mexico, Zone-tailed Hawks usually place their nests in walnut, cottonwood, or pine trees. *Nest:* Made of sticks, lined with bark and green leaves. *Eggs:* 2 to 4; bluish white.

ROUGH-LEGGED (AMERICAN) HAWK
Buteo lagopus

19—23″ long. Color pattern of sexes similar.

The Rough-legged (American) is a midwinter visitor to the state. The designation, "Rough," evidently has reference to the feathered legs. The plumages of the bird are varied, ranging from the normal light phase to dark or black individuals. *Adults, normal plumage:* Upperparts brown, marked with white, rusty, and yellowish brown; tail white at base, barred beyond, and with dusky terminal band; underparts from white to yellowish brown. The dark phase may vary from bluish to real black, and this coloration may bring it into confusion with melanistic individuals among Red-tailed and Ferruginous Hawks. In the normal phase there is a wide blackish band across the underparts which is lacking in the Ferruginous and Red-tailed. Charts and paintings of the bird provide the best clues to sight identification.

DISTRIBUTION. Breeding in the far north, the Rough-legged arrives in New Mexico in late fall and leaves in early spring, being present for only a brief period. It is most common in the plains country east of the Pecos River and northward. Few are seen as far south as the southern border. Less active than most other large hawks, the Rough-legged remains perched on telephone or fence posts much of the time in the more open country which it seems to prefer. It now frequents the highways, to feed on rabbits and other rodents which have been killed by motor cars, hence it is vulnerable to both cars and the hunter's gun. The author has observed more Rough-legged Hawks in northern Lea, in Roosevelt, and Curry Counties and on the vast open, high country centering about Vaughn, than elsewhere. They are listed as "winter resident, uncommon" at both Bosque del Apache and Bitter Lake Refuges. In Union County they are "common winter resident" (Krehbiel). They rarely occur in the western part of the state.

❰ FERRUGINOUS HAWK
Buteo regalis
22—24" long. Color pattern of sexes alike. (Pl. VII)

The Ferruginous, or the Ferruginous Rough-legged, as formerly listed, is the largest of the Buteos, being next to the Eagles in size. The designation regalis, stately, splendid, is most appropriate for this aristocrat, the handsomest of the birds of prey. The typical adult Ferruginous Hawk, so named from the iron-rust color of upperparts and leg feathers, with the conspicuously white underparts, wide wingspread and rather slow, methodical wingbeat is readily identified in normal plumage. In the dark or melanistic plumage, identification is often difficult. Adults,

normal plumage: Upperparts, flanks, and feathers of legs ferruginous, the upperparts streaked; flanks and feathered legs barred with blackish; tail white, washed with gray and ferruginous; wing linings white with some rufous; underparts white, sometimes streaked with dusky; legs, feathered to toes; feet bright yellow. Dark phase: Body dark brown and rusty.

Few other birds are so beneficial as Ferruginous Hawks. They shun habitations of man. Although appearing awkward in getting into the air, once aloft, they move with apparent ease, soaring gracefully about in wide circles as they rise higher and higher. The exceptionally large eyes possess magnifying power at incredible distances. On calm, clear days, from heights beyond vision of man, and evidently unobserved by its prey, this Hawk seeks out rabbits, ground squirrels, prairie dogs, and other rodents which are active by day. Before the black-tailed (plains-dwelling) prairie dogs were destroyed over the high plains and valleys, the author on several occasions observed the cleverness

YOUNG FERRUGINOUS HAWKS, IN NEST
ON SAND DUNE. Allen E. Anderson,
N.M. Dept. of Game & Fish

with which the Ferruginous Hawks secured one of these rodents as it fed some distance from its burrow. Upon seeing a Hawk, one or more of the dogs would give the alarm, whereupon all would scurry to the safety of the burrows. At times, however, the Hawk would be soaring beyond vision, and without warning plummet straight to earth with closed wings, banking only feet above the victim. At the point of attack, only a swish of wings would be audible—a warning much too late to save the chattering, panic-stricken rodent. Under more primitive conditions, the many plains-dwelling prairie dogs, which are active throughout the year, constituted a good portion of this Hawk's food. With the passing of all but isolated remnants of the prairie dogs, as the result of poisoning campaigns, the Hawks feed largely on rabbits, ground squirrels, and other rodents. However, on the high Continental Divide country, where white-tailed prairie dogs are still to be found, they constitute a major portion of the Ferruginous Hawk's summer diet. (This species of prairie dog hibernates in winter.) Like the Rough-legged and some other birds of prey, the Ferruginous has also succumbed to the temptation of ready meals in the great numbers of rodents which are killed on highways by speeding motor cars. Thus they, too, become vulnerable to both gun and automobile. The Ferruginous deserves and must have—and soon—adequate protection if it is to escape extermination.

DISTRIBUTION. Although Ferruginous Hawks formerly were found statewide in both summer and winter, they were most numerous in the eastern portion in winter because their prey is here most abundant. Since they are the largest of the Hawks and prefer a mesa-plains habitat, they have provided tempting targets few hunters could resist. As a result, their numbers are dangerously depleted. Today comparatively few are seen anywhere.

NESTING. The Ferruginous Hawk nests sparingly throughout the state. Nests are usually placed in juniper, pinyon, pine or cottonwood trees. It also resorts to rock and soil ledges, and in the eastern sandhill country, nests may be found on high sand dunes. On June 5, 1937, a pair (evidently breeding birds) was noted north of Hachita, in the top of a tall yucca, where two years previously the author found a nest containing three well-feathered young. Nesting birds have also been found on the semi-forested ridges and mesas of the Continental Divide, up to 9,000 feet, from upper end of the Black Range (Franks Mountain) to north side of the San Augustin Plains. Of interest was the high percent of the dark, or melanistic phase, in the nesting birds of this area. At that time, dark-phase birds were uncommon in the eastern section of the state. At Point of Rocks, about 18 miles southwest of Magdalena, one of the large white-breasted birds was noted sitting upright on the side of its nest. Curious as to why the bird was not on its eggs, the author climbed the tree to investigate, and soon discovered the reason. In lining the nest, the birds had used a piece of white rag, an end of which had blown over and covered the three eggs. Nest: Like those of Eagles, nests of the Ferruginous are usually old ones with evidence of annual repairs until they may be two or more feet high. This repeated use probably is often due to the serious lack of suitable nesting places over much of their range. Always with a spacious platform and central depression, nests are made with a mass of sticks, lined with bark, grass, rags, or strings, and invariably contain chips of cattle manure. Usually they are placed on a ledge or tree crown, permitting easy access for the large birds. Eggs: 3 or 4; creamy or pale greenish, usually conspicuously marked on large end with brown or lavender. If more than 2, the third or fourth egg is usually plain or with scant blotching.

GRAY HAWK
(MEXICAN GOSHAWK)
Buteo nitidus

16—18″ long. Color pattern of sexes alike.

This rare little Buteo, because of its size and unusual markings, is of special interest to bird observers. Preferred food includes mice, ground squirrels, lizards, fish, beetles, grasshoppers, and other insects as well as some small birds. *Adults:* Upperparts ash gray, top of head and back of neck with fine blackish shaft streaks; upper-tail coverts white, tail black, tipped with gray or white and crossed by two or more white bands; underparts closely cross-barred with gray and white, except throat and breast whitish; legs and feet bright yellow.

DISTRIBUTION. The Gray Hawk (Mexican Goshawk) is one of the rare Buteos found in the state. It is migratory and occurs in the southwestern part only. Since its chosen haunts are large cottonwood groves along stream bottoms where it can easily be overlooked, it is probably somewhat more common than the few authentic records might lead one to believe, and provides a challenge to the bird watcher. It may be looked for in southern Hidalgo County, the Gila and Mimbres River Valleys, and in cottonwood groves about Fort Bayard.

NESTING. Authentic nesting records of the Gray Hawk are few for the state. Two nests were found near Fort Bayard by Frank Stephens, an early-day ornithologist, on April 23, 1876. Levon Lee, of the State Game Department, observed adults, and young out of the nest, on the Gila River, July 24, 1953. He states in a letter: "I was terribly puzzled for quite a while; couldn't recognize the bird; being an immature bird, it didn't fit any description too well. Finally the parent bird came in and squealed in that peculiar manner and we followed the two birds around for, I

suppose, 30 minutes. The young was easily observed and sometimes was not more than 30 or 40 feet away. The old one was more shy; but I was able to see it quite clearly. The location was a section of dense (cottonwood) bosque along the Gila east and a little north of Cliff." *Nest:* Usually high in cottonwood trees; made of leafy twigs, lined with dry leaves and strips of bark. *Eggs:* 2 to 4; pale bluish white, unmarked, or with a few indistinct buffy spots.

HARRIS' HAWK
Parabuteo unicinctus

18—22″ long. Color pattern of sexes alike.

The Harris' Hawk is another of the Buteo group with a limited New Mexico range. It was named in honor of Edward Harris, 1799-1863, companion of Audubon on the Missouri River Expedition of 1843. The Latin, *unicinctus*, has reference to the one white girdle around base of tail. The Harris' Hawk is about the size of the Swainson's Hawk, though more streamlined, and more highly colored, and with longer tail. Other distinguishing characteristics are the alternate rapid wingbeat, repeated sailing, and a tendency to remain perched for extended periods in trees or on telephone or power-line poles. Unlike most other Hawks, it is rather social, three or four usually occurring together. *Adults:* Upperparts dark sooty brown; reddish brown on shoulders, underwing coverts and thighs; tail black with white base and broad white tip. Its preferred habitat is valleys or draws of arid areas where hackberry, native chinaberry and mesquite trees are available for resting and nesting. The Harris' shuns mountains and heavy forested land. It is usually resident where found, or only locally migratory. On January 5, 1919, great numbers were seen along Monument Draw near the New Mexico–Texas line, southeast of the pres-

BLACK HAWK. *Drawing by Fred Patton from photograph by Elmo Traylor.*

ent town of Eunice. At that time a cold wind prevailed and groups of several of the Hawks would often sit on the ground on the leeward side of the many large, spreading squaw *(Rhus)* and Condalia bushes. That locality had a heavy rabbit population at the time. A few days later, many of the Hawks were seen about the San Simon Ranch, about 20 miles farther west, where they spent much time perched in the tops of large willow and hackberry trees. Their principal food seemed to be cottontail rabbits. Because of its shyness, the Harris' Hawk has not been exposed to slaughter as have some of the other Buteos. Where domestic fowls are available, these Hawks at times become persistent killers and may have to be eliminated.

DISTRIBUTION. A line drawn from about Lovington west through Artesia to the north end of the Guadalupe Mountains, then south to the state line would enclose almost all of the range of the Harris' Hawk in the state. It is still fairly common, particularly east and southeast of Carlsbad, and ranges south into western Texas to and beyond Fort Stockton.

NESTING. The principal nesting range of the Harris' extends from the vicinity of Carlsbad eastward, where fresh eggs may be found by early April. Nests:

Usually placed in hackberry, native chinaberry trees, and sometimes in cottonwoods. Where mesquites attain tree size, these, too, are utilized, as are taller bunches of squawbush. Nest: Rather bulky, made of sticks, twigs and weed stems, lined with grass and mesquite or other leaves. One examined was lined with hair, along with an old flattened nest of an Oriole. *Eggs:* 2 to 4; soiled white or greenish; unspotted or spotted with pale brown.

(BLACK (MEXICAN) HAWK
Buteogallus anthracinus

20—23″ long. Color pattern of sexes alike.

The Black Hawk, a handsome representative of the Buteo group, is one of the two rare nesting Hawks with distribution confined to the southwest part of the state during warm periods of the year. Its nature of remaining close to heavily timbered watercourses and its consistently black plumage are diagnostic. *Adults:* Coal-black, except white tip of tail and white patch under wing, near end; tail with white tip and a broad white band around center; bill blackish; legs and feet yellow. In sight identification it may be confused with the Zone-tailed since their ranges overlap. The latter, however, is more slender or streamlined, wings narrower, tail without white terminal border, and it usually has three white bands rather than one. Like the Zone-tailed, it noisily protests intrusion about nest or young. It is not a bird Hawk. It feeds almost entirely on snakes, small mammals, crustaceans, and insects. Its beauty and its economic value warrant complete protection.

DISTRIBUTION. Distribution of the Black Hawk is confined to the southwestern part of the state, north to the upper San Francisco River (Reserve), upper Gila River (Hot Springs), and east to the Rio Grande. Black Hawks are migratory and are usually out of the state by early November. The author has observed them most commonly on the Gila River, upstream to the junction of the Middle and East Forks of this stream (Gila Hot Springs). He also has records for the upper Mimbres River, north of San Lorenzo. There are a few records for the Rio Grande about Las Cruces. Since Black Hawks are rather shy and frequent heavily wooded stream bottoms and canyons, they may avoid observation.

NESTING. Black Hawks nest regularly in giant cottonwoods along the Gila River and have been found nesting along the San Francisco and upper Mimbres Rivers. *Nest:* Usually high in cottonwoods, but sometimes in pines; rather bulky, made of sticks and herbage, usually lined with cottonwood limb tips and leaves. *Eggs:* 2 or 3, laid from April to June; generally white, moderately spotted with light and dark brown.

EAGLES

THE TWO native Eagles—the Bald and the Golden—are readily recognized by their size, wide wingspread, slow, alternating wing flapping, and graceful sailing and circling in mid-air. They have powerful legs, talons, and bills, well suited to taking and killing their prey. Both species are indigenous to the state. The Golden is resident or semi-resident, and far more common than the Bald, which occurs more as a winter visitor, although it breeds sparingly in the state.

GOLDEN EAGLE NEST AND EGGS. *Photograph by the Author.*

❦ GOLDEN EAGLE

Aquila chrysaetos

Male, 32—40" long; wingspread 7—8'. Color pattern of sexes alike. (Pl. VIII)

The adult Golden Eagle is predominantly black, or with some white at base of tail, and golden wash on head and upper neck, whence it takes its name, and these features distinguish it from the adult Bald Eagle which has a pure white head and tail. The young are apt to cause confusion when and where the two occur together in the fall and winter. The typical young Golden, in flight, shows white patch beneath the primaries and white tail with broad black terminal band, whereas the young Bald is uniformly dark brown. Larger size of the Golden in any plumage distinguishes it from the large black Hawks.

As with the larger beneficial Hawks, Golden Eagles have been slaughtered, often for no other reason than to satisfy a lust to kill. Unfortunately, Eagles at times prey on young lambs and kids, at which times control measures become necessary. Their preferred natural food is the destructive jack rabbit, and as a rule it is where such prey is scarce or lacking that they turn to other sources of food. Wildlife conservation organizations are vigorously protesting the destruction of Eagles by such drastic means as shooting them from airplanes manned by trained gunners—a method that has long been used in the control of Eagles throughout the vast sheep and goat raising empire of the Trans-Pecos country of west Texas. In a letter, dated February 23, 1957, Ray Williams of Alpine, states that no less than 10,000 Golden Eagles have been killed by the use of planes alone since the inception of this means of destruction. Fortunately, it has not been necessary to employ such drastic means of control elsewhere for livestock protection. While no doubt many of the Texas victims drift into the region from the north in the fall and winter, the majority of them probably cross over from adjacent Mexico. That the Golden Eagle is native to all of North America offers some solace, because localized control is not likely to endanger over-all populations of these majestic birds. However, should such destruction become general or assume the aspect of shooting sport, legal steps prohibiting the use of planes, other than to protect livestock, seem inevitable. The economic value of Eagles throughout most of the country far outweighs livestock losses sustained as result of their depredation. Especially true is this of sandhill terrain where rabbits and other rodents, when freed of Eagles and other natural enemies, do serious damage to range and agricultural crops.

Eagles at times prey on game animals, particularly the young of deer and antelope. However, when such game is favored by normal populations, their depredation is rarely serious. This fact, however, does not alter the need for local control where necessary in the interest of restoration, in localities where game animals are few or where "transplants" have been made. Of significance is the fact that when Eagles and other predacious species were in normal abundance in primitive times, deer and turkey were also usually in abundance, and antelope numbered millions. Even mountain sheep were far more numerous than they are today, despite man's attempts at restoring them. When, in 1825, the explorer-naturalist, James Ohio Pattie and his party visited the San Francisco River badlands, which include a portion of southwestern New Mexico, he stated in his *Journal*: "There were multitudes of mountain sheep." Yet the gorges of the San Francisco River and adjacent Mogollon Mountains are favorite retreats of the Golden Eagle.

In the U.S. Fish and Wildlife Service Bulletin on the Golden Eagle, Lee W.

Arnold concludes with the poignant statement: "In the final analysis of any wildlife situation, in which the Service is involved, its management calls for local appraisal combined with an impartial and thorough understanding of the broader aspects of its influence. Let it not be forgotten that the Golden Eagle will always be looked upon as a noble and priceless heritage of our Mountains and Western Plains." (*The Golden Eagle and Its Economic Status*, U.S. Fish and Wildlife Service, Circular No. 27, 1954.)

DISTRIBUTION. The Golden Eagle is statewide in distribution. Since it is more or less migratory, particularly so far as the eastern section is concerned, it is most in evidence in winter. At breeding time distribution is governed largely by suitable nesting places.

NESTING. The preferred nesting places of the Golden Eagle are on shelves or in recesses of ledges and cliffs of mountainsides, mesas, and canyon walls—locations usually inaccessible to man without the use of mountain-climbing equipment. Such chosen places have been used by the birds for untold ages. In the absence of such nesting sites they resort to tall, ancient pines—as in the Spur Lake area of Catron County. In the eastern section of the state, they may nest in lone cottonwoods along sand washes or they may even build bulky nests on the platforms of abandoned windmill towers. However, under such conditions the nesting efforts usually fail because of human interference. In past years, the author located or mapped from notes of reliable observers, no less than 75 utilized Golden Eagle nests in the state. Because of intensive land use and other disturbances some of these are no longer used. The greatest number still in use are in the Black Range, San Andres, and Mogollon Mountains. The huge nests invariably are located so as to permit the unrestricted use of the bird's wide wingspread in taking off or in landing. Nest:

Bulky, made of sticks, lined with grass, yucca tufts, and often cattle manure. *Eggs:* 2 or 3; whitish base, faintly or heavily blotched with brown and with pale lavender undershell markings. Only rarely does a clutch consist of 3 eggs; in such cases 1 egg will usually have little or no blotching.

(BALD EAGLE
Haliaeetus leucocephalus

Male, 32—37" long; wingspread, 6—7½'. Color pattern of sexes alike. (Pl. VIII)

The white head and white tail of the adult Bald Eagle distinguish it from the Golden which has a golden head and solid dark brown or black body. *Young (first year):* Black except white bases of feathers of underparts, in which plumage the young might be mistaken for the Golden. The Bald Eagle does not acquire full adult plumage until about three years of age. These majestic birds seem to revel in their strength and liberty, symbolic of the freedom and independence so cherished in American tradition. Since June 20, 1782, when Congress declared the Bald Eagle to be the national emblem, it has been so dramatized in song and legend that it is more familiar than almost any other bird. It enjoys rigid Federal protection. For a more complete history of the Bald Eagle, see *The Bald Eagle and Its Economic Status*. (U.S. Fish and Wildlife Service, Circular No. 30.)

DISTRIBUTION. Increasing numbers of Bald Eagles are occurring in the state, obviously influenced by the more recent creation of water impoundments for irrigating purposes. The Bald Eagle, for the most part, is a winter resident only. For some years, 1920 to 1930, Bald Eagles were common along the upper reaches of the Gila River and over the San Augustin Plains, where lakes usually contain water in winter. In recent years they are more in evidence about such large impoundments as Elephant Butte, Conchas and Alamogordo Lakes. On December 22, 1957, 2 adult Bald Eagles were observed in Sixteen Springs Canyon, about eight miles north of Elk, in the Sacramento Mountains, an unusual record for this area. During the winter of 1950-51, Elmo Traylor, State Conservation Officer, reported that some 30 were wintering at Conchas Lake. He had previously reported as many as 50. It is listed as "winter visitor, rare" at both Bosque del Apache and Bitter Lake Refuges. Like the Golden, it is both scavenger and predator in its food habits.

NESTING. The author has but two nesting records for the Bald Eagle in the state. One nest was situated on a pinnacle in the gorge of the Middle Fork, and the other in a cliff on the East Fork of the Gila River, north of Silver City. Since this is in an isolated section of wild country, searching will probably result in others being found. *Nests:* On cliffs or in tall trees; bulky masses of sticks, lined with grass, rushes, or weed stems. *Eggs:* Usually 2; white, unmarked.

(MARSH HAWK
Circus cyaneus
18—24" long. Color pattern of sexes different.

The Marsh Hawk is alone in classification among American Hawks. It is a member of the Harrier group, widespread in different parts of the world. *Adult male:* Bluish gray streaked with white; underparts white, sparsely spotted with reddish brown; tail with 4 or 6 dusky bands. *Female and young:* Upperparts brown, in sharp contrast to white tail coverts; underpart buff. The scientific name, *Circus* (Latin), "circle," refers to its nature of circling in the air. Marsh Hawks are actually small and of light weight in contrast to their rather bulky appearance in flight. Plumage is loose and fluffy, on the order of that of the Owl, thus exaggerating its size.

In flight, Marsh Hawks may be distinguished by their long wings, long tails, white rump patches, and by their slow, erratic flight over grasslands and meadows, with heads generally pointed downward as they seek their prey. They are almost incessant hunters, or "harriers"; their food consists largely of mice and other small mammals, along with lizards, snakes, and small birds. However, since they are not swift of wing, except when darting and wheeling near surface ground cover, much of their bird prey consists of injured and weaklings. Audubon charts rate their beneficial and injurious qualities about equal. In the Southwest, however, where rodents are usually so abundant, their economic value is probably higher.

DISTRIBUTION. In fall and winter the Marsh Hawk is now the most abundant Hawk in the state. Migrants begin entering the northern section in early August, reaching the southern portions somewhat later, with the majority passing on south for the winter. They are usually most in evidence in the Pecos Valley and on the high plains to the eastward. Although they are slow flyers and range over prairie and valley lands, they are adept at keeping out of gun range. The main northward spring movement has usually cleared the state by the end of March.

NESTING. The Marsh Hawk is not a common nesting bird in the Southwest; however, authentic records include practically all of New Mexico. The limited nesting is, apparently, a result of scarcity of marshes containing rank rushes, one of their nesting preferences. On June 6, 1935, the author found two nests in the San Simon Marshes, near Rodeo in the southwest part of the state. One of these contained 4 young about three days old, and 1 egg; the other, 3 young, about the same age, and 1 egg. He also found them nesting regularly in the rushes of marshes on the Dexter Federal Fish Culture Station. On April 16 to 19, 1949, three nests were located with 3, 4, and 5 eggs, respectively. Nests also have been found in the marshes near the mouth of Salt Creek, 18 miles northeast of Roswell. "It breeds at the Bosque del Apache Refuge" (Fleetwood). On June 12, 1951, the author and Robert Lebow, of the State Game Department, located a nest containing 6 small young in a rank-grass drain adjacent to the large salt lake southeast of Portales. *Nests*: Usually on or near ground, on mats of rushes or other rank marsh vegetation; bulky masses of dried grass. *Eggs*: 3 to 6; dull white, or greenish white, generally immaculate but sometimes faintly spotted with pale brown or lilac.

OSPREY

Family: PANDIONIDAE

THIS FAMILY is represented by only one species. Commonly referred to as Fish Hawk, the Osprey usually is to be found about lakes or streams. At a distance, it bears some resemblance to the Bald Eagle. However, the dark upperparts, white neck and white underparts isolate it from other members of the bird-of-prey group.

(OSPREY (FISH HAWK)
Pandion haliaetus

21–25″ long; wingspread 5½′. Color pattern of sexes alike.

Commonly referred to as Fish Hawk, the Osprey is an expert at fishing. Its diet consists principally of fish, and it preys on undesirable as well as desirable kinds. It catches fish by plunging, feet first, from the air into the water. Apparently it sees its prey in the water—not always clear or still—from a height of 100 feet or more, and rarely fails to score. Being nearly the size of a Bald Eagle, it can be confused with that species. However, certain characteristics and markings make identification certain. *Adults*: Black or blackish above, and pure white below. No other bird of prey is so colored. Top of head is white with black side streaks. In flight the Osprey can be distinguished by a bow or crook in the wings; the other large Hawks and Eagles fly with wings straight. Another characteristic is its manner of suspending itself in mid-air while seeking out its prey below, and plunging into the water, often disappearing completely, and laboriously taking wing again with its catch. Its powerful, sharp talons, with each toe of equal length, constitute ex-

OSPREY
J. L. Ridgway, U.S. Fish & Wildlife Service

cellent equipment for grasping slippery fish. The close, firm, and oily plumage is water-repellent.

DISTRIBUTION. The Osprey cannot be regarded as a common bird in the Southwest. On rare occasions it may be seen any place where there are streams, ponds, or lakes containing fish. One is occasionally seen and sometimes shot near fish hatcheries where it may do considerable damage to brood fish. Elsewhere it may be regarded as more beneficial than harmful when it feeds on carp, suckers, or other undesirable fish.

NESTING. Few Osprey nests have been located in the state. On April 24, 1916, the author secured 2 fresh eggs from a nest on the West Fork of the Gila River just above its junction with the Middle Fork of that stream, about 50 miles north of Silver City. The nest was atop a dead pine snag about 30 feet from the ground. Another nest was located farther up the same stream, in the summer of 1920, at about 7,500 feet. This nest was in a tall pine, and conduct of the birds indicated that it contained young. At that time the Gila and its tributaries were infested with what was known locally as "Gila trout," which is not a trout but a sucker-like bony fish of little use as human food. The Ospreys were feeding on these. Nests have been broken up near the Seven Springs State Fish Hatchery northwest of Jemez Springs, where the birds preyed on fish in the several large brood ponds. *Nests:* Bulky, made of sticks, lined with weeds or bark, and usually found atop dead trees or snags, but sometimes on pinnacles or cliffs. *Eggs:* 2 or 3; highly colored, varying from whitish to reddish, heavily spotted and blotched with brown.

CARACARAS AND FALCONS
Family: *FALCONIDAE*

VULTURELIKE in habits, the Caracara, though classed with *Falconidae*, differs from the Falcons in its larger size, longer legs, and heavier beak. The bare red face and long, dark horizontal crest further separate it from the true Falcons. The Falcons, except the friendly little Sparrow Hawk, are streamlined, swift-flying Hawks, with long, pointed wings and rather long tails. Keen, narrow wings fit them for speed rather than for leisurely sailing, such as indulged in by the large-winged Buteos. Of the six North American Falcons, five— Prairie Falcon, Peregrine (Duck Hawk), Aplomado Falcon, Pigeon Hawk, and Sparrow Hawk—occur within the state, all of which, with the exception of the Pigeon Hawk, nest here.

(CARACARA
Caracara cheriway
21—24″ long. Color pattern of sexes alike.

The Caracara, known both as Mexican Buzzard and Mexican Eagle, is a long-legged, dark bird with a combination of the habits of Hawks, Vultures, and Eagles. Like the Vultures, it is a scavenger. *Adults:* Skin of face is practically bare; crown, crest, and body blackish, contrasting sharply with white of sides of head, neck, and throat; tail with 13 or 14 narrow dusky bars and wide, terminal band; legs rather long; feet yellow. *Young:* Similar but brownish; body streaked vertically.

DISTRIBUTION. It is of extremely rare

occurrence in New Mexico, a challenge to the alert observer. The first Caracara record was that of Henry at Fort Thorn (now Hatch) in 1856. The bird was next taken near Las Cruces in 1914. The latest and most surprising record is that by James Peckumn, who located a family of the birds in the Rio Grande Valley near Belen in the summer of 1953. One, in immature brown plumage, was secured. These birds appeared to be resident, at least temporarily, in the wide cottonwood bottomlands. Their periodic presence may be confined to the Rio Grande Valley. However, they are apt to occur also in the extreme southwestern part of the state, where they have not been recorded, probably because of few competent observers. They occur in southern Arizona, where they are known to nest.

NESTING. Since the family of Caracaras referred to was observed near the center of the state and the bird secured was not in adult plumage, the species merits nesting status. Nest: In various kinds of trees; in the Rio Grande Valley probably in cottonwoods. Eggs: 2 or 3; beautifully marked with clusters of rich, reddish brown, and yellowish spots and blotches, usually obscuring the creamy white ground color.

(PRAIRIE FALCON
Falco mexicanus
Male, 16—17"; female, 18—20" long. Color pattern of sexes alike.

The swift-flying Prairie Falcon is well named since it is a bird of the wide open spaces. In size, shape, and flight it is a close counterpart of the Peregrine, or Duck Hawk. Plumage coloration of the Prairie Falcon is distinctive, and it is primarily a prairie dweller, whereas the Peregrine prefers watercourses and large bodies of water where water birds and shore birds occur. The Prairie Falcon's plumage is a pale gray or sandy color. Adults: Underparts pale white, lined and streaked with brown; tail tipped with creamy white and rather distinctly barred; feet yellow.

Although birds, including game birds, constitute a considerable proportion of its food, the Prairie Falcon also feeds on rodents, grasshoppers, and other insects. As is true of other able killers of birds, such as the Goshawk and Peregrine, it is not a common species. For the most part it is resident, although some wandering within the state occurs in fall and winter. It is a serious enemy of the Lesser Prairie Chicken. The superior speed of the Falcon over its potential flying victim is largely dependent on the aid of gravity for a killing downward strike. Many so-called game birds are favored with a flight speed almost comparable to that of the Prairie Falcon's straightaway or ascending flight. Despite its dashing speed, this Falcon does not always succeed in bringing down its quarry, as was witnessed on one occasion several years ago near Pecos, Texas. A lone Mourning Dove, flushed from a weed patch, rose and had been on wing only a short distance when a Prairie Falcon swooped down and swung in behind it. The Dove, evidently aware of its pursuer's limitations, not only increased its speed, but began circling and gaining altitude. Without the benefit of gravity for a downward swoop, the Falcon was at a disadvantage and soon gave up the chase, swinging back and on its way.

DISTRIBUTION. In winter, wandering Prairie Falcons may be seen anywhere in the state except the high forested mountains. They are most common in the Pecos Valley and on the high plains to the eastward, but most of them desert such land types in spring, doubtless because of lack of suitable nesting places. Some of the wintering birds probably are migrants from farther north. Because of their shyness and speed of flight, they usually are out of gun range, thus their numbers probably have remained about stationary over most of their range.

Nesting. Far more exacting in its nesting requirements than are most of the other raptors, the Prairie Falcon invariably selects protected crevices or recesses in high, perpendicular canyon walls or mountain cliffs. Sites which meet nesting requirements are limited. The lack of suitable breeding places, no doubt causing some of the birds to go through a season without nesting, may have a direct bearing on the scarcity of these Falcons. It is conceivable that the preferred nesting places have been used and re-used for ages. Being rather quarrelsome and aggressive at nesting time, pairs of the birds are intolerant of close neighbors of their own species, as well as of other large birds of prey.

An incident which occurred in the gorge of the upper Middle Gila River near the confluence of Snow Creek, attests this Falcon's apparent dislike of Owls. The author was traveling up the canyon by saddle horse, driving a couple of pack animals. Near the end of the gorge, where more open ridges appear, a pair of Prairie Falcons began chattering and screaming protests at this intrusion of their nesting grounds. At a point where the trail led near some trees growing beneath the east wall of the canyon, a Great Horned Owl dashed out, but before it could reach the cover of the opposite wall, some 300 feet away, the screaming Falcons, like a couple of rockets, were upon him, one striking with a loud thud which sent the Owl diving into heavy treetop foliage.

Nesting. Prairie Falcons may be found breeding wherever there are suitable cliffs or canyon walls, particularly adjacent to open mesa or valley lands. They require pockets, crevices, or caves in the higher portions of such stone walls. Apparently, the wilder the country, the better they like it. The rugged walled canyons that dominate the upper drainage systems of the Pecos, Canadian, Rio Grande and Gila Rivers provide the most suitable nesting places. Especially preferred are sites on and adjacent to the Continental Divide, from the New Mexico–Colorado line southward. Breeding pairs usually betray nest locations by chattering and screaming as they glide back and forth, or swooping down in efforts to drive an intruder away. In New Mexico, nesting usually begins about the first of April. No nest material is provided, eggs being laid on such dust or litter as may be present. *Eggs:* 4 or 5; creamy white or reddish ground color; heavily blotched with brown or chocolate. Collecting them is usually a hazardous undertaking.

CLIFFS NEAR BEAVERHEAD, PREFERRED NESTING SITE OF PRAIRIE FALCONS
Photograph by the Author

PEREGRINE FALCON
(DUCK HAWK)
Falco peregrinus
Male, 15½—17″; female, 18—20″ long.
Color pattern of sexes alike. (Pl. IX)

The Peregrine Falcon represents the ultimate in speed and grace. The Latin designation *peregrinus*, means "a wanderer." Like the Bald Eagle, the Peregrine is a symbol of courage and daring. Favored with terrific speed and sustained endurance, this Hawk defies the elements, takes its prey with ease, and usually avoids proximity to habitation of man. Its chances for survival, therefore, are good. Preferred habitat includes streams and large bodies of water, since waterfowl and shore birds make up a good part of its diet, although it also feeds on other birds. Though similar to the Prairie Falcon in many respects, the Peregrine is more spirited and colorful. *Adults:* Upperparts bluish slate, top of head, sides of throat (mustache) black, sides of head, throat and breast white or buffy; lower underparts barred; legs and feet lemon yellow. The black of the throat is a distinctive identification mark.

This dashing master of the airways seems at times to delight in pursuing and tantalizing birds of much larger size. Rate of speed of its downward swoop is estimated as high as 170 miles an hour, a record equaled by few other birds. While recording the northward spring flight of Hawks at Whitefish Point, northern peninsula of Michigan, the author had an opportunity to observe the conduct of Peregrines in contrast to that of the many other species funneling through this "jumping-off place" for the flight across Lake Superior to the Canadian shore, invisible from the Point. Quite an assembly of Sharp-shins, Cooper's, Broadwings, Red-tails, and Goshawks would at times be banked up as if summoning courage to proceed. Hesitatingly, they would make several starts, only to return to the safety of land and cover. Not so the Peregrines! One would cruise straight ahead, far above the grounded travelers, seemingly on some sort of radar beam beyond the comprehension of man.

The Peregrine is capable of overtaking most of its prey by sheer superiority of speed, plucking it from the air, even on a straightaway flight. In pursuing the swiftest Ducks and shore birds, it relies largely on the advantages of elevation, sweeping down and striking the victim with powerful talons. So persistent is it that probably few individual birds chosen for the kill escape. A demonstration of its persistence was witnessed at a shallow lake in the Tularosa Valley, southwest of Alamogordo, where there was a concentration of Mallard Ducks and shore birds. A Peregrine suddenly appeared, causing a general alarm which sent some of the birds into the air. Having singled out what appeared to be a medium-sized Sandpiper flying well above the lake, the Peregrine followed in hot pursuit, but failed on two or three passes to connect with the darting Sandpiper now wisely maneuvering for elevation. Undaunted, the Peregrine pressed the pursuit. Finally, the hard-pressed Sandpiper outwitted its pursuer by dashing into a compact group of a dozen or more high-flying Mallards, and thus remained obscured in the midst of the speeding convoy, causing the Peregrine to abandon the chase and go its way.

With all its apparent love for wild places, the Peregrine is not always averse to the habitation of man. For some years a pair had their lair in the tower of the U.S. Post Office Building in the center of Washington, D.C. Pigeon fanciers for some time were puzzled by the mysterious disappearance of their birds. When an investigation was finally made of the tower, many pigeon legs, still encircled by identification bands, were recovered from the remains of prey that the Peregrines had brought to their young.

DISTRIBUTION. The Peregrine must be regarded as uncommon, although it may be looked for statewide in winter. The author has a study skin of a male, in the bluish plumage, taken just south of San Antonio in the Rio Grande Valley. He has records of the birds at the Dexter Federal Fish Culture Station lakes, also in the Tularosa Valley, the Jemez Mountains, and at Burford Lake. It is reported as "winter visitor, uncommon" at Bitter Lake Refuge. It probably occurs about the larger lakes and reservoirs more often than is reported, but because of speed of flight, shyness, and cruising altitudes, it may escape notice.

NESTING. There are but few authentic nesting records for the Peregrine in the state. One reason is the lack of suitable places for nests near water. On July 18, 1921, the author observed parent birds with young at Seven Springs State Fish Hatchery northwest of Jemez Springs. James Peckumn stated that they had nested in the rimrock of the canyon wall above the hatchery for several years. Their usual presence in canyons of the upper Gila River, about the junction of the West, Middle, and East Forks, leaves little doubt as to Peregrines nesting in this rather inaccessible and rugged area. Dudley DeGroot and W. W. Hill found them nesting in the high cliffs west of North Lake, near Datil, in 1951. At Burford Lake, "a family of young left the nest about June 10, 1918" (Wetmore). The author, on two occasions, found them nesting in the high cliffs near this lake. In New Mexico, the Peregrine, like the Prairie Falcon, invariably nests in pockets or crevices of canyon or mesa walls; near lakes or streams. Eggs: 3 or 4; creamy ground color, often obscured by heavy markings and blotchings of chocolate brown, varying to almost wholly reddish

brown; laid on stone dust or rubbish which has accumulated in the chosen site.

❨ APLOMADO FALCON
Falco femoralis
15—18″ long. Color pattern of sexes alike.

The Aplomado, now the rarest of the five true Falcons occurring in the state, occupies only a small portion of its former range in the southwest section. A very slender, medium-sized Falcon, it is usually found in the more arid, open sections where there are clumps or "forests" of tall-growing yucca. Thus both the bird and its habitat are distinctive. *Adults:* Upperparts dark bluish, white line each side of crown; tail with six or more white bands; throat and chest white, "mustache" black, middle underparts black, anterior underparts creamy white.

The food of the Aplomado Falcon consists almost wholly of small reptiles, lizards, mice, other rodents, grasshoppers, and various other kinds of insects, rarely small birds except in winter when other food is lacking. On the Jornada del Muerto, east and southeast of Engle, in summer, when the bats emerged from their day abode in and under the drooping blades of the tall yuccas, a pair of these Falcons—they almost invariably occur in pairs—could occasionally be seen darting after bats, and plucking them out of the air as a Kingbird does a moth.

DISTRIBUTION. This graceful little Falcon was formerly resident, or at least semi-resident, in all of the open valley and prairie land in the southwest part of the state, from the Guadalupe Mountains westward. Their range extends north to base of the Sacramento Mountains, San Antonio, and to Silver City. Preferred resting perches are the dried stalks of yuccas. Aplomado Falcons, at present, seem to be almost wholly confined to open yucca desertland from the Rio Grande westward, and north to Deming and Separ. Considering the permanent source of their food and the abundance of suitable nesting places, the disappearance of the bird from most of its former range remains somewhat of a mystery. Since Aplomado Falcons are not very shy and are usually resident, spending much of their time at rest, thoughtless hunters may be responsible for their scarcity. The author recalls the thrill experienced by the late Dr. A. K. Fisher, author of *Hawks and*

PIGEON HAWK
J. L. Ridgway, U.S. Fish & Wildlife Service

Owls of the United States (Government Printing Office, 1893), upon seeing a pair of Aplomado Falcons from the window of a Santa Fe passenger train, on which he and the author were riding, north of Engle in late November 1918. The birds were roosting on the crossbar of a telegraph pole not far from the railroad track, giving Dr. Fisher his first sight record of the birds in the wild.

NESTING. The tall, forked or branched yuccas are used by the Aplomados almost exclusively for nesting in the state. The crotches or "saddles" provide secure supports for the nests. In western Texas, in the Pecos and Fort Stockton areas, where there are very few "tree" yuccas, nests are usually placed in mesquite or on tops of "all-thorn" (crucifixion bush).

In mid-May 1952, a nest was located southwest of Deming by Arnold Bayne, of the U.S. Fish and Wildlife Service. On May 20, the author visited this nesting site and found the nest contained 2 young, four or five days old. The nest was 15 feet above ground, in the fork of a branching yucca. In contrast to the protesting conduct of the Prairie Falcon when nests are approached, the two Aplomados remained perched on tall, dead yucca stalks a fourth of a mile away from the nest. *Nest:* In this case the nest was made of twigs and weed stems, lined with grass. *Eggs:* Usually 3; creamy white, dotted with light brown and blotches of dark brown; usually laid from the fifth to the twenty-fifth of April.

PIGEON HAWK
Falco columbarius
10—12″ long. Color pattern of sexes similar.

The Pigeon Hawk, so-called from its Pigeonlike size, is not common in New Mexico. So far as is known, it occurs only as a migrant, not as a breeding bird. The long, pointed wings distinguish it from the more streamlined Sharp-shinned, which has shorter, rounded wings. *Adult male, normal plumage:* Upperparts bluish, streaked with rust or buff; feathers of back with black shaft streaks; throat white; underparts tawny, streaked with darker brown; legs and feet yellow. *Females and young:* Upperparts dark brown; underparts whitish or buff. This Falcon is sometimes seen in dark brown or black plumage.

DISTRIBUTION. There are records of Pigeon Hawks for Silver City, Shiprock, Tularosa, and the Black and San Mateo Ranges, indicating that during migration, they are statewide in distribution, occurring even on the eastern high plains. "One was taken 25 miles south of Albuquerque, October 30, 1917" (Leopold). They seem to be most common in the Silver City area, where R. T. Kellogg collected specimens on November 14, 1920, November 2, 1922, and October 19, 1924.

⟦ SPARROW HAWK

Falco sparverius

9—11″ long. Color pattern of sexes similar. (Pl. VII)

The Sparrow Hawk is the smallest of the Falcon group and does not have the bird-preying nature of its larger relatives. The southwestern form is referred to in most bird publications as the Desert Sparrow Hawk. Both its common and scientific names indicate its Sparrowlike size. Although wholly beneficial and showing little fear of man, it is, unfortunately, classified with the spirited and able killers of birds, but its friendly, trusting ways have won for it a place in the hearts and affections of man shared by few other birds of prey. *Adult male:* Side of head with two black stripes; crown mainly rufous, bordered with bluish gray; wing coverts bluish gray; rest of upperparts buffy brown or pale cinnamon rufous; back and wings spotted with black; underparts buff, spotted on sides; tail rufous. *Adult female:* Similar but duller, and back, wings, and tail barred with dusky. Although the males and females differ slightly in coloring, they are, unlike most other Hawks, of about equal size. Their habit of hovering in mid-air while locating grasshoppers, beetles, and other insect life is another distinguishing feature. They evidently possess highly acute vision, for, from their suspended positions well above ground, they can spot small insects over a considerable area. If they fail to spot something from their first "stand," they usually swing down, rising some distance away to repeat the performance. A few other birds, particularly Ospreys, Bluebirds and Kingfishers, do their hunting in this manner.

DISTRIBUTION. The range of the friendly little Sparrow Hawk differs from that of most other birds in life-zone preferences. Preferred nesting habitat seems to be from 5,000 to 7,000 feet elevation, probably because trees with suitable nesting cavities are found at these altitudes. However, it also breeds at the lowest elevations, in the southeastern part of the state. In the fall, it may be seen almost anywhere, even around timber line (12,000 feet). Although the majority of Sparrow Hawks leave the state for the colder part of the winter, a considerable number remain within its southern borders.

NESTING. The author has found Sparrow Hawks nesting from Carlsbad (3,100 feet) and Las Cruces (3,900 feet), to the Chama area (about 8,000 feet). *Nest:* Commonly placed in Flicker excavations or in natural hollows of trees. If these are lacking, they utilize holes in soil banks, crevices in cliffs, or even lofts of deserted buildings. *Eggs:* 4 to 7; creamy white, generally evenly marked or blotched with brown. A unique thing about the egg is that while fresh the coloring can be rubbed or washed off easily, leaving the plain creamy white surface.

UPLAND GAME BIRDS

MEMBERS of this group, designated as Upland Game Birds to distinguish them from water, marsh, and shore species, are largely ground-dwellers. Most of them are equipped with strong claws for scratching, since the food of all (except that of the Sage Grouse which feeds mostly on sage and other succulents), is obtained largely from the soil. Most of these birds are swift of foot, as well as of wing. They are adept at evading their many enemies. Some birds of this group, such as Quails, are monogamous. The Pheasant, Turkey, and Grouse, except the Ptarmigan, are polygamous, and it is the precarious duty of the female to incubate the eggs and care for the young. The White-tailed Ptarmigan male usually, if not always, assists in the family duties. The young of all are precocial, that is, they are active soon after hatching.

No phase of wildlife administration in the Southwest today poses more serious problems than that of Upland Game Birds, mainly because of modern practices of land use and abuse, aggravated by the recurrence of devastating drought. Conversion of valley, prairie, and sandy lands to agricultural use has restricted habitats for some species, such as Quails and Prairie Chickens. This curtailment has been partially offset in places by such agricultural developments providing cultivated grain as additional winter food, in the field, and in feed-lots about farms and ranches.

Waterfowl, marsh and shore birds, and the Pigeon-Dove group are more or less subject to habitat disruption and the hunter's gun, but these birds are capable of swift and sustained flight, and therefore are free to seek the safest and most favorable living and nesting environments. On the other hand, upland species, Quails in particular, are virtually grounded wherever they may be and must contend with whatever local conditions confront them. Forest-dwelling species like Turkeys and the Blue Grouse, are less subject to habitat disruption than the prairie-dwelling species, since the high forested country is favored more consistently with moisture and, therefore, with sustained food and cover. Yet these advantages are often offset somewhat by the effects of forest fires and excessive use by livestock. The Ring-necked Pheasant, alone, as a bird of irrigated fields and meadows, is less affected by drought and excessive grazing. Game birds cannot live and thrive without two essentials: food and cover. The future welfare of such game in this region therefore is intimately linked to reformed land use which will permit a fair cover of native vegetation, and local supplemental feeding during the recurrent critical periods.

GROUSE and PTARMIGAN
Family: TETRAONIDAE

MEMBERS of this family are medium to large Chickenlike birds with feathered legs. Males have combs and most of them have air sacs, conspicuous at mating time when they inflate them during strutting or courtship performances. The prevailing bluish to brownish plumage of the Grouse is a remarkable camouflage of environmental features. Even more remarkable is the white winter plumage of the Ptarmigan.

❆ BLUE (DUSKY) GROUSE
Dendragapus obscurus

Male: 17—23″ long. Color pattern of sexes similar. (Pl. X)

The Blue Grouse is next to the largest—the Sage Chicken being the largest —Grouse in the state. *Male in breeding plumage:* Head with orange comb above each eye; skin of inflatable air sacs purple red; upperparts bluish slate; tail blackish, with terminal gray band; underparts dark bluish slate varied with white on flanks and under-tail coverts; legs feathered to toes; comb and air sacs lighter in winter. *Female:* Without comb; similar but smaller and grayer in color.

As is true of other Grouse, population of this species is subject to radical fluctuation, from moderate abundance at the peak, to near the vanishing point at time of the low cycle. Late spring freezes in the high country are sometimes disastrous to both eggs and young. The Goshawk appears to be the most serious predacious enemy of the adults, but it is uncommon.

DISTRIBUTION. The Blue Grouse ranges in the higher life zones, from 7,000 feet to timber line. Its principal haunts are in the north-central part of the state—the Sangre de Cristo, Jemez, and San Juan Mountains. It occurs in limited numbers also in the extreme western section. The oak-covered divide and the canyons between El Rito Creek and the Chama River drainages north to the Colorado line, periodically have perhaps the greatest populations, since the birds seem to thrive best where there is a liberal spread of Gambel oak (Quercus gambelii) which provides mast, and some yellow pine, Douglas fir, and aspen groves to complete the habitat. It also is to be found at times in fair abundance from the upper Pecos country northward. Since the mountains in western New Mexico contain only limited suitable habitat, the birds are never abundant there, occurring only at higher elevations, above 8,000 feet, as on and adjacent to Eagle Peak; and in the high country west of Reserve. A remnant also has survived in the north end of the San Mateo Range, southwest of Magdalena. In recent years the birds seem to have disappeared entirely from some of the isolated mountainous areas, such as Fox and Apache Mountains north and northeast of Reserve, and from the Zuñi Range. These mountains, however, are more or less borderline range of limited extent. During summer and fall— until snow blankets the mountains—they live for the most part on the ground, although when disturbed or flushed they generally take to the trees. After snow becomes too deep for free walking, the birds live almost entirely in trees, seeming to prefer Douglas fir and spruce, the needles of which provide their principal winter diet. Insects, including grasshoppers, constitute their main summer food, while acorns, kinnikinnick and other berries are the staple fall diet.

NESTING. The severity of the climate in the high country occupied by the Blue

Grouse undoubtedly is a factor in the population fluctuations. Broods of only two or three are often seen when the young are the size of Quails, indicating that serious mortality has taken place. Often females with no young are observed at the end of the nesting period. However, following a series of favorable nesting seasons, populations again rise, at times sufficiently to justify a hunting season. The Blue Grouse usually nests in protected positions, at bases of sheltering spruce or other evergreens, or beneath logs. The female is reluctant to leave the nest during incubation. There is no conclusive evidence that the male assists in the raising of the family. When disturbed, the young resort to aspens or other trees and conceal themselves in foliage so quietly and completely as to be all but invisible. *Nest:* A slight depression in the ground, usually at base of spruce or other evergreen, or beneath a log, lined with grass and leaves. *Eggs:* 7 or 8, buff, spotted with brown.

BLUE GROUSE ON NEST. *Photograph by the Author.*

NEST AND EGGS OF BLUE GROUSE. *Photograph by the Author.*

WHITE-TAILED PTARMIGAN IN SUMMER AND WINTER PLUMAGE
Robert W. Hines, U.S. Fish & Wildlife Service

(WHITE-TAILED PTARMIGAN
Lagopus leucurus

13″ long. Color pattern of sexes essentially alike.

Unusual interest attaches to the Ptarmigan, both because of the arctic character of its restricted range in the state, and its seasonal garbs—immaculate white in winter, simulating its snowy surroundings; and a mottled black, white and brown pattern in summer with the partial clearing of snow, to harmonize with the vegetation and the snow that remains on the ground. Drifts and banks of snow remain year-round on its lofty habitat. This phenomenal change in raiment, the Ptarmigan's principal protection, is effected almost simultaneously with the seasonal change in color pattern of its environment. So perfectly do the seasonal garbs blend with the surroundings, that the birds are practically invisible when motionless. Although the change in plumage coloration

presumably is achieved through a process known as "feather-wear," Dr. Ira Gabrielson states that he has never obtained a Ptarmigan that was not molting, indicating that they undergo an almost continuous molt. Legs and feet are completely feathered, the feathered toes serving as snowshoes. Bill, eyes, and claws are black. In summer the red comb over each eye of the male becomes very conspicuous.

DISTRIBUTION. The former range of this Ptarmigan, or "Snow Grouse," included all of the ridges and peaks of the Sangre de Cristo Range above timber line, from Lake Peak near Santa Fe to the Colorado line, a distance of about 130 miles. Today it is restricted in the state to a few peaks in the northern extremity of its former habitat.

How numerous Ptarmigan were in primitive times—before man and his flocks of trampling sheep and other disturbances disrupted their normal lives—is not known. Indians and adventurous pioneers reported them on all of the high peaks, "in flocks of twenty to fifty." In early days, few white explorers visited the then almost inaccessible, isolated retreats of the birds, so that definite information is lacking. The author has seen Ptarmigan in the state on only two occasions: on Wheeler Peak (elevation 13,160 feet) and Costilla Peak, the latter near the Colorado line (12,634 feet) where, on November 28, 1926, two in their snow-white plumage were taken. These were mounted and are in the State Game Department collection in Santa Fe. In mid-July 1952, John Brewer of Vermejo Park Ranch saw a "female with 4 or more small young at the head of Ricardo Creek, Costilla Peak," which is an extension of the Culebra Range of Colorado. Few, if any, remain south of Costilla Peak. Other peaks in New Mexico formerly occupied by Ptarmigan are Truchas, 13,024 feet; Pecos Baldy, 12,529 feet; Santa Fe Baldy,

12,622 feet; Lake Peak, 12,409 feet, and Gold Hill and Latir Peak, both lying north of Wheeler Peak.

If vegetative life in keeping with their requirements can be restored, and rigid protection can be given these arctic dwellers, they can be re-established on their original range through transplantation from some of the higher peaks to the north in Colorado where they are still quite common. However, until the herds of summer-ranging sheep are reduced or eliminated, there is little hope for their restoration. Though their treeless habitat is narrow, but long, and with the intervening high ridges between the peaks listed above, there is in the aggregate considerable Ptarmigan range in New Mexico. Since this skyland is becoming more accessible to hikers and trail-riders the presence of these birds would be an asset.

WINTER SCENE WITH PTARMIGAN, SANGRE DE CRISTO RANGE. *Photograph by Mrs. J. V. Flanigan.*

NESTING. As the Ptarmigan is a resident of the treeless peaks and ridges of the high country, it is there that it nests and raises its young. So well do the bird and its eggs blend with their surroundings that little or no effort seems to be made at concealment. *Nest:* A slight depression, lined with grass and, when the bird is incubating, partially lined with feathers. *Eggs:* 8 to 14, beautifully colored with creamy base, heavily marked and blotched with dark brown. The fact that large clutches are laid indicates that the birds are subject to considerable mortality in addition to that arising from man's use of their restricted habitat.

(LESSER PRAIRIE CHICKEN
Tympanuchus pallidicinctus

Male, 16″ long. Color pattern of sexes similar.

In some respects the Prairie Chicken is truly a Chicken. In others, it is quite different from the domestic fowl. The Lesser Prairie Chicken is found in southwestern Kansas, western Oklahoma, the Texas Panhandle, and eastern New Mexico, hence it is a semiarid-land dweller, somewhat smaller and lighter in color than its eastern and southern relative, the Greater Prairie Chicken. *Adults:* A brownish color that blends remarkably with their native vegetative surroundings, principally rank bluestem and other grasses which much of the time are a brown shade. They have feathered legs. The male has a slight crest most evident when it is excited, erectile neck tufts, 2 or 3 inches long, which give it the name Pinnated Grouse, and an inflatable orange-colored air sac on each side of the neck, very conspicuous when fully expanded in courtship rituals. Back and underparts are barred. The female is similar, but with rudimentary neck tufts and no visible air sacs.

In many respects the Prairie Chicken is a unique and spectacular bird, the male particularly so in the breeding season. When the impelling urge of the spring mating season dictates, these dwellers of the rank grasslands assemble in groups of a dozen to twenty or more—depending on local populations—on their established "booming grounds" which have been used for courtship rituals probably by countless generations of the birds, to participate in one of the most interesting performances known among birds. The males are the principal participants in this animated drama, the sole purpose of which, it seems, is to entice the demure females to call and consort with them.

With pristine and unpremeditated art the erstwhile somber male deftly employs all his adornments. The generally inconspicuous air sacs of his neck are brought into play by inflation until they resemble small oranges. The pinnates—tufts of elongated feathers generally compressed against his neck, but now mobile and erect —serve as a striking head adornment, while the double comb, which has deepened into bright yellow and is drawn pertly over his eyes, lends a dashing effect to his festive raiment. Thus adorned for the occasion, the feathered Don Juan, head down, tail spread and wings drooping, performs his antics of ecstatic dancing, strutting and parading, all the while stomping his feet to his own accompaniment of cooing, cackling, and booming, emphasized at intervals with repeated bowing of his head as he advances forward or describes a circle. His attitude may be relaxed momentarily as he dashes after a rival who has dared to invade his limited pre-empted domain. Though vicious fighting does occur at times among rivals, the conflict generally amounts to little more than routing, bluffing, and sparring.

At times the vocal strains and the resonant booming of the assembled performers, though in unison, sound as if produced in rapid sequence, resulting in a most harmonious chorus. How such precise timing on the part of so many of the birds is achieved is a mystery. Here and there a cock, as though deeming himself unworthy, offers himself prostrate in a most resolute overture before the lady of his choice who, not unlike the other members of her sex, appears indifferent to all the pageantry before her. Though a most persistent suitor, never does he force his attentions on the object of his affections. One fortunate enough to witness the nuptial dance of the Prairie Chicken is struck by its similarity to that of some Indian tribal dances.

Beginning at daybreak, the weird sessions of these gallants of treeless lands continue through the early part of the morning and are repeated, though with perhaps less animation, in the late afternoon, and continue until darkness silences some of them—the more exuberant participants often performing during the night. The rituals are carried on from late March to early May.

DISTRIBUTION. Formerly, the Lesser Prairie Chicken was found on the sandhill, bluestem sage grass plains of eastern New Mexico, from the Texas line on the south to near the Colorado line on the north. This ancestral range extended west to the Pecos River, with an average width of about 75 miles. In the Fort Sumner area, distribution included the sandhill, tall grass country across the Pecos, to approximately 30 miles west of the river. While the birds are still to be found over a considerable portion of this former range, the greatest number are semi-resident in northern Lea and southern Roosevelt Counties, which constitute the most stabilized range in the state. The principal range south of the main line of the Santa Fe Railway, west from Texico, is characterized by a dwarf oak, known as shinnery oak (Quercus havardii). North of this shinnery zone the prevailing habitat component is similar to that to the southward except that the oak is lacking. However, a dependable substitute, a low-growing bunch sumac (Rhus), better known as squaw bush, occurs here. The presence of these two shrubs is an important factor in keeping the range habitable for the birds, where other vegetative life has been depleted. The sand, or plumed, sage (Artemisia filifolia), found throughout practically all of the original Chicken range, is also an important component of the habitat of the birds since it constitutes a major part of their diet in winter and during periods of drought, and serves as a free water substitute. The present Chicken distribution is reduced by half or more compared with range formerly occupied. Formerly, probably because of scarcity of suitable winter food, the birds migrated south as far as Fort Stockton and the upper drainages of the Devils and San Saba Rivers in Texas. Such long migratory movements no longer take place, and it is well that they do not in view of the radical changes that settlement and intensive land-use practices have brought about. No doubt agriculture, particularly with the growing of grain crops which usually provide winter food, is largely responsible for bringing about the change in the Prairie Chicken's ways of life.

The State Game Department has transplanted some Prairie Chickens to their hereditary range, but with only limited success. The transplanted birds have a tendency to return to their home range. Such restoration efforts will probably avail little until better native forage conservation is practiced so that the birds will have living conditions—cover and food—comparable to those of the past, necessary for their survival. Research has been conducted in the management of the bird, and key areas have been acquired for its benefit, but since the species requires extensive spreads of normal native vegetation, reformed land use is the first requisite in restoration. Such direct aids have been confined largely to southern Roosevelt and

LESSER PRAIRIE CHICKEN DRUMMING. Photograph by D. E. Brown, Amarillo Globe-News.

LESSER PRAIRIE CHICKENS. Photograph by B. E. McKechnie.

Harding Counties, where the principal remnants of the birds are now found. The Prairie Chicken is regarded as royal game for wing-shooting, but as harvestable game it is little more than a token species so far as the hunter and his retriever are concerned.

NESTING. So cleverly are Prairie Chicken nests concealed, and so completely does the nesting bird blend with the drab surroundings, few nests are found, and probably not many are located by natural enemies so long as normal cover is present. A nest located by the author in western Oklahoma was destroyed, both eggs and hen, by a coyote. It was evident that the author was the guileless betrayer of this nesting female; the coyote doubtless had followed his trail to the spot. Nest: Slight depression in the ground, well concealed beneath rank grass or shrub, such as shinnery oak. Eggs: 10 to 14; pale white or buffy, spotted with small reddish-brown dots.

(SHARP-TAILED GROUSE
Pedioecetes phasianellus

15—18″ long. Color pattern of sexes alike.

In appearance, the Sharp-tailed is somewhat similar to the Prairie Chicken, the principal distinguishing feature being the shape of the tail. The Prairie Chicken, or Pinnated Grouse, has a square tail, and also has "pinnates"—neck tufts—which the former lacks. Both participate in spectacular nuptial performances on booming grounds, in the spring. The two occupy distinct types of habitat in the state. Adults: Head with inconspicuous crest except when raised; upperparts buffy and grayish, with broken black transverse bars; underparts mainly white.

DISTRIBUTION. Distribution of the Sharp-tailed Grouse is confined to Johnson Mesa and adjacent slopes and canyons east of Raton. This restricted area (around 8,000 feet elevation) adjoins like habitat occupied by Sharp-tailed in Colorado. When the author first visited Johnson Mesa in 1926, the area contained a considerable number of the birds. At that time grass and weeds were rank. Oak brush, cherry, wild rose, and conifers grew in profusion about rimrocks and on adjacent slopes, creating suitable natural habitat. The grain fields of the mesa and valley lands also contributed to their welfare. In recent years excessive grazing by livestock, combined with drought, has resulted in impairing the range to such an extent that only a small remnant has been able to survive, notwithstanding attempts on the part of the Game Department to revive the stock by the introduction of additional birds. Until habitat is restored, there can be little hope for restoration of the Sharp-tailed. Like the Prairie Chicken, this Grouse is dependent on rank grass and weeds for survival and for successful reproduction. The Sharp-tailed, however, relies largely on berries and buds of shrubs for food in winter, while the Prairie Chicken is now reliant on grain of cultivated crops. Nest: A hollowed-out depression, lined with grass, usually well concealed in bunches of rank grass. Eggs: 9 to 14; buff or olive brown, usually lightly spotted.

(SAGE GROUSE
Centrocercus urophasianus

21—30″ long. Color pattern of sexes similar.

The Sage Grouse is the largest of American Grouse. Male: About twice the size of the female, mottled gray, black underneath; in breeding season has a conspicuous white collar and breast, and black wiry plumes; yellow air sacs. Black bill; graduated and spiked tail; legs feathered to toes. Female: Similar in appearance, but without ruffs, spiked plumes, or air sac adornments. Like the Prairie Chicken, the males become very active and conspicuous before and during the laying season, when they congregate on established strutting and booming grounds.

DISTRIBUTION. The high valleys, mesas, and mountain slopes covered by solid or broken spreads of the big, or purple, sage (*Artemisia tridentata*) constitute the Sage Grouse range in the state. This Grouse is well named, for it is truly a sage dweller. Its habitat in New Mexico therefore is limited, since distribution of the big sage is from 5,500 to 8,000 feet; its potential range is confined to the northwest part of the state, from the Upper Rio Grande drainage, from about Embudo north and west to the Arizona line. Much of this country is mediocre or marginal Sage Grouse habitat. During primitive times the birds probably ranged over a considerable portion of it, but there seems to be no record of extent. According to information obtained from the older inhabitants of the Chama section, the birds survived longest in the Tres Piedras area and along the Continental Divide southwest of Chama, the last being killed about 1912.

While the author was conducting field work for the State Game Department an exchange agreement was made with the Wyoming Game Department whereby Sage Grouse were obtained in exchange for wild Turkeys, Ring-necked Pheasants, and Scaled Quail. During 1933 and 1936, 310 of the Grouse were netted by the author, and brought down by truck and released at the most promising points in the northern part of the state. The "plantings" were followed by later releases by other Game Department personnel. These releases have resulted in the re-establishment of the birds over some of their former range, mostly between Taos and Tres Piedras and the Colorado line, and on the Jicarilla Apache Indian Reservation. They have thrived best adjacent to alfalfa fields west and northwest of Taos, and in the Burford Lake area, where on May 5, 1956, Wayne Bohl observed nine males on a booming ground. On November 12, 1953, "17 were seen crossing a road near Lake Burford" (E. R. Gomer, U. S. Bureau of Indian Affairs). Further restoration of the Grouse will depend largely on habitat conditions and respect for game laws. *Nests:* Usually rather well concealed under clusters of sage, yet coyotes seem to be a serious enemy at nesting time. *Eggs:* Usually 7 to 9; grayish drab, spotted with reddish brown.

MALE SAGE GROUSE ON BOOMING GROUND
Courtesy of Wyoming Game Dept.

NEST AND EGGS OF SAGE GROUSE
Photograph by the Author

QUAILS, PHEASANTS, AND PARTRIDGES
Family: PHASIANIDAE

THE MEMBERS of this family are of varying sizes. With the exception of the more highly colored male Ring-necked Pheasant, their garb pretty much conforms to their surroundings. For the most part, they are swift of foot as well as of flight. Quails are native species, while the Pheasant and Chukar Partridge are exotics, of European and Asiatic origin.

The Quails are perhaps better known and more beloved by Americans than any other group of game birds. Being largely ground-dwellers, with limited power of flight, they are practically resident wherever they may be. They are equipped with deep, strong beaks, and stout legs and feet for running and scratching in the ground for various kinds of food. Seasonal movements do occur, governed largely by availability of food and protective cover, but their home range is radically restricted compared with that of mammals and birds capable of long migrations. Quail, particularly Scaled and Gambel's, are gregarious. Following a favorable nesting season, they often collect in large coveys by late fall. Both male and female Quails share family duties. When tragedy overtakes the nesting female, the male may assume the incubating chore and proceed to raise the brood. The chicks are precocial and on provocation scurry to cover when only a few hours old. Although vulnerable to a great array of enemies and to the elements, they usually manage to survive in numbers, due largely to the fact that Quails lay large clutches of eggs and some species, under favorable conditions, may even raise two broods a season.

⟦ BOBWHITE
Colinus virginianus
9½—10½" long. Color pattern of sexes different.

The native Bobwhite, wherever it occurs, is a cherished part of farm and woodland. Its cheerful "Bobwhite" call, early and late, adds interest to any countryside. The Bobwhite is a bird of rank weed and brush cover types. When such cover is destroyed, it soon disappears. The early dawn "all-is-well" call of coveys in the fall is a pleasant reminder to sportsmen and bird lovers in general that this interesting American is still around. Where Bobwhite populations are low and where their ranges overlap, these birds are often seen with Scaled Quail. *Adult male:* Readily distinguished by the black and white head markings, white throat, brownish upperparts and thickly barred tan and brownish underparts. *Female:* Buff and yellow head markings.

DISTRIBUTION. The hereditary range of the Bobwhite in New Mexico consisted of a north-south strip along the eastern side, ranging in width from about 60 miles in the south to about 10 miles, north of Clayton. Although the westward limit of its range was sometimes regarded as coextensive with that of plum thickets, this designation does not apply to the southeastern portion of the state, from the Texas line to near Artesia and Carlsbad, where the birds formerly occurred, since there are no plum thickets in this section. However, the native shinnery (Havard oak), mesquite, catclaw, and other low-growing shrubs were fair substitutes. The most desirable habitat for the Bobwhite in New Mexico now is the plum-thicket sandhill type about Portales and north and south of Logan.

By 1915, long and excessive grazing by livestock had so completely destroyed practically all of its former habitat that the Bobwhite had all but disappeared from the state. Restocking of the most suitable remaining range was begun about 1934, with propagated birds, the original brood stock having been obtained in northern Oklahoma and from the Waggoner Ranch near Vernon, Texas. Agricultural activities have contributed to the success of their reintroduction.

NESTING. Like the Meadowlark, the Bobwhite is skilled in the art of nest construction. *Nest:* Where there is normal growth of vegetation, especially perennial grasses, a dome-shaped bower is made of grass, providing shelter for bird and eggs, as well as some concealment from the many enemies. *Eggs:* 10 to 15; pure white.

MASKED BOBWHITE
Colinus virginianus ridgwayi

9—10″ long. Color pattern of sexes different.

The Masked is a semidesert-dwelling relative of the common eastern Bobwhite. However, its ancestral range, southern Arizona and Sonora, Mexico, is more than 500 miles west of the hereditary range of the common species *(colinus virginianus)*. Although habits of the two species are similar, the color pattern of the male Masked, with its black, masklike head markings, which has given the bird its name, is quite different. *Adult male:* Neck feathers finely streaked with white; back cinnamon brown, black and buff mottling; breast and underparts deep salmon. *Adult female:* Without black of head and salmon underparts. In appearance, similar but lighter in color than the female of the common Bobwhite. Call notes of the two strains are similar, except in the Masked the "Bobwhite" note is somewhat higher pitched. For a fuller account of the Masked Bobwhite, see "The Vanishing Masked Bobwhite," by this author, *Condor*, Vol. 54, January-February 1952.

DISTRIBUTION. There seems to be no conclusive evidence that the Masked Bobwhite is a native species of New Mexico. However, its ancestral range, as known to ornithologists, is fairly close to New Mexico, in southern Arizona. It is quite probable that it formerly occurred in the Animas Valley of Hidalgo County, where there is still limited habitat comparable to that of its original Arizona range.

The ancestral range of the Masked in Arizona extended approximately 100 miles from the Baboquivari Mountains eastward to about Douglas and included a zone of approximately 50 miles in width adjacent to the Mexican border. Definite information seems to be lacking as to the time the birds disappeared from Arizona. In 1937, 1949, and 1950, the author, in company with Arizona Game Department officials, made trips to Sonora, Mexico, when a number of the birds were secured for propagation and stocking in both Arizona and southwestern New Mexico. A "planting" was made in the Animas Valley, south of Animas, New Mexico, and for a time the birds thrived. Because of devastated rangelands, however, there is some doubt as to whether any remain. There is little doubt that this interesting Quail, under more favorable land-use practice, permitting of more normal growth of vegetation, can be established in some parts of the southern and southwest sections of the state. Because of denuded habitat throughout its ancestral range, it is now near the brink of extermination. The main hope of saving it from extinction now seems to rest on restored habitats and propagated birds for stocking. It should be kept apart from the common Bobwhite to avoid hybridization.

Nest: Nests similar to that of Bobwhite, a bower made of grass and usually well concealed in deep grass or weeds. *Eggs:* 8 to 10, pure white.

《 SCALED QUAIL

Callipepla squamata

9½–12″ long. Color pattern of sexes alike. (Pl. XI)

The Scaled Quail, also widely known as Blue Quail, Cottontop, Blue Racer, and Cactus Quail, is listed in most bird publications as the Arizona Scaled Quail. The qualifying term, Arizona, however, is misleading since the principal range of the bird in the United States is confined to west Texas and New Mexico, while its historic range in Arizona covers only the southeastern corner of the state.

So alike in appearance are the male and female Scaled Quail that it is difficult to determine the sex. Both male and female are of a prevailing gray and bluish color, with a one-inch or longer gray, upright crest tipped with white. The adult male has a slightly bluer and larger head than the female. The most dependable identifying mark of the male, however, is the yellowish wash of throat, this part being grayish in the female. The designation *squamata*, squamous, "covered with scales," has reference to the pattern of the breast feathers, which has given the bird its common name.

The Scaled Quail is a bird of arid lands; few desert areas are too inhospitable for it. This unusual adaptation subjects it to many adversities. Yet so hardy and resourceful is it that it usually thrives in spite of them. Its distribution is largely coextensive with that of mesquite, blue chaparral (*Condalia*), and cholla cactus. It shuns heavily wooded areas. Average annual precipitation of its principal range is 8 to 16 inches although, periodically, this may be reduced to one-fourth or less over much of the range, a variation accounting largely for the serious fluctuation in populations. Winter storms, especially during periods of deep snow, at times cause serious mortality, although when a stable food supply is available, their resistance to adverse winter conditions is amazing.

During the period from late fall to spring, when the Scaled Quail are in coveys, the Cooper's Hawk is their principal winged enemy. However, where vegetative cover is near normal, their alertness serves them remarkably well in evading predaceous enemies.

The Scaled, like the Bobwhite, roost on the ground, and employ a clever precautionary means of self-defense against night-prowling enemies by forming a circle, tails together, heads outward; thus every bird represents a night sentinel on guard against surprise attack.

DISTRIBUTION. The Scaled is by far the most widely spread of the Quails in New Mexico and the Southwest. Its distribution includes practically all of New Mexico except the forested mountains above 7,000 feet elevation. There has been some contraction of range from the higher altitude, where the birds were never numerous. However, this altitudinal range still extends to 6,990 feet, as in the Santa Fe and Taos areas. The heaviest populations occur, as has always been true, in the southeastern part of the state and north to the Tucumcari–Logan section. In former years, the sandhill terrain of southeastern New Mexico supported probably the heaviest and the most evenly spread populations to be found anywhere in the Southwest, but late in 1953, after a series of dry years and barren lands, populations of this Quail reached an all-time low in this section and in west Texas.

NESTING. Fortunately, most of the range of the Scaled Quail because of mild climate favors a long breeding season and— below 4,500 feet elevation—a pair may produce two broods in a season, provided nesting conditions are favorable and the birds are successful in raising an early-season brood. When loss of eggs and mortality of young are taken into account, without second broods, it would seem impossible, after a series of droughts, heavy hunting, and other decimating factors, for populations to bounce back as they do in the span of one or two seasons. The nesting period of the Scaled Quail throughout most of its range extends from mid-April to early September. *Nest:* Under bushes, gourd or other vines, in clusters of prickly pear, and in various other locations. Cup-shaped cavity in the ground, lined with grass and leaves. *Eggs:* 10 to 14; creamy white, or buff, usually rather evenly dotted with reddish brown.

(GAMBEL'S QUAIL

Lophortyx gambelii

9½—10½″ long. Color pattern of sexes different. (Pl. XII)

The Gambel's is one of the most handsome and dignified of the Quail. It is named in honor of William Gambel (1819-1850), who did outstanding pioneer ornithological work in the Southwest. *Adult male:* Has a long decurved, black plume, carried at varying angles according to the mood of the bird. Crown reddish brown with narrow white U-shaped line separating it from black face; throat black encircled by white band; upper neck feathers bluish, lined with brown; back uniformly bluish gray; breast gray; underparts light buffy with black patch; sides rufous striped with white. *Adult female:* Crest brown and shorter; head and body without the more striking markings except that she too has the rufous or reddish sides striped with white.

The Gambel's is well endowed with admirable Quail qualities, including the ability for self-defense. It is quick to discover lurking or aerial enemies and rarely fails to reach protective cover when pursued. Its favorite habitat is brushy or timbered stream valleys and canyons flanked by brushy drains. The Gambel's is one of the

most vocal of the Quail, and its varied notes with their implications serve it well for group communication. Usually a male serves as sentinel on some lookout perch, ready to give warning, when danger threatens, to the foraging covey.

Roosting above ground in thick bushes and vines, Gambel's Quail have a protective advantage which ground-roosting species lack. Where populations are normal, they often congregate in large bunches, and forage in weed patches or, where available, in fallow fields. For "loafing" they prefer thick brushy cover. In the spring when other succulence is scarce or lacking, they also feed on swelling buds of hackberry, cottonwood, or other trees. They are less affected than other Quails by habitat deficiencies because their favorite retreats —stream and canyon bottoms—are less impaired by recurrent drought and excessive livestock grazing such as at times seriously devastate the range of the Scaled and Bobwhite.

DISTRIBUTION. The original range of the Gambel's Quail in the state was limited, confined as it was, largely to the Rio Grande Valley, north to Belen, and west to the Arizona line. In more recent years the birds have become well established in the San Juan Valley (Farmington) section, Española portion of Rio Grande Valley, and along the west slopes of the Sacramento and White Mountains, all outside the hereditary range, through transplanting. The Gambel's Quail is fully adjusted to a wide variety of climatic conditions, from desert areas to upper reaches of canyon watercourses, as high as 6,500 feet on the Upper Gila River (Beaverhead) and the San Francisco River (Reserve and Apache Creek). Although often referred to as the "Desert Quail," it is not, as above indicated, confined to the desert.

NESTING. In the lower altitudes Gambel's Quail usually begin nesting in early April. They are prolific layers. *Nest:* Usually under bushes or in vines. *Eggs:* 10 to 15; rather highly colored, in various shades with white to buff ground color and spotting and blotching with brown and drab.

❲ HARLEQUIN (MEARNS) QUAIL
Cyrtonyx montezumae

8—8½″ long. Color pattern of sexes different.

Because of the rugged, wooded type of its habitat, and its retiring nature, the Harlequin or Mearns Quail, in the wild, is all but a rank stranger even to the majority of ornithologists. It is unique among American Quail in conduct, type of range occupied, and ways of garnering food. Unlike other American Quail, the conspicuously marked plumage of the male is in sharp contrast to that of the somber garb of its mate. None has a stronger covey attachment. *Adult male:* Head banded and streaked with contrasting black and white and with a wide fawn-colored crest, usually slightly raised when the bird is suddenly disturbed or excited; upperparts mottled light and dark brown with white barring, primaries long, almost concealing the short, pointed tail; outer wing coverts brown with distinct black dotting; median

PAIR OF HARLEQUIN QUAIL
Photograph by the Author

underparts rich chestnut brown, anterior underparts and under-tail coverts coal black; sides bluish gray, thickly spotted with Guinea-like white dotting; bill and legs, in life, pale blue, toenails long (½ to ⅝ inch), an adaptation for scratching and digging. *Adult female:* Upperparts, rather uniformly mottled brown; crest as in male; head, pinkish brown; underparts, cinnamon brown to glossy lavender; bill and legs as in male.

When in danger, the Harlequin Quail rely for protection on inaction and on simulating surroundings by "freezing" to the ground rather than by seeking cover as do other quail. They are best observed from horse or car, of which they usually are quite fearless. Although appearing awkward in taking wing, they are strong, swift flyers. Their conduct probably accounts for their numerous aliases, some disparaging, as Crazy Quail, Fool Quail, and Squat Quail. They spend much time scratching out their preferred food—nut or cocoanut grass (*Cyperus esculenta*). However, when available, they also eat pinyon nuts and acorns as well as a variety of insects during the warmer period of the year.

DISTRIBUTION. Occupied range of the Harlequin Quail is now greatly restricted, while nowhere, except periodically where normal vegetative cover, particularly rank grass, has been permitted to develop, do populations approach those attained in former times. No other Quail of the Southwest has such altitudinal range variation as the Harlequin. They occur as low as 5,000 feet in some mountain foothills, and as high as 12,000 feet (White Mountain Baldy) in summer. They also range to the summits of the Capitan, Sacramento, San Mateo, Black, and Mogollon Ranges, but are found at high elevations in summer only, moving down onto south slopes and canyons for the winter, rarely remaining as high as 8,000 feet. They are also still found in the extreme southwestern part of the state—Animas and Peloncillo Mountains.

The only hope for restoring them to much of the formerly occupied range lies in reformed land use so that native vegetative ground cover may again thrive. Even then, restocking in most cases will be necessary.

NESTING. Because of the skill with which Harlequin Quail conceal their dome-shaped nests in rank grass or other concealing cover, nests are difficult to locate. Furthermore, an incubating bird generally sits tight, giving no clue to nest location. *Nest*: Usually a grass-made bower or dome, like that of the Meadowlark, with a small front entrance. Both parent birds take part in caring for the brood and are very attentive to the young. *Eggs*: 8 to 14; glossy white. See "Nesting of the Mearns Quail in Southeastern Arizona," by O. C. Wallmo, *Condor*, Vol. 56, No. 3, May-June 1954.

❨ RING-NECKED PHEASANT
Phasianus colchicus

Male, 25—35"; female, 20—24" long. Color pattern of sexes different. (Pl. XIII)

The Ring-necked Pheasant, a popular exotic game bird which was introduced to America from the Old World, is now so well established in the northern states and in irrigated sections of the West as to be regarded by most sportsmen as a native species. Thriving as it does in captivity and in the wild or semi-wild state, it fills what would otherwise be largely a void in upland game bird distribution. Unlike any native species, particularly the adult male, in its gorgeous colors and long tail, it is readily identified. Two strains—Mongolian and Chinese, natives of different parts of Asia—or crosses of the two—comprise most of the adjusted American birds. Males of both strains have dark green, iridescent head and neck coloring, white lower neck ring, and variegated body markings. The Mongolian, however, is somewhat larger and is more richly colored with its mahogany, black-dotted breast and

sides. The true Chinese is more stream-lined, has a less brilliant red breast; flanks are yellowish with black spots; wing bluish gray and chestnut; lower back grayish green. However, differing degrees of hybridization result in varied color combinations, which are most conspicuous at the height of the breeding season. The pure-strain Chinese is of wilder nature and more adaptable to the arid conditions of the Southwest than the larger, more brilliantly colored Mongolian. At Sand Lake near Aberdeen, South Dakota, the author secured an unusually large Mongolian cock which was 35 inches in over-all length, tail 17 inches long; weight 3 pounds, 10 ounces. Color pattern of females varies from deep buff to brownish, sharply contrasting with the highly colored males.

DISTRIBUTION. With respect to Ring-necked Pheasants, New Mexico is a borderline state. The birds are not adapted to desert or mountain, hence stocking experiments in the southern section have met with limited success, and then only in the irrigated valleys. Summer heat seems to have a serious adverse effect on nesting, and the growing of cotton, the dominant crop, is not in keeping with habitat requirements. They thrive best where alfalfa is grown, but cotton has largely replaced alfalfa as a major crop in southern New Mexico. Illegal hunting also is a limiting factor. Irrigated valleys in the northern part of the state constitute the principal range of Pheasants at the present time. However, even in the aggregate these areas are too limited to provide the type of hunting enjoyed farther north; in South Dakota, for instance, four million or more of these fine birds have been bagged in a single season. There is much potential Pheasant habitat in the state, involving sections from Lovington northward, where the elevation provides a favorable climate. Through the cooperation of farmers, the Game Department, and organized sportsmen, shelterbelts of shrubs and trees could be provided, with adjacent border zones where weeds would be permitted to grow, particularly sunflowers. Some corn or other grains also could be planted to round out the habitat. Such strips would provide additional Pheasant as well as Quail habitat, now lacking. Since shelterbelts and other permanent ground cover are the main hope for holding valuable top soil, such conservation measures will no doubt ultimately be rigidly employed. Game birds, as well as song and insectivorous species of birds of high economic value in insect control, may then become important by-products of such land use.

NESTING. Hay meadows and alfalfa fields are the preferred nesting places of Pheasants. Unfortunately, machinery used in harvesting such crops often destroys both birds and nests. There seems to be no practical means of preventing such losses although flushing bars attached to mowing equipment have proved to be of some benefit. Birds that nest on canal banks and other marginal cover are little less secure since they are subject to disturbance from prowling dogs, raccoons, and skunks. *Nest*: A depression scratched in the soil, lined with grass, weeds or leaves, usually well concealed in grass, weeds or hay field. Laying usually begins in early April. *Eggs*: 8 to 12, olive brown or pale blue.

《 CHUKAR PARTRIDGE
Alectoris graeca

11—12" long. Color pattern of sexes alike.

The Chukar Partridge, which is native to portions of Europe and Asia, has in recent years been introduced in the Southwest. The Chukars which have been propagated in the United States for the past thirty years are probably a fusion of subspecies. However, the New Mexico Game Department, at its game farm at Carlsbad, is now propagating the Turkish—from brood stock which was secured direct from the native habitat by the U.S. Fish and Wildlife Service through a cooperative agreement. *Adults*: Upperparts brownish gray; throat white encircled by a conspicuous black band from base of bill through eyes and extending to and around breast; lower breast and mid-underparts bluish gray, anterior underparts tawny; sides conspicuously barred with dark brown and white; bill reddish. The black head-throat band and barred sides are distinctive, no native species being so marked. Field biologist Wayne Bohl, formerly in charge of the Chukar Partridge project in New Mexico, states: "The Indian Chukar is larger by a few ounces and darker in color than the Turkish Chukar." Experiments show the Turkish bird is more adaptable to Southwest conditions than is the Indian.

DISTRIBUTION. While several thousand Chukar Partridges have been released in the state, for the most part in the south, south-central, and southwestern sections, the birds apparently are nowhere fully established. However, nests and young have been recorded at different points of release. The more rugged semidesert mountains and canyon terrain types favored with living water appear to be preferred habitat. So remarkably does the color pattern of the Chukar simulate its surroundings when motionless that it is practically invisible against typical background of desert cacti and shrubs. Horned Owl is the most serious enemy of Chukar Partridges.

Nest: Usually a depression, sparsely lined with grass, under plant or shrub or other protective covering. *Eggs*: 8 to 10, white base, speckled with light brown.

CHUKAR PARTRIDGE
Wayne Bohl, N.M. Dept. of Game & Fish

TURKEYS
Family: *MELEAGRIDIDAE*

THE LARGEST of the American game birds, Turkeys are also generally regarded as the swiftest on foot. The males have conspicuous bristly breast appendages, or beards. The heads and necks are without feathers, but are adorned with highly colored wattles and overhanging crown appendages. The females are smaller and without the head and throat adornments. They, too, occasionally have abbreviated beards.

The Mexican Wild Turkey, which was taken to Europe by early Spanish explorers, is the progenitor of all domestic Turkeys. The Wild Turkey occupies a dramatic place in early American history, and it is generally regarded as our most royal game bird. Yet few other native species were so ruthlessly destroyed. Fortunately,

here and there, remnants survived. These, under protective laws, have been restored to stabilized populations in suitable habitats throughout the country. In some instances, through transplants, occupied range has been extended beyond hereditary boundaries.

Since the three Turkeys—Rio Grande, Merriam's and the Mexican (subspecies of *Meleagris gallopavo*)—all indigenous to New Mexico, differ somewhat in plumage and in ancestral range, and as all are rather distinct birds, there seems to be justification in treating them separately as subspecies, although this treatment is a deviation from the regular procedure in this publication of featuring species and generally disregarding subforms.

MERRIAM'S TURKEY HEN, SHOWING CAMOUFLAGE. *Photograph by the Author.*

(RIO GRANDE TURKEY

Meleagris gallopavo intermedia

Male, 45–50″ long. Color pattern of sexes essentially alike.

The Rio Grande Turkey differs from the other two subspecies—the Merriam's and the Mexican—in being somewhat smaller, and in the chestnut markings of tips of upper-tail coverts and tail. This strain, according to early explorers, was common along the North and South Canadian Rivers of northeastern New Mexico, but probably nowhere did its range extend more than 50 miles within the state. Its distribution was confined almost wholly to the cottonwood-bordered streams and valleys, for outside of such watercourses and adjacent hill slopes, there is no timber, the prevailing pattern of the land being open, grassy plains. It is quite evident that there was a north-south foothill zone between the mountains and the plains where neither the Rio Grande nor the mountain-dwelling strain, Merriam's Turkey, regularly occurred, hence

NEST AND EGGS, MERRIAM'S TURKEY
Photograph by the Author

there were probably few, if any, points of contact to permit hybridization of the two.

When Lt. J. W. Abert explored the valley of the Canadian River in 1845, he found Turkeys "abundant" about ten miles west of the present New Mexico–Texas line. This location was east of the present location of Tucumcari. Other pioneers reported killing Turkeys along the North Canadian River. This Turkey's range most certainly extended into New Mexico along the Dry Cimarron River, west of what is now Kenton, Oklahoma. Since this range was accessible to hunters, the Turkeys all were killed before 1900. Restoration by the State Game Department on this former range, through transplanting from the Texas Panhandle, has met with promising success.

(MERRIAM'S TURKEY

Meleagris gallopavo merriami

Male, 45–50″ long. Color patterns of sexes essentially alike. (Pl. XIV)

The pure-strain Merriam's, or mountain-dwelling Wild Turkey, in some respects is distinct from the Eastern or Rio Grande, a bird of lower altitudes. (*History and Management of the Merriam's Wild Turkey*, by J. Stokley Ligon. University of New Mexico Press, 1946.) It is named in honor of Clinton Hart Merriam (1855–1942), first chief of the U.S. Biological Survey from its founding in 1885 to 1910, and Harriman Research Associate of the Smithsonian Institution, 1910–42. "Tail coverts and feathers of lower rump [are] broadly tipped with buffy whitish" (Bailey), whereas in the Rio Grande these are brown or a rich chestnut, and in the Mexican almost pure white. In general color pattern of plumage, the Merriam's differs little from the domestic Bronze Turkey. In body streamlining it is radically different. Considering the size of the bird, its natural enemies and severity of winter climate where it dwells, its ruggedness and self-reliance are amazing. In primitive times, no doubt, populations fluctuated to some extent but not to the degree observed in recent years. An early-day explorer wrote about "multitudes of them on the Gila River." Although remnants have managed to survive over most of their ancestral range, habitat depletion, predation, and hunting combined have resulted in the critical situation that has periodically confronted them. At the time (1925–26) the author made a statewide game survey, population of this Turkey in the state was placed at 21,000. (*Wildlife of New Mexico: Its Conservation and Management*, by J. Stokley Ligon. State Game Department, Santa Fe, 1926.) That figure was a liberal estimate. Prior to 1900, the Turkey population in the state probably exceeded 40,000 in peak years. During the winter of 1912–13 the author spent considerable time on the west slope of the Black Range, in the upper drainage of the Gila River, where at that time he estimated there were 500 Turkeys in a 25-square-mile area.

In addition to its superior rating as big game, the Merriam's Turkey has a high economic value as a destroyer of beetles and other forest tree pests and their larvae, which it scratches from the litter and needles of the forest floor.

DISTRIBUTION. The ancestral range of the Merriam's Turkey was confined to the conifer-oak mountain forests of the Southwest, including southern Colorado, New Mexico, and Arizona, from the lower limits of the pines (approximately 6,000 feet) to the summits of the highest mountains. It occurred in Texas, so far as is known, in the southern extension of the Guadalupe Mountains only. It still is to be found either as a descendant of the original stock or of transplants on practically all of its ancestral range.

Because of disruption of winter range as result of excessive grazing by livestock, the Merriam's in recent years has periodically become a problem species, due to scarcity or lack of a sustained winter food supply—the principal limiting factor. Winter storms, even with deep snow, seem to have little adverse effect on them so long as there is sustained mast—acorns, juniper berries, pinyon and other pine nuts. Unfortunately, heavy mast is periodically lacking. At such times the Turkeys must find a substitute to carry them through the winter. Under more primitive conditions they found such a substitute in weed seed, succulent plants, rose-haws, and more especially in native grass seeds of many kinds, more or less abundant in the lower levels of their mountainous range. Because of heavy livestock grazing on the lower elevations, such foods are now too often scant or lacking, with the result that the Turkeys, in the absence of masts, cannot find sufficient sustaining food to carry them through in good physical condition. Hence, they become emaciated, and thus rendered highly vulnerable to the elements and to predators, particularly the coyote. One of the most direct benefits that could be provided for these Turkeys would be complete elimination of all coyotes from forested mountains which are entirely out of their hereditary range, and more effective control of bobcats. Other predators, with the possible exception of the gray fox, are of minor consequence. Fortunately, the State Game Department is now aware of the recurrence of emergencies, and is usually prepared, so far as is practicable, to provide supplemental feed. Yet locating and aiding all of the birds in remote places is a difficult assignment. Planes are being used for dropping feed during such emergencies. In addition to such supplemental feeding as can be provided, the practical approach to the problem seems to be the acquisition of potential key wintering areas where native grasses and other plant life may be permitted to grow and mature so as to be available to the Turkeys in time of need. As a further provision for their welfare, portions of such desirable areas could be planted to oats, barley, and hardy clovers. No game is more highly prized by the sportsman, and no other is in greater need of intensive management, nor does any other offer greater opportunities for restoration and stabilization under such management.

NESTING. The pure-strain Merriam's Turkey does not breed until the second year. A nesting group usually comprises one gobbler and two or three hens. A majority of nests observed by the author were in the Transition Zone—7,000 to 8,500 feet. One in such location was found May 13, 1951, in the Sacramento Mountains, about fifteen miles southeast of Cloudcroft. It contained 11 slightly incubated eggs. Location of nesting sites is variable. They may be under fallen treetops, near logs; often they are in open position. But the preferred site seems to be on the upper side of the base of a tree growing on the north slope of a mountain or canyon. Such places are preferred probably because of shade and more uniform temperature and because of the vantages thus gained; when leaving the nest, the hen has only to take a step or two to sail away, thereby leaving no trail which might lead prowling enemies to the nest. She generally follows the same precaution by flying back to or near the nest. Successful raising of the brood depends very largely upon the presence of normal vegetative cover and insects, particularly grasshoppers. After the young are hatched, the hens of a group invariably consolidate their broods, accounting for the usual large bunches of young when nesting conditions are favorable. This trait, in keeping with the gregarious nature of the species, serves a mutual protective purpose, since it enables more adults to be on the lookout for enemies. The gobbler takes no part in family duties; in fact the hens shun his presence. Nest: A slight depression in the ground, under fallen tree tops; by logs; at base of trees or even in comparatively open places; scantily lined with grass, chips of bark or needles. Eggs: 9 to 12, creamy white, thickly sprinkled with dots of brown. Eggs are usually partly covered when the hen leaves for food and water.

(MEXICAN TURKEY
Meleagris gallopavo mexicana
Male, 45–50″ long.

In most respects the Mexican, or Gould's Turkey, is almost a counterpart of the Merriam's. In a letter to the author dated September 17, 1957, A. Starker Leopold, who has had an opportunity to study the comparative differences in wild Turkeys, states: "M.g. mexicana differs from M.g. merriami in having the white tail tips and white tail coverts, top and bottom. That is to say, the end of the tail and the tail coverts instead of being buffy as they are in the Merriam's Turkey are pure white, as, for example, in the bronze domestic turkey. In all other respects the two birds are essentially the same in coloration and in size." The following description of the mexicana as given by John W. Aldrich, of the U.S. Fish and Wildlife Service: "Tips of tail feathers and upper tail-coverts very light, almost pure white. Secondaries as in merriami, with darker bars and mottling, broader white margins less rusty and higher metallic gloss. Size large, particularly the legs, which are especially long"— is virtually the same as that given by Leopold.

DISTRIBUTION. The range of the Mexican Turkey in New Mexico is limited to extreme southern Hidalgo County, adjacent to the Mexican boundary, and confined to the Animas and Peloncillo Mountains. As the adjacent higher forested and well watered Sierra Madres, just south of the International Boundary, constitute much better Turkey habitat, the birds usually cross into New Mexico only when seasonal moisture provides water, food, and suitable ground cover. The habitat north of the line is definitely marginal. It could, however, be improved and stabilized through better conservation of rangeland and forests and the establishment of strategic watering places. The fact that the range of the Mexican Turkey is separated from that of the Merriam's by 75 miles or more of treeless, broken and valley country, precludes the possibility of the former having come in contact with the Merriam's. Any attempt at crossing this sterile barrier would have resulted in the birds falling prey to coyotes, Golden Eagles, or other enemies. Although in recent years Merriam's Turkeys have several times been transplanted from the Reserve section of Catron County to the range of the Mexican Turkey, these transplants seemingly were not successful. It is doubtful whether any survived long enough to crossbreed. There are several definite records of the Mexican Turkey having been seen and taken on the New Mexico side of the line, the most recent being that of May 23, 1957, when a female was taken at the Pendleton Ranch, in the Peloncillo Mountains. This specimen was definitely identified by Leopold as belonging to the Mexican variety.

NESTING AND EGGS: Probably essentially the same as that of the Merriam's.

CRANES
Family: GRUIDAE

THE TRUE CRANES are large, long-legged, long-necked birds, easily distinguished from the Herons, which are smaller. The position of head and neck, in flight, is also distinctive in that these are extended forward rather than drawn back between the shoulders as is true of the Herons. Their far-carrying trumpetlike notes are further means of identification, even when the birds themselves are beyond ordinary vision. The Sandhill Crane, with its subspecies, the Little Brown, is the commonest Crane in New Mexico, but only in migration and during the winter. The majestic Whooping Crane is now so rare in the state, if in reality it occurs at all, that viewing it is an event to be remembered.

WHOOPING CRANE
Grus americana
50—54" long; wingspread, 7½'. Color pattern of sexes alike.

Although it has not been reliably reported in the state for many years, this majestic Crane of massive size merits consideration. The beautiful Whooping Crane, which formerly "assembled by many thousands" during migration, is today precariously near the brink of extermination. Renewed hope for its survival is based on the fact that 32 of the birds, 9 of which were young, returned to the Aransas National Wildlife Refuge, on the Gulf Coast of Texas, their principal wintering grounds in 1958. Under date of December 31, 1958, an official statement issued by the U.S. Fish and Wildlife Service, principal guardians of this near-vanishing species, concludes as follows: "In addition to the 32 birds on Aransas, there are 6 in zoos: 2 adults and 3 young, in the New Orleans Zoo, and a crippled adult in the San Antonio [Texas] Zoo. These 38 birds represent a recent all-time high, but they are the only representatives remaining of the species."

The welfare of few other birds has provoked a greater degree of public interest and concern. To emphasize wildlife conservation, the Post Office Department, on

November 22, 1957, issued as one of a wildlife series, a postage stamp depicting the Whooping Crane. In little more than a year one hundred million of the stamps were sold, and the demand for them continues.

The Whooping Crane is distinguished by its large size and all-white plumage except black on tips of primaries, and red on crown and lores, and in flight by the fully outstretched head and neck. Young are mainly white, mottled with brown. Thomas C. Henry (1855) reported the birds in the Rio Grande Valley about Fort Thorn (now Hatch). No doubt there have been more occurrences, but absence of competent observers or the possibility of the migrating Cranes having passed over with few or no stops may account for lack of later records. The present spring and fall migration route of the few remaining birds seemingly adheres rather closely to a line from Canada into the northwest corner of North Dakota, thence direct to the Gulf Coast of Texas. Thus the regular route crosses north Texas, approximately 250 miles from New Mexico. There is a possibility of sighting one in eastern New Mexico during migration.

WHOOPING CRANE, ARANSAS REFUGE, TEXAS
J. O. Stevenson, U.S. Fish & Wildlife Service

SANDHILL CRANE
Grus canadensis

40—48″ long (Little Brown Crane: Approximately 35″). Color pattern of sexes alike.

Adults: Bare red face; grayish brown body; long neck and legs; bill 5 to 6 inches.

The Sandhill Crane is the largest of the Heron-Crane group of birds now occurring in the state. Its great size, gregarious nature, and loud, far-carrying clarion call are clues to identification. Prior to the enactment of the Migratory Bird Treaty Act, Sandhill Cranes had become greatly reduced in numbers, but under present rigid protection they have increased to the point where they now enter New Mexico by the thousands. While no Sandhills probably nest within 500 miles of New Mexico, they do grace much of the state with their presence, either in migration or as winter residents, almost six months of the year —from early October to early March. The Little Brown Crane, presumably a subspecies, occurs in far greater numbers than does the true Sandhill. The two are so similar that it is difficult for the average observer to tell them apart.

Few birds seem so well organized in their seasonal migratory movements, nor display more apparent joy in mass association and mastery of the flyways than do Sandhill Cranes. Few other birds are so dignified, or deliberate in action when their welfare and security are involved. In the Pecos Valley the main pattern of flight is southward down the Valley to a point about Carlsbad, where they rather consistently alter their course, swinging to the southwest, around or over the point of the Guadalupe Mountains. It is probably the old, experienced birds that lead their trusting followers unerringly into the lake-dotted valleys of northern Chihuahua, and it may be assumed that the purpose of this flight pattern is to avoid opposing mountain air currents which might be encountered to the west of the Pecos Valley.

The conduct and maneuvering of these cruisers of the airways are fascinating. Wave after wave moves through at such great heights as to be at times almost invisible to the unaided eye, but even unseen, they can be traced through the clarion notes coming from somewhere in the distant blue of a calm fall or spring day. Methodically, in their wide, arrowpoint formation, they coast gracefully along, gradually losing elevation until suddenly they break rank, falling more or less into a state of confusion. Becoming quite vocal they circle and rise again to the desired height, when a leader again takes command and the flock assumes formation for another long, easy glide. Only when the birds are gaining altitude, flying low in search of feeding grounds or roosting grounds or lake shores, do they abandon their orderly flight formation. On March 2, 1950, about 3,000 Sandhill Cranes were approaching their regular roosting grounds in the southeast corner of the Dexter Fish Culture Station land. Flock after flock of the noisy incoming birds, from irrigated fields to the southwest, began to arrive just before sunset and continued to arrive until dark. When all had settled a great chorus arose as result of some disturbance, and seemingly all took wing. While some resettled, most of them headed north towards Bitter Lake, 35 miles away. In a few days the Cranes of the Valley had moved northward, leaving only stragglers behind.

DISTRIBUTION. During spring and fall migrations, Sandhill Cranes may be seen or heard almost any place in the state, but because suitable feeding, resting, and roosting places are few, or lacking, elsewhere, their continued presence is confined almost wholly to the Rio Grande and Pecos Valleys where they have the benefit of lakes, marshes, and grain fields where they feed. They are winter residents at Bosque del Apache Refuge, and Harry Williams lists them also as winter residents in the Las Cruces section. The lakes of the eastern high plains section of New Mexico and the Muleshoe National Wildlife Refuge (just over the line in Texas) provide roosting and rallying retreats for the birds. The Pecos Valley lies along the western edge of the migration route of vast numbers of Cranes, so often observed in Nebraska and Kansas.

The vanguard of the fall flocks usually reaches the middle Pecos Valley around October 10 to 15. These early flights, strangely enough, usually pass through with little or no delay. Apparently it is the later arrivals that stop over or winter in the farming districts of Curry and Roosevelt Counties, and in the mid-section of the Pecos Valley (Roswell, Dexter, and Artesia) where they congregate at times in vast numbers. At the time of the Roswell-Bitter Lake Christmas Count (December 22, 1956), it was estimated there were 35,000 Sandhill Cranes in that area. (See Christmas Bird Counts.)

In recent years, as result of the great increase in numbers of the Cranes, there has been considerable complaint by farmers in eastern New Mexico of early-season damage to grain and peanut crops; otherwise the great birds are welcome visitors. They are far more abundant, in season, in the Pecos Valley than in the Rio Grande Valley. On November 5, 1956, Raymond Fleetwood of the U.S. Fish and Wildlife Service, wrote: "Last week the census showed 1,853 Cranes [on Bosque del Apache], the largest number ever reported on the Refuge."

RAILS, GALLINULES, AND COOTS
Family: RALLIDAE

THE RAILS, being shy, retiring birds of concealing marshland cover, are usually difficult to see and identify. Their streamlined bodies and long, strong legs permit them to slip rapidly through dense marsh vegetation, while their long toes serve to support them in mud and on floating vegetation. Their crackling notes during the nesting season are heard more frequently than the birds are seen. When flushed, they skim over the marsh, with legs dangling, and suddenly drop as if totally exhausted. Two species of Rails—the Virginia and the Sora—occur and nest sparingly in the state. The Coot and Common Gallinule are dark, Ducklike birds, but unlike Ducks they are partial to the protective cover of rushes and other aquatic vegetation, and are adept at threading through such growth in water or on land. In these species the sexes are similar in appearance, and seasonal plumage changes are slight.

(VIRGINIA RAIL
Rallus limicola

8—10½" long. Color pattern of sexes alike.

The Virginia Rail, a reddish marsh-dwelling bird, smaller than a Bobwhite Quail, should not be confused with the Sora. The Virginia is larger and has a much longer bill, and short tail. *Adults:* Sides of head gray; upperparts olive brown streaked with black; wing with rufous patch; throat and breast cinnamon brown streaked with black; flanks black, barred with white.

DISTRIBUTION. The Virginia Rail is found sparingly in various parts of New Mexico during the nesting season; more frequently in migration. The author has observed the birds in summer, both in the Rio Grande and Pecos Valleys; also at Burford Lake where specimens were secured. They were common in the marshes about Albuquerque in early September 1920. They have been observed and specimens were taken at the Bitter Lake Refuge, and they are permanent residents and breed at Bosque del Apache Refuge.

NESTING. The author has secured breeding birds at Burford Lake and also at Wade Lake north of Lake McMillan delta. Since the birds are adept at concealment they no doubt nest far more commonly than might be suspected. *Nest:* Usually placed in marsh grass and made of grass. *Eggs:* 7 to 12; buffy irregularly spotted with brown.

(SORA (CAROLINA RAIL)
Porzana carolina

7½—9½" long. Color pattern of sexes alike.

The Sora, also known as Carolina Rail, is more common in the state than the Virginia, both in summer and in migration. *Adults:* Front of head and throat black; upperparts olive brown streaked with black and lined with white; breast gray; flanks and sides barred with white and black; bill short, yellowish with dark tip; legs and feet yellowish green. Like the Virginia, it is a shy, active bird of rushes and similar vegetation growing in marshes and on shores of ponds and lakes.

DISTRIBUTION. At nesting time Soras may be found around any marsh or pond bordered with rank aquatic vegetation. They were formerly most common in the Rio Grande Valley, northward to Albuquerque; but less so in recent years because of the draining of marshes and swamps.

In September 1920, the author found them common in marshes both above and below Albuquerque. Some may be observed all winter in suitable habitat in the southern part of the state. "They winter in the Las Cruces area" (Williams). Migrants were observed at Carlsbad on September 16.

NESTING. The height of the breeding season in the central Rio Grande Valley is in May. Soras nest in the San Simon marshes and on Bosque del Apache and Bitter Lake Refuges. At Burford Lake and other high-altitude lakes in northern New Mexico, nesting takes place in June. *Nests:* Made of marsh grass, may be on the ground but are more often in rushes above ground or water, with the grass blades sometimes bent over to provide shade and concealment. *Eggs:* Usually 10 to 12; buffy-drab, spotted with reddish brown.

([COMMON (FLORIDA) GALLINULE
Gallinula chloropus

12—14″ long. Color pattern of sexes alike.

The Common Gallinule, although smaller, resembles the Coot, but crownplate and base of bill are bright red, whereas the Coot has a white bill. Though a good swimmer, it is very shy and is inclined to spend more time than does the Coot in marsh grass cover, particularly where there are rushes and cattails. *Adults:* Dark slate or lead color, darker on back, and blackish on head; edge of wings and flanks streaked with white; under-tail coverts white. *In winter:* Underparts whitish.

DISTRIBUTION. There were no records of Gallinules in the state prior to July 14, 1928, on which date Harry Williams, of

SORA (CAROLINA RAIL). *Edwin Sheppard, U.S. Fish & Wildlife Service.*

U.S. Bureau of Reclamation, saw one in a drainage canal south of Las Cruces. After that time, Williams states, the birds became progressively more numerous until by 1940 they had become well established in the Rio Grande Valley from El Paso north to the vicinity of Hatch. In more recent years the Gallinule has extended its range northward to Bosque del Apache Refuge and Socorro. In the Las Cruces area it seems to prefer the many drainage canals containing a variety of aquatic plant life, and bordered by rank rushes and willows. On several occasions, more recently, the author has accompanied Williams on investigating trips in the Rio Grande Valley when numbers of the birds were seen slipping about shyly, Rail-like, in the heavy cover. On May 10, 1955, the Common Gallinule was observed at Bitter Lake Refuge by Leslie Beatty, Refuge manager. This seems to be the first authentic record for the Pecos Valley. It may be only a question of time until it will be established in this valley also.

NESTING. On May 15, 1955, Harry Williams, Wayne Bohl, and the author located a nest of the Common Gallinule in a drainage canal three miles west of Las Cruces. The nest was situated in a small patch of rushes growing on the side of the bank, just above running water, in the drain. It contained 10 eggs, apparently incubated about ten days. Nest: Substantially made of blades of marsh grass. Eggs: 8 to 12; buffy white, rather heavily spotted with brown.

(AMERICAN COOT
Fulica americana

13–16″ long. Color pattern of sexes alike.

The American Coot is often appropriately called the Mud Hen. Distinguishing marks are the white bill, slaty plumage, darkening to brown or black on head and neck; wings and under-tail coverts marked with white. Coots are gregarious, often gathering in great flocks during winter. The jerky, head-bobbing motion while swimming is diagnostic. At nesting time at Burford Lake the author found the males very antagonistic toward Ducks and Grebes that ventured near their pre-empted nesting places. So abundant were they that they dominated much of the tule-bordered shorelines. Resourceful and prolific, their excessive numbers are out of proportion to their benefits; they consume food needed by Ducks and other more beneficial birds. Liberal bag limits are usually allowed sportsmen, but excessive populations persist.

DISTRIBUTION. The summer range of the American Coot is statewide, wherever there are marshes, ponds, and lakes with rank growths of aquatic vegetation. In migration they are abundant in the Rio Grande and Pecos Valleys. Few are observed in midwinter, even in the southern part of the state. On October 20, 1956, more than 200 in a comparatively compact raft were observed by Wayne Bohl and the author on Lake McMillan, near the dam.

NESTING. The American Coot nests wherever it finds suitable environment. In 1913 the author estimated 200 pairs were nesting at Burford Lake. "In May–June 1918, it ranked next to Eared Grebes and Yellow-headed Blackbirds in abundance at Burford Lake, with about 150 pairs nesting on the lake" (Wetmore). Nest: Floating among rushes or other rank water vegetation; made of blades of grass pulled together and built up a few inches above waterline. When nests become waterlogged they are built up to keep the depression above the surface, whereas Duck nests which are built in water sometimes become waterlogged and are lost. Eggs: 8 to 12; buffy, evenly dotted with brown. The young take to water soon after emerging from the shell.

SHORE BIRDS
TOP: LONG-BILLED CURLEW. ROW 2: AVOCET
ROW 3: BLACK-NECKED STILT, MOUNTAIN PLOVER, SNOWY PLOVER
BOTTOM: KILLDEER, SPOTTED SANDPIPER
Orville O. Rice, courtesy of Mrs. G. F. Coope, Carlsbad

PLOVERS
Family: CHARADRIIDAE

PLOVERS are both shore and upland birds of variable sizes. They have relatively large heads, short bills, and long, pointed wings. Their middle and outer toes are webbed at base. Of the six species which occur in the state, three—Snowy, Killdeer, and Mountain—nest within its borders. The precocial young, with their concealing coloration, are virtually invisible, even when crouched on barren ground.

SEMIPALMATED (RINGED) PLOVER
Charadrius semipalmatus
6½—7″ long. Color pattern of sexes alike.

The Semipalmated Plover must be regarded as uncommon in New Mexico. Until recently this Plover had not been recorded here. It is a small Killdeer-like shore bird. *Adults:* Upperparts brown; entirely white underneath except for the single black collar, or ring, around the neck. Base of bill orange; legs yellowish. The species is listed as "transient visitor, uncommon" at both Bosque del Apache and Bitter Lake Refuges. "Seen on two occasions, spring 1954 at lake 13 miles west of Clayton" (Krehbiel). In the Roswell area Montgomery recorded it on September 27, 1952. "September 17, 1939, 5 seen and specimen taken, in New Mexico, northwest of El Paso. There are six to ten records for the El Paso area" (Lena McBee).

❲ SNOWY PLOVER
Charadrius alexandrinus
6—7″ long. Color pattern of sexes alike.

In its light plumage which blends perfectly with its surroundings of barren gypsum flats, the shy and extremely active little Snowy Plover often is difficult to see.

The speed with which two or more of these dainty Plovers whip about in devious courses just above the surface of the bare white or gray ground is no less amazing than are their movements in "streaking" across the surface of the ground at such speed as to leave one wondering whether they are running or flying. Like most Plovers, the Snowy has no complete ring, but black bars on each side of chest. *Adults:* Upperparts buffy gray with black barring; ear coverts black; remainder of body white.

DISTRIBUTION. The Snowy Plover is a summer resident about the barren alkali-bordered lakes of the Rio Grande, Estancia and Pecos Valleys. As such habitat type is limited, nesting distribution is likewise limited. Snowy Plovers are most common in the Pecos Valley above Roswell (Bitter Lake and Salt Creek), and the shallow salt lakes in the Estancia Valley. In June 1951, Lon Hunter, Refuge manager, estimated there were between 75 and 100 of these Plovers at Bitter Lake Refuge. Jack Campbell and W. W. Hill recorded them April 28, May 12, 19, 22, and 30, 1951, at salt lakes in the valley southeast of Estancia.

NESTING. Bitter Lake Refuge is the principal Snowy Plover nesting area in the state. The several barren alkali flats adjacent to the shallow, brackish ponds provide the nesting conditions that the little Plovers require. On June 29 downy young were seen there. Although the birds are unusually shy and scoot away when approached, the author found them on this occasion rather fearless in their ruses to lead him away from nests or newly-hatched young. In their feigning antics they are not unlike Killdeers at nesting time. They dash up, then swiftly "streak" away for some distance, only to fall over with a wing extended, and flop about on the ground as if seized by agonizing pain. Should the ruse fail, the agitated performers play a game of "hide and seek," running away and crouching behind a tuft of grass or a stick, and then repeat their antics behind some other object, in an attempt to lure one in pursuit so that search for the skillfully concealed nest or young will be abandoned.

The Snowy Plover is also a summer resident and breeds at Bosque del Apache Refuge. *Nest:* A slight depression lined with small pebbles, usually on barren ground near a trail or roadway where there is gravel to camouflage nest and contents. *Eggs:* 3 or 4; clay color base thickly sprinkled with blackish-brown splotches and lines. The eggs are large for size of the birds.

([KILLDEER
Charadrius vociferus

10—11″ long. Color pattern of sexes alike.

The Killdeer is the most common Plover in New Mexico. Its "Killdeer" notes are diagnostic. *Adults:* Forehead, eye stripe, collar, underparts and wing linings white; neck with two black bands, the wider one a complete collar. Unlike the Mountain Plover, which it resembles in some respects, it generally is found near lakes, ponds, or streams, whereas the Mountain Plover's chosen habitat is high, open mesa or plain, short-grass land, with little or no regard for proximity to water. Killdeers seem to prefer association with man and his utilization of soil and water, and are so adaptable that their numbers fluctuate little if at all. The Killdeer wears the same dress throughout the year, whereas most male shore birds undergo a change of plumage from winter to summer.

DISTRIBUTION. During the nesting period and in warmer seasons of the year, Killdeers are found practically statewide. Although a majority of them leave the state during the colder part of the winter, some remain, even as far north as Albuquerque, at places where water from springs or spring-fed marshes does not freeze. They are more evenly distributed throughout the state in summer than any other shore or water bird.

NESTING. The Killdeer nests throughout the state. Full complements of eggs were noted at the Dexter Fish Culture Station as early as March 21. It breeds from the lowest part of the state to 8,000 feet (Burford Lake); nesting time, however, is correspondingly later as altitude increases. A favorite nesting site is the center of gravelly roadways or near trails about lakes or streams. Such barren, gravelly surfaces provide a perfect camouflage for the eggs. Were it not for the fact that the birds may be observed leaving the nest when approached, few nests would be located. When disturbed, other than by man, the Killdeer usually stays and defends the nest. When they "freeze" on the ground, the downy young are practically invisible. The alarm notes of the parent birds are sufficient to keep them hidden as long as danger threatens. Few other birds are more skillful at feigning affliction in efforts to lead intruders away from nests or young. The newly-hatched are led to stream or lake shore where they forage for themselves, but they remain intact as a family unit until young are well developed. *Nest:* Usually on gravelly hillside, at side of or in middle of road, or on grass hummock; a slight hollow in the ground, lined with small gravel, bits of grass, or weed stems. *Eggs:* 4, dull buffy, heavily marked with dark brown, black, and lavender.

([MOUNTAIN PLOVER
Eupoda montana

8—9½″ long. Color pattern of sexes alike.

In size and coloration, the so-called Mountain Plover resembles the Killdeer, though it is slightly smaller. *Breeding plumage:* Forehead and line over eye white; crown with black patch; prevailing body color plain light brown, simulating the usual drab surroundings of its short-grass prairie or mesa habitat. Underparts whitish. *Winter plumage:* Without black or white markings.

The name Mountain Plover is a misnomer since it is not a mountain dweller. "Prairie Plover" would seem a more appropriate name. Although its breeding range includes plains and high mesa country up to 7,000 feet elevation, it adheres strictly to open plain, mesa, or ridge, short-grass terrain, preferably with a gravelly surface.

DISTRIBUTION. Mountain Plovers are somewhat sporadic in their annual occurrence. If a previously occupied breeding area has had scant moisture and consequently is lacking in suitable food, they will move on to more favorable habitat. Water is not a nesting-range requirement. This Plover, so far as the state is concerned, is only semi-migratory, since it may be observed as late as mid-December, or even January, depending on weather conditions, and by early March may be seen whipping about close to the surface in groups of three, six, or more, on preferred breeding range. So completely do Plovers blend into typical habitat environment that they are difficult to see, either on the surface or in flight. Even their ground movements tend to conceal them, since they run rapidly for short distances and then stand motionless, thereby often escaping notice. The greatest concentration of the birds ever recorded by the author was on July 3, 1937, when approximately 150 were seen in a hard-land basin near the Price Ranch about ten miles northwest of Tatum. This mass assembly indicated that the nesting season had passed and that young of the year were on their own.

NESTING. The most extensive breeding grounds are in Lea, Union, Roosevelt, and Harding Counties, and on mesa country south of the Sacramento Mountains in Otero County. The Mountain Plover also nests locally on the short-grass, mesa lands east and northeast of Tres Piedras in Taos County; on the valley land north and east of Domingo in Santa Fe County; and on the San Augustin Plains of Socorro and Catron Counties, where on June 5, 1940, the author found a nest containing three fresh eggs, ten miles southwest of Horse Springs. It also breeds on the gravelly mesas both north and south of the Animas Mountains, Hidalgo County. The male Mountain Plover assumes the duty of raising the young. Whether he incubates the eggs seems yet to be determined. In lower altitudes (Otero, Lea, and Roosevelt Counties) nesting begins in late April. *Nest:* A slight depression in the ground, lined with grass and rootlets. *Eggs:* 3 or 4, brownish drab, heavily marked with blackish brown, mixed with paler spots mostly on the larger end.

AMERICAN GOLDEN PLOVER
Pluvialis dominica

10—11″ long. Color pattern of sexes similar.

The American Golden Plover is a winter visitor to the state. While it must be regarded as uncommon, it is probably less so than the comparatively few authentic records might indicate. In association with other Plovers or shore birds it may be overlooked. Unfortunately, it is seen in the state mostly in its plainer plumage—mottled brownish upperparts and dusky underparts, rather than in its beautiful summer garb—upperparts rich golden-brown mottled (which give the bird its name), and black underparts; sides of head white. The Black-bellied Plover, which it resembles, is larger, with upperparts grayish, mottled black and white. In the spring the Golden begins to assume the black underpart markings. "Thirty-five American Golden Plovers were seen at Bosque del Apache Refuge on May 11, 1954" (Fleetwood). It is recorded as "transient visitor" at Bitter Lake Refuge.

BLACK-BELLIED PLOVER
Squatarola squatarola

10½—13" long. Color pattern of sexes alike.

The Black-bellied Plover, like the American Golden, which it resembles, is generally regarded as an uncommon visitor to the state. As its name implies, the underparts, in summer plumage, are black; back is grayish with black-and-white spotting. In winter dress the underparts are whitish; upperparts grayish or brown without black spotting so conspicuous in summer plumage.

The Black-bellied is listed as a rare transient visitor at Bosque del Apache and Bitter Lake Refuges. For the Clayton area: "Only one record here, September 22, 1954, at East Three Mile Lake" (Krehbiel and Cook). In the Roswell area: "Occasional, May, September, October, December" (Montgomery).

SNIPE, SANDPIPERS, ETC.
Family: *SCOLOPACIDAE*

THE SNIPE and Sandpipers belong to a large group of rather plain-colored birds of various sizes, most of which are waders. Of the twenty-two species that have been recorded in the state, only two—the Long-billed Curlew and the Spotted Sandpiper —are known to nest here. Although the larger species of the group are not difficult to identify, the several smaller ones of similar winter plumage may be somewhat confusing.

COMMON (WILSON'S) SNIPE
Capella gallinago

10½—11½" long. Color pattern of sexes alike.

The Common Snipe, also known as the Jacksnipe, is widely distributed in migration; some spending winter in the state. It is a shy marsh-dweller, very much resembling the Eastern Woodcock, and may well be regarded as a smaller edition of that popular game bird. It has a rather large, long bill (2½ inches), and an upper mandible which overreaches the lower. *Adults:* Top of head with narrow buffy or whitish median stripe between broad black lateral stripes; upperparts variegated, dark brown, black, tan striped with buffy or whitish, giving a lengthwise striped pattern to head and neck; underparts white. The bird lies so close in marshes or along stream shores that it is rarely seen until it bursts from its hiding place and dashes away on a devious course, probably to drop into similar cover and again disappear. It may occur alone, or in twos or threes where there are sedges and other marsh vegetation. Its food is obtained by probing in the mud, thereby leaving holes as evidence of its recent presence. It is probable that it nests about the high marshy-bordered lakes in the northern section of the state, although there seems to be no record on which to base this assumption. However, it is known to nest in Colorado, not far to the north. It has a high rating, both for wingshooting and as a table delicacy.

([LONG-BILLED CURLEW

Numenius americanus

20—26″ long. Color pattern of sexes alike.

The exceptionally long, decurved bill (in mature birds, 8 inches), brown streaked body, long legs, and clarion calls as it flies, readily identify the Long-billed Curlew. The long, sensitively-pointed bill serves it well in probing spiders and other insects from the ground. In the Pecos Valley, concentrations of the birds may often be seen, particularly in spring and fall, in newly-mown alfalfa fields where they feed on the insect life brought to the surface by irrigation water. Under rigid protection there has been a rather marked increase in numbers of these Curlews in recent years.

DISTRIBUTION. During migration the Curlew may be seen anywhere in the state except in the forested mountains, but it is usually most common along the high plains and in the Pecos Valley. The author has seen great flocks at Bitter Lake Refuge and Dexter Fish Culture Station, resting in close formation apparently without fear, on the smooth alkali flats bordering shallow ponds, or even standing in the water. Most of the birds pass out of the state with the coming of cold weather, but some may be seen throughout the winter in the southern part.

NESTING. Although not consistently, the Long-billed Curlew nests in several localities in the north-central, eastern, and northeastern sections of the state. Moisture and vegetation have a direct bearing on whether it remains to nest. If one locality is dry, with few insects, and pond and lake basins are without water, the breeders will move on to "greener fields." Under such conditions most of them may leave. On May 23, 1954, a nest containing four eggs was examined by Wayne Bohl, southwest of Mosquero (elevation about 4,500 feet), San Miguel County. When an observer gets within the vicinity of nests or young, he is met with shrill calls or broken clarion notes, thereby revealing the location of the nesting grounds, which are always on open terrain—plain, mesa, or valley. Curlews use clever ruses or decoys to deflect from nesting areas. So well do nests, eggs, or young simulate the surroundings that few are found, even with intensive searching. *Nest:* A slight hollow in the ground, lined with grass or weed stems. *Eggs:* 4; unusually large for size of bird, olive clay color, spotted and blotched with chocolate and blackish markings.

WHIMBREL (HUDSONIAN CURLEW)

Numenius phaeopus

16—18″ long. Color pattern of sexes alike.

The Whimbrel, a smaller relative of the Long-billed Curlew, occurs rarely in the state. Identification as a Curlew is simplified by its similarity to the latter. *Adults:* Head striped, rest of upperparts grayish brown mixed with buffy to whitish; tail and wings marked with pinkish or cinnamon; underparts buffy or whitish streaked with grayish brown. For Bosque del Apache Refuge it is listed as "transient

COMMON SNIPE
Edwin Sheppard, U.S. Fish & Wildlife Service

visitor, rare." "Recorded near Roswell, May 16, 1953" (Montgomery and Sikes). One was taken by Thomas C. Henry at old Fort Thorn (now Hatch) in 1854.

UPLAND PLOVER
Bartramia longicauda

11—12½" long. Color pattern of sexes alike.

In the state the Upland Plover, as its name suggests, is a bird of the short-grass, high plains country and prairies and meadow farmlands to the eastward. Since it is an upland dweller, free water does not appear to be a requisite of its summer range. The Curlew-like habit of holding its wings aloft for an instant on alighting and the waterless type of its chosen habitat, as well as its trait of alighting on posts or stumps on its nesting ground, simplify identification when compared with Sandpipers which, for the most part, are strictly shore birds.

"They are birds of peculiar attractiveness and interest, which we can ill afford to lose" (Bailey). It was formerly known, also, as Tattler, or Prairie Pigeon. *Adults:* Upperparts brownish streaked with buff. Underparts mainly creamy white; head small, crown blackish with median buffy lines; remainder of head streaked with buffy brown; tail graduated, buff tipped with white.

DISTRIBUTION. The Upland Plover is now rare in the Southwest. It formerly occurred in migration in great numbers in the Pecos Valley and on the high plains to the eastward. Elliott Coues, in his *Birds of the Northwest*, refers to these Plovers occurring in Texas in flocks of thousands about 1880. Unrestrained hunting resulted in almost total extermination of the species. Especially was excessive killing along the Gulf Coast of Texas disastrous to these birds. Laws for their protection were enacted almost too late. Migrants over the high plains bore the brunt of the Gulf Coast slaughter. Formerly at the height of the fall and spring migrations their pleasing clarion contact calls as they coursed along their flyways delightfully dispelled the stillness of a cool calm night. Ranchmen and cowboys loved "the lonely Plover's call." They are now rarely seen or heard in the state. Fortunately, they have fared better in states to the east of New Mexico, since birds of that region seem to have been saved the persecution that befell those that formerly abundantly populated the high plains. Their recovery in the Southwest has been disappointingly slow. They formerly nested along the east side of the state, but there are no recent breeding records. Upland Plovers winter in South America—Paraguay and Argentina—where excessive hunting could prevent their hoped-for recovery in our own Southwest.

Nest: Slight depression, some with but little lining, others lined with grass, weed stems, or feathers. *Eggs:* 4; creamy or white; heavily spotted with brown, chocolate, or violet or lilac spots, more numerous on larger end.

(SPOTTED SANDPIPER
Actitis macularia

7—8" long. Color pattern of sexes alike.

The Spotted is one of the few Sandpipers nesting commonly in New Mexico. The conspicuously spotted breast, and habit of teetering as it runs along canal, lake shore or stream bank, are identifying clues. *Adults, breeding plumage:* Upperparts greenish or bronzy-brown, with faint metallic gloss; wing and flight feathers brown and white; line over eye white. Underparts white with large, dark round spots except on chin. *In winter:* Upperparts grayish olive; underparts unspotted.

DISTRIBUTION. In summer this Sandpiper is widely distributed about high mountain streams in central and northern New Mexico. It also remains during breeding season in the Rio Grande Valley as far south as Bosque del Apache Refuge. Although largely migratory, some may remain throughout the winter as far north as Socorro and Roswell.

NESTING. Favorite nesting environment of the Spotted Sandpiper is gravelly margins of mountain stream and lake shores. On July 15, 1951, the author and Raymond Fleetwood found the birds nesting commonly along mountain streams and lakes in the Canjilon section of Rio Arriba County. Four young, just hatched, were noted at one nest. Three broods of four each were observed along Upper Canjilon Creek, while previously breeding birds were noted along the Chama and Brazos Rivers. They also nest commonly at Bosque del Apache Refuge. "Somewhat common in the Roswell area from May to September" (Montgomery). "Nests sparingly along spring-fed portions of Perico Creek, 6 and 7 miles west of Clayton" (Krehbiel). Nests: Killdeer-like, usually in gravelly ground near water; sometimes near some object, as tuft of grass, stone, or piece of driftwood, but often on barren ground, on a gravel bar; usually lined with grass or leaves but sometimes the cavity contains only small gravel. Eggs: 4; creamy buff with reddish- or blackish-brown spots, mostly at larger end.

SOLITARY SANDPIPER
Tringa solitaria
7½—9" long. Color pattern of sexes alike.

The Solitary Sandpiper is a little larger than the Spotted and somewhat resembles the Lesser Yellowlegs. Upperparts brownish; underparts white; white eye-ring and white bars on tail. It is an uncommon migrant in the state. In the Roswell area, "Occasional, May, August and September" (Montgomery). Union County: "Fall migrant. In 1954 observed from July 10 until September 22" (Krehbiel). For Bit-

ter Lake and Bosque del Apache Refuges it is listed as "transient visitor, occasional."

WILLET
Catoptrophorus semipalmatus
15—16" long. Color pattern of sexes alike.

The Willet is a moderately large shore bird, smaller than a Curlew and very conspicuous in flight with its black-and-white wing pattern both above and below. Adults: Top and sides of head blackish; bill straight, 2 to 2½ inches long; back mainly black, lower underparts white; sides streaked and spotted; tail gray, white at base; front toes webbed at base.

DISTRIBUTION. Willets are rather common throughout the state in both spring and fall migrations. They are usually observed in groups of six to a dozen or more, although the author has observed as many as 25 or 30 in the southwestern section in the spring. While they may be observed sparingly even in the summer, there seem to be no authentic breeding records for New Mexico. It will be rather surprising if they are not found nesting within its borders since they are known to breed in

GREATER YELLOWLEGS
Edwin Sheppard, U.S. Fish & Wildlife Service

southern Colorado (Rio Grande Valley), not far to the north. They are absent from the state in the winter.

GREATER YELLOWLEGS
Totanus melanoleucus
14—16″ long. Color pattern of sexes alike.

So distinctive are the Greater Yellowlegs with their long, yellow legs, and long, slightly curved, black bill (2¼ inches), and the whitish rump and tail as seen in flight, they are readily identified. Among the largest of the shore birds, they are often seen feeding while standing in water almost body deep. Their loud, clear, rippling notes as they take wing are also distinctive. *Adults:* Upperparts gray, finely flecked with white; underparts mainly white.

DISTRIBUTION. Greater Yellowlegs are widely spread during migration, when they may be seen feeding in ponds or lakes, as far out as they can wade. They are among the earliest arrivals in the fall migration. The author recorded them August 7 at Dulce Lake. Vernon Bailey noted the Greater Yellowlegs in the Carlsbad area August 3 to 9. However, it has been noted here as late as early December. It is recorded as "transient visitor, common" at Bosque del Apache and Bitter Lake Refuges. Northbound migrants usually begin to arrive the latter part of April (Carlsbad). "May 1, 1955, one at Alcalde" (Hawkins). There are no nesting records for the state.

LESSER YELLOWLEGS
Totanus flavipes
9½—11″ long. Color pattern of sexes alike.

The Lesser Yellowlegs is almost a duplicate of the Greater, except that it is somewhat smaller, and the gray and white plumage pattern is more refined; bill shorter—1½ inches long. *Adults:* Head and upper part of neck streaked with black

and white, back mottled black and white, tail coverts white; breast and sides white dotted, median and lower underparts white; legs and feet bright yellow.

DISTRIBUTION. Like the Greater, the Lesser Yellowlegs is strictly a migrant. The birds begin to arrive in the state by the middle of August. "Koehler Junction August 21, 23 and 25" (Kalmbach). The author observed them commonly from Albuquerque to Socorro, August 28. They were noted at Carlsbad, September 3 and Lake McMillan, October 20. While they are widely spread and common during late summer and fall migration, there are very few records for the spring northward flight. One was recorded at Glenrio, April 15. "One was observed on May 18, 1952, on the Isleta Indian Reservation" (Fitzsimmons and Durrie). Lack of spring records may be due to brief tarrying of the birds in their northward flight or to their largely bypassing the state by the way of the Texas high plains, where at this season there are usually many small lakes which are more in keeping with their habitat requirements.

PECTORAL SANDPIPER
Erolia melanotos
8—9½″ long. Color pattern of sexes alike.

The Pectoral is a medium-sized Sandpiper, larger than the Spotted but with shorter legs and neck. *Adults:* Upperparts, including wings, light brown streaked and spotted with black, lined with white. Distinctive features are the brownish breast and white underparts. It is known also as Grass Snipe because it seemingly prefers grassy meadows rather than lake or stream shores; in fact it has characteristics of the Wilson's Snipe, such as flushing singly and zigzagging in flight. There are few records for the state. It is listed as "transient, occasional visitor" at Bosque del Apache Refuge. "One record, July 24,

1954, when 15 were observed at Prairie Lake, ½ mile south of Clayton" (Krehbiel and Cook).

WHITE-RUMPED SANDPIPER
Erolia fuscicollis
7½" long. Color pattern of sexes alike.

The White-rumped Sandpiper, with the Baird's, Least, and Western, constitutes a group that possesses fine points of distinction requiring careful observation for positive identification. Its name suggests one of the distinguishing marks, since the white rump is conspicuous, particularly in flight. *Adults:* Head and back striped with black and light rusty; underparts white; neck and breast spotted, washed with buffy. There are very few old records of the bird's appearance in the state. Competent observers consider it uncommon, if not rare. "Five at Bitter Lake, September 8, 1951, and one May 3, 1952" (Montgomery). It is listed as "transient visitor, unusual" at Bitter Lake Refuge, and "transient visitor, occasional" at Bosque del Apache Refuge. Krehbiel lists it "unusual transient" in the Clayton area. He states: "One observed May 30, 1955."

BAIRD'S SANDPIPER
Erolia bairdii
7½" long. Color pattern of sexes alike.

This little Sandpiper resembles the Least, but is a little larger. Baird's belongs to a group of small Sandpipers that are very confusing to the average bird observer. *Adults:* Upperparts pale grayish-buff streaked with black; throat white; breast with light buffy band lightly streaked or spotted; upper-tail coverts blackish; paler in winter. Like the White-rumped, it is uncommon in the state. Most of the records refer to its late summer appearance—August and September. From September 3 to 14, Vernon Bailey reported finding it common in alfalfa

fields about Carlsbad. Other old records list it as occurring at various points throughout the state. "A few seen in late fall migration of 1954 at lake, 3 miles east of Clayton" (Krehbiel). It is recorded as "transient visitor, unusual" at Bosque del Apache and Bitter Lake Refuges.

LEAST SANDPIPER
Erolia minutilla
5–6½" long. Color pattern of sexes alike.

The designation, "Least," is of little aid in identifying this mite of a shore bird since the other so-called "Peeps"—Baird's and Western—are but little larger. This trio of little busybodies is usually sufficiently tame to permit careful observation. *Adults:* Upperparts of the Least are buff and rufous, with black feather centers; broad chest band distinctively spotted or streaked; legs greenish. It is listed as a "common, transient visitor" and "present occasionally in winter" at Bosque del Apache and Bitter Lake Refuges. In the Clayton area, "A few seen during migration both in spring and fall of 1954" (Krehbiel). Like most others of the group, the Least Sandpiper begins to arrive early (July 26 at Carlsbad), and it must be a swift and long-distance flyer for its breeding range is some 2,000 miles distant from southern New Mexico. It is regarded as abundant during migration.

DUNLIN (RED-BACKED) SANDPIPER
Erolia alpina
7½–8½" long. Color pattern of sexes similar.

The Dunlin, a medium sized Sandpiper, is rare in the state. *Adults, winter:* Upperparts grayish; chest light gray, more or less streaked with dusky; rest of underparts, sides, rump, and upper-tail coverts white. Bill, 1¾ inches. *Adults, spring and sum-*

mer: Crown, back and upper-tail coverts bright rusty, more or less spotted or streaked with black; chest grayish white, thickly streaked with dusky; sides and underparts black.

DISTRIBUTION. The Southwest seems to be out of the regular migratory route of the Dunlin Sandpiper. There is at least one authentic record for New Mexico: "Two individuals were seen regularly with a flock of Dowitchers, from January 8 to February 22, 1941, on Bosque del Apache Refuge" (Monson). (*Condor*, Vol. 48, No. 3, September-October 1946). While seemingly extremely rare, at times the Dunlin may be overlooked. The one record should alert observers for this Sandpiper.

LONG-BILLED DOWITCHER
Limnodromus scolopaceus
11—12½" long. Color pattern of sexes alike.

The Long-billed Dowitcher may be recognized, even in winter plumage, by its long bill (2 to 3 inches), the broad white stripe down the lower back and on the tail, and white line over eye; upperparts grayish brown; underparts white; in spring, breast tinged with light brown. Old records of the bird in the state are few. It is now known to occur more commonly. "An adult male was taken June 21, 1921, on the Mimbres River, 30 miles southeast of Silver City in a flock of about 75 Western Willets" (Kellogg). It is listed as "transient visitor, common" at Bosque del Apache and "transient visitor, uncommon" at Bitter Lake Refuge. The author collected one at Wade Lake, above Lake McMillan Delta, October 1, 1954.

The Short-billed Dowitcher (*Limnodromus griseus*) probably also occurs in the state, but has not been recorded, because observers generally are unable to distinguish it from the Long-billed. The Short-billed is somewhat smaller than the Long-billed, and its bill is almost an inch shorter.

STILT SANDPIPER
Micropalama himantopus
7½—9" long. Color pattern of sexes alike.

The Stilt Sandpiper, one of the rarest of this large family of birds occurring in the state, has two distinctive plumages. The summer dress is readily recognized but in winter plumage it might be confused with the Lesser Yellowlegs, which it resembles, particularly in flight; however, it is smaller than that species with a slightly longer bill which is widened at tip. As seen in winter it has a conspicuous white line over eye; upperparts grayish brown; underparts white; mottled on side; legs greenish. *Adult, summer:* Upperparts mottled with black, buff, and brown; upper-tail coverts white; stripe along side of head brown; underparts thickly barred and spotted with buff and white.

DISTRIBUTION. There seem to be only two state records, but, since its winter plumage is similar to that of the Lesser Yellowlegs, it might be overlooked. On August 24, 1954, Montgomery recorded "six or eight at Bitter Lake." For the Clayton area, Krehbiel states, "accidental transient."

SEMIPALMATED SANDPIPER
Ereunetes pusillus
6" long. Color pattern of sexes alike.

This is one of the small, problem Sandpipers. The Semipalmated resembles the Western Sandpiper but is slightly smaller. *Adults, winter:* Upperparts dull gray, streaked with dusky; underparts white tinged with gray on breast; legs black. Krehbiel reports it as "accidental transient" in the Clayton area. The author picked up a dead Semipalmated Sandpiper at a small pond near Socorro, September 10, 1926. It may be overlooked because of uncertainty of identification.

WESTERN SANDPIPER

Ereunetes mauri

6—7″ long. Color pattern of sexes alike.

The Western is another of the "Peep" Sandpipers that may be difficult to identify. Among the finer points of distinction is its size; it is one of the smallest of the "Peeps"; the bill is about an inch long. It has the habit of flocking, either when feeding or in flight. *Adults, fall and winter:* Upperparts brownish gray; shaft feathers tipped with white, imparting a scaly effect; chin white; breast streaked; lower underparts white.

The Western Sandpiper now seems to be a common migrant although limited old records indicate otherwise. It is regarded as "transient visitor, common" at Bosque del Apache Refuge. In the Clayton area, Krehbiel lists it as "common migrant." There seem to be fewer northward spring migration records, indicating that the majority of Western Sandpipers might miss New Mexico.

MARBLED GODWIT

Limosa fedoa

16—20″ long. Color pattern of sexes alike.

The Marbled Godwit is one of the larger shore birds; in size almost a duplicate of the Avocet, the latter, however, being largely cinnamon, black and white. It is strictly a fall and spring migrant, but is apt to be seen any place in the state where there are ponds or lakes. *Adults:* Upperparts black and buffy brown; tail barred, cinnamon and black; underparts buffy white barred with black; bill 4 inches long, slightly decurved; feet black.

DISTRIBUTION. "Seen upon five occasions during 1954 (Clayton area), during spring. Largest number seen was 17, on May 2, 1954" (Krehbiel). "I saw three on Unit 16, Bitter Lake Refuge July 3, 1952"

(Montgomery). Listed as "transient visitor, common," Bosque del Apache Refuge and "transient visitor, uncommon," at Bitter Lake Refuge.

HUDSONIAN GODWIT

Limosa haemastica

15—16″ long. Color pattern of sexes alike.

The Hudsonian Godwit seems to be one of the rarest shore birds occurring in the state. It is a little smaller than the Marbled Godwit, with shorter bill. *Adults:* Upperparts, grayish with rusty and blackish mottling, upper-tail coverts black and white, tail white at base, black at end; underparts chestnut red with blackish barring. *Adults in winter:* Head, neck, and underparts grayish or buffy; upperparts grayish brown; bill about 3 inches long, slightly recurved. *Limosa* (Latin)—"mud" or "muddy," *haemastica* (Greek)—"a blood-red color."

DISTRIBUTION. There seem to be but two authentic records of this Godwit for the state. On December 12, 1955, John M. Campbell of New Haven, Connecticut, wrote the author: "On May 22, 1951, I collected this bird from the midst of about 20 Avocets which had occupied the pond area as a nesting site. The Avocets were harassing the Godwit in an attempt to drive it away from the pond." The pond referred to is near Estancia in the Estancia Valley. The specimen is now in the University of New Mexico Collection of Vertebrates. One was recorded at Bitter Lake Refuge, May 18, 1958 (Montgomery, Harris, Garrett, and Sikes).

SANDERLING

Crocethia alba

7—8½″ long. Color pattern of sexes alike.

The Sanderling is a conspicuous Sandpiper, in fall or winter, when seen in New

Mexico. Upperparts pale gray; bend of wing dusky, forming a dark splash against the whitish sides; bar of white on wing which flashes conspicuously in flight; underparts white; bill and feet black. Since it was recorded in the state a hundred years ago there have been few records of its occurrence. It still seems to be one of the rarest of the Sandpipers to enter the state.

It is possible that some go through with few or no stops. Union County: "One record here in spring migration, when on May 12, 1954, W. W. Cook saw four at lake 13 miles west of Clayton" (Krehbiel). "The only Sanderling I have seen in the area [Roswell] was a lone individual on the closed area at Bitter Lake, April 27, 1952" (Montgomery).

AVOCETS AND STILTS
Family: RECURVIROSTRIDAE

AVOCETS AND STILTS are rather large, long-legged wading birds. So striking are their highly contrasting plumage and long slender bills—definitely upturned in Avocets, less so in Stilts—they are easily identified. Both species are unique in their manner of flying some distance to meet an intruder and loudly protesting his presence in an attempt to divert attention from nest location. Male and female are very attentive in nesting duties.

(AMERICAN AVOCET
Recurvirostra americana

16—19″ long. Color pattern of sexes alike.

The American Avocet, a rather large long-legged, black-and-white shore bird, is not apt to be confused with any other species. *Adults:* Foreparts light cinnamon except for whitish area about eye and at base of recurved bill; rest of body white; wings mainly black. Its habit of wading about in shallow water, sweeping its long bill (3½ inches) from side to side as it gleans aquatic insects is distinctive.

DISTRIBUTION. Avocets may be seen sparingly statewide during migration, but their preferred summer habitat is about lakes and ponds of the Pecos Valley and high plains to the eastward. During periods of scant rainfall, when prairie

basins are dry, breeding Avocets are absent. They are most common in migration in the Rio Grande and Pecos Valleys. From September 5 to 20, 1954, many were observed at Bitter Lake Refuge and at Lake McMillan. The Avocet is listed as "a summer resident, common" at Bosque del Apache, and as "summer resident, uncommon" at Bitter Lake Refuge. Local lake conditions influence its presence elsewhere.

NESTING. The Avocet breeds sparingly and irregularly in the state, depending largely on upland lake water conditions. The author found fresh eggs on June 6 at Deep Lake, 30 miles northeast of Roswell, and several pairs, no doubt breeding birds, were observed at nearby White Lakes at that time. They nest sparingly about lakes in the Las Vegas and Wagon Mound sections and in the Estancia Valley. In the Clayton area: "Summer resident, breeding occasionally when adequate rains supply local lakes" (Krehbiel). Noisy, restless conduct of the birds upon approach of an observer usually betrays nesting grounds. When nest or young are approached, the birds become bolder, as they dash up on wing, alighting nearby, and in simulated affliction sneak away, or squat on the ground, in an effort to lead an intruder away. *Nest:* Usually on sloping ground near ponds or lakes, a slight depression in the ground, lined with grass and weed stems. *Eggs:* 4; plain olive or buffy clay, thickly spotted with chocolate or black and lavender. Unless the bird is seen leaving it, the nest is difficult to find, so perfectly do nest and contents blend with surroundings.

(BLACK-NECKED STILT
Himantopus mexicanus
13½—16″ long. Color pattern of sexes alike.

The Black-necked Stilt, with its long stiltlike legs, long pointed bill (2½ to 2¾ inches) and black-and-white body, is readily recognized, either on the ground or in flight. Female is similar to the male, but duller. So spectacular is the Black-necked Stilt that once seen it is not apt to be forgotten. Its extravagantly long legs are adapted for wading while feeding in deep water.

DISTRIBUTION. The Black-necked Stilt may be observed in migration throughout the state, mostly about shallow alkali lakes. It shuns timbered areas and prefers the Rio Grande and Pecos Valley flyways

NEST AND EGGS, BLACK-NECKED STILT
Photograph by the Author

where the small brackish ponds and lakes are in keeping with its nature. Although it may occasionally be observed in high mountainous country, it is transient at such elevations.

NESTING. Black-necked Stilts usually nest in groups of three or more pairs, or even in colonies. They are spectacular performers on their nesting grounds. Some distance from the nesting area seemingly all the local inhabitants join forces in loudly protesting the approach of an observer as they take wing and fly about distractedly, or they may alight and creep away in feigned affliction, only to rise and circle noisily should the ruse fail. When they have young, their conduct is even more dramatic—a half dozen or more of the protesting group may line up in the shallow water of a pond, all facing the intruder, wings flapping as though frantically beckoning or beseeching aid, in a valiant effort to divert attention from their young. Significantly, only man, dog, or other predaceous species arouse fear in these and similar shore birds. Cattle, horses, and sheep provoke no concern, unless they chance to get too near a nest, in which case, by complaining and flapping of wings, the birds endeavor to prevent their treasures from being trampled. The author has found Stilts nesting commonly on Salt Creek and on the Bitter Lake area about Roswell, and about shallow lakes near Dexter. They nest commonly at La Joya Refuge. On May 14, 1925, 30 to 40 of the birds were located at Willow Lake, 20 miles south of Carlsbad. At that time, six nests containing fresh eggs were located on an island in the lake. The nests were placed on dead salt grass hummocks. The Stilt is listed as an unusual summer resident at Bosque del Apache Refuge. *Nest:* A shallow depression lined with a few grass or weed stems, usually placed on grass hummocks above surrounding ground, near water. *Eggs:* usually 4; olive or buffy clay color, spotted with reddish and black or lavender.

PHALAROPES
Family: *PHALAROPODIDAE*

THE PHALAROPES comprise a group of three unique birds, two of which occur in New Mexico during migration. They resemble Sandpipers, but differ in habit in that they are more at home on water, usually whirling about, presumably for the purpose of stirring up small water insects that constitute their principal food. They have rather long necks and small heads, usually held upright. They are very active and appear light when riding high on the water. Unlike most other birds, the female Phalarope, rather than the male, wears the more conspicuous colors. The male, in somber plumage, also incubates the eggs and cares for the young.

WILSON'S PHALAROPE
Steganopus tricolor

8—10" long. Color pattern of sexes alike in winter.

So distinctive are its plump body, bill longer than head, quick action, and nature of spinning round and round on the water that the Wilson's Phalarope is almost self-identifying. *Adults in winter:* Upperparts light gray, white feather tippings giving scale effect; upper-tail coverts white; underparts mainly white; legs and feet yellowish. *Adult female in breeding plumage:* Top of head bluish gray, side of head white with black stripes, changing to reddish brown on lower neck and sides of breast; upperparts with broad brown V's, but without white markings on back or wings; upper-tail coverts white; underparts white. *Adult male in breeding plumage:* Upperparts mainly brownish.

DISTRIBUTION. Wilson's Phalarope is recorded as "transient visitor, common" at Bosque del Apache, and "transient visitor, uncommon" at Bitter Lake Refuge. In the Clayton section it is a "common spring and fall migrant" (Krehbiel). Wetmore noted 20 at Burford Lake as late as May 20, and the author observed six on a pond at the Dexter Fish Culture Station on May 6, 1950. While there are no nesting records for New Mexico, the Phalarope does nest in Colorado and probably will be found breeding here.

WILSON'S PHALAROPE. LOCALITY: JACKSON, WYOMING. *O. J. Murie, U.S. Fish & Wildlife Service.*

NORTHERN PHALAROPE
Lobipes lobatus

7—8" long. Color pattern of sexes different in summer.

The Northern Phalarope is similar to the Wilson's but slightly smaller. *Adults, winter:* Upperparts mainly gray, darker on head, with black ear patch; underparts white. *Adult female in breeding plumage:* Upperparts, including wings, tail, and sides of breast, grayish with tan stripes forming a V on back; rump white; wings with white patch; breast reddish; throat white. *Adult male in breeding plumage:* Similar to female but much duller; face largely white. The Northern Phalarope crosses New Mexico as a rare visitor in both spring and fall migration. Clayton area: "Occurs during migration; less common than Wilson's Phalarope" (Krehbiel). One was observed by Monson near Gallup, November 19, 1937. Henry states: "The only occasion of my meeting with this species was May, 1855, on the Rio Bonita [present site of Fort Stanton]. I met a large flock in full plumage, and secured a number of them."

GULLS AND TERNS
Family: LARIDAE

GULLS AND TERNS comprise a large group of long-winged, slow-flying ocean and interior water birds. Graceful in action as they wheel or spiral in disorderly fashion, they are capable of prolonged flight, and are at home in the air or on the water. At times great numbers may be observed flying at such great heights as to be barely visible. Both the Gulls and Terns have high economic value as destroyers of insects and as scavengers. Adults are predominantly white and bluish gray with distinctive black markings, such as the black cap of most Terns and black wing tips of Gulls. Gulls generally have larger bills and longer legs, and do not fly with their bills pointed down as Terns usually do when above water in search of food. Terns have more or less forked tails.

Seven species of Gulls—Herring, Ring-billed, Laughing, Franklin's, Bonaparte's, Heermann's, and Sabine's—have been recorded in the state, in migration, or as seasonal wanderers (see Rare Birds). There are questionable records of others, and unrecorded species may occur as result of larger reservoir impoundments created in recent years. There seem to be no nesting records of any of the Gulls for the state.

Much interest attaches to the Gull. It is protected under federal and state laws. In Utah, in the early history of the state, great numbers of Gulls came to the aid of farmers by preying on the hordes of crickets which threatened their crops. A monument was later erected commemorating the Gull for bounteous benefits rendered. The only other monument erected in honor of a bird is that to the extinct Passenger Pigeon. This plaque is on a bluff in Wyalusing State Park at the junction of the Mississippi and Wisconsin Rivers. Dedicated May 11, 1947, the legend on the bronze tablet reads: "Dedicated To the Last Wisconsin Passenger Pigeon. Shot at Babcock, Sept. 1899. This Species Became Extinct Through the Avarice and Thoughtlessness of Man. Erected by The Wisconsin Society for Ornithology."

Concentrations of different species of Gulls may frequently be seen in both the Pecos and Rio Grande Valleys, particularly when fields are flooded. Farmers may not always be fully aware of the significance of the presence of these destroyers of insects nor of the extent of benefits thus derived. Although Curlews, Blackbirds, or even Ravens perform like services, the Gulls and Curlews do not possess the undesirable traits of the others. When their more palatable food is lacking, Gulls also serve as scavengers. After heavy rains in August 1927 there was a "phenomenal" concentration of Gulls on the Cheyenne Bottoms in Kansas (now the site of a great federal aid project). Significantly, grasshoppers and cutworms disappeared concurrently on an adjacent area 50 miles in extent.

Terns occur periodically in limited numbers in the state. Four species—Forster's Common, Least and Black Tern—have been recorded, the Least being the only Tern so far known to nest within its borders.

HERRING GULL
Larus argentatus
23—26″ long. Color pattern of sexes alike.

The Herring Gull, one of the larger inland Gulls, is a rare visitor to the state. It may occur more frequently than records indicate but escape notice in the presence of other species. Uncertainty of identification may be the reason for so few listings. *Adults:* Top of head and neck pearl

RING-BILLED GULL
W. F. Kubichek, U.S. Fish & Wildlife Service

gray; lower back and wings dark gray, tips of wings black; underparts white; bill 2¼ inches long, yellow with red spot near end of lower mandible. In winter, head and neck streaked with grayish. It is listed as "accidental visitor, rare" at Bitter Lake Refuge, while for the Clayton section Krehbiel states, "accidental transient." It is listed "accidental visitor" at Bosque del Apache Refuge.

RING-BILLED GULL
Larus delawarensis
18—20″ long. Color pattern of sexes alike.

The Ring-billed is of medium size. It is by far the most common Gull that enters the state. *Adults:* White except wings which are gray above, with black outer tips broken by white spot at end: bill yellow with black ring near tip, accounting for the common name. In winter the underparts are streaked with brownish gray. As evidence of its periodic abundance, Willet estimated 300 on the Carlsbad (Avalon) Reservoir on January 1, 1915, and 500 in December 1916. The author has observed large flights on both Avalon and McMillan Reservoirs, and at Bitter Lake. It is often observed along the Rio Grande about Albuquerque. It is listed as "transient visitor, common" at Bosque del Apache, and "winter visitor, uncommon" at Bitter Lake Refuge. For the Clayton area, "occurs here in limited numbers during migration" (Krehbiel). Great numbers may often be seen at Playas Lake in Hidalgo County.

FRANKLIN'S GULL
Larus pipixcan
13—15″ long. Color pattern of sexes alike.

The Franklin's Gull inhabits the Great Plains and the interior regions to the westward. In size and color pattern it resembles the Bonaparte's Gull. In breeding plumage the head is black. *Winter:* Head mainly white, but sides with contrasting dark patch and back of head streaked with dusky; bill and feet dark red, bill tipped with orange reddish. It is recorded as "transient visitor, occasional" at Bosque del Apache and Bitter Lake Refuges. Wetmore found the Franklin's Gull to be "fairly common at Lake Burford during the spring migration of 1918—15 to 20 immature birds, molting into adult plumage, were seen June 11; about 20 more June 13; and a flock of about 30 in full adult plumage June 14-16."

BONAPARTE'S GULL
Larus philadelphia
12—14″ long. Color pattern of sexes alike.

The Bonaparte's is the smallest Gull that is likely to be seen in New Mexico. The conspicuous white outer primaries are in clear contrast with the gray of the remainder of the back. *Summer:* Head black. *Winter:* Head white with black spot behind eye. It is regarded as a rare migrant here. "Transient visitor, occasional" at Bosque del Apache Refuge. The author recorded a half-dozen on Conchas Lake, April 15, 1951, with full black heads of the breeding plumage.

FORSTER'S TERN
Sterna forsteri
14—15″ long. Color pattern of sexes alike.

The Forster's Tern may be distinguished from the Black and the Least by its greater size. *Adults, summer:* Top of head and nape wholly black; remainder of upperparts, including deeply forked tail, pale gray; underparts wholly white; bill orange, tipped with black; feet and legs orange or orange red. *Winter:* Head white; bill and feet duller. It is uncommon in

the state, listed as "transient visitor, rare" at Bosque del Apache and Bitter Lake Refuges.

COMMON TERN
Sterna hirundo
13—15″ long. Color pattern of sexes alike.

The designation "Common" is scarcely applicable to this Tern in New Mexico since it is rare here. In size and appearance it is similar to the more common Forster's Tern. Both have deeply forked tails. However, the Common has a white tail, while in the Forster's Tern the tail is gray, the same color as its back. *Adults, summer:* Top of head black; bill and feet bright orange red; bill tipped with black; tail mainly white; throat white; underparts grayish white. *Winter:* Crown principally white; underparts purer white. The Common Tern is recorded as "transient visitor, uncommon" at Bosque del Apache and Bitter Lake Refuges.

[LEAST TERN
Sterna albifrons
8½—9½″ long. Color pattern of sexes similar.

As its name implies, the Least is the smallest of the Terns occurring in the

NEST AND EGGS, LEAST TERN
Photograph by the Author

state. The small size and yellow bill and feet are distinguishing features. *Adults, summer:* Upperparts pearl gray, forehead and underparts white; top of head black. In winter, crown grayish.

DISTRIBUTION. Although the Least Tern has been recorded in the Rio Grande Valley, most of the records are for the Pecos Valley. However, since it is a small bird, fast-flying, and rather inconspicuous on the wing, it may escape notice. Roswell area, "occasional May, June, September" (Montgomery). The author has observed it at both McMillan and Avalon Reservoirs.

NESTING. The only nesting records of the Least Tern are for Bitter Lake Refuge. A nest with 2 fresh eggs in a barren alkali flat near a shallow pond was examined there, June 28, 1951. This nest was near a small dead grass stubble, on the barren ground. Refuge Manager Lon Hunter advised that the Least Tern had nested there in 1950. *Eggs:* 2, buff with brown spotting.

BLACK TERN
Chlidonias niger

9—10″ long. Color pattern of sexes alike.

The Black Tern is easily identified in summer plumage since it is the only Tern with almost wholly black body occurring in the state. *Winter:* Underparts white; upperparts gray, darker about head. Since it assumes breeding plumage early it is in the black garb in spring or early summer. This Tern may be observed throughout the state where there are ponds and lakes. On May 14, 1954, there were an estimated 300 at Bosque del Apache Refuge. Since it often flies high, it no doubt frequently passes unobserved. The author has recorded the species in considerable numbers at Avalon, McMillan, and Conchas Reservoirs. Montgomery regards it as common May to September, about Roswell.

BLACK TERN. *L. A. Fuertes, U.S. Fish & Wildlife Service.*

DOVES
TOP: MOURNING DOVE, WHITE-WINGED DOVE. BOTTOM: INCA DOVE, GROUND DOVE.
E. R. Kalmbach, courtesy N.M. Dept. of Game & Fish

PIGEONS AND DOVES
Family: COLUMBIDAE

PIGEONS AND DOVES are a distinctive group of birds which rely on their ample wings for self-defense, and on sustained, speedy and direct flight for covering space. They have small feet and move slowly on the ground. In drinking they do not raise the head to swallow as do most other birds, but keep the bill immersed. They feed their young by regurgitation. They are monogamous and males assist with incubating the eggs and care of the young. Few birds are more social. Except during the breeding season, they may congregate in great numbers. Pigeons and doves lay but one or two eggs; however, young develop rapidly, and two or more broods may be raised in a season.

(BAND-TAILED PIGEON
Columba fasciata
15—16″ long. Color pattern of sexes essentially alike.

The Band-tailed is the only large, true wild Pigeon found in the state. It often occurs about orchards and farms in foothills and mountains. In size and in flight it resembles the domestic Pigeon, but can be distinguished by the white crescent neck stripe and uniform bluish color which gives it the designation "Blue Rock." Only in hand or through binoculars can the exquisite coloration of this bird be fully appreciated. *Adult male:* Head and underparts mainly mauve; nape band white; upper neck to shoulders metallic bronze or greenish; bill yellow, tipped with black; eyelids red; legs and feet yellow; tail broad and rounded, gray at base, wide (2-inch) light band at end, giving the bird its popular name. *Adult female:* Very similar, but body somewhat grayer, yellow of bill and feet obscured. *Young:* Underparts grayer, tinged with brown on breast and without white neck crescent or metallic feathers.

The Band-tailed is eagerly sought by sportsmen when its numbers justify an open hunting season, for its shyness and speed of flight (up to 40 miles or more an hour) challenge wing-shooting skill. Although its movements are often limited to the state, it is considered migratory and is protected by federal and state laws.

DISTRIBUTION. In season the Band-tailed may be found anywhere in the forested mountains and in foothills of the state. Periodic abundance or scarcity of its selective foods, or mast, however, makes its distribution highly erratic. If acorns, pinyon nuts, manzanita, cherries, mulberries, juniper or other fruits or berries are scarce or lacking in the fall or early spring, the birds wander far and wide, and may be almost entirely absent from the state, whereas at other times great numbers may concentrate, and forego any migratory movement. In the absence of natural foods they are sometimes responsible for damage to orchards and grain crops. Pinyon mast, a preferred food, attracts and holds the birds in a locality as long as it lasts. During the fall of 1913, for example, there was a great concentration of Band-tailed on the west slope of the Black Range west of Chloride, where there was heavy pinyon mast. Although there was considerable snow and the temperature at times 20° or more below 0°, the Pigeons remained throughout the winter. As a rule, oak and pinyon mast is gone by late spring. It is then that the birds may do serious damage to fruit, particularly cherries. As the season advances there is usually an abundance of wild cherries, grapes, currants, elderberries, or other fruits and berries, which tend to break up the concentrations and level out distribution of the birds. The prolific everbearing mulberry is a favorite food. If systematic plantings of this tree were made in foothills and mountain meadows there probably would be more Pigeons and fewer complaints of damage by the birds.

Extensive surveys conducted by the U.S. Fish and Wildlife Service, with state game departments and individuals cooperating, provide reliable estimates on Pigeon populations in the Southwest. The census figures resulting from those studies placed the number of Band-tailed Pigeons in New Mexico during the census period (September 16 to 20, 1954) at 2,174, and for the same period in 1955 at 2,634. These figures represent only the number of birds tabulated during the 5-day periods. The totals indicate how the Pigeon populations may vary from year to year and from season to season, depending upon local food conditions and the percentage of birds in Mexico, or in adjacent states, at time of surveys. (*Survey of Band-tailed Pigeon Populations in Arizona, Colorado, New Mexico, and Utah, 1955.* Branch of Game Management, U.S. Fish and Wildlife Service, Albuquerque, New Mexico.)

NESTING. Band-tailed Pigeons may nest anywhere they chance to be during the nesting season. There is evidence that when a dependable food supply is lacking they may shift and wander and even forego normal breeding activities. Fluctuating populations seem to sustain such a theory. The life expectancy of the Band-tailed is rather long for a bird. They seem to be less vulnerable to natural enemies than most other game birds, and the periodic limited hunting seasons are not a serious decimating factor. The breeding season is long, extending from early April to September, and nesting occurs at elevations from 6,000 feet in the foothills to near timber line of the higher mountains. All nests found by the author contained one egg or a single young. Some observers,

however, have reported instances of two. H. Garven Smith, of the U.S. Forest Service, told of finding 14 nests, August 18, 1934, in one large Douglas fir tree close to a spring in the Magdalena Mountains, near Magdalena. One of these contained two eggs; the others, one egg or a squab. He observed nests in nearby trees, and noted much activity and fighting among the birds. There was a heavy Gambel oak mast in the mountains at that time. Such colony nesting seems to be most common when local food conditions encourage concentrations at the proper season. There are nesting records for all forested mountain sections in the state. "Three nests were located in the Guadalupe Mountains after the middle of August" (Bailey). The author has found nests in the Black Range, Pinos Altos, and Mogollon Mountains. Nests are usually in limber pine, locally known as sugar pine, Douglas fir, or oak, 10 to 30 feet from the ground. *Nest:* Of twigs and weed stems, similar to Dove nests. *Eggs:* 1 (rarely 2); glossy white.

(ROCK DOVE (DOMESTIC PIGEON)
Columba livia

Color pattern (stabilized strain) of sexes alike.

The Rock Dove, although not usually regarded as a wild game bird, readily reverts to a semi-wild state with only remote contact with man. The Pigeon has been domesticated for centuries. It is a descendant of the European Wild Rock or Blue Rock Dove, from which many strains of so-called Pigeons have been developed; among them the Carrier which through selective breeding and training has been used as a conveyor of messages from early times. *Color pattern of the adult wild bird:* Light gray and bluish mottling, with two black wing bars; wing and tail tips black; white rump patch. The most common of the roving domestic bird reflects a similar color pattern, a bluish shade, with dark wing bars, but lacking the white rump patch. It is this Pigeon that seems to revert most readily to the wild. Prairie Falcons and Duck Hawks seem to be the principal enemies of Rock Doves.

The feats performed by well-trained Carrier Pigeons, when released long distances from their "homing" cotes, in returning unerringly and with great speed, are amazing. Many have distinguished records as carriers of messages during times of war, when other means of communication were not feasible.

A homing pigeon, known as Black Jack, owned by the late Denis De Cooman, of Superior, Wisconsin, had a remarkable record for homing ability and speed. Mr. Con Shears, Secretary of the Superior (Wisconsin) Pigeon Club in 1926, advises that Black Jack, along with 94 other pigeons, was taken to Ft. Worth, Texas, in an express car, and released there at 5 A.M., August 15, 1926. "Black Jack was timed in (Superior) at 8:52:24 P.M., airline distance of 1,012 miles; flying time (15 hours, 52 minutes and 24 seconds) 63.7 miles per hour," which Mr. Shears states was "the highest speed by any pigeon during the existence of our Club."

DISTRIBUTION. At the present time, the distribution of the Rock Dove in the wild state is limited. In several instances it has abandoned its domestic ways in favor of independence to the extent of making its home on supporting timbers beneath long concrete bridges on highways. A colony of the birds has for years occupied such a bridge on Highway 18, north of Nara Visa. Here nests are placed on the timbers beneath the floor of the bridge. The birds which comprise the colony are shy, leaving the bridge and remaining in flight or perching on rock ledges some distance away as long as an intruder remains afoot about the bridge. Passing cars seem to be disregarded. There are no dwellings nearby. The author has also observed wild Domestic Pigeons living and nesting at deserted buildings in the sandhills near Milnesand, Roosevelt County; in most cases the occupants are of the prevailing bluish color. Krehbiel refers to them as "occasional residents" in Clayton area.

NESTING. Rock Doves are prolific breeders, and the young develop rapidly. The nesting season extends throughout the warmer period of the year. Several broods are raised in a season. Nesting ways are similar to those of other Doves and Bandtailed Pigeons, except that nests are placed under eaves of buildings, in lofts prepared for them, on sleepers of bridges, and in crevices of rock ledges. *Nest:* Flat, frail structure, made of twigs and straws. *Eggs:* 2, white.

ROCK DOVE. *Fred Patton, courtesy of Mrs. T. J. Godfrey.*

❨ WHITE-WINGED DOVE
Zenaida asiatica

11—12½" long. Color pattern of sexes similar.

In body size, the White-winged is intermediate between the Mourning Dove and the Band-tailed Pigeon. Unlike the Mourning Dove, which has a pointed tail and no white markings, the White-winged Dove has a wide, rounded tail, and white in wings and on end of tail. The conspicuous white of wings is an unmistakable identification mark. *Adult male:* Iridescent bluish shade about and back of eyes, with dark ear spot above golden-green patch; rest of upperparts brownish, except lower back, which has bluish shade; underparts fawn. *Adult female:* Similar but slightly duller. *Young:* White wing bars, but more brownish than adult.

DISTRIBUTION. The summer range of the White-winged Dove is confined almost wholly to the southwest section of the state, from the Rio Grande Valley westward to Arizona, and north to Glenwood, Cliff, Silver City, and the upper Mimbres River (San Lorenzo). It is uncommon in the Rio Grande Valley (Las Cruces); occurs occasionally on the east side of the Guadalupe Mountains near the Texas line, and in the Pecos Valley about Carlsbad. It is most common near the international boundary in the Big Hatchet, Animas, and Peloncillo Mountains, and in the Gila River Valley from the Arizona line to and beyond Cliff. "I saw a White-winged Dove on June 22, 1955, 12 miles south of Corona" (W. A. Humphries). This seems to be the most northerly record for the state. A permanent source of water seems to be a summer range requirement. The bird ordinarily is absent from the state in winter.

NESTING. Presence of the White-winged during the nesting season can be detected by the almost constant cooing. Their favorite nesting haunts are large sycamores that grow along the Gila River and in many canyons of southern Hidalgo County. "In June 1939 a pair raised one young in my yard at Las Cruces. April 22, 1940 the same pair (presumably) returned to the same nesting place" (Williams). On June 15, 1937, the author located a nest in Big Hatchet Mountain (6,500 feet) which contained two small young. In June 1953, Levon Lee, of the State Game Department, reported "great numbers of nesting birds about Sheridan Well, Big Hatchet Mountain, Birch Spring and Culberson Ranch, Animas Mountains, and Cloverdale and Guadalupe Canyons, Peloncillo Mountains." Because of lack of suitable mesquite forests, the birds do not nest in large colonies in this state as they do in southern Arizona and southern Texas. Water development by the State Game Department in the arid portions of the state should result in increased nesting and greater populations. *Nest:* Usual Pigeon-Dove nesting pattern, scant twig-straw nest barely sufficient to support the eggs; usually on horizontal limbs or branches of sycamore or oak trees, up to 25 feet above ground. *Eggs:* Almost always 2; white or creamy white when fresh.

❨ MOURNING DOVE
Zenaidura macroura

10½—12" long. Color pattern of sexes alike.

The Mourning Dove is one of the most widely distributed and familiar of American birds. In summer it is found throughout New Mexico from the lowest elevations to 13,000 feet. At this season it is one of the most abundant birds in the state. Detailed description of the Mourning, or "Turtle," Dove is unnecessary for anyone familiar with birds. It is much smaller than the Band-tailed Pigeon; much larger than the Inca and Ground Doves, and lacks the conspicuous white wing markings of the White-winged. It is the only one of the group that has a pointed tail. Of all the so-called game birds, the Mourning Dove is the least affected by drought, devastation of ground cover by livestock, or other uses and abuses of the land. The flight speed (40 miles or more per hour) and endurance permit this Dove to commute readily between watering, feeding, and nesting grounds. Few birds are more deliberate in conduct. In its swift, musical flight, it cleaves the air over plain, forest, or mountain, seemingly with fixed destination. Except at breeding time, it is tolerant and inoffensive in its relations with other birds.

Weed seeds and grain crops alike meet the feeding need of the Mourning Dove and if these are not found in one place it moves on to better feeding grounds. Because of its mastery of speed and space, it is not dependent on protective ground cover, an essential need for resident game birds. If winter food is lacking, it moves southward where food is available. It is a prolific breeder, usually raising two or more broods in a season, with two eggs invariably comprising a clutch. The young develop rapidly and seem to be less vulnerable to natural enemies than are most birds. Because of these advantages, Mourning Dove populations are consistently high, assuring wing shooting for a great number of sportsmen, although there is a widespread sentiment against Dove shooting since the birds are regarded as symbols of peace and tranquillity. Early hunting seasons often result in many birds being killed while they still have eggs or young in nests. Fewer Doves might be taken if the hunting seasons were later, but fewer eggs would be lost and fewer young birds left to starve. Agricultural development has benefited the Mourning Dove perhaps more than it has any other game bird because it takes advantage of various kinds of grains grown, and also of a great variety of seed-producing weeds that follow the cultivation of soil. Since the Dove feeds largely on dry seeds, it requires water and goes to it regularly even though it may be at some distance.

Few other birds are so resourceful in their own welfare as Pigeons and Doves. Especially true is this of the Mourning Dove, accounting largely for its consistent abundance. It not only seeks out the best feeding grounds, but employs unique means of obtaining food, such as using the wings to knock mature seeds from poppies and other plants. In more arid sections, Mourning Doves now feed commonly along shoulders of highways where runoff from the pavements often results in a growth of seed-producing weeds of various kinds, even in periods of drought. Incidentally, very rarely is one killed by a speeding automobile.

DISTRIBUTION. The Mourning Dove, during the warmer period of the year, may be found anywhere in the state, from the lowest to the highest elevation. It has an uncanny way of seeking out such preferred food-producing plants as Dove weed (*Croton*), Rocky Mountain bee plant (*Cleome*), thistle, sunflower, and harvested fields where there is waste wheat or other small grain on the ground. While a majority of the birds leave the state for the winter, local concentrations may remain as far north as Socorro in the Rio Grande Valley; Roswell, in the Pecos Valley; and Portales, on the eastern high plains, when ample food is available. At times it may succumb to extreme cold, but this can usually be attributed to lack of nourishment and protective "loafing" and roosting cover. The author recalls one winter when great numbers remained in the high semi-forested sand country near Montoso Mountain west of Magdalena, at almost 7,000 feet elevation. The winter was not severe, and the preceding summer there had been an unusually prolific growth of the Rocky Mountain bee plant, which provided abundant seed throughout the winter. Furthermore, the ground-spreading juniper (*Juniperus monosperma*) and other shrubs provided shelter from the wind and cold. Fortunately, also, snow did not cover the ground for long periods; otherwise mortality might have been heavy. Usually such concentrations occur where squawbush (Rhus), mesquite, catclaw, arrow-weed, or plum bushes are available for shelter against wind and cold. During the winter of 1950-51, an estimated 250 wintered at the James headquarters ranch about 35 miles southeast of Carlsbad, where there is ample brush cover.

NESTING. Nesting of Doves is statewide. In their nesting activities, Mourning Doves are resourceful. If suitable bushes or trees are not available, they nest on the ground. Even where trees are available, a pair may select a window sill, grape arbor, or other unpredictable site. Formerly, under more primitive conditions, there were few suitable nesting trees along the Pecos River. During the last twenty-five years the exotic salt cedar (tamarisk) has become well established along the Pecos and its floodlands, providing resting and nesting places for many birds. The Mourning Dove has taken advantage of the older and rugged cedars, particularly about McMillan and Avalon Reservoirs, to the extent that this segment of the river valley is probably the most heavily utilized Dove nesting area in the state. Of direct benefit to Doves also are the many trees now growing about urban and rural homes, along with the abundance of seed-producing weeds, and grain crops grown on the irrigated farms of the valley. The devotion of this Dove to nesting duties and young never fails to inspire admiration. On one occasion the author observed such parental devotion on a barren hill slope near Carlsbad when on a calm day in mid-August with temperature of 100° in the shade, and no shade on the slope, a parent Dove was standing over two small young, attempting to protect them from the sun's rays. Doves are monogamous, and both

parents share incubation of eggs and care of young. Nesting begins in early April in the southern section of the state; somewhat later in the northern part, and continues into September. Affliction ruses in their attempt to lead intruders or enemies away from nests or young are many. Nest: A frail platform made of stems and twigs, unlined; placed on horizontal limb of tree or bush, or on the ground. Eggs: 2; white.

❮ GROUND DOVE
Columbigallina passerina
6½–7″ long. Color pattern of sexes essentially alike.

This little Dove, usually listed as the Mexican Ground Dove, is a pygmy of the Pigeon-Dove group. Its wings are short and broad; tail almost square. Adult male: Back of head and entire neck bluish, feathers of a scaly appearance, rest of upperparts mainly grayish brown; tail blackish; wing coverts with lustrous steel blue spots; underwing feathers chestnut or bright reddish brown; face and underparts pinkish; bill coral or orange red; legs and feet pink. Adult female and young: Similar but duller; young with whitish edging to feathers. Ground Doves are usually shy and remain concealed except when on the ground feeding, when the least disturbance sends them dashing to cover. In flight the chestnut or red beneath primaries is a certain identification mark.

DISTRIBUTION. The Ground Dove is uncommon in the state. However, it is so retiring that its presence may not be suspected except prior to and during nesting, when the soft cooing notes may be heard, particularly in the early morning. It is known to nest sparingly at Carlsbad. It is most common in the Rio Grande Valley about Las Cruces, and seems to be resident there. When not disturbed it becomes tame, feeding in yards and gardens where its movements are limited to a small area. Although there seem to be no published records for this Dove in the Lower Gila River Valley, local residents advised that it is present about Virden in summer. "It is fairly common in Las Cruces" (Williams).

NESTING. Usually about residences or farm homes, not far above ground in willow or cottonwood trees and sometimes in mesquite bushes; rarely on ground. Nest: Of twigs and plant stems; may have some lining of straws, somewhat of a departure from nests of most other members of the Pigeon-Dove group. Eggs: 2; white.

(INCA DOVE
Scardafella inca
8" long. Color pattern of sexes alike.

The Inca, like the Mexican Ground Dove, is very small, rather retiring, and uncommon in New Mexico. The designation Scardafella (Italian) has reference to the scaly appearance of its grayish plumage, particularly upperparts—a distinguishing feature. Adults: Underparts dusky and buffy; tail rather long, round, middle feathers dark brown, outer tail feathers white, which clearly distinguish it from the Ground Dove. In flight it has a dashing movement, and is quick to seek cover of trees when disturbed. The name Inca implies sovereignty or a prince.

DISTRIBUTION. Distribution of the Inca Dove is limited to the southern and southwestern sections of the state. It has been recorded locally across the southern part of the state, but is nowhere common. Kellogg noted it at Silver City on July 17, 1924. The author recorded one June 17, 1926, 18 miles northwest of Lordsburg, and another on October 18, 1945, at Carlsbad. Karl W. Heller (Condor, Vol. 53, No. 3, 1951) states: "Several observed at Virden, April 21, 1950." On December 8,

1951, Harry Williams of Las Cruces, wrote: "I have seen in my yard 3 or 4 Inca Doves. They are probably present all the time; but they utter no sound now, so their presence is known only when I see them." On December 2, 1954, Judge Edwin Mechem, of Las Cruces, wrote the author: "I wish I could get a picture for you of the Inca Doves that come to my bird bath. Sometimes there are as many as 8 of them." Levon Lee states: "I saw a few of them in the summer of 1947 close to Virden along the Gila River." "Two were seen at Hatch, June 12, 1939" (Williams). "On September 30, 1956, an Inca Dove was observed on the Bosque del Apache Refuge" (Fleetwood). This record seems to be the most northern observation yet made. It is usually regarded as a "town" Dove, but irregularly distributed. House cats may be largely responsible for the low Inca and Ground Dove populations. Both species seem to prefer living in proximity to habitations of man in urban communities, and as they feed on the ground, often among weeds, the young particularly must be vulnerable to house cats.

NESTING. Most of the Inca Dove nesting records are for the Rio Grande Valley. However, their presence elsewhere, as on the Gila River, indicates they were breeding birds. On May 16, 1955, two well-feathered young were observed still in the nest, about 25 feet up in a Siberian (Chinese) elm tree, at the Gordon White home in Las Cruces. When disturbed in an effort to photograph them, they flew from the nest. A short time later they were back sitting side by side on a limb near the nest, both adults nearby. At the end of the nesting season, the Gordon Whites advised that the pair had succeeded in raising three broods. Nest: In bushes or trees, more compactly made of twigs and straw than that of other Doves. Eggs: 2; white.

PARROTS
Family: PSITTACIDAE

THICK-BILLED PARROT
Rhynchopsitta pachyrhyncha

ALTHOUGH its occurrence is rare and unpredictable, and its visits are of short duration, the Thick-billed Parrot has been reported in the southwestern part of the state, and it occurs in the Chiricahua Mountains, in adjacent Arizona. Several pioneer ranchmen, among them R. Winkler of southern Hidalgo County, have told the author about seeing this Parrot in the Animas and Peloncillo Mountains. "New Mexico (Animas Mountains)" (*A.O.U. Check-list*). Their periodic presence in these mountains may be expected since they occur in the adjacent Sierra Madres in Mexico. According to accounts, the Parrots may be present for a few days, and depart as suddenly as they arrived. There is little doubt that the birds observed were the Thick-billed Parrot, since the descriptions given fit the species: a large green bird; large hooked bill; red on forepart of head and wings.

CUCKOO, ROADRUNNER, AND ANI
Family: CUCULIDAE

THE CUCKOO and the Roadrunner are unique, both in appearance and habits. They are long slender birds, with long tails, and both have feet with two toes pointing forward and two pointing backward, but the feet of the Cuckoo, which is arboreal, are adapted strictly for perching, whereas those of the Roadrunner, which is terrestrial, are large and strong, suitable for running. A relative, the Groove-billed Ani, is primarily a semi-tropical species. It occurs rarely in southern Arizona and must be regarded as accidental in New Mexico.

❨ YELLOW-BILLED CUCKOO
Coccyzus americanus

12—13″ long. Color pattern of sexes alike.

Upperparts dull brown with greenish gloss; middle-tail feathers like back, tipped with black; underparts white; upper part of bill black; basal part of lower mandible bright yellow. White spotting underneath tail is conspicuous when bird is in flight. The Yellow-billed, formerly referred to as the California Cuckoo, is the common Cuckoo, or "Raincrow" of the South and Southwest. Its pleasing, repeated cooing is frequently heard during the warm period of the year. It is a shy, short-legged, streamlined bird of the timbered valleys and stream-bottom lands, by preference living in heavy-foliage trees. The cooing, or "crowing," notes are presumed by some people to forecast rain, hence the designation "Raincrow."

DISTRIBUTION. This Cuckoo ranges statewide in summer, from the lower altitudes to as high as 7,000 feet along mountain watercourses. It arrives in the southern portion (Las Cruces and Carlsbad), around May 10 to 15; later in the higher and more northern sections. By early September it usually has vacated the state.

NESTING. Unlike the European Cuckoo, which lays its eggs in nests of other birds which hatch and raise the young (as does the Cowbird in this country), the members of the American family incubate the eggs and care for their young. *Nest:* In trees, a frail structure, like that of the Dove; made of twigs and straws. *Eggs:* 2 or 3; blue or greenish blue, unspotted.

⟮ ROADRUNNER

Geococcyx californianus

20—24″ long. Color pattern of sexes alike. (Pl. II)

The long, heavy beak, brown camouflaging garb, and long pumping tail are distinguishing features of the Roadrunner, one of the most familiar birds of the Southwestern deserts and brushlands, either through observation or by reputation. It is resident or only locally migratory wherever found and although commonly referred to as a Roadrunner, it has other names, depending on locality, such as Chaparral, Paisano, and Ground Cuckoo. So much a part of the Southwest is the Roadrunner that in Texas, southern New Mexico, and particularly in Mexico, where it is regarded with affection and even reverence, it is commonly referred to as "Paisano," meaning "fellow countryman." In New Mexico it has the distinction of having been designated the State Bird. Although it is at times in disrepute with sportsmen for occasional killing of small Quail, its predaceous propensities toward valuable species are often exaggerated. Analysis of stomach contents of Roadrunners has revealed that their food consists principally of beetles, cutworms, grasshoppers, and other insect pests, mice and other small rodents. Their economic value therefore more than outweighs any loss as result of deviation from the usual pattern of conduct. They have been seriously persecuted in the past and, to some extent, up to the present time. They are now protected by law, and by strong public sentiment. The advent of motor vehicles and improved roads has made the familiar designation "Roadrunner" all but archaic. Although it may still be seen along highways, or dashing across the road ahead of a motor car, it has learned that its speed is no match for that of a motor vehicle. "Trailrunner" would seem more descriptive of the bird today. Occasionally it may be seen about farm or ranch home, even perching on buildings when its brown, black-tipped crest feathers may be compressed, or pulsated to a prominent, large crest. Probably no other bird has such sensitive control of crest feathers. On sunshiny mornings this comic may be seen indulging in one of its whimseys as it spreads its wings and raises neck feathers so as to expose its back, which is covered with coarse down rather than feathers, to the warm sunshine, repeating the odd performance for extended periods. The Roadrunner seems to prefer sunshine to shade, and only during the hottest summer days does it seek the scant shade of a mesquite bush or other desert shrub.

Where there is ample ground cover, remote from habitation of man, the telltale footprints (two toes pointing forward, two backward) are generally more in evidence than is the bird. So unique in many ways, the unusual should be expected of this streamlined racer. The short, rounded wings of the Roadrunner do not permit sustained flight. Its primary dependence for self-preservation is on its nimble brain and long legs which it uses as springboards to land effortlessly on bush, tree or building. It is one bird that is almost as speedy on foot as on wing in level flight. But wings serve it well for sailing from high perches or in gliding downgrade. As a foot racer the Paisano's principal competitor for ground speed, among American birds, would probably be an excited wild Turkey.

No other bird of comparable size can instantly and so completely vanish from sight. When danger threatens, it flattens itself into a streamlined streak close to the ground with head, body, and tail lined out as straight as a ruler, taking advantage of every surface object or curve of ground to avoid being seen as it makes a complete getaway. Yet at times, either through boldness or curiosity the Roadrunner may surprisingly spring into plain view to "coo-coo," or more often, to survey its surroundings.

Preferred summer food seems to be the common striped, or whiptailed lizards, which, although quick of action, are readily caught by the clever, dashing Paisano. During the winter months when the warm-weather life is hibernating, the Roadrunner is often hard-pressed for food. At such times it resorts to whatever may be available, even carrion. One held in captivity at the author's farm for a time seemed to prefer mice to any other food. (This bird was the model for the frontispiece painting.)

For a more complete account of the Roadrunner, see "The Roadrunner in Fact and Folklore," by J. Frank Dobie, *Arizona Highways*, May 1958.

DISTRIBUTION. The Roadrunner is confined largely to the more arid brushlands, comprising the Lower and Upper Sonoran Life Zones, but it does range into mountainous valleys and southern slopes of mountains up to 7,000 feet elevation—Fox Mountain and the village of Aragon, on the upper San Francisco River drainage. It also ranges up the Rio Grande Valley to Santa Fe, 7,000 feet, and into the Dry Cimarron Valley in the extreme northeastern section. It is most common in the Pecos Valley, the lower Rio Grande Valley and westward.

NESTING. Nesting ways of the Roadrunner are as unusual as is its unpredictable conduct. Nesting begins in early April in the southern part of the state, somewhat later in the northern sections. A nest with three eggs was found near Tatum on April 3. Nests are almost always placed near the center of thick bushes, such as squaw bush (sumac), Condalia, cholla, tree yuccas, live oak, cedar, or other low trees, 4 to 8 feet above ground. *Nests:* Made of sticks, lined with weed stems, grass, bark, and usually chips of cow or horse manure; well concealed. Since the young, like the adults, have enormous appetites, nature seems to ease the duty of satisfying their wants by permitting the laying of eggs at intervals of several days, so an egg and partly feathered young may be found in the same nest. Thus, not only are the young raised successively, but the first hatched serve as brooders for the younger members of the family, even incubating the eggs yet to hatch. *Eggs:* 4 to 8; white with chalky film.

GROOVE-BILLED ANI
Crotophaga sulcirostris
12½" long. Color pattern of sexes alike.

Specimens of this queer bird have not yet been taken in the state, nor is there supporting evidence by competent ornithologists that it has been seen. There are reports, however, which border so closely on authenticity as to justify its inclusion in the State List. The fact that it does occasionally occur in southern Arizona gives credence to the report that it has been seen near the Mexican border in extreme southwestern New Mexico. Of such unusual appearance is this coal-black bird, that it is not apt to be confused with any other species. In some respects it resembles the Great-tailed Grackle, but its heavy, large bill with grooved upper mandible is distinctive. Two birds which were seen about the middle of May 1953, at the Culberson Ranch near the New Mexico–Mexico line, about 50 miles southwest of Hachita, seemingly could have been no other than Anis. According to the ranch foreman, they stayed around the place, on the lawn and in the trees, for several days. Both the ranch foreman and his wife recall distinctly the grooving of the bill. Judge C. M. Botts, a close bird observer, is confident he saw one of the birds in the shrub-bery of his lawn in east Albuquerque in 1952. Since the bird was so far inland, it could well have been a captive bird which had escaped from its owner. Otherwise, since the Ani is not well favored with ability for long, sustained flight, some doubt would be cast on its occurrence there.

OWLS

Families: TYTONIDAE AND STRIGIDAE

OWLS are of many species and sizes, from the dainty 6-inch Elf (Dwarf) to the large and powerful Horned Owl, with a wingspread of 4 feet or more. Sexes look alike. Most of the Owls are nocturnal but are not always restricted to night movements, especially if their chosen food is scarce, requiring more time for foraging. Some have ear tufts or "horns"; others have round heads. All move on silent wings, nature's aid in surprising prey—rabbits and a great variety of smaller rodents that are keen of sight and quick of action.

Owls, even the Great Horned, when not in proximity to habitation of man, have high economic value but, like the beneficial Hawks, have been persecuted and destroyed to such extent that their numbers are now greatly reduced. In some areas where formerly they were periodically common, they are now absent. The prevailing apathy regarding their plight is largely responsible for this serious economic loss. Returns from range and crop lands would be far greater today had all species (with the possible exception of the Great Horned) long ago been rigidly protected. As is true of Hawks, most Owls, unfortunately, are more or less fearless of man and have therefore been subjected to widespread persecution. On the other hand, the Great Horned, the largest of the Owls indigenous to the state, is shy and capable of taking care of itself. Even if it were denied legal protection, its status would be little affected. The small, arboreal species are charming and wholly beneficial. They are the least known because most of them are usually concealed in Woodpecker excavations or in hollows of trees during daylight. Not only are they usually difficult to see, but their presence is often not suspected unless their varied notes are heard at night. Because of their small size and concealment, they have escaped some of the persecution accorded to others. Owls swallow their food regardless of bones, hair or feathers, regurgitating the indigestible portions in the form of pellets. Such pellets are often a clue to the bird's presence. Of the eleven species resident or occurring in New Mexico, only the Short-eared is a non-breeder here. In shape, the eggs of owls are more nearly round than eggs of most other birds. Not many species of Owls use nest material other than cuttings or natural decay of wood in holes of trees used for nesting.

TYTONIDAE

⟨ BARN OWL
Tyto alba

15—20" long. Color pattern of sexes alike.

The Barn Owl is resident throughout the United States, but is not common in the Southwest. It is so distinctive, both in appearance and nature, that identification is not difficult. The head is without ear tufts, but ears are large. The heartshaped facial disc has given rise to the widely used name "Monkey-face." Legs are long and closely feathered; feet with two toes pointing forward, two backward. Upperparts tawny yellowish; facial disc and underparts varying from white to yellowish; wings long and plumage of a downy texture. While the bird may appear to be rather large, a good proportion of its size consists of feathers and head, the body being light in weight. In the Southwest, including New Mexico, the designation "Barn Owl" is scarcely applicable, since there are few barns with suitable nesting and living lofts. Few other birds are more wholly beneficial, since the food of the Barn Owl consists almost entirely of mice and rats and various beetles and insects—very rarely birds. It is of such high economic value as to justify complete protection.

DISTRIBUTION. Scarcity of the Barn Owl in the state is partly due to the lack of suitable living and nesting conditions. The author has observed Barn Owls at Carlsbad, in southern Roosevelt and Hidalgo Counties, and in the Gila and Rio Grande Valleys. They are listed as "rare" at Bosque del Apache Refuge and in the Roswell area. Jensen has only two records for Santa Fe.

NESTING. The few nesting records for this Owl are not conclusive, as nesting sites are not readily located even by the most persistent observers. Jensen found nesting holes in an arroyo soil bank five miles south of Santa Fe. A nest containing eggs was located by the author in hollow of a willow tree in June 1925, on the Gila River near Red Rock. Young, nearly feathered, were seen at Las Cruces in June 1912. "Nest containing young was observed in a hollow cottonwood near Corrales, June 16, 1955" (Campbell, Mrs. Hibben, and Durrie). Nest: In hollow trees, holes in soil banks, in abandoned wells, mine shafts or deserted buildings. Eggs: 5 to 7; white.

BARN OWL. L. A. Fuertes, U.S. Fish & Wildlife Service.

STRIGIDAE

([SCREECH OWL
Otus asio

8—10″ long. Color pattern of sexes alike.

Two small "horned" Owls—Screech and Flammulated—occur in the state, the Screech Owl being the larger of the two, and with decidedly more prominent "horns." The New Mexico representative of the common Eastern bird is generally listed as the "Mexican Screech Owl." In daytime, this Owl is usually hidden in hollows of trees, but at times may also be seen on the ground or on a stone beneath a bush or spreading tree. *Adults:* Camouflaging ashy gray plumage and blackish shaft streaks; underparts with black cross-lines; short tail, long wings; ear tufts prominent. The brown or red color phase, common in the Eastern and some other forms, has not been recorded in the state.

DISTRIBUTION. The common Screech Owl is found almost throughout the state, wherever there are hollow trees, from the lowest elevation in the south to as high as 8,000 feet in the north. In the northern part a subspecies is referred to as the Aiken; in the south as the Mexican. However, so alike are they, it is difficult to distinguish them by sight alone. They are most common in the oak-pine zone, at about 7,000 feet elevation.

NESTING. In the southern part of the state the Screech Owl seems to prefer hollows in the scrub live oak, from 6,500 to 7,000 feet elevation, for nesting. Outside this belt, along watercourses, it usually resorts to holes or cavities in the old cottonwoods, and may be found as low as 3,000 feet, where nests may be some distance from the ground. Occasionally deserted Flicker excavations are appropriated, even though the Owl is rather large for such cramped quarters. Nesting usually begins in mid-March, even in the north. Jensen reported "nearly grown young," May 15, at Santa Fe. Fresh eggs April 22, near Chloride. Latitude seems to have little bearing on nesting time. *Eggs:* 4 or 5; ivory white.

([FLAMMULATED OWL
Otus flammeolus

6½—7″ long. Color pattern of sexes alike.

The Flammulated is a dainty little Owl. The designation *flammeolus*, from Latin *flammeus*, "reddish of color," refers to its reddish plumage. Few observers see this Owl since it is largely nocturnal and emerges from its hiding place in woodpecker hole or other day-abode cavity, under cover of darkness. Rarely one may be seen in thick foliage or on the ground beneath some concealing shrub. It is readily identified by its small size, being much smaller than the common Screech Owl, or by its small "ears" and its reddish color, although it does occur in a gray phase. In some individuals the entire head is brown, sprinkled with black.

DISTRIBUTION. With the exception of treeless mesas, or plains, the Flammulated is statewide in distribution, apparently without regard to altitude, but is most common in the higher forested mountainous sections. The author has found it in the Sacramento, Black and Mogollon Ranges, and in the northern section of the state (Tres Piedras area), and also at lower elevations (Carlsbad) in cottonwoods, and in the scrub timber foothills of the Animas Mountains. "One, North Spring River, Roswell, Apr. 27, 1955" (Montgomery).

NESTING. In high mountainous country, the Flammulated seems to prefer Woodpecker and Flicker holes in aspen trees as nesting sites. One nest, 30 miles west of Chloride, was in a dead yellow pine; others, near Tres Piedras and in the Sacramento Mountains, were in aspens. "A pair has nested for five years on the Indian

School Campus, Santa Fe" (Jensen, 1922). On May 22, 1952, the author located a nest containing two fresh eggs, in Pump Canyon, about three miles southeast of Cloudcroft in the Sacramento Mountains, elevation about 8,000 feet. In the same tree were nests and eggs of the Pygmy Owl and the Red-shafted Flicker. Williams reported a nest of the Flammulated Owl near Glenwood. *Nest:* Usually in aspens, but sometimes in pines; almost always in Woodpecker or Flicker holes. *Eggs:* 2; white. Three nests found by the author contained 2 eggs each. However, other observers report clutches of 3 and 4.

❨ GREAT HORNED OWL
Bubo virginianus
18—24″ long. Color pattern of sexes alike.

The Great Horned, or "Hoot Owl," is the largest of the Owls found in the state. It has a very conspicuous, large, wide head and prominent "horns." The Long-eared is much smaller, more streamlined and with slender "horns" close together. The Great Horned is swift of flight and is usually shy and adept at detecting danger. Although regarded as the most destructive of the Owls, its principal depredation when about habitation of man is on poultry. It is also often seriously disturbing about game bird farms. Elsewhere, particularly where rabbit populations are high, it is more beneficial than harmful, feeding on rabbits and other rodents. It is resident where found, or only locally migratory.

DISTRIBUTION. The Great Horned is more widely distributed than are most other birds of the state, ranging from the lowest elevations of the southern portion to the higher mountainous country. It is most common, however, in rugged foothills where canyons are characterized by cliffs and crevices that provide shaded recesses for spending daytime.

NESTING. It is not probable that Horned

Owls often construct their own nests, as do most Hawks and Eagles. When they nest in trees they take advantage of old nests made by other large birds, on which they may do some repairing. However, their preferred nesting sites are pockets and crevices in mountain or canyon walls. In the southern valley and plains sections they more often choose deserted Hawk or Raven nests in native chinaberry or hackberry trees or the large yuccas that cover much of the southwestern section. They are among the earliest birds to nest, eggs usually being deposited in late January or early February. *Eggs:* 2 or 3; white.

❨ PYGMY OWL
Glaucidium gnoma
7—7½″ long. Color pattern of sexes alike.

The Pygmy, as the name implies, is one of the smallest of the Owls, only the Elf being smaller. *Adults:* Rusty or gray-brown in color; striped breast; head round without tufts or "horns"; tail barred with white. Unlike most other Owls, the Pygmy is active by day as well as by night, feeding during mornings and late afternoons. It seems to enjoy the morning sun on high evergreen perches. Its summer food consists largely of small rodents, grasshoppers and other insects, another clue to its daylight activities. One of its preferred foods, in summer, seems to be the rock chipmunk *(Eutamias dorsalis)*. Because it is active by day, the Pygmy Owl is often the object of noisy sessions of small birds which endeavor to "mob" it. The author has often witnessed an animated gathering of small birds tormenting a Pygmy Owl. As the latter dashed away, perhaps across a clearing, in an effort to throw off the mob, an escort of such birds would follow in hot pursuit, as if to make certain that the intruder was leaving their pre-empted feeding ground. Since birds know their enemies, this little Owl must be assumed

OWLS
Top: Elf, Great Horned, Screech. Middle: Pygmy. Bottom: Burrowing, Saw-whet.
E. R. Kalmbach, N.M. Dept. of Game & Fish

to be a molester of smaller kinds, at least to some extent. Nuthatches, Juncos, and Hummingbirds particularly scold and flit about when they discover a Pygmy Owl. The author, however, has never seen evidence of bird predation. If it does feed on small birds, this is probably when more preferred foods are scarce, as in winter.

The repeated whistling of the Pygmy Owl issuing from a tall pine is heard oftener than the bird is seen. In the Sacramento Mountains one sunshiny morning, the author timed the whistling of a Pygmy perched near the top of a pine. The clear, evenly pitched notes—at about two-second intervals—continued two minutes. Such continued whistling is most often heard in springtime but, since it is obviously a contact call, may be expected at any time.

ASPEN TREES USED FOR NESTING
BY FLAMMULATED AND SCREECH OWLS
Photograph by the Author

DISTRIBUTION. Pygmy Owls may be looked for wherever the Yellow or Ponderosa pine grows, at elevations ranging from 6,000 feet upward. They also occasionally may be seen, or the familiar whistling heard, in cottonwoods or oak below the pine belt. They seem to be resident where found. They appear to be most common in the Sacramento and White Mountains and the Black Range. There is little or no evidence that they resort to concealment in tree cavities by day as do most other small Owls.

NESTING. The few nests located by the author were in Woodpecker holes in aspen trees, at rather high altitudes, since aspens do not often occur much below 7,000 feet elevation. Young birds out of the nest were observed in the Sacramento and Magdalena Mountains in late June. On May 22, 1952, a nest was located in a Flicker excavation in an aspen three miles southeast of Cloudcroft, elevation about 8,000 feet. The nest hole was located 15 feet up in the 75-foot tree, which grew near some dense spruce at the edge of an open drain, and it contained 6 partly incubated eggs. Nest cavity was without lining. *Eggs:* 4 to 6; white when fresh and without stain.

(ELF OWL
Micrathene whitneyi
5½–6″ long. Color pattern of sexes alike.

The Elf, the smallest of the Owls, is one of the least of the raptorial birds. The common name "Elf" has reference to the diminutive size. *Adults:* Round head, without ear tufts; upperparts grayish brown; underparts mottled reddish brown; whitish about eyes; wings spotted with whitish and pale rusty.

DISTRIBUTION. The Elf Owl, a summer resident, occupies a zone about 50 to 75 miles wide in the southwestern part of the state adjacent to the Arizona line, from the Mexican border north into the Gila River Valley, where it is not uncommon. On July 25, 1955, Wayne Bohl and E. M. Lang observed one on White Creek southeast of Mogollon Baldy at about 7,000 feet elevation, the most northern and highest elevation at which it has been recorded. The author observed in late summer of 1918 numbers of the birds at the entrance of the Gila River gorge above Cliff, sitting on the ground or on rocks beneath the thick scrub bushes of the ledges at base of the canyon wall. This concentration probably preceded the southward migration for the winter. Previously some had been noted along the river about Red Rock, roosting in dense cottonwood foliage as well as in heavy clusters of mistletoe. These records indicate that the Elf Owl is not wholly nocturnal, at least on its New Mexico range. Since winter records are lacking, the birds are evidently migratory in New Mexico. They are out of the state by late September, returning in early May.

NESTING. In late June, a family of Elf Owls was seen near Red Rock, on the Gila River. They were occupying a Woodpecker hole—probably that of a Gila Woodpecker—in a dead cottonwood tree, about 20 feet above ground. For nesting, the Elf Owl prefers the giant cactus (saguaro), such as is found in Arizona. Since this cactus is not native to New Mexico, the Elf nests in hollows of trees or in abandoned Woodpecker or Flicker holes. *Eggs:* 2 or 3; white.

(BURROWING OWL

Speotyto cunicularia

9—10″ long. Color pattern of sexes alike.

The Burrowing Owl, a bird of the earth, is active by day as well as by night. It is most often seen on the ground at or near its home burrow, or perched on lookout point—a low bush, snag, or fence post. It is so unlike other Owls in appearance, in habits, and in its type of habitat, that it is readily identified. Bowing and bobbing of the head when disturbed are characteristic of its conduct. At such times, too, rather than turn to follow the movements of an observer, it twists its neck as though pivoted, thereby achieving an almost complete about-face. *Adults:* Upperparts dull brown, spotted and barred with buffy, head round; wings and tail barred with white; whitish line over eye; chin and throat white; underparts buffy dappled with brown; legs long and almost bare.

Although it is the consensus that Burrowing Owls are migratory, the author has never found evidence in support of this contention for the Southwest. While the birds move about at times, particularly when in search of suitable winter burrows, they are practically resident where found, remaining underground during severe winter weather. Whether or not they resort to any degree of torpidity during periods of inaction, seems yet to be determined. The fact that in winter they cache food, particularly mice, in their burrows seems to indicate that they use their "Owl wisdom" to provide for the proverbial "rainy day." In the Milnesand area of Roosevelt County, where old prairie dog burrows are still found, the little Owls are present year-round. On January 30, 1952, the author and a companion visited an old prairie dog "town" 35 miles west of Portales where many Burrowing Owls were present in summer. Not an Owl was in evidence, but upon excavation of a burrow with indication of occupancy by Owls, one was found snugly settled in the bottom of the hole, 6 feet from the entrance. Since about 40 of the Owls were noted there a little later, when weather became milder, there is little doubt that all were underground at the time this bird was taken from its burrow. Because of depth of burrows—and many are deep—and the uncertainty as to which are being occupied by the birds while at rest, much time and labor are involved in excavating them. However, such research carried to conclusion would yield valuable information.

Poisoning of the Black-tailed prairie dog over the vast central plains country has resulted in eliminating the living quarters of the Burrowing Owl. When the old mounds weather away and holes become sodded over, most of the Owls are without homes, hence are found only in limited numbers anywhere, and are absent from vast areas where once they were abundant and their presence was a factor in controlling infestation by grasshoppers, beetles, and small mammals, including young cottontail rabbits. The great assortment of beetle shells and small rodent bones about burrows where 8 or 10 young Owls may have been raised is conclusive evidence of their economic value.

DISTRIBUTION. Burrowing Owls were formerly found statewide wherever plains, treeless valleys, and mesas predominate. They shun the more rugged canyon, mountain, and forested types of terrain. They still occur sparingly over the state, but their numbers are only a shadow of former abundance in sections formerly occupied.

NESTING. Burrowing Owls nest in burrows underground. In the absence of prairie dogs to provide burrows, the birds resort to other excavations such as those made by badgers, kangaroo rats, or other ground-workers. Nest: Usually at end of burrow, and almost always consisting of flakes of horse or cow manure which is also conspicuously in evidence at the mouth of the occupied quarters. The author collected a set of 8 fresh eggs of this Owl from a prairie dog burrow south of Rosebud in Harding County, May 13, 1926. The nest, made of horse manure, was at the end of the burrow which extended under the surface for a distance of about eight feet at a 10-degree angle. The nesting area was occupied by quite a colony of the Owls, such colonization often occurring where there are numerous suitable burrows. Broods of young Burrowing Owls present an animated sight, when after they are well developed, they come to the surface to form a dignified circle on the burrow mound, like so many little soldiers, while the foraging parents endeavor to provide for the 8 or 10 insatiable appetites. At the least disturbance, all vanish into the safety of their underground abodes. Eggs: 8 to 10; white.

⟨ SPOTTED OWL
Strix occidentalis

16½–19″ long. Color pattern of sexes alike.

The Spotted Owl has a large round head, spotted with white; without ear tufts or "horns," and big, deep blue eyes; upperparts chestnut brown with white spotting; breast and underparts distinctly marked with white and brown spotting; tail rather long with white bands. The designation occidentalis signifies "western." One of the larger resident Owls of the state, this dweller of remote mountain fastnesses is a relative of the Barred Owl of the Eastern States. White droppings (feces) in caves and under fir trees are clues to the Spotted Owl's presence.

Spotted Owls are for the most part high-altitude dwellers, preferring by day the semi-dark recesses of spruce- or fir-covered mountainsides and canyons. They generally are found in dense Douglas fir growing in box canyons where there is little or no penetration of sun rays. Their clear, far-carrying who—whoo—whooo notes breaking the stillness of some remote canyon, or a sudden piercing scream overhead at night can evoke apprehension on the part of even a resolute woodsman. Its rarity and retiring nature, and rugged type of its retreats usually reached afoot or on horseback only—make the acquaintance of the Spotted Owl difficult. These trusting Owls usually are observed 20 to 30 feet above

SPOTTED OWL, NEST AND EGGS. *Photograph by the Author.*

ground, in pairs perched side by side near trunk of tree. A few have been noted, however, roosting in the semi-darkness of caves in canyon walls. Generally they pay little attention to an intruder other than to glance down drowsily with half-closed eyes. In one instance an adult bird was caught by hand, from its perch on a shelf in a cave. On another occasion, near Monument Park in the Black Range, no difficulty was experienced in getting pictures of a pair from a tree adjacent to the one in which the two birds sat. Prior to 1920, the author made a rather exhaustive study of this Owl in its principal retreats in the state, and collected specimens for the U.S. Biological Survey. Findings were published, in part, as "Habits of the Spotted Owl" (*The Auk*, Vol. XLIII, No. 4, Oct. 1926). A set of three eggs—now in the National Museum—was taken. So wholly beneficial is this fine Owl—feeding as it does on rodents, particularly wood rats, and on beetles—complete protection should be accorded it.

DISTRIBUTION. The Spotted Owl is resident where found. It has been recorded in all of the higher forested mountains of the state, but is nowhere common. It is most common in the Mogollon, Black,

and San Mateo Ranges. However, these records may be due to these ranges having been more thoroughly worked than others. It was found in the Sangre de Cristo Range, near Taos. Henshaw and Jensen recorded it in these mountains, east of Santa Fe. Jensen also observed a pair in the Jemez Mountains. This owl occurs in the New Mexico and Texas portions of the Guadalupe Mountains, which represent the extreme southeastern extension of its range. On February 21, 1958, Levon Lee saw a single Spotted Owl at Black Bill Spring, Animas Mountains, near the Mexican boundary, the most southern record for the state.

NESTING. Nesting of the Spotted Owl usually begins in late March or early April. Preferred nesting sites are pockets or crevices in well-shaded caves in canyon walls. Among several nests located by the author was one which contained 3 fresh eggs, April 4, 1926. It was situated in a cave in a canyon wall, in the San Mateo Mountains about 25 miles northeast of Winston (Fairview), at about 6,700 feet elevation. A few nests have been found in the thick growth or clusters of fir tree branches, 10 to 20 feet above ground, near the bole of the tree. Wherever the nests are found, they are likely to be difficult of access and well concealed. *Nest:* Made of dry sticks and twigs, lined with bark, twigs, and feathers. *Eggs:* Usually 3; white.

(LONG-EARED OWL
Asio otus

13—16″ long. Color pattern of sexes alike.

The Long-eared Owl, a retiring, brush- and tree-dwelling nocturnal species, is much smaller than the Great Horned. To avoid detection it assumes a clever pose: standing upright, long "ears" close together, the streamlined body so lined up as to present a remarkable resemblance to the upright limbs of a concealing perch. Thus it is often overlooked. The lengthwise streaking of the underparts perfects the barklike camouflaging pattern. When startled, it dashes away with ease and, threading through heavy cover, is soon lost to view. In flight the "ears" are depressed and little in evidence. *Adults:* Upperparts brownish black, mottled with grayish white; underparts whitish, lined and cross-barred with black; "ears" rather long and held upright.

The Long-eared is migratory, and in the state in winter it is more or less gregarious where cover and available food encourage concentrations. So skillful at evasion is this Owl, it is not subject to as serious persecution as are some other species. In flight, its wide wingspread gives it the appearance of being much larger than it is. Plucked, the body is little larger than that of a Quail.

DISTRIBUTION. In winter the Long-eared Owl is widely distributed, occurring even on the high plains of the eastern section, where orchards, hedgerows, and suitable natural cover are available for diurnal concealment. Wherever found it should be given complete protection since it feeds almost entirely on rodents, particularly mice and rats. On January 18, 1951, several were observed in a shelterbelt hedge near Milnesand, southern Roosevelt County. On October 30, 1950, a small concentration was located in a large, protected willow thicket near Beaverhead. A short time later several were seen in a live oak grove south of Animas.

NESTING. The Long-eared nests sparingly in the state. The author has observed but two nests, both containing young— one on June 28, 1916, on the rim of Mount Taylor Mesa about 35 miles north of Grants at 7,500 feet elevation; the other in a lone clump of tamarisk about 10 miles west of Tularosa, in the wide, semidesert Tularosa Valley. "Collected set of three incubated eggs at Abo, Torrance County, New Mexico, May 20, 1955. Nest fourteen feet from ground in juniper. Collected set of five fresh eggs of this species in this locality in 1955" (Campbell). *Nest:* In bushes or trees, 6 to 30 feet above ground, usually the nests of other raptors or of Ravens or Crows, have been repaired and used by Owls. *Eggs:* 4 or 5; white.

LONG-EARED OWL
J. L. Ridgway, U.S. Fish & Wildlife Service

SHORT-EARED OWL
Asio flammeus

13½—16″ long. Color pattern of sexes alike.

This Owl is too large to be confused with the smaller Screech Owl, and too small to be mistaken for the Great Horned. The Short-eared, as its name implies, has much shorter "horns" than its more streamlined relative, the Long-eared. The Latin, *asio*, refers to "horns"; *flammeus*, "reddish of color." *Adults:* White facial disc; black ring around eye; heavily striped above, lighter below, with individual variations.

Primarily a surface-ground dweller, it prefers grassy meadows and rank-grass plains, mesa and valley lands. Unlike the other larger Owls which are usually abroad by night only, the Short-eared is active in late afternoons, beating about slowly over meadows or other grasslands in search of rodents. Serious depletion of native grasses and persecution by man have resulted in all but eliminating this valuable Owl formerly common in fall flights and often found wintering in the state. In late years, day concentrations have been observed on the ground under spreading thickets of chaparral *(Condalia)* and other brush growing along the foothills and canyons adjacent to the Pecos River in southeast-ern New Mexico and in western Texas. Periodic absence of rank upland grasses in which they prefer to live, probably influences their concentration in thickets. In areas where formerly these Owls could be flushed or be seen coursing above "seas of grass," one rarely is observed now.

DISTRIBUTION. The Short-eared formerly occurred statewide in winter. As was true in former times, it is most in evidence, though in far less numbers, in the open grasslands east of the Pecos River. Even here it is now confined mostly to the sandhill, bluestem terrain, which constitutes the best remaining ground cover. In March 1949, six were flushed from an abandoned field overgrown with shinnery (Havard) oak and bluestem grass, six miles southeast of Milnesand, Roosevelt County. A few days previously, two had been seen farther west when a notation was made "A rare Owl in recent years." It usually begins to enter the state in late September, and is absent by mid-March. There is no nesting record for the state.

(SAW-WHET OWL
Aegolius acadicus

7—8½″ long. Color pattern of sexes alike.

The Saw-whet Owl, so named from its notes which sound like the filing of a saw,

NEST AND EGGS OF LONG-EARED OWL. *Photograph by John M. Campbell.*

is seemingly a rare bird in the state. However, like some of the other small Owls, it is nocturnal and so retiring that its presence may often be unsuspected. It is smaller than the common Screech Owl and has no "horns" or ear tufts. *Adults:* Upperparts brown; wings and tail spotted with white; conspicuous black spots at inner corner of eyes; underparts whitish streaked with wide brown stripes. This little Owl is unique in its facial disk pattern in that the discs are lined above with white, and divided by an inverted V below.

DISTRIBUTION. The few authentic state records of the Saw-whet indicate that although it is nowhere common, it is widespread in the mountainous sections. It has been recorded in the Rio Grande Valley at Las Cruces. One was taken 3 miles north of Silver City on January 23, 1923. "The species was observed at Santa Fe during the winter of 1922-23" (Jensen). The au-

thor has a specimen of this Owl which he picked up, dead, in Jordan Canyon, southwest of Black Mountain about 75 miles north of Silver City. One was picked up, dead, by John M. Campbell, near Santa Fe, October 24, 1954. The Saw-whet is known to be at least semi-migratory.

NESTING. As is also true of most other small owls, authentic nesting records of Saw-whet Owls are usually difficult to secure. They nest in Flicker holes and hollows of trees, and are abroad mostly at night, leaving few or no clues as to nesting locations. "Nest with young reported by General G. Ralph Meyer, at Cloudcroft, summer of 1948; family of 4 at Alto, New Mexico, seen by Jack Stewart and sons about August 1, 1956" (Lena McBee). The repeated rasping notes of the Saw-whet often are a clue to its presence. *Nest:* In hollow trees, Flicker excavations, or nesting boxes. *Eggs:* 4 to 7; white.

GOATSUCKERS
Family: CAPRIMULGIDAE

NO OTHER birds have been so much the object of misconception and myths as members of this group. Even the origin of the group designation is steeped in superstition. In ancient times European goatherders, imbued with the absurd belief that these foragers of the night visited their herds and helped themselves to milk, attached to them the incongruous stigma, "Goatsucker." Soft, pencilled, inconspicuous plumage—a perfect simulation of their environment—is characteristic of members of this family. Their long, pointed soft-feathered wings permit easy, noiseless flight. Bills are small, but mouths are wide, providing an efficient trap for catching insects in the air. Long, wiry bristles at

sides of bill help prevent escape of insects when caught. Legs of the Goatsuckers are short; feet small, and used very little as a means of ground locomotion. Ample wings fit them for cruising the airways in search of food or in migration. Few other birds are of higher economic value as harvesters of injurious insects, or so completely harmless. They make no nest, laying their eggs on barren ground. Although they are generally regarded as crepuscular or nocturnal, their activities are not restricted to twilight or darkness. The New Mexico group consists of Whip-poor-will, Poor-will, and two species of Nighthawks —the Common and the Lesser, also known as the Texas.

❲ WHIP-POOR-WILL (STEPHENS)

Caprimulgus vociferus

9—10″ long. Color pattern of sexes alike.

So rare, retiring, and restricted in range in the state is the Whip-poor-will that only a favored few observers are aware of its occurrence. It may be found, in summer only, in the southern and south-central mountains. Since the bird is rarely seen, it can best be identified by its early evening and night call: *Whip— whip— whip-poor-will*. The Poor-will, a somewhat smaller member of the group, occurs more often in the foothills, and its call, *Poor-will*, is distinctive. The Whip-poor-will, on the other hand, is usually confined to the denser forests of the mountains. In their concealing color pattern, both members may be overlooked on the ground, where they spend much of their time. *Adults:* Upperparts mottled grayish, barred with blackish; underparts mixed tawny and black.

DISTRIBUTION. The Whip-poor-will is a migrant found in the state in summer only. Its range is confined almost wholly to the Guadalupe, Sacramento, and Mogollon Mountains and Black Range. It is very rare, however, east of the Rio Grande. It is most common in the Black and Mogollon Ranges, north to Reserve and Chloride. Both Mearns and Goldman recorded it in the Peloncillo and Animas Mountains in southern Hidalgo County. It has been recorded in Upper Dog and Dark Canyons, Guadalupe Mountains. On May 18, 1913, the author observed Whip-poor-wills in Monument Pass, Black Range, 12 miles west of Chloride, at 8,000 feet, and west of the pass, in Turkey Canyon. "A Whip-poor-will called repeatedly, after dark, near our camp above Bonito Lake" (Montgomery). Bonito Lake is about 6 miles north of Alto, in the White Mountains.

NESTING. The Whip-poor-will builds no nest but lays its eggs on barren ground. The only nesting record for the state, so far as the author is aware, is that of a "nest" found by him on upper South Diamond Canyon, 50 miles northeast of Silver City, at 7,500 feet. It was located in a small opening in heavy forest on the north exposure of the canyon. One of the birds was on the "nest," which contained a small young and an infertile egg. *Nest:* On barren ground. *Eggs:* 2; white with faint markings.

❲ POOR-WILL

Phalaenoptilus nuttallii

7½—8½″ long. Color pattern of sexes alike.

In color and action, the Poor-will and the Whip-poor-will are similar, but the Poor-will is smaller and ranges mainly in the valleys and foothills, while the Whip-poor-will prefers the heavy forests of high mountains. Both are primarily ground-dwellers and neither is often seen in bright daylight, unless virtually kicked out of a shady hiding place. The repeated evening and early morning *Poor-will* notes herald its arrival in early spring. *Adults:* Head narrowly barred with black; upperparts soft and velvety, mothlike, in bronzy gray color, with wavy, frosty crossbar markings; tail (except two middle feathers), banded with black, gray and buffy, tipped with white; throat, silky white, bordered by black or brown; underparts barred.

DISTRIBUTION. During the summer months the Poor-will is found in the entire state, except open mesas and plains, up to about 9,000 feet. It may occur sparingly on the high southeastern plains in migration but it does not remain long on such terrain. It enters the southern part of the state in late March (Carlsbad, March 25) while the latest observation here is December 8 (1954). The first arrival in 1953 was noted on March 26. Usual arrival in northern New Mexico in late April. During migration it is often seen on lawns, in gardens and driveways about Carlsbad, after sunset, alternately vaulting upward for insects, returning to crouch motionless on the ground, then repeating the aerial feeding maneuver, occasionally taking time out to repeat its distinctive *Poor-will* notes over and over. Jensen reported it in Santa Fe Canyon, east of Santa Fe, at 9,500 feet elevation, in June. It is most common in the rugged foothills about Magdalena and southward, and in the Guadalupe Mountains. At night, the pink glow from its eyes may often be seen reflected by automobile headlights.

NESTING. Although the Poor-will is a rather common breeder in the state, nests are rarely located because the bird so closely simulates the ground about it, and because it is most reluctant to leave its "nest." It breeds from the southern border of the state northward. *Nest*: On barren ground. *Eggs*: 2; white.

⟨ COMMON NIGHTHAWK
Chordeiles minor
8½—10″ long. Color pattern of sexes similar.

Neither of the terms, "Night" nor "Hawk," fully applies to the bird that is known by this combined term. It is a hawk only to the extent that it preys on insects in flight. The Common Nighthawk is no better equipped as a bird of prey than is the Hummingbird; neither are its activities restricted to darkness. In fact, in the lower Pecos Valley of the state, about Artesia and Carlsbad, swarms of the birds at times may be seen in bright, sunshiny weather, vaulting, turning, flitting, and diving in involved gyrations, while harvesting the concentrations of aerial-moving insects. These midday congregations are probably influenced by flying insects that are not so abundantly airborne at other times. The birds are readily recognized,

POOR-WILL. *L. A. Fuertes, U.S. Fish & Wildlife Service.*

either at rest or in flight. *Adults:* Upperparts with white and buffy markings; throat and band near end of tail white; white bar on primaries; underparts barred with dusky; throat patch of female usually buffy and no white tail patch.

When not on wing, they take advantage of their protective coloration by sitting lengthwise and motionless on limb or other perch, or crouched on the ground. As an example of their adaptability to local conditions: in 1940, in the open mesa country northwest of Roswell, when it was common practice for hunting crews to hang the skinned carcasses of coyotes on the posts of fences bordering the highway, the author observed, for some distance along Highway 285 near the Macho Wash Bridge, Common Nighthawks sitting very well concealed, on most of the brown carcasses.

DISTRIBUTION. The Common Nighthawk is a late spring arrival, reaching southern New Mexico in late April or early May. By early June, the birds occupy practically all parts of the state, up to 8,000 feet, shunning only the most heavily forested mountainous areas. They are most in evidence in August before departing for the winter, when heavy concentrations occur, usually in late afternoons, wheeling and flitting about over meadows or irrigated fields. Such concentrations are especially common about Carlsbad and other Pecos Valley points. At this season, numbers of them may be seen at times flying ahead of approaching rainstorms. Following the nesting season they have a tendency to "tour" the country leisurely, even getting up around timber line. In their erratic aerial movements, they seem to tarry or proceed as if destination were of little or no consequence.

NESTING. Since Common Nighthawks are late in arriving, nesting activities begin soon after they become distributed and settled. The aerial antics and booming sweeps of the males are at their peak at this time.

One will start upward, repeating the characteristic sharp mating call until high in the air, whereupon he relaxes and starts a downward swoop, climaxed by a booming note that has given rise to the term, "bullbat," commonly applied to the bird. At the conclusion of the downward dive, a low-flying female—the incentive for the acrobatic plunge—can usually be seen, leisurely going her erratic way, whereupon the male may swing upward to complete the wide aerial arc or, with wide beat of wings, trail after the object of his overtures. The booming sound—a thunderous bang for so small a performer—is the result, presumably, of air rushing through the wing feathers during the downward swoop.

The author found fresh eggs 8 miles north of Roswell on May 30. Jensen reported the Common Nighthawks nesting regularly over the pinyon flats near Santa Fe in early June. The affliction or "cripple" ruse employed upon leaving eggs or young

NIGHTHAWK. *U.S. Fish & Wildlife Service.*

is characteristic. In a straightaway flight, the tail is usually pointed directly down, and to make the simulated affliction seem real, the pretender may repeatedly bob along off and on the ground for some distance. There is little need for all of this make-believe, for the eggs and ashy gray young are all but invisible, so well do they simulate the surroundings. *Eggs:* 2; creamy buff, or gray, finely blotched or speckled with brown or lavender; laid on bare ground.

⟦ LESSER (TEXAS) NIGHTHAWK
Chordeiles acutipennis

8—9″ long. Color pattern of sexes essentially alike.

The Lesser is confined to the southern portion of the state, while the Common occurs statewide, but is less in evidence in summer over the lower, southern parts. The Lesser is more of a ground dweller, even flying near the surface early and late as it feeds, while the Common usually flies higher. Both have white wing bars, but those of the Lesser are narrow and nearer the wing tips. The author has rarely known the Lesser to swoop down and make the booming sounds common to its larger relative, during the mating season. The most frequent mating note, presumably that of the male, is a soft yodeling, continuously sounded on an even scale, in the early evening, at night, and in the early morning. Where the birds are numerous the yodeling, performed while the bird sits on the ground, is often heard from different directions in late spring and early summer. The males also utter mewing or whining notes in flight as they swing about near the ground with slow downward sweep of wings in devious pursuit of the females. *Adult male:* Upperparts brownish gray; tail mottled and broadly barred with buff; throat with large triangular white patch; breast dark brown and mottled; rest of underparts buff with dark brown bars. *Fe-*

male: Similar but browner; throat patch tawny. Although in general color and flight pattern, the Lesser Nighthawk bears a close resemblance to the Common Nighthawk, the former is smaller and has a different note.

DISTRIBUTION. In the Southwest, the distribution of the Lesser Nighthawk is largely coextensive with creosote bush. It ranges up the Rio Grande Valley and along the foothills to Monticello, and is listed as "summer resident, uncommon," at Bosque del Apache Refuge. It also occurs north to Tularosa in the Tularosa Basin. In the Pecos Valley the Lesser Nighthawk is fairly common as far north as Dexter and is an uncommon summer resident at Bitter Lake Refuge. In the early 1930's it was far more common in the Carlsbad area in season than it now is. Some bird observers, including the author, are of the opinion that the dusting of cotton fields with lethal insect sprays is proving fatal to Nighthawks and other insectivorous species as well as to bats, as a result of their eating the affected insects. The Lesser is still common, however, in the southwest part of the state. On May 26, 1951, an estimated 100 Lesser Nighthawks were seen milling about over a pond in the San Simon Marshes southwest of Lordsburg. It is among the latest migrants to arrive in the spring, and among the earliest to leave in the fall. It usually appears at Carlsbad from May 6 to 10, and about the same date at Las Cruces and Lordsburg.

NESTING. The height of the nesting season of the Lesser Nighthawk is in June. A "nest" containing 2 fresh eggs was located by the author, June 2, near Big Hatchet Mountain, 20 miles south of Hachita. Fresh eggs that may have been second clutches were also noted near Las Cruces as late as July 15. *Nest:* On barren ground, usually by a creosote bush. *Eggs:* 2; clay color, washed with pinkish, blotched with gray and lilac.

SWIFTS
Family: APODIDAE

AS THEIR common name indicates, members of this family are swift of wing. In some respects Swifts resemble the Swallows, but they are far more streamlined, and fly with rapid, gliding movements. They have long, narrow, stiff wings. Their feet are used mainly in clinging to vertical cliffs or interiors of chimneys. They are seldom seen perching. While the Chimney Swift is extremely rare in New Mexico (see Rare and Stray Birds), it is an abundant summer resident in Eastern states.

BLACK SWIFT
Cypseloides niger

7—7½" long. Color pattern of sexes alike.

The Black Swift must be regarded as rare in the state, unless it flies high and thus escapes observation in migrating between Mexico and Colorado, where it is known to breed. The adult is sooty black, except chin and throat grayish, and some white about bill; tail slightly forked, more in evidence when spread in flight. It is the largest of the Swifts that occur in the state.

DISTRIBUTION. There seems to be no recent record of this bird's occurrence in the state. Henshaw noted it in fall migration at Willis (now Cowles), and it has been recorded at Burford Lake in September. According to Bendire: "In 1883 Mr. Anthony found them abundant in southwestern Colorado; nesting in all of the highest crags, but never in places accessible to anything not provided with wings." Thus, Black Swifts may nest in northwestern New Mexico.

⟨ WHITE-THROATED SWIFT
Aeronautes saxatalis

6½—7" long. Color pattern of sexes alike.

Gliding about cliffs and ledges, the White-throated Swift is readily distinguished by the white throat and line that extends back to near base of tail. Often these rockets of the air may be observed swiftly racing or gliding by some lofty canyon or mountain wall, reminding one of skilled performers on roller skates. The Greek-Latin term aeronautes means "air sailor," while Latin, saxatalis, means "rock-inhabiting," which the White-throated Swift most definitely is. Adults: Upperparts, sides and under-tail coverts black; throat, breast, and flanks white.

DISTRIBUTION. Altitude seems to be no barrier to summer distribution of the White-throated Swift. It is common from about 5,000 feet to about timber line. From early March (southern section) to mid-April (northern part) the bird observer may see one after another whiz by some high creviced ledge uttering its bat-like squeak, then reverse its course to race back with characteristic grace and ease. It has a tendency to colonize at nesting time. The birds are usually out of the state by mid-October, but there is one record as late as December 15, at Hachita.

NESTING. The White-throated Swift nests almost entirely in crevices of perpendicular or overhanging cliffs. Seemingly it prefers the higher and more inaccessible nesting sites. So quickly do they enter and leave the chosen crevice that only the most alert observer can follow them in the act. The author has found them nesting in Big Hatchet Mountain in the extreme southwest; Black and Mogollon Ranges in the central section; and Sangre de Cristo Range and about Burford Lake in the north. "In 1920 a good-sized colony was nesting in the 300-foot perpendicular cliff in Canyon el Diablo near Buckman, northwest of Santa Fe" (Jensen). The height of the nesting season is from mid-May to late June. Nest: Made principally of feathers, glued to each other as well as to the rocks. Eggs: 4 or 5; white.

HUMMINGBIRDS
Family: TROCHILIDAE

HUMMINGBIRDS are distinctive in many ways. They are the smallest members of the class Aves, and are the only birds known to have the ability to fly backwards. They are indigenous to the Americas. More than 400 species occur in the Western Hemisphere, most of them in the tropics.

Hummingbirds have a rare faculty of displaying their scintillating beauty which is heightened by reflection of the sun's rays. Diffusing iridescent splendor through reflex action, with a magic akin to optical illusion, they dart from flower to flower extracting with protrusile tongues nectars and the tiny insects which invade the blooms. It is, however, when momentarily hovering in midair that they bring into focus the "most gorgeously brilliant metallic hues known among created things."

Other than emitting a squeaking note, the Hummingbird is not vocal. The humming—which has given the bird its name—is the result of rapid vibration of its wings —"as rapidly as 75 a second when progressing straightaway" (Bent).

In late summer, Hummingbirds occur in migrating concentrations and at such times their performance in competing for preferred food is most impressive. A spectacular avian exhibition was one that had its setting in a field of "red hot poker" (Tritoma) at the Cadwallader Nurseries at Mountain Park, on August 15, 1951. Judg-ing by the whirring hostility, punctuated by explosive squeaks, each of the hundred or more participants—Rufous, Broadtailed, Black-chinned, and Calliope—was asserting its prerogative over the mass of flaming blossoms that spread about him. The dainty, iridescent jewels were now cast in roles of fierce warriors in aerial combat, their brilliant vestments flashing defiantly during a melee of counterattack. Few birds are so maneuverable on wing, a gift that serves them well in aerial battle, in procuring food, and in evading potential winged enemies.

The diminutive size distinguishes the Hummingbird from other birds, but separating females of the different species by sight alone is a challenge to the most exacting observer. Color of males and females in some is so radically different that only through very close observation can the species be determined. At nesting time, when pairs are together, identification is simplified. Of the nine species which have been recorded in New Mexico, four—Black-chinned, Broad-tailed, Rufous, and Calliope—are widely distributed and common to abundant locally, particularly in mountainous areas. The rarer Costa's, Rivoli's, Blue-throated, Violet-crowned, and Broad-billed—are confined in season to the southwest part of the state.

Hummingbirds are all migratory, and

their summer appearance is governed largely by the abundance or scarcity of flowers. Although nectars, and the small insects which infest flowers, are the preferred foods, Hummingbirds are quick to find and partake of supplements, such as sweetened water, when placed about yard or garden, especially during the late summer migration.

(BLACK-CHINNED HUMMINGBIRD

Archilochus alexandri

3¼—3¾" long. Color pattern of sexes different. (Pl. XVI)

Adult male: The most conspicuous identification marks of the adult male Black-chinned Hummingbird are the black throat and white collar. Upperparts, including top of head and middle tail feathers, metallic bronze green; outer tail feathers purplish black; wings dusky, glossed with purple. Gorget, above, velvet black, below, a narrow band of metallic violet. Underparts mostly whitish gray; sides greenish. *Adult female:* Upperparts dull metallic bronze green; head duller or grayish; tail rounded, middle feathers like back, tail feathers with white tips; underparts grayish or whitish. Young similar to female, but best identified by presence of adults.

DISTRIBUTION. The Black-chinned, in summer, is widely distributed in the state, but confined mainly at breeding time from 3,500 to 7,000 feet elevation. "It was common at 5,000 feet on the Hondo, west of Roswell, June 9, 1899, and continued common to the foot of the Capitan [Mountains] at 6,000 feet" (Bailey). "It was noted June 23, 1904, at Espanola, 5,500 feet" (Surber). "Fairly common at Shiprock, 5,000 feet" (Gilman). "It was taken, July 28, at 5,100 feet, near the base of the Animas Mountains" (Goldman), where the author observed it at the north end of these mountains on May 8, 1920. On July 18, 1951, the author found it common in association with Rufous, Broad-tailed, and Calliope, at Jemez Springs, in the foothills of the Jemez Mountains. It leaves the state in late September, returning about mid-April.

NESTING. The various early summer records (late May and June) of the Black-chinned no doubt represent breeding birds. "It was nesting at 4,500 feet at the Carlsbad Cave [Caverns] in 1924" (Bailey). Bailey reported another nest "under the arched entrance to the Bighorn Cave [Guadalupe Mountains], where the White-throated Swifts also nested," higher up in the Guadalupe Mountains. The Gordon Whites report that the Black-chinned hummer nests commonly in trees of their yard and in those of adjoining lawns (Las Cruces, 3,900 feet). The author noted a nest containing two eggs in the White's yard on May 15, 1955. *Nest:* In bushes or trees, two to 20 feet from the ground; made of plant down, sustained by the bird's saliva, and coated with spider web; sometimes with oak blossoms on outer walls. *Eggs:* 2 or 3; white.

(COSTA'S HUMMINGBIRD

Calypte costae

Male, 2¾—3¼"; female, 3½—3¾" long. Color pattern of sexes different.

Adult male: "Entire head, gorget, and long, flaring ruff glittering metallic violet or amethyst-purple, changing to black, blue-green, or magenta in varying lights; rest of upperparts, including middle tail feathers, dull metallic bronze green; lateral tail feathers grayish or brownish, glossed with green; wing quills dusky, faintly glossed with purplish; upperparts whitish, glossed with golden-green. Tail is slightly forked. *Adult female:* Entire upperparts, including middle tail feathers, dull metallic bronze green; other tail feathers green or gray, black tipped or white tipped; underparts brownish gray, whitish on throat, often with a few amethyst feathers." The female is considera! 'rger than the male. Young similar to adult female.

DISTRIBUTION. Although a common summer resident in Southern Arizona, the Costa's Hummingbird seems to be of rare occurrence in New Mexico. It is one of those rarities that test the patience of the most avid bird watcher. In a letter, September 2, 1958, Lena McBee states: "Another exceptional record for us is the Costa's Hummingbird on the west or New Mexico side of the Rio Grande, July 25, in a tornillo (Prosopis odorata) thicket that is bordered on three sides by desert wasteland, and on another by a field of cotton. There were two male adult birds, a female, and an immature bird. I had once seen the Costa's at Ash Spring, in the San Andres Mountains, New Mexico, May 13, 1942, but never since then until this summer, in this area."

NESTING. The early-day ornithologist, Frank Stephens, found a nest of the Costa's Hummingbird on the Gila River in May 1876, which appears to be the only authentic breeding record of this hummer in the State. According to J. B. Dixson, they have a tendency to colonize at nesting time. Where they are numerous, several nests were found on a limited but preferred area. Apparently they prefer desert or semidesert habitat. Nest: Usually placed near the ground on cactus, vines, or dwarf shrubs or bushes; made of plant down, leaves and bits of flower stems; attached to supporting branch by cobwebs; lined with down or small feathers. Eggs: 2; white.

(BROAD-TAILED HUMMINGBIRD

Selasphorus platycercus

4—4¾" long. Color pattern of sexes different. (Pl. XVI)

The Broad-tailed is a common and widespread summer resident hummer in the state. Adult male: Entire upperparts, including top of head and middle tail feathers, bronze green; outer tail feathers dull purplish or bronzy black; gorget metallic deep rose pink or reddish purple; rest of underparts pale grayish, sides overlaid with green, and flanks tinged with cinnamon. Adult female: Upperparts metallic bronze green, including middle tail feathers which are sometimes dusky at tips, dusky portion wider on adjoining pair; three outer pairs brown at base, and broadly tipped with white, with purple, bronzy, black and green between; throat whitish, with dusky or bronzy specks; rest of underparts more or less brownish white or buffy; sides brownish.

The Broad-tailed Hummingbird is endowed with cunning, which, with the aid of its awesome whirring, it employs to advantage in putting to flight birds many times its size, or in appropriating nest material from their nests, as was witnessed by the author near Chloride, when his attention was attracted by the buzzing of a hummer about a branch of a walnut tree where a Broad-tailed darted up and looked into a newly constructed Solitary Vireo nest. Finding the owner absent, it dropped slightly down, thrust its long bill into the side of the nest, pulled out a bit of material, and dashed away to add it to its own nest which was in process of construction.

DISTRIBUTION. Broad-tailed Hummingbirds have a statewide summer distribution. They usually arrive in the southern part (Carlsbad and Las Cruces) about April 1 to 10, and crowd the frost line as they move north. Their spring arrivals and fall departures are influenced by the nature of the season. They occur in all the higher mountains in August, when valleys and mountains are aglow with wild flowers. Especially attractive to them are the fields of Rocky Mountain bee plant, Indian paintbrush, and the lupines, while various cultivated flowers about Mountain Park and James Canyon, in the Sacramento Mountains, and elsewhere in the high country attract them in great numbers after the peak of the breeding season, and hold them temporarily during the fall migration. They were observed at Cloudcroft, September 8, Albuquerque, September 16 and 18, and Carlsbad, early October.

NESTING. The Broad-tailed Hummingbird is the only hummer that nests statewide, from 3,100 feet elevation about Carlsbad, to near timber line in the Sangre de Cristo Range. "Nest with two fresh eggs, June 29, in Santa Fe Canyon at 8,000 feet, and two pairs were nesting on the Indian School Campus, Santa Fe, 1921 and again in 1922; and a pair observed on Lake Peak, at 12,000 feet elevation, June 26" (Jensen). Nest: Usually only a few feet from the ground at the lower altitudes; but in the forested mountains may be 12 or 15 feet from the ground; often about porches, as on light fixtures, or in lower branches of fruit trees. Made of plant down, coated with lichen, bark fibers, moss, or leaves. Eggs: 2; white.

RUFOUS HUMMINGBIRD
Selasphorus rufus
3¼—3¾" long. Color pattern of sexes different. (Pl. XVI)

The Rufous Hummingbird is common to abundant, but only as a migrant in the higher mountains of the state, particularly in August when, in association with the Broad-tailed, Black-chinned, and Calliope, it animates the flower-bedecked mountain meadows and valleys with its whirring challenge as it engages in battle over pre-empted areas. It is then that the bright rufous body markings, the flaming red throat, contrasting with the white on chest of the male, appear to greatest advantage. Since no other red or rufous hummer occurs in the state, identification of the male is simplified. Adult female: Upperparts metallic bronze; tail feathers with brown at base, three outer tail feathers broadly tipped with white; throat and chest dull whitish; slightly larger than male.

DISTRIBUTION. There seem to be no spring or early summer records for this hummer, indicating that it goes north in the spring, west of the state. By early August, however, it begins to appear over practically all of the mountainous sections of New Mexico, fanning out in limited numbers even to the eastern portion. In the Clayton area, Krehbiel reports: "They were fairly common during fall migration," and in 1954, "observed them from July 25 to August 23." Fleetwood and the author found them abundant, in company with the Broad-tailed, near Cumbres Pass, northeast of Chama, around 9,000 feet, July 14, 1951. Flowers were blooming in profusion at the time, and the cool mountain air was vibrant with the buzzing and squeaking of the spirited contestants. On July 18, the Broad-tailed, Black-chinned, Calliope, and Rufous were observed in considerable numbers above Jemez Springs, where their feeding activities were divided between the luxuriant garden flowers and the self-feeders containing sweetened water which hung about buildings for their benefit. On August 3, 1951, Homer Pickens observed great numbers of the Rufous in association with the Black-chinned, in the extensive patches of blooming Rocky Mountain bee plant, north of Reserve. Their arrival in the extreme southwest portion (Animas and Peloncillo Mountains) coincides with the blooming of the mescal (agave) in late July.

NESTING. Although New Mexico has been included in the breeding range of the Rufous Hummingbird for the past 35 years, there appears to be no verification of its nesting up to the end of 1958. The persistent observer may, in time, be rewarded by finding it nesting in the highest mountains in the northern section. Nest: In bushes, trees, or vines overhanging ledges; made of down and covered with moss and shreds of bark. *Eggs:* 2; white.

CALLIOPE HUMMINGBIRD
Stellula calliope
Male, 2¾"; female, 3½" long. Color pattern of sexes different. (Pl. XVI)

The poetic Latin designation, *Stellula*, meaning "dim star," seems most appropriate for this diminutive bird, one of the smallest of the Hummingbirds that enter the state. Like the Rufous, the Calliope seems to bypass New Mexico in the spring migration, but overflows the mountains of the state in late July and early August as it moves southward. *Adult male:* Gorget red barring on white base; upperparts, including top of head, metallic bronze green; tail feathers dusky, usually with paler tips and more or less brown at base; underparts grayish brown. *Adult female:* Upperparts metallic bronze green; middle tail feathers duller, others green or gray, crossed with black; throat dull brownish white; median underparts buffy or dull whitish.

DISTRIBUTION. The pattern of the late summer southward flight of the Calliope follows rather closely that of the Rufous, though in smaller numbers. The distribution of the Calliope is confined almost wholly to the mountainous sections, influenced by the abundance of wild or cultivated flowers. There are no nesting records. It is out of the state by mid-September.

RIVOLI'S HUMMINGBIRD
Eugenes fulgens
Male: 4½–5" long. Color pattern of sexes different. (Pl. XVI)

The Rivoli's and the Blue-throated Hummingbirds are the largest of the hummers that occur in the state. Likewise, both are rare and restricted to the southwest part. *Adult male:* When seen in flight the male Rivoli's appears almost black. Top of head metallic violet or purple; gorget brilliant metallic emerald green; chest velvety black or bronze green in different lights; rest of body mainly green, including tail. *Adult female:* Upperparts metallic bronze or green; feathers of chin and throat with scaled appearance.

DISTRIBUTION. In 1892, from June 26 to July 23, Mearns, while serving on the United States–Mexico Boundary Commission, found the Rivoli's in the San Luis Mountains, which comprise the southern part of the Animas Range on both sides of the International Boundary. He did not report it nesting, but probably the height of the breeding season had passed. The author and Maj. Allen Brooks recorded it in Cherry Canyon, north of Silver City, in May. Bird watchers going into the southwestern corner of the state at the proper time may find that this Hummingbird is more common during favorable seasons than the few records indicate.

NESTING. Nests are usually placed in sycamore, alder, or walnut trees; made of mosses and lichens and sustained by spider web. *Eggs:* 2; white.

BLUE-THROATED HUMMINGBIRD
Lampornis clemenciae
4½–5½" long. Color pattern of sexes similar.

The large Blue-throated is one of the more somber members of the hummer family, and is a challenge to the ambitious observer, since there are few records for the state. *Adult male:* Upperparts dull metallic green; tail feathers bluish black, lateral feathers tipped with white; wings dusky; head with conspicuous white streak back of eye; throat metallic blue; remainder of underparts brownish gray. *Adult female:* Similar, but throat like underparts—brownish gray.

DISTRIBUTION. Mearns took a specimen in July 1892 in the San Luis Mountains. On May 16, 1934, "one was seen perched on a wire at Mesilla Park, and May 4, 1941, one was recorded near Anthony" (McBee and Keefer).

❮ VIOLET-CROWNED HUMMINGBIRD
Amazilia verticalis

3½—4¼″ long. Color pattern of sexes essentially alike.

The beautiful Violet-crowned Hummingbird is a new addition to the New Mexico bird list. Mr. Seymour Levy, who knows the bird, gives the following account of it in a letter to the author, dated August 15, 1957: "This medium sized Hummingbird is unmistakable! Its pure white underparts contrast sharply with the brownish back; bill red tipped with black; in good light the crown and forehead appear either violet-blue or purple. Since this bird has no white lines on sides of its head, in either sex, there can be no confusion with females of other species that have whitish underparts. In the violet-crowned there is little or no difference in the sexes. It has been my experience that this bird is easiest of any of the Hummers to distinguish without binoculars." Mr. Levy states further that the Violet-crowned is very pugnacious, and chases other hummers which stray into its territory. He is of the opinion that the Violet-crowned and Black-chinned are the most common of the Hummingbirds in the Guadalupe Canyon area. (See Guadalupe Canyon, Bird Watching Region 1.)

DISTRIBUTION. Records of the Violet-crowned Hummingbird apply only to Guadalupe Canyon, Hidalgo County. A male was taken on the New Mexico–Arizona line in the canyon, July 24, 1957.

NESTING. Regarding the Violet-crowned Hummingbird, Dale A. Zimmerman, of Silver City, states: "I found 3 pairs of this hummer in the New Mexico portion of Guadalupe Canyon this summer [1959]. July 5, I found a nest with an incubating adult. This nest, and the one I found in Arizona, were quite white in appearance, decorated with a few green lichens. The New Mexico nest was in a sycamore, about 32 feet above ground where I could not reach it in any way."

BROAD-BILLED HUMMINGBIRD
Cynanthus latirostris

Male, 3½″; female 4″ long. Color pattern of sexes different.

The black-tipped red bill, wide at base and slightly decurved, and the bright metallic greenish blue gorget are distinguishing marks of the Broad-billed. *Adult male:* Back of head and body metallic bronze green; tail feathers blue black with white spots; wings dusky, glossed with purple. *Adult female:* Upperparts green, with grayish or brown on head; fine white streak back of eye; tail feathers green; wing quills grayish brown; underparts gray.

STATE RECORDS. The earliest record of the occurrence of the Broad-billed Hummingbird in New Mexico is that by Mearns, who took a specimen on August 31, 1893, in Guadalupe Canyon (Cloverdale Range, now generally known as the Peloncillo Range), in the extreme southwestern part. Regarding the Broad-billed Hummingbird, Dale A. Zimmerman states: "I found this bird common in Guadalupe Canyon this summer [1959], but found no nests. This surprised me inasmuch as we found 7 Black-chinned, plus the Violet-crowned in a half mile of the canyon. In that area were at least 3 male Broad-billed. We saw no females there but did note them elsewhere in the New Mexico portion of the canyon."

TROGONS
Family: TROGONIDAE

THE ONLY member of this family of highly colored birds that occurs in the United States is the Coppery-tailed Trogon. The short thick bill, short and rounded wings, relatively long tail, and small feet are distinguishing characters.

COPPERY-TAILED TROGON
Trogon elegans
12″ long. Color pattern of sexes similar.

The Trogons are among the most beautifully colored of the tropical and semitropical North American birds. *Adult male:* Upperparts bright bronzy green; middle feathers of the long tail green to copper bronze, broadly tipped with bluish black, outer tail feathers mostly white; primaries slate black; face and throat black; naked parts about eyes orange; chest green or bronze bordered by white crescent; rest of underparts rose red; flanks blackish with pinkish wash. *Adult female:* General color pattern similar to male, but gray replaces black and green is replaced by brown; underparts lighter.

DISTRIBUTION. The Coppery-tailed Trogon is a regular summer resident in the mountains of Southern Arizona. It is of rare occurrence in the Peloncillo and the Animas Mountains of New Mexico. A visit, in mid-June, to Cave Creek Canyon, Chiricahua Mountains, just across the state line in Arizona, should be rewarding, for here an observer is almost certain to hear the hen turkeylike call from some lofty pine, or perhaps get a glimpse of this Trogon's gorgeous plumage as it wings its deliberate way from tree to tree. The only record of the bird being taken in New Mexico is that of a female by Oliver Milton, of the Peabody Museum, New Haven, Connecticut, June 18, 1957, in Guadalupe Canyon, Peloncillo Mountains. (See Guadalupe Canyon, Bird Watching Region 1.) Mearns secured a specimen in breeding condition about five miles south of the line, probably near where the author found the birds in Devil's Canyon. Chances of seeing this visitor in New Mexico are best in years of bounteous moisture and consequent luxuriant vegetation, when streams run clear in the mountain canyons.

NESTING. The Coppery-tailed Trogon nests in hollows or Flicker excavations in cottonwood, sycamore or other large trees.

KINGFISHERS
Family: ALCEDINIDAE

THE KINGFISHER, as its name indicates, is an expert in catching small fish which it secures by plunging headlong into the water from a limb or snag above water, or even from a suspended position in mid-air. Food is swallowed whole, the indigestible parts later ejected. The head is large, legs are short and the feet small, being used only for perching or trundling back and forth in nesting burrows. The plumage is compact and oily, hence impervious to water. The Belted Kingfisher is the dominant species. Although not definitely recorded, there is little doubt that the little Green (Texas) Kingfisher occurs in the southwestern corner of the state since it is regularly found a few miles south of the International Boundary.

❰ BELTED KINGFISHER
Megaceryle alcyon

11—13½″ long. Color pattern of sexes different.

So distinctive is the Kingfisher, with its bushy crest that covers the entire head, and its large pointed beak, that its identification is simple. Its nature of staying near water, the irregular wingbeats in flight, and the raucous, rattling notes, are diagnostic. This bird is in disrepute about fish hatcheries, where young of valuable species of fish are easy prey and are taken as readily as those of the less desirable species, which it takes from streams or lakes. *Adult male:* blue gray above, underparts white, except the bluish gray breast band, or belt, which gives the bird its name. *Adult female:* Similar to male but with two belts; flanks rufous.

BELTED KINGFISHER
R. J. Sim, U.S. Fish & Wildlife Service

DISTRIBUTION. The Belted Kingfisher, although not common in the state, is widely spread during migration and may be seen sparingly throughout the summer. It occurs on practically all streams and about clear-water ponds and lakes from the lowest altitudes to more than 9,000 feet (Costilla River, Taos County). The author has recorded the bird at Carlsbad, San Simon Marshes, Gila River, and the Dry Cimarron River. It was found wintering on Alamosa Creek above Monticello, where minnows were abundant and springs and swift current of the creek prevented the water from freezing during the coldest weather.

NESTING. There seems to be no authentic record of the Kingfisher nesting in New Mexico, but no doubt it does nest, since it is present in summer along many of the mountain streams. "It occurs in summer and probably breeds in the banks of the Rio Grande, west of Santa Fe" (Jensen). *Nest:* In self-excavated tunnels in soil cutbanks, 5 to 15 feet long. *Eggs:* Usually 6 to 8; laid on bones and fish scales and other ejected food particles at end of burrow.

GREEN (TEXAS) KINGFISHER
Chloroceryle americana

8—8½″ long. Color pattern of sexes similar.

The little Green, or Texas, Kingfisher, with its exceptionally large and long bill for so small a bird, and its typical Kingfisher ways, is not apt to be confused with any other species. *Adult male:* Upperparts glossy green; white of throat extending around lower neck forming collar; breast band rufous; wings spotted with white; sides and flanks mottled with green. Bill black, 1¾ inches long. *Adult female:* Similar to male, but rufous of breast replaced with greenish.

DISTRIBUTION. While there seems to be no definite record of the little Green Kingfisher's occurrence in the state, there is little doubt that it occasionally occurs in the extreme southwestern part. It is most likely to be seen on Adobe Creek northeast of the Animas Mountains; in Guadalupe Canyon, adjacent to the Arizona line; about the San Simon Marshes, or along the Gila River. The author has observed it on Cajon Bonito Creek, Mexico, only a few miles from the New Mexico line. It has been recorded on the San Pedro River to the west, near Fairbanks, Arizona. While it is generally regarded as resident where found up to about 5,000 feet, it would probably be transient if found in the state, returning to Mexico for the winter.

WOODPECKERS
Family: *PICIDAE*

THIS GROUP is represented by a large family. The aptitude of Woodpeckers for clinging to trunks or branches of trees, in almost any position, is made possible by their short, strong legs, and feet with two toes pointing forward and one or two toes, depending on the species, pointing backward. Their stiff pointed tail feathers serve as a support when the birds are in an upright position on tree trunks. Woodpeckers have long, strong bills that enable them to chisel or drill into wood. Their long extensible tongues, barbed at the tip, are used in spearing and withdrawing larvae of insects that infest trees. Hence most of these birds nave a high economic value since the pests on which they feed are often very destructive to fruit and forest trees alike. The so-called Sapsuckers, particularly the Yellow-bellied, may at times girdle trees to obtain the sap from the cambium or sapwood. However, there is some question as to whether such girdling seriously affects trees.

Some members of this family are resident while others are migratory. Their source of food is little affected by winter storms and cold weather, and they are further favored by being able to resort to nesting holes which they may have excavated in trees or to natural cavities for security. Although they are not regarded as songsters, most of the Woodpeckers do have shrill, rattling voices, and, during the breeding season, produce a melodic substitute by beating or drumming a far-carrying tattoo on snags or hollow limbs—evidence of their presence even though the birds are not seen. Woodpeckers use no nesting material other than wood cuttings or natural decay in the nesting cavities.

YELLOW-SHAFTED FLICKER
Colaptes auratus
12½—14″ long. Color pattern of sexes similar.

The Flickers (Yellow- and Red-shafted) are among the largest of the Woodpecker family found in the state. The Yellow-shafted can be distinguished in flight from its relative, the more common Red-shafted, by the conspicuous yellow of wing lining and under-tail feathers. *Adult male:* Red patch on back of head; throat and side of head pinkish brown, with black "moustache" and black crescent on chest; upperparts, except for red crescent, brown, barred with black; underparts brownish white, washed with yellow, overlaid with black spotting. *Adult female:* Similar, but without the well-defined black "moustache."

DISTRIBUTION. This Flicker, free from hybridization, is uncommon. Fall and winter records only indicate that it does not nest within the state. It is recorded as "winter visitor, rare" at Bosque del Apache and Bitter Lake Refuges. Krehbiel states that in the Clayton area, "It occurs very rarely, one having been seen March 20, 1954 by W. W. Cook and Paul Shoeberger." On January 17, 1951, the author, by use of a flashlight, secured four Flickers that were roosting in an abandoned chickenhouse, six miles southeast of Milnesand, about twelve miles from the New Mexico–Texas line. Two of these proved to be typical Yellow-shafted, and two were Red-shafted. Of interest is the fact that these Flickers had been feeding almost entirely on hard grain, hegari in particular.

(RED-SHAFTED FLICKER
Colaptes cafer

12½—14″ long. Color pattern of sexes similar. (Pl. XVII)

The Red-shafted, the commonest Flicker in the Southwest, is the most widely distributed Woodpecker in the state. It is readily identified by its large size and, in flight, by the red of under side of wings and tail, which give the bird its common name. It has a unique way, on being disturbed, of bowing and swinging its body back and forth on some elevated perch. Were it not for the fact that Red-shafted Flickers lay large clutches of eggs in the security of self-drilled holes or natural cavities of trees, they would probably be far less common than they are since their rather large size, slow erratic flight, and nature of feeding, usually on the ground, render them easy prey for Goshawks, Cooper's Hawks, and Prairie Falcons. So intent are they in probing for ants—more than 50 percent of their diet, it is estimated, consists of ants—they may appear oblivious to possible surprise attack by their winged enemies.

Adult male: Head and body brownish; back and wings barred; a conspicuous white rump patch; red "moustache," and black chest crescent; remainder of underparts brownish spotted with black; lacks red patch on the nape, which is conspicuous on the Yellow-shafted. *Adult female:* Similar but brownish stripe in place of red moustache.

DISTRIBUTION. Red-shafted Flickers occur statewide in summer, and although there is a blanket southward movement in the fall, many of the birds winter here, particularly in the southern half. This southward drift may be influenced by the inaccessibility in winter of certain ants on which they feed. Like most Woodpeckers, the Red-shafted roosts in cavities of trees or in self-excavated holes. In the absence of trees containing such winter retreats, as on the high plains, they often resort to outbuildings, and sometimes persist in pecking their way into attics of rural homes and school buildings; thus at times making their presence objectionable.

NESTING. Red-shafted Flickers nest wherever suitable trees for nest holes are found, from the lowest elevations to near timber line; or, in the absence of trees, may utilize telegraph or power-line poles. *Nest:* In natural tree cavities, as well as in self-drilled holes, or in holes in soil banks. A nest containing six fresh eggs was found on May 22, near Cloudcroft, Sacramento Mountains, at about 8,000 feet. Nest hole was 10 feet from the ground, in an aspen tree. *Eggs:* 6 to 10; white.

(GILA WOODPECKER
Centurus uropygialis

8—9½″ long. Color pattern of sexes different.

The Gila is a relative of the Golden-fronted Woodpecker, a species found in south Texas, as far west as the Big Bend of the Rio Grande. Both have zebra-colored backs. *Adult male:* Head, neck and underparts grayish or brown, except for red crown patch and yellow lower underparts; back and rump with black-and-white mottling, forming the zebra pattern; primaries black marked with white; iris orange. *Adult female:* Crown without red; underparts paler, yellow more restricted.

DISTRIBUTION. The Gila Woodpecker seems to prefer the sycamore bottomlands of the extreme southwestern part of the state, particularly along the Gila River from the Arizona line to a point above Cliff. It may be observed some distance from the river in the timbered side canyons, and there is one record as far east as Silver City. The author has never noted it elsewhere in the state. Within its limited habitat it is resident and fairly common.

NESTING. On April 10, a pair was observed preparing a nesting hole 35 feet up in a dry sycamore snag near Red Rock. *Eggs:* 4 or 5; white.

⟨ RED-HEADED WOODPECKER

Melanerpes erythrocephalus

8½—9½″ long. Color pattern of sexes alike. (Pl. XVII)

The Red-headed Woodpecker is not common in New Mexico. Its presence is irregular and unpredictable. It seems to prefer telegraph or telephone lines from which it may repeatedly sail out or upward to pluck insects, Flycatcher-like, from the air. The head, as its name indicates, including neck, is entirely red. No other Woodpecker found in the state has a completely red head. Also distinctive is its black-and-white dress. *Adults:* Underparts, base of tail, and wing patch white; remainder of wings, back, and tail black.

DISTRIBUTION. The Red-headed Woodpecker may be seen occasionally almost anywhere in New Mexico, except in the southwest portion, but it is most common in the north central part (upper Rio Grande Valley), Pecos Valley, and along the Dry Cimarron River in the northeastern section. Since the species rarely occurs in the southern part of the state, it is quite evident that migration flight of the species runs counter to the usual north-to-

south movement of most birds. This west-east migration pattern is followed by the Eastern Kingbird, Catbird and some others, and probably is influenced by the west-east drainage of the Canadian and Dry Cimarron Rivers and their tributaries. There seem to be no old records of its occurrence in the state and some observers are of the opinion that the invasion of this Woodpecker into eastern and northeastern New Mexico was a result of the progressive advance westward along the telegraph lines paralleling the Santa Fe and Rock Island Railway lines. The fact that the birds seem to have a preference for the poles which support such lines lends credence to this opinion. The author has only three records of this bird as far south as Carlsbad.

NESTING. The Red-headed Woodpecker nests most commonly both north and south of Albuquerque, in the Rio Grande Valley, and in the Pecos Valley near Roswell. "In 1919 and 1920 a pair nested in Santa Fe" (Jensen). "June 8, 1949, one was taken near Señorita, Sandoval County" (Gabrielson). This was probably a breeding bird. "Three young on the Berrendo north of Roswell August 1950; and nest May 16, 1953 in Roswell" (Montgomery). *Nests:* In holes in telegraph poles, or in stubs or trunks of cottonwoods and other trees. *Eggs:* 4 to 7; white.

⟨ ACORN WOODPECKER

Melanerpes formicivorus

8—9″ long. Color pattern of sexes similar. (Pl. XVII)

The Acorn Woodpecker, formerly referred to as the Mearns or California, is sometimes mistaken for the Red-headed. The entire head and neck of the latter species are red, whereas only the crown of the Acorn is red. *Adult male:* Feathers around base of bill, black bordered with white; face band becoming yellowish on throat;

crown red; sides of head, upperparts and chest band, glossy greenish blue black; underparts white streaked with black. In flight, all of back and tail appear black except white patch at base of tail. *Adult female:* Like male except black band separates white of forehead from red of crown. Iris in both male and female is usually white, but may vary to yellowish. The Acorn Woodpecker is well named, since at times of oak mast it industriously stores the acorns, usually in circular holes previously prepared as storage cells, in trunks of pine trees. Sometimes the bark or wood of the large dead trees or snags has been used to such extent that the trees have a pepperbox-top appearance. A 30-foot pine snag examined in upper O-Bar-O Canyon, about 80 miles southwest of Magdalena, was peppered with literally thousands of these acorn stalls, many of which contained dried acorns, some still sound and palatable, which had been placed there probably the year before. The birds are more or less communal in conduct. Just before dark one cold December evening a number were seen to enter a hole in an oak tree. When the tree was struck with an axe, five of the birds emerged from their roosting retreat.

DISTRIBUTION. The Acorn Woodpecker is resident or semiresident throughout practically all forested mountains of the state except along the extreme northern portion. Areas where various species of oaks and pines overlap, at elevations ranging from 7,000 to 8,000 feet, are preferred habitat. In this zone type it is usually by far the most abundant Woodpecker. The author has found it especially common in the Black and San Mateo Ranges.

NESTING. The Acorn Woodpecker's nest holes—self-excavated—are usually in oaks; but sometimes in pines. Nest hole may be 8 to 25 feet or more from the ground. *Eggs:* 4 or 5; white; usually laid early June.

❨ LEWIS' WOODPECKER

Asyndesmus lewis

10½—11½″ long. Color pattern of sexes alike. (Pl. XVII)

The Lewis' is one of the most handsome and distinctive of the American Woodpeckers. It is named in honor of Meriwether Lewis, 1774-1809, leader of the Lewis and Clark Expedition, 1803-06. Members of this expedition were the first to note and describe the bird. In summer it is a bird of high pine valleys and parks. Its distinctive markings and conduct simplify identification. The Lewis' Woodpecker makes Flycatcher-like upward sallies from its high perch to catch airborne insects. *Adult male:* Entire upperparts, including crown, glossy greenish black except for gray collar; face dull crimson; chest gray, changing to soft rose on underparts. Feathers of collar and underparts are more like bristles than true feathers. *Adult female:* Chest gray usually mixed with dusky. Rose underparts are distinctive; no other Woodpecker is so marked.

DISTRIBUTION. In summer the Lewis' Woodpecker is found most commonly in the higher mountain parks and valleys of northern New Mexico, although it does occur uncommonly at this time in the Mogollon and Sacramento Mountains. Most of the birds move south in the fall in considerable numbers along the Continental Divide and westward, and in the Rio Grande Valley, but they seem to shun the Lower Pecos Valley. Some remain for the winter in the southern section. They were observed in late December in the Guadalupe Mountains west of Carlsbad. By late March they begin to return to their summer range.

NESTING. This Woodpecker usually nests high in dead pines. On June 15, 1917, the author found a nest in a yellow pine on the Apache Indian Reservation about 20 miles east of Mescalero. No nests have been recorded farther south. On the Dry Cimarron it nests high in the cottonwoods as well as in pines. Young were being fed in the nest near mouth of the Chama River, July 13. On June 6, Jensen found a nest containing 6 fresh eggs in a cottonwood north of Santa Fe. *Eggs:* 6 or 8; dull white.

❨ YELLOW-BELLIED SAPSUCKER
Sphyrapicus varius
8–8½″ long. Color pattern of sexes different. (Pl. XVII)

The Yellow-bellied, formerly known as the Red-naped Sapsucker, is one of the common Woodpeckers occurring in the state. The red forehead and red throat patch are distinguishing features. *Adult male:* Crown red; upperparts black with two white longitudinal stripes; tail black except middle feathers white with black bars; sides of head with white stripes, black band between red of throat and yellow underparts. *Adult female:* Similar to adult male, but top of head duller, sometimes wholly black; throat white, sometimes washed with red.

During fall and winter Yellow-bellied Sapsuckers descend to lower altitude, when they are seen about trunks of trees, particularly the Siberian (Chinese) elm, "drilling" for sap by girdling the trunk. However, approximately 50 percent of their food consists of insects. Thus any damage they may do to trees is largely offset by their economic value as destroyers of insects.

DISTRIBUTION. In summer these Sapsuckers are common in most of the timbered high country. In winter they are more in evidence in the lower slopes and valleys of the southern section, and even over the eastern high plains. Although there is a late fall southward drift out of the state, many remain for the winter.

NESTING. During the nesting period, the Yellow-bellied Sapsucker is largely con-

fined to the Transition and Canadian Life Zones of all the mountainous areas. However, the preferred nesting tree seems to be the aspen; thus its nesting range extends to 10,000 feet elevation or higher. A nest examined June 4, three miles west of Alto, in the White Mountains, was ten feet above ground in an aspen, and contained 4 fresh eggs. *Nest:* Usually in green aspens, ten to thirty feet above ground. *Eggs:* 4 or 5; glossy white.

❨ WILLIAMSON'S SAPSUCKER
Sphyrapicus thyroideus
9–9½″ long. Color pattern of sexes entirely different. (Pl. XVII)

Adult male: Crown, breast, throat, back and tail black. Narrow white band or crescent between crown and neck, and white line from bill to back of neck, and a conspicuous red throat stripe; outer-wing coverts white; underparts, lemon yellow; sides with black-and-white barring and dotting. *Adult female:* Zebra color, white rump and brown head, and rarely, a red median stripe on throat. The female Williamson's Sapsucker differs so radically from the male that for a time it was regarded as a different species. Henshaw discovered and corrected the error in 1873, when he saw the two supposedly different species entering the same hole to feed the young. In all other Woodpeckers the color pattern of the sexes is much alike. Robert Stockton Williamson (1824-82) was a lieutenant in charge of a party of the Pacific Railway Survey, 1856, when the Sapsucker, later named for him, was collected.

DISTRIBUTION. The Williamson's Sapsucker is confined in summer largely to cool dense forests of the Canadian and Hudsonian Zones of the northern mountains. The author has recorded it at this season, however, on the continental divide of the Black Range. While many of these Sapsuckers are known to remain in the state for the winter, they drift into west

Texas and Mexico. The Pecos Valley is off-center of the main migration route, but they occasionally occur here. One was noted in Carlsbad on April 1, 1938, during the northward movement. "In migration they occur in the Las Cruces area" (Williams).

NESTING. At nesting time the tattoo of the Williamson's Sapsucker in the heavy forests reminds one somewhat of the broken tinkling of a bell. Regarding this tattoo, Jensen states (Auk, July 23, 1923): "He strikes two blows and after a short pause, four blows." The main nesting range consists of the high, forested mountains in the northern section, although the author found a nest at 8,000 feet near the summit of the Black Range west of Hermosa, in an aspen growing among dense conifers. Wetmore recorded it as a breeder about Burford Lake, May to June, 1918. The author found it nesting rather commonly from 9,000 to 9,500 feet in the Sangre de Cristo Range southeast of Taos. "June 1922, a pair nested in a pine stump in Santa Fe Canyon [east of Santa Fe] altitude about 9,500 feet" (Jensen). This nesting record is unusual since the nesting holes are usually in green aspens. Entrances to nests are seemingly quite small for size of birds. *Eggs:* 5 or 6; white.

(HAIRY WOODPECKER
Dendrocopos villosus

8½—9½" long. Color pattern of sexes similar. (Pl. XVII)

The Hairy is a rather large black and white Woodpecker with a scarlet patch on back of head. *Adult male:* White median stripe down the back; four middle feathers of tail black, two outer pairs entirely white; wings barred with white; sides of head with black bands enclosed by two white bands; underparts white. *Adult female:* Like male but without red head patch.

The Hairy is resident where found. The species has been divided into many forms.

Although in the various parts of the state in which it occurs there is a noticeable difference in size, and also some modification in color pattern, whether these variations all merit distinction as subspecies is a matter of opinion. Birds of the northern portion of the state have been described as the "Rocky Mountain"; those of the west and south central part, the "White-fronted"; and those of the extreme southwestern corner, the "Chihuahua." Such subdivisions offer much of interest for the advanced bird student who may wish to explore the status of this species.

DISTRIBUTION. The range of the Hairy Woodpecker includes practically all forested mountains of the state with elevations from 6,000 feet (Cloverdale, Pinos Altos, Silver City) to 11,600 in the Sangre de Cristo Range. It is one of the most beneficial Woodpeckers, feeding almost wholly on destructive tree-infesting insects and larvae, with quantities of wood ants.

NESTING. Nesting time of the Hairy Woodpecker varies considerably with the great variation in altitude where it lives. Young were located in nest hole near Chloride at 6,300 feet on May 16. In the Sangre de Cristo Range, Jensen found a nest with young 30 feet up in an aspen at 11,000 feet, June 21, with 3 feet of snow at foot of tree. He states that in that area, "all nests located were in aspen trees 4 to 70 feet up." At lower altitudes, far to the south, nest holes may be in small trees in canyon beds. No matter where located, if the nest hole contains young, their noisy squeaking will identify the occupied tree. *Eggs:* 4 to 6; white.

(DOWNY WOODPECKER
Dendrocopos pubescens

6½—7" long. Color pattern of sexes similar. (Pl. XVII)

The Downy Woodpecker, referred to in some publications as the "Batchelder," is merely a small counterpart of the Hairy.

It has the scarlet patch on the head, white median stripe down the back; tail with four middle feathers black, two outer ones entirely white; wings barred; sides of head with black band enclosed by two white bands; underparts white. *Adult female:* Like male but without red head patch. It is the smallest Woodpecker occurring in New Mexico.

DISTRIBUTION. The Downy is an uncommon species in the state but it appears to be resident, ranging mainly from 6,000 to 8,000 feet elevation. Although most bird publications indicate that the bird is confined to the northern section, more recent field work reveals that it occurs sparingly throughout all of the forested mountains. Except at nesting time, it is often found in association with other small birds.

NESTING. Nests containing young were found by the author June 28 around 7,500 feet elevation in the Black Range, 30 miles southwest of Chloride. The many summer records elsewhere indicate breeding birds. *Nest:* Five to 50 feet from the ground, with small entrance—evidence that the birds excavate their own nesting cavities. *Eggs:* 5 or 6; white.

([LADDER-BACKED WOODPECKER
Dendrocopos scalaris
7½″ long. Color pattern of sexes different. (Pl. XVII)

The Ladder-backed, Texas, or Cactus, Woodpecker is a small black and white bird of arid sections of the state. The color pattern is somewhat like that of the Hairy and Downy, but with red of the male covering entire top of head. *Adult male:* Crown to nape red; remainder of upperparts bordered with alternate black and white cross-barring, giving the ladder-like effect that accounts for its name. Four middle tail feathers black, others white, barred with black; side of head with black stripe under eye extending past middle of head; underparts smoky, lightly dotted and lined with black. *Adult female:* Similar to male but head without red, top of head black.

DISTRIBUTION. The little Ladder-backed is common and for the most part resident up to about 6,300-feet elevation over the more arid parts of the state. It ranges over practically all of the southern section and occupies a finger up the Rio Grande to beyond Taos and up the Pecos Valley to Santa Rosa and along the eastern side to Tucumcari and beyond.

NESTING. Nest cavities from two to twenty feet above ground according to availability of sites in mesquite, hackberry, native chinaberry, cottonwood, oak, willow, walnut, mescal stalks, fence posts or telephone poles. *Eggs:* 4 or 5; glossy white.

([ARIZONA WOODPECKER
Dendrocopos arizonae
7–8″ long. Color pattern of sexes different. (Pl. XVII)

The accepted common name of this odd-looking Woodpecker is applicable since it barely enters New Mexico, but is common over much of southern Arizona. Its color pattern is such as to distinguish it from other species. Like other Woodpeckers, it is highly beneficial as a destroyer of insects. *Adult male:* Upperparts plain brown except red crescent at back of head; dark barring on white outer tail feathers; white band encircles dark patch on side of head; underparts white, thickly spotted with dusky. *Adult female:* Similar but without red on nape.

DISTRIBUTION. In New Mexico this Woodpecker is indigenous only to the extreme southwest corner—Peloncillo and Animas Mountains. It is resident in the oak-juniper foothills up to 7,000 feet elevation.

NESTING. On June 28, Wayne Bohl and the author observed young ready to leave the nest hole, 10 feet up in an oak, in Indian Creek Canyon, Animas Mountains, 6,500 feet elevation. *Nest:* In oak, sycamore, cottonwood or ash, unlined. *Eggs:* 4 or 5; white.

([NORTHERN THREE-TOED WOODPECKER
Picoides tridactylus

9–9½″ long. Color pattern of sexes similar. (Pl. XVII)

This handsome alpine-dwelling Woodpecker is indigenous to the higher, forested elevations of the state, but is nowhere common. The Northern Three-toed Woodpecker is unique, as the common name suggests, in that it has but three toes —two pointing forward, the other extending backward. Bill is broad and flattened at base. *Adult male:* Crown patch yellow, upperparts black except white neck band and white streak down back; back of head metallic green bordered by white; inner-wing coverts black with white blotching; outer-wing feathers black with narrow white bars; middle tail feathers black, outer ones with white margins; underparts white, sides more or less mottled black and white; white line through metallic green back of eye; white bar below eye from base of bill extending back to neck band. *Adult female:* Similar but without yellow crown; forehead and crown sometimes spotted with white.

DISTRIBUTION. The Northern Three-toed, sometimes called the Alpine Three-toed Woodpecker, is found in greatest numbers in the heavy forests of the Sangre de Cristo Range centering around the highest peaks; less numerous in San Juan, Jemez, and Zuñi, and even occurs sparingly in the highest parts of the Black and Mogollon Ranges. Noted by Bailey in the Mogollons at 10,500 feet, near top of White Water Baldy, October 23. The author observed it in Monument Pass, Black Range, 12 miles west of Chloride, at 7,800 feet, December 28.

NESTING. The Three-toed breeds wherever it is found. "In the Zuñi Mountains it was fairly common and nesting between 8,000 and 9,000 feet in June" (Goldman). "Several breeding birds were seen on top of the Chuska Mountains 8,000 to 9,000 feet, June 30 and July 2, 1918" (Wetmore). *Nest:* Two recorded by Major Charles Bendire in spruce and yellow pine, 15 and 30 feet above ground. *Eggs:* 5; white.

BECARDS
Family: *CONTINGIDAE*

ONLY one member of this family of unique birds crosses the International Boundary in the southwestern corner of the state. Representatives of this group have thick bills and large heads.

ROSE-THROATED BECARD
Platypsaris aglaiae
6–6½″ long. Color pattern of sexes similar.

Of this bird, Seymour Levy—probably more familiar with the Becard than most observers, wrote the author: "A very shy and inconspicuous bird. It resembles closely the Wood Peewee, but has a bigger head and shorter tail appearance. The male has a dark pink or rose colored throat, dark crown and dark grayish body. The female is similar but browner and with a buffy collar."

DISTRIBUTION. The assumed range of the Rose-throated Becard is the extreme southwestern corner of the state, particularly Guadalupe Canyon. The source of this canyon is in the Peloncillo Mountains from which it drains to the southwest into Mexico. While the greater portion of the canyon lies in New Mexico, it also cuts the corner of Arizona before reaching the International Boundary. The bird's occurrence even here is sporadic and unpredictable.

NESTING. The only clue to possible nesting of the Rose-throated Becard in New Mexico is that of a deserted nest found in June 1957, by Seymour Levy and his brother James, in a cottonwood tree in mid-Guadalupe Canyon, in Arizona, a few hundred yards west of the New Mexico line. Regarding the nest of the Becard, Levy states: "This species is best known for its comparatively huge and unique nest: A large pear-shaped object, about 1½ to 2 feet long and 3 feet in circumference at the widest part, hung from a sycamore or cottonwood branch 20 to 50 feet above ground."

TYRANT FLYCATCHERS
Family: *TYRANNIDAE*

ALTHOUGH the Flycatchers (so-called from their habit of catching insects on the wing) are classified as *Passeriformes*, they are normally regarded as songless perching birds. Some of them are loudly vocal, with harsh notes which they probably use as a means of self-defense. Since food is taken almost wholly in flight, their feet are used primarily for perching and are therefore small and weak. In general, bills are flat and slightly hooked at tip, and the wide gape is guarded by flaring bristles which also aid in "trapping" and holding insects. Most Flycatchers conform to a plain coloration pattern. Unlike the Nighthawks, Swallows, and Swifts, which obtain their insect food by continuous flight, Flycatchers usually select a commanding perch, where they watch and wait. When they spot their prey they dash out or upward to pluck it from space, often with a snap of bill.

Most Flycatchers are highly migratory. The larger ones are more readily identified than are the smaller, plainly colored species classified as *Empidonax*. These "Problem Flycatchers"—Traill's, Hammond's, Dusky (Wright), Gray, Western, and Buff-breasted—can best be distinguished on their nesting grounds. In migration, with young of the year, they are most confusing. Their retiring nature, monotonously plain coloring, and the character of their habitat—usually rather dense undercover—further complicate identification. Illustrations and descriptive text are helpful in learning to recognize them. *Empidonax* (Greek) signifies "Gnat King," in this case implying that the birds are of the highest order in garnering small insects from the air. Very likely these small Flycatchers are more numerous than records indicate. They are shy, particularly at nesting time, and the average observer often hesitates to attempt their identification. Much intensive field work remains to be done before the status of this group can be conclusively established.

❰ EASTERN KINGBIRD
Tyrannus tyrannus
8–9″ long. Color pattern of sexes alike.

The handsome Eastern Kingbird, or "Bee Martin," as it is sometimes called, is an uncommon summer resident in the state. It is readily distinguished from the other two more common Kingbirds—Western and Cassin's—by its dark, almost black, upperparts and by a white embroidered band on end of tail, which the bird displays by flitting about in the air with tail spread fanwise. *Adults:* Head slightly crested with central orange patch (usually concealed); wings dusky with lighter edgings; chest gray; underparts white.

DISTRIBUTION. The Eastern Kingbird follows the contradictory migratory pattern of entering and leaving the state from west to east, instead of following the normal north-south migration routes. It is listed as "transient visitor, rare" at Bosque del Apache Refuge. It occurs more commonly about Albuquerque and throughout northeastern New Mexico. The author has often observed it about Tucumcari, Logan, and northward to the Colorado line, but there seem to be few records for the southern section.

NESTING. The Eastern Kingbird nests throughout its restricted New Mexico range. On June 13, 1949, a pair with young was observed in an orchard eight miles north of Albuquerque. A pair was also noted feeding young out of nest six miles west of Folsom on August 18. Jensen reported it nesting commonly about Santa Fe in 1923 and 1926. "It was common along the Dry Cimarron River, August 29, 1913" (Kalmbach). *Nest:* Cup-shaped, made of weed stems and plant fiber, lined with soft material such as wool, cotton, or hair, usually placed on horizontal branch of tree. *Eggs:* 3 or 4; white, pink, or creamy, spotted or blotched with reddish or dark brown and lilac markings.

❰ WESTERN KINGBIRD

Tyrannus verticalis

8½—9½″ long. Color pattern of sexes alike.

This friendly Flycatcher, almost the size of a Robin, is a common summer resident about rural homes and ranches throughout the more open, arid sections of New Mexico. Kingbirds seem to prefer habitat in proximity to habitation of man, probably because the growing of trees and agricultural development have created a suitable environment for them. The Western and the Cassin's, both of which occur in the state, are rather difficult to separate by sight alone, but they are rather fearless, thus permitting careful comparison. The most reliable distinguishing feature in adults is the difference in pattern of tail feathers. The outer half of the outside tail feathers of the Western (formerly called the Arkansas) is white; that of the Cassin's, brownish. Both have the scarlet crown patch. Foreparts of the Western are light ashy gray, fading to white on chin; back grayish olive; tail black except completely white web of outside feathers; underneath canary yellow. Notes of the Western are less harsh than those of the Cassin's. Few birds are more animated on the wing, or are more vocal, although their noisy chatter can scarcely be called a song. Their acrobatic stunts in the air, flitting, diving, and chasing each other, can normally be regarded as play rather than warfare.

Robert Ridgway (1850-1929), leading American ornithologist of his time and Curator of Birds in the National Museum for more than fifty years, gives an interesting account in the *American Naturalist* (Vol. 111, No. 6, August 1869) of a Western Kingbird which became part of the company attached to the U. S. Geological Exploration of the Fortieth Parallel. Obtained from the Indians in Nevada, who had taken him from a nest with three others, all fully fledged, Skippy, as he was named, soon captivated all those about him with his ingratiating and trusting ways. Until he had learned to catch insects, he tested the grasshopper-catching skill of the personnel for, Ridgway states, he had an "almost insatiable appetite." By actual count, in one day, he consumed 120 grasshoppers, however, with their legs pulled off. Skippy spent several months with the Exploration Company, moving with it from camp to camp, even flying along on a horseback hunting trip with the eminent ornithologist. He would occasionally leave to sport with other birds of his kind, or dart out after an insect, but always returned to his seat upon the pommel of the saddle or to Ridgway's shoulder or hat.

DISTRIBUTION. Summer range of the Western Kingbird is statewide, except for the wooded mountains above about 6,000 feet elevation. Probably only the Horned Lark and the Mourning Dove are more widely seen at this season. After nesting and during late summer migration the birds may occur at higher elevations. They arrive in the southern part from late March to mid-April, depending on the nature of the season; and are out of the state by late fall.

NESTING. This Flycatcher seems to prefer large trees as nesting sites, cottonwoods being commonly selected below 6,000 feet elevation. When cottonwood trees were not as numerous in the Pecos Valley as they are today, the birds often resorted to substitutes for nesting sites, such as V's of the mile boards on telegraph poles along railway lines. *Nest:* Compactly made of weed stems, twigs, plant fiber, mixed with down, wool, or feathers; placed 10 to 40 feet from the ground in trees or other convenient places. *Eggs:* 4 or 5; creamy, spotted with dark brown.

THICK-BILLED KINGBIRD
Tyrannus crassirostris
8½—9″ long. Color pattern of sexes essentially alike.

Although somewhat precariously, the Thick-billed Kingbird was added to the list of New Mexico birds as result of observations of its occurrence in extreme southwestern New Mexico, by R. F. Johnston and J. W. Hardy, of the University of Kansas, who reported seeing one in Guadalupe Canyon on June 22, 1958. *Adults:* Head dark brown; upperparts light gray; crown patch yellow; throat white; lower underparts pale yellow.

NESTING. In regard to the Thick-billed Kingbird, Dale A. Zimmerman, Department of Biology, New Mexico Western College, Silver City, advised: "In the New Mexico portion of Guadalupe Canyon, I located two pairs of the birds, June 20, 1959. On June 20 they began building a nest about 60 feet above ground, in a sycamore tree. This pair was still present, and one bird apparently incubating on June 28. On June 28, I located the completed nest of the second pair one half mile to the northeast. This nest also was in a sycamore tree, and at least 50 feet above ground. The two birds frequently changed places on the nest, and were undoubtedly incubating. The male of the pair was collected."

Mr. Zimmerman further states: "None of the nests I have seen, including one in Arizona, of this species, have been low enough to reach. I have not seen the eggs or description of them. The nests, however, are very unlike the compact nests of other *Tyrannus* I know. They are thin and frail-looking; are constructed apparently of slender twigs and grass stems, the ends of which project outward and upward from the rims, imparting a bristly, unfinished appearance to the nests. One was thin enough to enable me to see daylight through it, even after completion, and I was on the ground 50 or 60 feet below it, using binoculars."

([CASSIN'S KINGBIRD
Tyrannus vociferans
8½—9″ long. Color pattern of sexes alike.

The Cassin's Kingbird is almost a duplicate of the Western. A fine point of distinction in the adult is the marking of tail feathers. In the Cassin's, tail is dark

TYRANT FLYCATCHERS
TOP: EASTERN KINGBIRD, WESTERN KINGBIRD, CASSIN'S KINGBIRD
BOTTOM: BLACK PHOEBE, SAY'S PHOEBE, ASH-THROATED FLYCATCHER
Orville O. Rice, N.M. Dept. of Game & Fish

brown tipped with light gray, while in the Western the outer web of outer-tail feathers is white. The neck and upperparts of the Cassin's are darker gray and the throat is distinctly white. Also, as the Latin designation *vociferans* denotes, its notes are harsher, and the Cassin's is inclined to be more tyrannical toward its potential enemies than is its more tolerant relative. When in numbers preceding nesting activities, Cassin's Kingbirds often participate in a lively blended chorus. The author recalls hearing such a choral session in Engle. The chorus began just before daybreak in a nearby cottonwood. The perfectly timed "click-click" notes would be uttered on a rising scale by one and repeated by another until apparently all were united in an enthralling blended chorus. Following an intermission of a few minutes, the theme of sequence would be repeated until the performers dispersed with the coming of day. The bird is named in honor of John Cassin (1813-69), American ornithologist, author of *Illustrations of the Birds of California, Texas, Etc.*, 1856.

DISTRIBUTION. In migration, the Cassin's Kingbird may be observed throughout the state up to 8,000 feet elevation. Its summer distribution is confined largely to wooded areas and forested zones from 6,000 to 7,500 feet, particularly the yellow pine association. Although found statewide at this season within the limits of such habitat, it is more common in the southern half. It is usually out of the state by mid-October, returning about the first of April.

NESTING. It is the author's opinion that many of the former lower altitude (below 5,000 feet) nesting records of this Kingbird were in error, the Western having been mistaken for the Cassin's. The author made such errors in some earlier observations. Considering the similarity of the two birds, it is not surprising that errors occurred in sight records. *Nests*: Well made and compact, of stems, twigs, and plant fiber, lined with cotton, wool, or other soft material; generally securely saddled on or in crotches of horizontal limbs of cottonwoods or other trees, 25 to 50 feet from the ground. *Eggs*: 4; like those of the Western Kingbird but not so heavily spotted.

SCISSOR-TAILED FLYCATCHER
Muscivora forficata
12—15″ long. Color pattern of sexes similar. (Pl. XVIII)

The Scissor-tailed Flycatcher, often called the "Texas Bird of Paradise," is one of our most beautiful and beneficial birds. It is a summer resident in eastern and southeastern New Mexico. *Adult male:* Foreparts ashy, paler on throat; crown with small scarlet patch; back suffused with pinkish or salmon; "scissor" tail, 8 to 10 inches long, deeply forked, feathers of fork white tipped with black; underwing coverts salmon; sides and flanks from pinkish salmon to blood red. *Female:* Similar, but colors less brilliant and tail shorter.

Prior to leaving for their winter home, dozens of the birds at times congregate in roosting trees in late evening and early dawn and offer a lilting chorus not unlike that of Cassin's Kingbirds. Under such roosting trees may often be found the beautiful long feathers they molt, many of which the author collected in his boyhood rambles. Few birds excel them in aerial acrobatics and aggressiveness, or are more courageous in pursuit of birds they regard as intruders. Upon the approach of a winged enemy, the watchful sentinels usually take to the air, vaulting, chattering, and screaming. Size of bird does not intimidate them. Ravens and hawks when in the vicinity of nesting grounds are immediately challenged. At such times one may perch on the back of the intruder, riding it, wasplike, with outstretched wings until it is out of the pre-empted zone, and then sail triumphantly back. "In effervescent spirit, original, fantastic, aerial evolutions, it outdoes all of its kin— this Kingbird raised to the nth degree." In anticipated pursuit of an enemy, Scissor-tails first execute upward gyrations, repeatedly opening and closing the white-bordered scissor-blades, thereby gaining the advantage and security of elevation, in pouncing down on the intruder, giving vent all the while, by wing and vocally, to their indignation. They favor living in proximity to habitation of man, where they take advantage of shade and other trees for nesting; yet they live in the open, preferably perching on telephone or other wires from which their animated conduct and beauty may best be enjoyed.

DISTRIBUTION. The sociable Scissor-tailed Flycatcher has a limited summer distribution, being confined to eastern and southeastern New Mexico. Formerly it was rather uncommon, but in recent years it has become more numerous and apparently is extending its range. It is a welcome visitor, for in beauty, economic value, and spectacular performance it occupies a place of distinction among birds and a warm place in the affections of people wherever it dwells. The growing of more trees where formerly there were few, along with the development of land, has been a factor in its wider distribution and increasing numbers. At present it is most common in the Pecos Valley north to Artesia and over the Staked Plains north to Portales, and west to Hope, where a pair was noted (two miles west) on May 14, 1955. "A few of these birds wander in here [Clayton] briefly in the spring. Likewise I have one fall record, namely September 19, 1945" (Krehbiel). "They are here in nesting season, especially south and east of Roswell" (Montgomery). Normally they begin to arrive at Carlsbad about April 15, and remain until late fall. On October 8, 1954, 25 were noted on telephone and fence wires three miles northwest of Carlsbad. On October 14, two were observed, and one or more have been noted as late as early November.

NESTING. For nesting, the Scissor-tailed Flycatcher prefers trees with rather scant foliage, such as black locust and mesquite, but also utilizes Siberian (Chinese) elm and cottonwoods. Nest: Usually five to 20 feet above ground; compactly made of plant stems and rootlets, well lined with plant fibers, and the ever-present Indian tobacco, or "goosewax" as it is often called. This soft, cotton-like fiber seems invariably to be used as nest lining, as is a piece of discarded snakeskin in the nest of the Ash-throated Flycatcher. Where wool is available it also is commonly used for lining. Eggs: 4 or 5; white or creamy white, heavily blotched with reddish or dark brown and lilac spots.

(GREAT CRESTED FLYCATCHER

Myiarchus crinitus

8—9" long. Color pattern of sexes alike.

The only account of the occurrence and nest of this large eastern Flycatcher in the state is that by Krehbiel, of Clayton, who is positive that the Great Crested Flycatchers have been present at Clayton during several seasons. Clayton is considerably west of the regular breeding range of the species, but far too distant from the summer range of the Mexican form to be mistaken for that bird. Furthermore, Krehbiel and his bird-observing teammate, W. W. Cook, have noted the Ash-throated, indicating that they clearly distinguish one from the other. In describing this Flycatcher (manuscript) Krehbiel states: "Most ornithologists confine the breeding range of the Northern Crested Flycatcher to eastern United States and as far west as central Kansas, eastern Texas and eastern South Dakota. However, I observed specimens of this bird in Clayton, New Mexico, the summers of 1945, '47, '48 and '49. These records range from as early as April 24th and May 12th until as late as September 11th and 16th, with other records scattered throughout each summer month. On July 22, 1948 an immature pair was seen here." Krehbiel continues: "The birds are readily distinguished from our common Western or Arkansas Kingbird. They are appreciably larger than the Kingbird, slightly crested, have a rather yellow color on the breast and the tail is a reddish or cinnamon brown, not black and without white edging. The tail is the distinguishing feature. When it is fanned out, flooded with sunlight as the bird sways on a tiny poplar limb the reddish brown presents a truly handsome picture. The scolding of this species of Flycatcher reminds me somewhat of that of a Jay."

A similar unusual case is that of the Common Grackle, whose breeding range is far to the east and north, yet the author found a nesting colony on the Cimarron River north of Clayton less than a mile from the Oklahoma line.

NESTING. In hollows of trees, but also now in bird houses. *Nest:* Lined with fur or hair and plant stems and, like the Ash-throated, almost always contains pieces of shed snakeskin. *Eggs:* 4 to 8; creamy buff, highly colored with blotches and lines of brown and purple.

([WIED'S CRESTED FLYCATCHER
Myiarchus tyrannulus
9¼—10″ long. Color pattern of sexes alike.

The Wied's Crested Flycatcher, formerly referred to as the Arizona Crested, is larger than the Great Crested Flycatch-

er of Sonora and other parts of Mexico. *Adults:* Upperparts uniformly grayish olive, brownish head, upper-tail coverts and wings brownish, throat and breast ashy gray; underparts pale yellow. The slender bill is almost an inch in length.

DISTRIBUTION. The seasonal (summer) range of the Wied's Flycatcher is confined to extreme southwestern New Mexico, from the lower Gila Valley to the Mexican boundary. The birds seem to occur most commonly in Guadalupe Canyon and about its tributaries adjacent to the Arizona line. The first record for the state seems to be that of Frank Stephens, who collected one June 12, 1876, on the Gila River, about 40 miles from the Arizona line. More recently the birds have been observed in Guadalupe Canyon.

NESTING. On September 7, 1959, Dale A. Zimmerman, of Silver City, advised: "Observed a pair of Wied's Crested Flycatchers feeding young in a nest in Guadalupe Canyon, New Mexico, about 1½ miles from the Arizona line, July 4, 5, and 6." *Nest:* Like others of this group of Flycatchers, the Wied's Crested nests in cavities or hollows of trees. In Arizona, its preferred nesting place is in Flicker excavations in giant cactus.

([ASH-THROATED FLYCATCHER
Myiarchus cinerascens
8—8½″ long. Color pattern of sexes alike.

In some localities the Ash-throated may be confused with other Flycatchers by the inexperienced observer. It is smaller and more streamlined than the Kingbirds, and has two white wing bars, white throat, yellowish underparts, and rufous tail. The Kingbirds have dark tails. Head of the Ash-throated is slightly crested and gape bristles or "whiskers" are strongly developed. *Adults:* Upperparts grayish brown, darker on head; tail with middle feathers dusky brown, the others cinnamon rufous on inner webs; throat and chest pale ashy; lower underparts pale sulphur yellow. The other Flycatcher with which it might be confused is the smaller, more slender Olivaceous, extremely rare, occurring only in the southwest corner of the state.

DISTRIBUTION. The Ash-throated is a common summer resident throughout the state, except along the east side where it is less numerous. It ranges up to 7,500 feet in the more mountainous sections, but shuns the denser forests. Ash-throated Flycatchers usually enter the state by April 1, and almost all are gone by September 1. They are rather silent birds in contrast to most of the larger Flycatchers.

NESTING. The Ash-throated Flycatcher nests throughout its summer range, from as low as 3,100 feet (Carlsbad) to 7,500 feet at Glorieta, and at about the same elevation near Grants. *Nest:* In Woodpecker holes, cavities in trees, or ends of exposed pipes, or in nesting boxes; rather compact, with mat of hair, weed stems, and almost always a piece of snakeskin. *Eggs:* 4 to 6; light cream or pinkish buff with streaks and scrolling of purple and sometimes with irregular spots.

(OLIVACEOUS FLYCATCHER
Myiarchus tuberculifer
7¼″ long. Color pattern of sexes alike.

This Flycatcher resembles the Ash-throated, but is smaller and decidedly more streamlined. *Adults:* Head and back grayish olive; throat and breast ash gray, in sharp contrast to the yellow of rest of underparts.

DISTRIBUTION. There are but few records of this Flycatcher for the state. While he was on the United States–Mexico Boundary Survey, two were taken by Mearns in the San Luis Mountains on the New Mexico side. The author found it just south of the International Boundary,

in Devil's Canyon. It was noted also in Cajon Bonito near the same place. No doubt the species occurs in the Animas and Peloncillo Mountains but there have been few observers to record it.

NESTING. The bird's habits, including nesting, are recorded as similar to those of the Ash-throated Flycatcher. Its eggs are somewhat smaller than those of the Ash-throated. Regarding the breeding of the Olivaceous Flycatcher, Dale A. Zimmerman advises: "Several pairs in June and July [1959], young just out of nest caught by hand July 5, and seen again, being fed by parents, the next day. These birds were two miles from the Arizona line, and the young could not fly more than a few feet."

(EASTERN PHOEBE
Sayornis phoebe
6½–7″ long. Color pattern of sexes alike.

The Eastern Phoebe, a rare visitor to the state, is a little smaller than the Say's Phoebe and slightly larger than the Wood Pewee, which it resembles. *Adults:* Upperparts grayish olive; crown blackish; outer web of tail feathers whitish; underparts washed with yellowish; sides of breast grayish; throat white.

DISTRIBUTION. Fleetwood recorded the Eastern Phoebe at Socorro in December 1953. Listed as "transient visitor, occasional" at Bosque del Apache Refuge. Krehbiel lists it as "occasional" about Clayton. Richard F. Johnston collected a female at his home in Las Cruces, November 28, 1956. Fleetwood reported two, October 15, 1956, at Elephant Butte Dam.

NESTING. Nesting Phoebes were recorded by Bailey in the Santa Rosa area May 29 to June 2, 1903. Several nests were located, although this seems to have been the only place where the birds have been found breeding. *Nest:* Under bridges or culverts, about residences or outbuildings, in caves or beneath rock ledges; made of grass, feathers and mud. *Eggs:* usually 5, pure white.

(BLACK PHOEBE
Sayornis nigricans

6½–7″ long. Color pattern of sexes alike.

The Black Phoebe lives about water, preferably near falls and rock ledges, intakes to canals, and other irrigation installations. It is black, except for pure white posterior underparts; the blackness distinguishes it from all other Flycatchers. This color pattern and the fact that it is almost always found in plain view, near or over water, facilitate identification. It sits restlessly on some convenient twig or stone, all the while flitting its tail, and then takes wing to pluck an airborne insect, returning to the same or another perch, to repeat the performance. It usually makes its presence known by its liquid chipping note.

DISTRIBUTION. The range of the Black Phoebe is confined largely to watercourses and irrigation projects in the southern half of the state. It is rather common along all main watercourses of the Black and Mogollon Ranges; the upper San Francisco River to Reserve; Gila River to Beaverhead; and along the upper Mimbres River. In the Rio Grande Valley, Black Phoebes regularly range to Socorro and Albuquerque. There is one record as far north as Alcalde by Leslie Hawkins. In the Pecos Valley it occurs as far north as Roswell. While most are out of the state before cold weather, some remain throughout the winter, about springs or waterfalls, protective caves or ledges. In recent years, flume outlets from reservoirs or other irrigation structures also provide winter shelter.

NESTING. Nests are placed in protected locations, as in pockets under ledges, entrances to caves, or under bridges. *Nest:* Made of weed stems, grass, or hair, with bits of mud as binding material; lined with rootlets, hair, or plant fiber. *Eggs:* 4 to 6; white, sometimes dotted with reddish brown around larger end.

(SAY'S PHOEBE
Sayornis saya

7–8″ long. Color pattern of sexes alike.

The Say's Phoebe is one of the common summer-dwelling birds of New Mexico. Like the Barn Swallow, it prefers living in proximity to habitation of man, taking advantage of the safety of residences or other buildings for nesting and roosting. It is slightly smaller than the Kingbird, more slender, and has rusty rather than yellow underparts. *Adults:* Upperparts plain brownish gray; crown and hind neck darker; tail brownish black, outside feathers edged with whitish; throat, chest and sides of breast rusty or buffy brownish gray; rest of underparts cinnamon buff.

It lives near the ground, usually perching on fence wires or low bushes. In flight it has a hesitant, uneven wingbeat, and is usually seen solitary. It is named in honor of Thomas Say, 1787-1834, ornithologist, member of Long's Expedition to the Rocky Mountains, 1819-20.

DISTRIBUTION. The Say's Phoebe, like the Western Kingbird, inhabits the entire state up to about 6,000 feet, and like that bird, shuns heavily forested areas, preferring more arid, open terrain. It is largely migratory. Most of the birds leave the state at approach of cold weather; some, however, remain throughout the winter in the southern section, utilizing outbuildings, caves, canal flumes or other protected places for shelter during storms. Migrants begin to arrive from the south the latter part of March and progressively move northward.

NESTING. A favorite nesting site of the Say's Phoebe is about porches of either occupied or vacant dwellings, wherever a plate, shelf, or other projection is available. It prefers exposed rather than the concealed locations selected by the Ash-throated Flycatcher. It also commonly places nests on ledges under overhanging cliffs, beneath bridges, in entrances to caves and mining shafts, or on offsets in abandoned open wells. Often the same nests are used in bringing off two, sometimes three, broods in a season. Like other Flycatchers, the Say's Phoebe feeds on insects and is wholly beneficial. Its acceptance of diversified habitat and nesting places gives it advantages over most other birds. *Nest:* Made of weed stems, dry grasses, plant fiber, and hair; lined with hair, wool, cotton, or other soft materials. *Eggs:* 4 or 5; usually white, but sometimes with a few reddish spots around the larger end.

([TRAILL'S FLYCATCHER
Empidonax traillii

5½—6″ long. Color pattern of sexes alike.

Adults: Whitish eye ring and two whitish to brownish wing bars; crown brownish; lores yellowish; upperparts and tail dark brown; underparts creamy white, shaded with gray on breast; wide bill brownish. It is named for Thomas Stewart Traill, 1789-1862, Scottish professor and editor of the 8th Edition of the Encyclopedia Brittanica, who befriended Audubon on his visit to Liverpool, where Traill was head of the Royal Institution.

DISTRIBUTION. Bailey noted the Traill's Flycatcher at Santa Rosa on May 26. It was noted at Fort Bayard July 27, and Hachita July 30. Goldman recorded it in the Magdalena Mountains, at 6,500 feet, on August 30, indicating a preference for the intermediate rather than the high ele-vations—a clue in identification at nesting time. It arrives in the southern part of the state in early May. The summer distribution and therefore breeding range of the little Traill's Flycatcher seems to be confined largely to the southern half of the state, for the most part below 7,000 feet elevation.

NESTING. "Seen from May to September. Nest, June 5, 1946, 3 eggs, above El Paso; on July 4, one near Anthony, with one Flycatcher and one Cowbird egg. Nests 6 to 10 feet above ground, pendent, or nearly so, in salt cedars, tornillos [*Prosopis odorata*] or vines" (Lena McBee). *Nest:* In bushes, vines, or low trees, usually near water; made of dry grass, shreds of bark, lined with grass tips, down and hair. *Eggs:* 2 to 4; white or pinkish buff, with blotches of brown on larger end.

HAMMOND'S FLYCATCHER
Empidonax hammondii

5—5½″ long. Color pattern of sexes alike.

It is generally conceded that very few bird students, regardless of their familiarity with the Empidonax, or problem group of Flycatchers, can distinguish between the Hammond's and the Dusky (Wright) by sight alone. According to Chapman, "The bill of the Hammond is the smallest of the Empidonaces, a rather fine point of distinction, and one that offers little consolation to the puzzled observer." *Adults:* Lower mandible brown; throat and breast gray; breast and lower underparts slightly washed with sulphur; above grayish with a slight olive tint.

DISTRIBUTION. Hammond's Flycatcher seems to be uncommon, but widely spread during summer and fall; but there is little data on spring migration. One was taken by Mearns, May 4, 1892, on the International Boundary "100 miles west of the Rio Grande." Recorded "August 25, 1906 in Santa Clara Canyon [Jemez Mountains]" (Bailey). "A specimen taken September 27, 1908, at Redrock" (Goldman).

NESTING. There seem to be no authentic accounts of its breeding in the state, but there is little doubt that it does, since it has been recorded at breeding time. *Nest:* In willows, cottonwoods or other trees, near or high above ground; made of plant stems and bark. *Eggs:* 3 or 4; creamy white.

(DUSKY (WRIGHT) FLYCATCHER

Empidonax oberholseri

5½—6″ long. Color pattern of sexes alike.

The Dusky and the Hammond's Flycatchers are generally regarded as separate species, but so alike are they as to be indistinguishable to the average bird observer. The two seem to constitute the most perplexing of this very confusing group. The main distinction is in the smaller size of bill in the Hammond's. *Adults:* Upperparts, grayish; wing bars whitish; web of outer tail feathers white; underparts, whitish without the "slight" washing of sulphur attributed to the Hammond.

DISTRIBUTION. The Dusky reaches the southwestern part of the state in early April, but its summer distribution seems to be confined almost wholly to the higher northern mountainous section, from 7,000 to 8,000 feet. It was recorded at Fort Wingate, and the author and Jensen found it to be rather common in the mountains near Santa Fe.

NESTING. A favorite nesting place is in sage bushes. A nest in such a location, containing young, was found by Bailey near Taos at 7,400 feet, on July 18. *Nest:* Usually near the ground; made of plant stems fastened to branches, lined with feathers, hair, or moss. *Eggs:* 3 to 5; dull white, unspotted.

GRAY FLYCATCHER

Empidonax wrightii

6″ long. Color pattern of sexes alike.

The Gray is a close relative of the Dusky Flycatcher. It seems to prefer a semidesert habitat—with sage or other low-growing shrubs—where other similar species are not likely to occur at nesting time. It has a longer wing and shorter tail, and longer and narrower bill than the Dusky. *Adults:* Upperparts grayish with brown tinge; underparts grayish white, with little or no yellow. The Gray Flycatcher apparently spends most of its time on or in low bushes, and when disturbed it disappears near the ground, making careful observation difficult.

DISTRIBUTION. Formerly the Gray Flycatcher was presumed to be confined, in summer, to southwestern New Mexico. More recent observations indicate it may occur statewide. Mearns collected it on the International Boundary, west of El Paso, Texas, May 5, 1892. "One was taken near San Antonio, April 12, 1942" (Monson).

NESTING. Although there seem to be no records of this Flycatcher nesting in the state, there is prospect that it may be found as a breeder. *Nest:* Made of bark, placed in bushes or in small trees, near or considerably above ground. *Eggs:* 4; creamy buff, unspotted.

(WESTERN FLYCATCHER

Empidonax difficilis

5½—6″ long. Color pattern of sexes alike.

The Western Flycatcher is a widely distributed summer resident in the state. Its preferred range consists of the cool, heavily forested areas of the higher inaccessible mountains. Its delightful high-pitched "sweetie-sweetie" is heard more often than the singer is seen. *Adults:* Key distinguishing marks—upperparts brownish or grayish olive; eye ring white; tail grayish brown with lighter edgings, wings dusky with two or three buffy bars; chest and sides pale buffy olive, rest of underparts pale yellow.

DISTRIBUTION. In migration this Flycatcher may be observed in the lower areas or foothills, but during midsummer it should be looked for in the higher forested areas, from 7,000 to 11,500 feet. It is seemingly most common in the Black, Mogollon, and Sangre de Cristo Ranges. The birds are usually out of the state by late September, back about mid-May.

NESTING. On June 20, 1927, Jensen and the author found two nests each containing four fresh eggs, in Santa Fe Canyon, seven miles east of Santa Fe, at 8,000 feet. *Nest:* Usually in stump or upturned roots, under banks or rock ledges; made of plant stems and fibers, inner bark, rootlets, and moss; lined with feathers. *Eggs:* 3 to 5; white, blotched and spotted with brown and buffy pink.

ℂ BUFF-BREASTED FLYCATCHER
Empidonax fulvifrons
5" long. Color pattern of sexes alike.

This is one of the smallest of the Flycatchers. The conspicuous buff breast, white eye ring, and white wing bars readily distinguish the Buff-breasted from its relatives of the Empidonax group. *Adults:* Upperparts grayish brown; throat, breast and sides buffy.

DISTRIBUTION. This little Flycatcher is uncommon and has a very restricted summer range in the state. The author's observations of the Buff-breasted have been confined to the canyons and foothills adjacent to the Mogollon Mountains and the west slope of the Black Range, at 6,000 to 7,000 feet. However, it has been recorded as far north as Ramah.

NESTING. A pair observed in May, in Apache Canyon near Aragon, were definitely breeding birds. A pair were found feeding young near Ramah on July 24. Since it nests commonly in southern Arizona it will no doubt be found breeding in extreme southwestern New Mexico where the summer bird life is yet to be fully explored. *Nest:* On the order of the Blue-gray Gnatcatcher nest; small, deep and compact, usually well above ground; made of dried grasses, vegetable fiber and spider web binding. *Eggs:* 3 or 4; pale buff or dull whitish.

COUES' FLYCATCHER
Contopus pertinax
7½–8" long. Color pattern of sexes alike. (Pl. I)

This medium-sized Flycatcher is a rather rare species in the state. In size and plumage the Coues' resembles the Olive-sided, but may be distinguished by its uniformly dark chest, lacking the white stripe up middle of breast which the Olive-sided has. It has a slight crest. It is named in honor of Doctor Elliott Coues, 1842-99; one of America's most able and prolific writers among early-day ornithologists. *Adults:* Upperparts gray; crown darker; chest lighter gray; underparts whitish or pale buffy yellowish; bill black above, yellow below.

DISTRIBUTION. According to the few authentic records, the summer range of this bird seems to be restricted to southwestern New Mexico, north to the Zuñi Mountains. The Olive-sided is confined in summer almost if not entirely to the mountains in the northern part.

NESTING. There seem to be no authentic nesting records for the state. *Nest:* Well formed and compact, deeply cupped; made of grasses and leaves covered with fragments of moss, lichens, and cobweb. *Eggs:* 3; creamy white, spotted with reddish brown.

❬ WESTERN WOOD PEWEE
Contopus sordidulus

6—6½″ long. Color pattern of sexes alike.

The Western Wood Pewee is one of the commonest of the smaller Flycatchers, found at lower and intermediate elevations in the state. *Adults:* Upperparts dark grayish; tail grayish brown with lighter edges; wings dusky with two light bands; without white eye rings; throat and underparts whitish. An active, restless bird, it is usually seen in the open atop some shrub or tree, from which it dashes out or upward to pluck a flying insect, returning to the same or another commanding perch.

DISTRIBUTION. Settlement of valley lands, with building of irrigation systems and growing of trees, has favored this widely spread Flycatcher. Summer range extends from the lower altitudes, but the bird is met with more commonly in the Upper Sonoran and Transition Zones. "It occurs up to 8,000 feet in the Santa Fe area" (Jensen), and "Zuñi Mountains" (Goldman). The author's records include Mt. Taylor (near Grants), 8,000 feet; Chloride, and Albuquerque, and it was common in southern Hidalgo County, May 18, 1955, around 6,000 feet.

NESTING. Like its eastern relative, the Western Wood Pewee nests late in New Mexico, usually from June 1 to 15. Nesting range includes practically all of the state below 8,000 feet elevation. It nests commonly about Chloride, 6,000 to 6,500 feet, fresh eggs being found June 2 and 13. Adults were feeding young, July 4, on Mt. Taylor, and on August 4 at Winston (Fairview). *Nest:* Usually 6 to 20 feet from ground, either saddled on limbs or in their forks; compactly made of dead grass, plant fiber, inner bark and often wool, sometimes covered with spider web. *Eggs:* Usually 3; white, irregularly wreathed around larger end with black and specks of brown and purple.

❬ OLIVE-SIDED FLYCATCHER
Nuttallornis borealis

7½—8″ long. Color pattern of sexes alike.

The Olive-sided is one of the most tyrannical of the tyrant Flycatchers, particularly on the breeding range. Its harsh, far-carrying notes, heard from the top of some lofty fir or spruce at nesting time, are definite clues to identification. One observer wanted to know what bird said: "What-you-doing-there"—and truly the notes could be so interpreted. It also makes a loud whistling sound as if to warn would-be enemies that a sentinel is on guard, and few other birds are more alert or more successful in protecting their preempted nesting areas. Judging by the conduct of the Olive-sided, the Steller's Jay appears to be at least a potential enemy. A pair of the Flycatchers will viciously attack the Jay, dashing down and striking at it with such speed and snapping of bills that the Jay instantly seeks the heaviest cover and at first opportunity leaves the vociferous warriors in complete command. The Olive-sided's distinctive notes and nature of living about the tallest treetops of high country, as well as its rather large size and the white patches on flank are distinguishing features. *Adults:* Upperparts dark olive gray, darker on crown; wings and tail blackish; throat white; chest darker with white stripe down center; posterior underparts lighter with yellow tinge. When the Olive-sided Flycatcher is perching, a cottony white patch is visible behind the wing.

DISTRIBUTION. In migration Olive-sided Flycatchers, because of their silence at that time and quick passage over lower country, are rarely seen. After they reach the high country in late spring, their loud, raucous notes and tyrannical conduct soon proclaim their presence. The author has found them established in summer only, in the higher, forested mountains, usually in fir or spruce. Thus at this season they are confined largely to the Sangre de Cristo Range. They are usually out of the state by early September, returning about mid-April.

NESTING. Since the Olive-sided Flycatcher occupies high, inaccessible country and chooses the tallest trees for its abode, its nests are difficult to find or to reach when located. However, the many summer records and observations of pairs defending pre-empted places are sufficient proof of their nesting. Vernon Bailey recorded the bird from July 15 to 25 at 7,500 feet altitude near Cowles, to 11,000 feet around Pecos Baldy. The author observed the birds caring for young at head of Pot Creek southeast of Taos (about 11,000 feet) in late July. Nest: 30 to 60 feet from the ground in coniferous trees; shallow, made of twigs, rootlets, bark ravelings and, sometimes, moss. Eggs: 3 (as is true of almost all Flycatchers); beautifully marked, creamy or pinkish, wreathed around larger end with reddish brown and lilac.

❮ VERMILION FLYCATCHER
Pyrocephalus rubinus
5½–6½″ long. Color pattern of sexes different. (Pl. XIX)

Few birds are more highly colored than the male Vermilion Flycatcher or display their charms to better advantage on their breeding grounds. So distinctive is this Flycatcher in his bright red and grayish brown vestments that he is not likely to be confused with any other bird that occurs in his summer range. Inconspicuous only by comparison is his somber mate, which has only a dash of red on underparts. *Adult male:* Head adorned with full vermilion crest; upperparts and stripes on side of head grayish brown; underparts bright red. When the male is seen sitting on some low perch, ready to sally forth for insects, or apparently falling to pieces in mid-air in his nuptial display, his more

modestly garbed mate is usually not far away. His chosen place of action is usually an opening among mesquite, oak, cottonwood, or similar types of trees without dense foliage, where there are convenient perches from which he can flit out and upward to display his plumage to best advantage. *Adult female:* Slightly crested, head and upperparts grayish brown; underparts white; breast and sides streaked with brown; lower underparts tinged with yellow, salmon, or red.

DISTRIBUTION. The summer range of the Vermilion Flycatcher is confined largely to the southern section of the state, from the Arizona line to the Pecos Valley. The bird makes its appearance in the Gila and Rio Grande Valleys in late March. It is common in the Gila Valley as far up as Cliff, and occurs as far north as Reserve and Beaverhead. In the Rio Grande Valley it ranges north to the vicinity of Socorro. In the Pecos Valley it occurs sparingly to Roswell, and there are two records even farther north. "On March 26, 1956, Elmo Traylor and I saw a Vermilion Flycatcher at Clayton Lake, a few miles north of Clayton" (Krehbiel). On June 2 and 5, David M. Niles observed a male of the Vermilion Flycatcher at Conchas Lake.

NESTING. The Vermilion Flycatcher usually nests in May. A nest containing three fresh eggs was found by the author, May 4, on the Gila River, near Cliff. "It nested at Bosque del Apache Refuge in 1954" (Fleetwood). Montgomery reported "adults feeding young out of nest, on the Hondo River, 18 miles west of Roswell, July 10, 1957." Nest: Shallow and compact; usually in cottonwood, willow or mesquite; placed in fork of limbs or saddled on horizontal branches, 6 to 20 feet above ground. Made of twigs, plant fibers and down, lined with feathers, hair, and wool when available. Eggs: 2 or 3; cream or buff, heavily marked about larger end with blotches of brown and purple.

188

LARKS
Family: ALAUDIDAE

THE HORNED LARK is the only American representative of this large family of Larks of Europe and Old World countries. It is a small, Sparrow-like ground dweller, and is not related to our common Meadowlark. Its plain-colored plumage blends with the surface of the open land where it dwells. The American Horned Lark runs about on the ground with jerky movements, perching only occasionally on bush, post, or fence wire. Few other birds are so intimately attached to open, short grass terrain. Although the American Horned Lark has been divided into many subspecies, so far as a single state and the average observer are concerned, these are scarcely separable by sight alone.

(HORNED LARK
Eremophila alpestris

7—8″ long. Color pattern of sexes similar. (Pl. I)

The typical Horned Lark, Desert Horned Lark, or Skylark, as the bird is variously listed, is statewide in distribution and is among the most abundant year-round birds in the state; no other occupies such extremes in elevation. The pointed tuft of feathers, or "horns" on each side of head, which has given the bird its common name, is most prominent at nesting time. Except about the head, the plumage pattern varies little with the seasons. Male, in breeding plumage: Front of crown with "horns," cheek stripe and breast shield black; forehead and stripe over eye usually yellow, sometimes white; back of head, neck, and upper-tail coverts pinkish cinnamon; back, wings, and middle tail feathers dark brown edged with

buffy; throat yellowish white; rest of underparts white. Winter plumage: Similar, but black areas and "horns" less prominent. Female, in breeding plumage: Similar to male but head brownish and buffy instead of black. Winter plumage: Similar.

It is surprising and regrettable that so fine a songster as this common resident species, and one so wholly beneficial, should be unfamiliar to many bird lovers. Although not as spectacular as the Roadrunner, this fine little Lark might very appropriately have been designated the State Bird. No other bird remains as steadfast on short grass, arid and desert plains, mesas and valleys, through drought, heat, cold, rain, or shine. How it finds sufficient food to survive under the many adverse conditions which prevail in its typical habitat is a mystery.

On December 19 and 20, 1918, while conducting field work from one of the Diamond A Ranch substations, a few miles north of Engle, the author observed these Larks under stress of most severe winter conditions. After snow had covered the ground to a depth of several inches, during the worst blizzard in many years, the Horned Larks gathered about the ranch in great numbers. So hard-pressed for food were they that they collected in the corrals, under sheds, even entering the residence when they found an open door. At such times, they must subsist primarily on seeds of weeds and grasses which stand above snow.

DISTRIBUTION. The common Desert Horned Lark is resident or semi-resident throughout the state. Apparently there is no well defined seasonal migration although there is some local movement or adjustment of distribution in the fall, particularly when great numbers flock together. If some migrate and leave the state for the winter, it is quite evident that others move in from the north to fill the vacated habitat. Horned Larks avoid rank vegetation, preferring to cling to short grass, open terrain. They are common over the eastern buffalo-grass plains and on Jornada del Muerto, from near Las Cruces to east of Socorro, and on the Deming Plain. They are in greatest abundance in the upper Animas Valley or Basin, south of Animas to the International Boundary, around 6,000 feet elevation.

SUBSPECIES. There is convincing evidence that one form of the Horned Lark in the state merits subspecies status, for there obviously is an Alpine form which is much lighter in color than the typical desert bird. The pale form occupies the bleak ridges and slopes above timber line of the Sangre de Cristo Range. On July 3 and 4, 1955, Wayne Bohl and the author observed Horned Larks on the barren ridges and slopes of Wheeler Peak and Gold Hill, from the 11,000-foot level upward. Breeding birds were noted near the summit of Wheeler Peak (13,160 feet). At the time there was still considerable snow in drifts and banks, and the birds had conspicuously lighter plumage than those of lower sections of the state. Most of these birds probably move down onto the lower, yet high, mesas and valleys for the severe part of the winter, but some may remain in the Arctic Life Zone, where the prevailing strong winds sweep snow from the surface, or where seeded weeds and grasses stand above the snow, providing food.

NESTING. It is before and during the nesting season that the Horned Lark approaches perfection in plumage, aerial conduct, and song. As a prelude to the aerial melody, the male may sit on a stone, grass hummock, or fence post, to twitter or warble. But when overjoyed, he spirals upward, often to a height barely visible to the unaided eye, to flit and float while delivering his soft, flowing song that proclaims his presence somewhere in the infinite blue. It is then that the designation "Skylark" becomes wholly fitting. Jensen has recorded nests with fresh eggs from April 20 to May 13, and on June 4, on the mesas about Santa Fe. In the southern section, nesting begins in late March. Later nesting records no doubt represent second clutches. Bailey reported young at 12,000 feet, on Pecos Baldy, on August 20. *Nest:* A cup scratched in the soil, usually beside or under tufts of grass in order to provide protection from enemies and from prevailing winds; compactly lined with grass. *Eggs:* Usually 3, occasionally 4; varied color shades but most often gray with greenish tinge, profusely sprinkled and spotted with shades of light brown.

SWALLOWS
TOP: PURPLE MARTINS, PAIR. MIDDLE: BARN SWALLOW, TREE SWALLOW, BANK SWALLOW
BOTTOM: VIOLET-GREEN SWALLOW, CLIFF SWALLOW
Orville O. Rice, N.M. Dept. of Game & Fish

SWALLOWS

Family: HIRUNDINIDAE

SWALLOWS have long, pointed wings which permit easy sustained flight, and they spend most of the daylight gracefully cruising the air, low and high, in pursuit of winged insects. Their bills are short and mouths widely cleft, facilitating the taking of insects on the wing. Their legs are short, and feet small, unsuited for ground movement. Tails are more or less forked. Most members of this family seem to prefer telephone and power line wires for resting and preening their plumage. The Barn Swallow is the most familiar of the group because of its preference for living in proximity to the habitation of man.

(VIOLET-GREEN SWALLOW

Tachycineta thalassina

4½–5″ long. Color pattern of sexes similar.

The Violet-green is the most highly colored of the several Swallows found in New Mexico. When feeding, it resembles a bat as it darts about over a restricted area. *Adult male:* Crown and back of neck bronzy green to purplish bronze, nape often with narrow purplish collar; back and point of wings bronzy green tinged with purple; tail and wings black glossed with blue; underparts pure white. *Adult female:* Color much duller; crown and back of neck vary from brownish to greenish or purplish bronze.

DISTRIBUTION. The Violet-green Swallow is found in summer in all of the high forested mountains of the state, from about 7,000 feet in the Sacramento and Mogollon Mountains and the Black Range to more than 11,000 feet in the Sangre de Cristos. While not abundant, it is most apt to be found in the yellow pine zone. It usually arrives in the southern mountains around April 1 and most of

the birds are out of the state by the middle of September.

NESTING. Nesting usually begins in early June. On June 12, a nest containing four fresh eggs was located at 7,000 feet in the San Mateo Mountains, 30 miles northeast of Chloride; and a pair was noted feeding young July 3, above Twining, northwest of Wheeler Peak, at about 11,300 feet. On June 6, several pairs of the Swallows were entering nesting crevices in a rock cliff above water at the junction of Haut Creek and the East Fork of the Gila River, 20 miles west of Chloride. *Nest:* Usually in Woodpecker holes, often in dead yellow pines or in natural tree cavities, or crevices in rock ledges; lined with grass and feathers. *Eggs:* 4 or 5; white.

(TREE SWALLOW

Iridoprocne bicolor

5–6″ long. Color pattern of sexes similar.

Tree Swallows are readily recognized by the greenish- or bluish-black upperparts and white underparts. They appear on their northward flight in early May, and on their southward drift about the middle of September.

DISTRIBUTION. Tree Swallows are most in evidence in New Mexico during spring and fall migrations, at which time they seem to occur statewide. Identification may at times be difficult because they often fly high, or in association with Bank Swallows, thereby lending confusion.

NESTING. The only nesting records of the Tree Swallow seem to be those at Bosque del Apache Wildlife Refuge, where Fleetwood and the author found a pair nesting on July 2, 1954. Fleetwood believed that the pair had nested near the same place the previous year. The nesting place was a Woodpecker hole in a dead willow standing in three feet of water, and about fifteen feet above the surface of the water. According to nesting accounts in other states, the birds may select Woodpecker holes, hollows in trees, or bird boxes. *Nest:* Lined with grasses, leaves, and feathers. *Eggs:* 4 or 5; pure white.

([BANK SWALLOW
Riparia riparia

5—5½" long. Color pattern of sexes alike.

This small Swallow may be recognized by the dark band across its white underparts and brown back, darkest on head and wings. Bill very small; legs with tuft of feathers near insertion of hind toe; throat often speckled. The Latin term *riparia* refers to river bank. There is often confusion in identifying and separating the Bank, the Tree, and the Rough-winged Swallows. This is not surprising, since there is considerable resemblance, particularly among the young in the fall migration. During the spring northward movement, close attention to color patterns of the different adult species will simplify identification.

DISTRIBUTION. No doubt closer observation of the similar small Swallows in migration will disclose that all, including the Bank, are more numerous than records indicate. The Bank has been recorded at various points. Bailey noted it at Carlsbad on September 3, and it was recorded at Mesilla and in the Burro Mountains near Tyrone by Dayton E. Merrill.

NESTING. In recent years the Bank Swallow has been found nesting commonly in the Middle Rio Grande Valley. On July 23, 1950, Fleetwood located a breeding colony, with ten nesting burrows, in a clay bank six miles northeast of Socorro. On July 6, 1954, 40 to 50 pairs were nesting in sand banks along a drainage canal in the southern part of Bosque

del Apache Refuge. They were also found nesting in the stabilized sand banks about San Marcial. "A nesting colony in the sand banks on the west side of the river (in New Mexico, northwest of El Paso) was first discovered May 10, 1940. Young were observed at doors of nests [burrows]. Later observations disclosed that there were 150 holes in the bank" (Lena McBee). According to Mrs. McBee's field notes, the swallows were still using the nesting banks in 1955. She states: "Dr. Allan Phillips states this is the southern-most known nesting colony of Bank Swallows." Nest colonies were previously located in the Jemez Mountains, near Jemez Springs. *Nest:* Clawed out by the birds, 14 or more inches deep in clay or sand banks. *Eggs:* 4 to 6; white.

([ROUGH-WINGED
SWALLOW
Stelgidopteryx ruficollis

5—5¾" long. Color pattern of sexes similar.

By means of its brownish underparts and lack of dark chest band, the Roughwinged can be distinguished from the Bank Swallow, which has white underparts. There are few authentic records of this Swallow in the state, but as is true of the Bank Swallow, it may be overlooked because identification without a specimen is often difficult.

DISTRIBUTION. Henshaw recorded the bird and secured specimens at Zuñi. It also was recorded by Marshall F. Gilman at Shiprock. At Burford Lake, "One pair and a few others were noted between May 23 and June 9, 1918" (Wetmore).

NESTING. The Henshaw record at Zuñi included breeding birds as did the Gilman record near Shiprock. "It arrived El Paso Jan. 19, 1941, and was present throughout the summer. Nest burrows were in banks above El Paso, on New Mexico–Texas line, near where Bank Swallows were nesting" (Lena McBee). *Nest:* In holes or crevices, often in abutments of bridges; lined with straws, dry leaves, grass stems, and twigs. *Eggs:* 3 to 6; white.

(BARN SWALLOW
Hirundo rustica

6—7½" long. Color pattern of sexes similar.

The Barn Swallow is the common, fork-tailed Swallow which is seen in summer rising and dipping in devious courses about barns and dwellings. The males are somewhat more highly colored than the females. The long, more deeply forked tail is the mark by which this Swallow can definitely be distinguished. The fact that it usually lives in proximity to habitation of man insures its easy acquaintance. *Adult male:* Forehead and underparts tawny brown; upperparts glossy steel blue with partial collar of the same. Tail and wings dusky, faintly glossed with greenish; all but middle feathers of the conspicuously forked tail have white spots. *Adult female:* Similar, but underparts usually paler, and outer tail feathers shorter.

DISTRIBUTION. The summer range of the Barn Swallow is statewide, from the lowest sections up to 8,000 feet altitude. It usually arrives in the southern section in early April: Las Cruces, April 2; Chloride, April 3; Albuquerque, April 5; Las Vegas, April 20. It may remain in the southern part of the state (Las Cruces and Carlsbad) as late as mid-October. The number of nesting birds in the state seems to be on the decline, due, perhaps to vandalism at nesting time.

NESTING. Favored nesting site is under eaves of porches of occupied houses or in garages with suitable joists or projecting plates on which nests may be placed. If a suitable nest support is not available, the birds sometimes prepare one of mud on a perpendicular wall. If not molested they usually return annually to their former nesting places. Boys with air-guns or acts of vandalism often drive them away. As a rule, an undisturbed pair will raise two or three broods in a season. Harry Cowan of Hagerman advises that in 1948, three pairs nested under the eaves of his front porch, and that he believes each raised three broods. He stated that at migration time there were about 40, but that boys had disturbed them and probably killed some. Swallows are resourceful to the extent that if preferred nesting places are lacking, they accept substitutes, as was the case of a pair found nesting in an abandoned dugout. At the Pat Birmingham ranch, 70 miles west of Magdalena, young were still in the nest on September 5, this being the third brood in the same nest, under the eaves of the front porch. *Nest:* A somewhat shallow pocket, made of bits of mud mixed with straws and hairs, lined with feathers. *Eggs:* 3 or 4; white, speckled with brown and lavender.

(CLIFF SWALLOW
Petrochelidon pyrrhonota

5—6" long. Color pattern of sexes similar.

The Cliff, the most common Swallow found in New Mexico, may best be distinguished from other Swallows in flight by its conspicuous reddish-brown rump. *Adults:* Forehead cream color; crown, back, and chest patch glossy steel blue; chin, cheek, and collar chestnut; wings and short, squared tail dusky with greenish gloss; underparts whitish. The Cliff Swallow has been divided into a bewildering variety of subspecies, but to the average observer they are the same bird.

DISTRIBUTION. Cliff Swallows, both at nesting time and preceding fall migration, often concentrate in great numbers. They normally enter the southern part (Carlsbad and Las Cruces) in late April and by early June are spread throughout the state. Colonies of them may be found from the lower elevations along the Pecos and Rio Grande Valleys to 8,000 feet in the northern section. Altitude seems to have little bearing on summer distribution. Fall concentrations in the lower Pecos and Rio Grande Valleys may run into hundreds. Such concentrations may occur as early as the last of June. On June 29, 1951, many hundreds of the birds were observed on power line wires near Wade Lake about eight miles southeast of Artesia. In late August probably 3,000 were noted on the power line wires by irrigated fields north of Loving, where they were closely spaced between several poles. On October 13, 1954, many of the birds were still present in the Carlsbad area; but immediately thereafter they moved on southward ahead of the first cold wave.

NESTING. Nesting colonies of the Cliff Swallow may be found from late May until early August wherever there are suitable nesting cliffs, concrete highway bridges, or canal flumes, and mud for nest building. One colony with approximately 500 nests was observed under two overhanging ledges about two miles below Elephant Butte Dam; and on June 14, 1949, about 400 were occupying nests under the limestone walls along Peñasco Canyon eight miles below Mayhill. So resourceful are Cliff Swallows that they do not confine their nest building to natural situations. In recent years many concrete highway bridges, even on the high plains, have been appropriated as nesting sites where formerly there were none. On June 28, 1951, five pairs had placed their mud nests against the joists in the large garage at the Bitter Lake Refuge headquarters. At the time, six pairs of Barn Swallows and Say's Phoebes were sharing the building in apparent amity. *Nest:* A retort-shaped structure made of pellets of mud securely set with a few weed stems or grass straws and usually lined with feathers. Usually great numbers of nests are clustered together, with all entrance openings or pipes drooping outward—a marvel of bird architecture, both in construction and in location for protection against the elements, and a factor which probably favors the birds' high reproductive rate. *Eggs:* 4 or 5; white, speckled or spotted with brown and lilac.

SEPTEMBER CONCENTRATION OF MIGRANT CLIFF SWALLOWS. *Photograph by the Author.*

《 CAVE SWALLOW
Petrochelidon fulva

5½″ long. Color pattern of sexes alike.

The Cave Swallow, a recent discovery in the state, is somewhat similar in appearance to the common Cliff Swallow. Principal distinguishing marks of the adults are color of forehead and throat. The Cave Swallow has a dark chestnut forehead and light buff throat, whereas the Cliff Swallow has a light buff forehead and dark throat. The nesting conduct of the Cave Swallow, however, is so different from that of the Cliff it can readily be separated on that feature.

DISTRIBUTION AND NESTING. Richard Prasil, former Park Naturalist at Carlsbad Caverns National Park, is credited with recording the first Cave Swallows in the state. In June 1952, he located a breeding colony at Goat Cave in Slaughter Canyon, about eight miles southwest of Carlsbad Caverns, in the foothills of the Guadalupe Mountains, at about 4,000 feet. At time of discovery Prasil estimated there were about 40 of these birds. On July 21, 1953,

Edgar Kincaid, ornithologist of Austin, Texas, accompanied Prasil to Goat Cave, an account of which trip appears in the *Texas Ornithological News Letter* (Vol. 3, No. 6, 1955) of which Kincaid is editor, and reads in part:

"When I visited Carlsbad Caverns National Park on July 21, 1953, Prasil very kindly showed me, not only specimens, but also 24 live Swallows and 11 nests in Goat Cave. Prior to Richard Prasil's discovery, the Cave Swallow was officially known in the United States only from Kerr County, in central Texas, although Alexander and Sandy Sprunt knew of its presence at the Devil's Sinkhole in Edwards County, Texas, in 1950 or earlier."

In a letter, September 15, 1955, Kincaid advised the author relative to comparing the common Cliff and the Cave Swallows:

"Obviously the two birds are closely related, but in every classification I've seen they are regarded as separate species. Besides differing somewhat in appearance their nesting habits are rather different. All the nests I have seen of Cave Swallows in this country were built in the twilight

CAVE SWALLOW IN NEST. *Courtesy of U.S. Park Service.*

zone of real caves, whereas all the Cliff Swallow nests I've seen were built on the sides of well lighted cliffs, ledges, dams, bridges, etc. All the Cave Swallow nests I've seen were open cups and not roofed over affairs with entrance at the side such as the Cliff Swallow usually builds. The Cave Swallow doesn't have to put a roof on his nest because the top of the cave itself offers protection from above."

On June 26, 1956, the author, with Austin Roberts and James King, visited Goat Cave and observed the Cave Swallows for some time. As nests were on shelves or in crevices high in the roof of the cave, in semi-darkness, they could not be reached.

During the 1959 nesting season, Carlsbad Caverns National Park naturalists Paul Spangle and James K. Baker made a study of the Cave Swallow. They found the birds nesting in four caves, Goat, Ogle, Rainbow, and Vandalized, all in Slaughter Canyon. They estimated there were as many as 200 of the birds at the four caves.

On nesting Cave Swallows, Baker says: "The nest is an open cup-shaped nest made of mud. Occasionally chips of rock and straw materials may also be included in the nests. The birds line the nests with feathers, pieces of string, paper, and straw materials. There is a wide variation in nest sizes, due largely to additions of new layers of mud in successive years of use. The nests are separated from one another on the walls of the Cave and not nearly so grouped as with Cliff Swallows.

"Eggs: Average number of eggs 4. The eggs are white and mottled with brownish-purple, and quite similar to Cliff Swallow eggs, except for possible differences (slight) in shape. The birds, at least in Vandalized Cave, have two broods, the second broods not being as large as the first. Second brood clutches are usually 3. In the first week of September all but 2 or 3 nests still had young left of the second brood."

(PURPLE MARTIN
Progne subis

7½–8″ long. Color pattern of sexes similar.

The Martin of the Southwest differs from the Eastern Martin in that it rarely lives about habitation of man, preferring a heavily forested summer habitat. It is therefore confined almost wholly to the high mountainous regions. Even in migration Martins cling rather closely to the high wooded or forested country. Being the largest of the Swallow group, they are readily distinguished. Other than in type of habitat occupied, the general habits and conduct of the birds in this region are similar to those of the Martin in the Eastern United States. *Adult male:* Uniformly glossy, violet or steel blue both above and below; tail forked; tail and wings dull black. *Adult female and young:* Forehead and collar grayish; upperparts duller and less uniform than those of the male; tail and wings black; throat, breast, and sides grayish, more or less tipped with white; rest of underparts pale grayish, usually more or less streaked.

DISTRIBUTION. Martins range from 7,000 to 9,000 feet, but seem to prefer the yellow pines in parks, valleys, or canyons where the timber is not dense. They are listed as "a transient visitor, unusual" at Bosque del Apache Refuge. They usually arrive in the southern extension of mountains in late April (April 18, Chloride), and most of them are out of the state by the end of August.

NESTING. With one exception, all nesting sites recorded by the author have been at considerable height, and almost always in natural cavities or in Woodpecker holes in dead pines. The exception was one noted at the Velmer Lane home, in James Canyon about ten miles below Cloudcroft, where a small nesting box placed in a pine tree about 40 feet from the ground was appropriated by a pair of Purple Martins. They were found nesting near Ruidoso, 7,500 feet, in summer, 1955. The author has also found them nesting sparingly in all of the higher forested mountains of the state. *Nest:* Usually in Woodpecker or Flicker holes or in natural tree cavities 60 to 80 feet from the ground. Two or more pairs often may occupy the same large tree. *Eggs:* 4 or 5; plain white.

JAYS, MAGPIES AND CROWS
Family: *CORVIDAE*

THE CONDUCT of few other birds indicates greater intelligence or curiosity than that of members of this family of medium to large size birds. The undesirable traits of some, notably the Steller's Jay, and the aggressiveness and cunning of others are apt to be somewhat obscured, either by an illusion of beauty, such as that of Jays, or by their beguiling ways. Although larger than Crows, Ravens, particularly the White-necked, may sometimes be mistaken for Crows. Crows are rarely seen outside of wooded or forested areas, while the White-necked Raven, for the most part, inhabits semidesert types, hence their ranges rarely overlap. Representatives of this group are usually rather common over a well-defined range. None, however, are statewide in distribution at nesting time. They are more or less migratory, with the exception of the Gray (Canada) Jay, which is virtually resident over its restricted range. Shifting of range of others generally can be attributed to absence of preferred winter food, such as acorn, pinyon, and other mast.

⟨ GRAY (CANADA) JAY
Perisoreus canadensis

11½—13″ long. Color pattern of sexes alike.

The deliberate inquisitive conduct, soft fluffy feathers, and leaden gray plumage pattern of this Jay combine to make identification certain. *Adults:* Bill short; head and collar white; rest of upperparts leaden gray; tail blackish with white tips; throat and breast whitish; rest of underparts brownish gray. Depending on locality, this bird is variously referred to as Canada Jay, Rocky Mountain Jay, Camp Robber, or Whiteheaded Jay, all of which are to some degree applicable. The designation *Perisoreus* (Greek), meaning "heap-up," supposedly alludes to their hoarding instinct.

In comparison with other members of this family, the Gray Jay is a unique character. Lacking the shyness or caution displayed by most other Jays, it seems to be fearless of man. A pair or family may move about from tree to tree intently searching the branches, or descend near the ground and curiously observe an intruder or search for surface food, and then move on to continue their methodical ways. Or if camp is established, two or more may appear and with abandon solicit any available tidbit, perhaps to carry it away to cache for future use. Not only do they help themselves to whatever is thrown on the ground, but they may boldly alight close at hand if some object appeals to them. This boldness may be influenced by their unawareness of the ways of man, or by a desire to appease an insatiable appetite or hoarding instinct.

DISTRIBUTION. The Gray Jay is largely resident from the Colorado–New Mexico line south through the Sangre de Cristo Range to Lake Peak and along the summit of the San Juan Range, west of the Rio

Grande as far south as Lake Hopewell. The 9,000-foot level is about the lowest elevation at which the Gray Jay may be seen in summer. From that altitude it ranges up to 12,000 feet or timber line. It seems to be resident over its restricted range.

NESTING. According to definite records for south-central Colorado (10,000 feet), the birds begin nesting about the middle of April. No doubt nesting activities start about the same time at comparable altitudes in northern New Mexico. The author noted young barely distinguishable from adults on June 29, near the head of Santa Barbara River, 20 miles north of Cowles, at 11,000 feet. "In Wheeler Peak amphitheatre, at 11,400 feet, the young were nearly grown July 20 but were still being fed by the parents" (Bailey). Nest: Usually on branch of spruce or other conifer; large and well made of twigs, grasses, mosses, and plants, down and feathers. Eggs: 2 to 4; varying in size and in coloration from yellowish gray to pale green, finely dotted with brown and slate, or lavender about larger end.

BLUE JAY
Cyanocitta cristata
11—12" long. Color pattern of sexes alike.

The common Blue Jay of the Eastern states is a rare visitor to the arid Southwest. However, there are a few records of its occurrence in New Mexico. It can be distinguished from the other more common Jays indigenous to the state by its pale blue crest, grayish blue upperparts, white markings on wing and outer tail feathers; underparts grayish. The Steller's is the only other crested Jay occurring here, but its crest is dark blue or blackish, and it lacks white markings of wing and tail feathers.

STATE RECORDS. Birdseye recorded one October 17, 1908, at Fruitland, and three the following day at the same place. One was seen at Carlsbad in November 1932. "December 28, 1955, two Blue Jays were seen in Roswell" (Montgomery). During the winter of 1955-56 several were reported at Las Cruces. On March 7, 1956, Judge Edwin Mechem of Las Cruces advised: "This morning a pair of Blue Jays were at my place." He further stated that his neighbors, W. P. Bixler and Rufus Garland, had previously seen these Jays at Las Cruces. There seems to be no record of its nesting in the state.

(STELLER'S JAY
Cyanocitta stelleri
12—13" long. Color pattern of sexes alike. (Pl. XX)

For color, aggressiveness, and mimicry of voice, the beautiful Steller's Jay, also listed as Crested Jay and Long-crested Jay, is in a class by itself. Its striking appearance and winning ways are somewhat overshadowed by its predacious inclinations. In its dark blue vestments, with a striking white-streaked high crest and white line over eye, it is not apt to be confused with any other Jay. Like the Mexican Jay, the Steller's is often seen in groups of eight or more, systematically working a canyon or mountainside in search of food. In cunning and thievery the Steller's is unsurpassed. When engaged in seeking out nests of smaller birds in order to rob them of their eggs or young, it does not proclaim its presence in its usual noisy manner but quietly and slyly moves about bushes or trees. From whom it pilfers—other birds or man—concerns it little so long as its hoarding instinct is appeased. Where corn is used as bait by the State Game Department in trapping wild Turkeys for transplanting, these aggressive foragers carry away a good portion to cache for the proverbial rainy day. The first Jay to locate the grain apparently notifies all others within cruising range, for soon numbers are shuttling back and forth until much of the corn has been carried away. With its screaming protests against any intruder, it alerts Turkey, deer, and bear of impending danger, hence it is unpopular with hunters. But in judging its general behavior, one is likely to overlook the faults of this audacious culprit, which are obscured by its beauty.

DISTRIBUTION. In the summer Steller's Jays are confined almost entirely to forested mountainous country from 7,000 to 10,000 feet, or higher. Although some always are to be found in the high country, many descend in winter to the lower edge of the pine belt, and when mast is scarce or lacking, some may wander far and wide, even into the Lower Rio Grande and Pecos Valleys, or to the high plains of the eastern section of the state. In the western portion there evidently is at times a decided fall or winter southward drift into Mexico. As late as May 28, 1951, the author recorded a northward flight of approximately 50 of these Jays which extended a fourth of a mile along the west slope of hills lying north of the Animas Mountains in Hidalgo County. These mountains, with hills extending northward to the Burro Mountains and Black Range, constitute a continuous migration route to and from Mexico. In 1951, from January 27 to the end of February, a half-dozen or more were feeding in association with Scrub Jays and a variety of other birds at the feeding station at Doepp's residence in north Carlsbad. Such occurrences in the low country may be regarded as evidence of scarcity of winter food elsewhere.

NESTING. Nesting usually begins the latter part of April in the southern mountains, later to the northward. A nest with one egg was recorded April 26 at 8,000 feet in the Black Range west of Chloride, another with four fresh eggs on June 8 in the same area. "Nest with fresh eggs in Santa Fe Canyon April 30" (Jensen). A nest of unusual interest was one located by the author, May 31, 1951, containing four incubated eggs. It was situated among exposed roots of a small pine on the edge of a steep soil bank, about 5 miles south of Mountain Park in the Sacramento Mountains. Nest: Usually 8 to 15 feet above ground in pine, Douglas fir, or other conifer. Rather bulky, made of twigs, grass and moss, sometimes cemented with mud, lined with rootlets or pine needles. Eggs: 4 to 6; dull pale bluish green, spotted and blotched over the entire surface with brown and lavender.

(SCRUB (WOODHOUSE) JAY
Aphelocoma coerulescens
11½—12½" long. Color pattern of sexes alike. (Pl. XX)

The Scrub, so named from its nature of inhabiting scrub timber, is a rather long-tailed pale blue Jay, without crest. Adults: Upperparts dull blue except for gray back and whitish streak over eye; underparts gray except for throat, which is grayish white, streaked with bluish gray.

It may also be recognized generally by its habitat—scrub oak or other foothill woodland type—and by its noisy flight from cover to cover near the ground, or sitting atop bush or tree on lookout. Aggressive and resourceful like most other Jays, in winter, when natural food, as mast or insects, is scarce or lacking, the Scrub readily seeks out other sources of food. The extent of wandering usually depends upon what food may be available about human habitation.

DISTRIBUTION. In summer the Scrub Jay occurs statewide, wherever there is scrub oak, pinyon, juniper, and other woodland type, from 5,000 to 7,000 feet elevation. In winter, in the absence of their mast, particularly acorns, the birds may appear anywhere in the lower sections of the state, as in the Rio Grande and Pecos Valleys. On January 17, 1947, a dozen or more were at the Golden place on the plains, 6 miles southeast of Milnesand, Roosevelt County, and two or more were seen about almost every farmhouse in that section of the plains where there were a few shrubs or trees. They were still in that area as late as April 12. On January 27 and later in 1951, and during the winters of 1952 and 1953, as a widespread drought continued, several were noted about Carlsbad and in the Rio Grande Valley about Las Cruces.

NESTING. Nesting of the Scrub Jay usually begins about the middle of April. A nest containing young was found May 4, on the east slope of the Cuchillo Hills, east of Chloride, at 6,000 feet. Although most nesting occurs from 5,000 to 7,000 feet, it may occasionally take place at lower altitudes, as about Tucumcari, 4,000 feet, or higher, and in the Mt. Taylor area where a nest was found at about 7,500 feet. *Nest:* Usually in scrub oak, but may be in other small trees or thick shrubs, four to six feet from the ground; made of twigs, weed stems and rootlets, lined with hair. *Eggs:* 4 to 6; bluish green, sparingly flecked over the entire surface with rusty brown.

(MEXICAN (ARIZONA) JAY
Aphelocoma ultramarina

11½–13″ long. Color pattern of sexes alike.

The range of the Mexican, one of the largest and noisiest of the Jays, is confined to a limited area in the southwestern corner of the state. This Jay's reputation is not good, since, like other members of the family, its conduct toward small birds which nest in exposed positions is predatory. The large size and plain gray feather pattern, its habit of ganging up, and its inquisitive nature combine to assure unmistakable identification. *Adults:* Without crest; upperparts, including wings and tail pale blue; sides of head blackish; underparts bluish gray. The Mexican some-

what resembles the Scrub Jay but is larger and less streamlined and lacks the whitish gray-streaked throat of the latter. The Mexican Jay prefers the upper levels of the tall oaks rather than the ground story, which the Scrub usually occupies. The beautiful large, heavily-acorned Emory oak, one of the dominant trees of this Jay's habitat, is a favorite retreat. Its shy, yet inquisitive conduct often causes its presence overhead to be unknown until an outburst of raucous notes and a thumping of wings of a group suddenly break the silence for a brief spell. They almost always move along in groups of a half-dozen or more when systematically searching for food along canyon sides and bottoms.

DISTRIBUTION. The Mexican Jay, apparently resident, is confined to a strip of southwestern New Mexico, comprising the Peloncillo, Animas, and Burro Mountains, northward to Glenwood; the Pinos Altos Mountains, eastward to the Upper Mimbres River (San Lorenzo), and the south end of the Black Range. It is quite common within the wooded foothills and lower extremity of yellow pine, from 5,000 to 7,000 feet.

NESTING. The Mexican Jay is communal in conduct, even during nesting time; two or more pairs often nest in the same or adjoining trees. Nesting usually takes place from early April to mid-May. On May 16, a nest containing four eggs was found near Cloverdale, and another containing two fresh eggs was found on May 20, near the same place. *Nest:* Usually in oaks, 10 to 30 feet from the ground; made of small sticks and twigs, lined with rootlets and hair. *Eggs:* 4 or 5; greenish blue.

(BLACK-BILLED MAGPIE
Pica pica

17½–21½″ long. Color pattern of sexes alike.

Adult: Mostly black with bronzy metallic gloss; white on wing and lower underparts; white lines each side of back terminating in a V at base of tail; tail 9½ to 12 inches; bill black, 1 to 1½ inches. So striking in its black and white garb is the Magpie, it is easily identified. No other land bird with so long a tail is similarly marked. The wide, graduated, iridescent tail in erratic flight conspicuously fans out, while the white of outer wing feathers and shoulders flashes in the sunlight. The expression "chattering like a Magpie" is most applicable to a talkative person, for few birds chatter so incessantly, or display so much curiosity. Although the Magpie has high economic value as a destroyer of grasshoppers and other injurious insects, it is nevertheless in disrepute because of its predatory inclinations and its fondness for eggs. Its alertness and shyness keep it well out of ordinary gun range. Its shyness may stem in part from unfavorable association with man. Even so, it prefers to live in proximity to habitation of man, possibly because of the advantages gained in obtaining daily meals. The Magpie avoids dense forests, preferring foothills, meadows, and wooded valleys.

DISTRIBUTION. In summer the Black-billed Magpie is common in the northern part of the state, from 5,000 to 10,500 feet, from about Las Vegas, Santa Fe, and Cuba, northward, and eastward along the Dry Cimarron River to the Oklahoma line. In winter it occurs as far south as Socorro, in the Rio Grande Valley, and rarely into the Sacramento Mountains. Stragglers have been reported as far south as Las Cruces.

NESTING. The Black-billed Magpie constructs one of the largest and most unusual nests of any bird of comparable size. The nest is usually about 2 feet high and 12 to 14 inches in diameter, hooded or domed, with entrance on the side. The cover is for protection against inclement weather, since snow storms often occur in May in the high country where these birds

nest. *Nest:* Usually in willows, cottonwoods, or oaks, 8 to 10 feet above ground; made of sticks and completely covered; cavity made of twigs and grass cemented together with mud, lined with grass and other soft material. *Eggs:* 7 to 10; grayish, blotched with purple or brown over entire surface.

(COMMON (AMERICAN) RAVEN

Corvus corax

21½–26″ long. Color pattern of sexes alike. (Pl. XXI)

The largest of the Crow-Raven group, the Common Raven is easily distinguished. It is larger than its desert-inhabiting relative, the White-necked Raven. *Adults:* Entire plumage glossy black. When at rest, flushed throat feathers are usually conspicuous; bill 2¾ inches long, and nostrils completely concealed by coarse, bristly hairlike tufts that are more than half the length of the bill. The Common Raven ranges for the most part in the forested mountains and rugged foothills, while the smaller White-necked is a plains or desert dweller. Except when accompanied by young, Common Ravens usually are seen in pairs, and they seem rarely to leave their chosen habitat. The Crow is so much smaller, and its flight so erratic that it is not likely to be confused with its larger relatives.

DISTRIBUTION. The range of the Common Ravens includes most of the wooded foothills and forested mountains of the state. They may be seen in lower country but usually in broken canyon-rent sections or about mesa rims; rarely if ever are they seen on the more desert areas, or the eastern high plains. They are largely resident where found, but no doubt have a rather large cruising range. Their habitat varies from about 5,000 feet to the top of the highest mountains.

NESTING. Nesting of the Common Raven takes place from early April into May. The preferred nesting sites are cliffs and ledges of canyon walls, mesa rims and soil banks. In the absence of such preferred locations, as in the forested Sacramento Mountains, they may nest in pines or Douglas firs, high above ground. Jensen reported seeing one on May 20 east of Santa Fe on a cliff near the Lake Peak Trail, at 10,500 feet altitude. The author has examined several nests on the sides of soil banks or rock ledges along Cuchillo Creek between Cuchillo and the Rio Grande; also in the cliffs of Monticello Canyon above Monticello. Young in nest were found near Santa Rosa, May 26. They were common and nesting at Burford Lake (about 8,000 feet) May 23 to June 18. *Nest:* Of sticks, with deep well-padded bowl, lined with bark, moss, and hair. *Eggs:* 5 to 7; pale green, olive, or drab, the whole surface dotted, blotched, and clouded with purplish and various shades of brown.

❨ WHITE-NECKED RAVEN
Corvus cryptoleucus
19—21" long. Color pattern of sexes alike. (Pl. XXI)

"Desert Raven" would seem to be a more appropriate designation for the White-necked Raven. *Cryptoleucus* (Greek), "hidden white," has reference to the white at base of neck feathers, visible only when neck feathers are raised or agitated. The White-necked prefers the more arid lands, avoiding forested areas, the chosen habitat of the Crow and the Common Raven. It may be distinguished from the Common by its smaller size, the smaller and shorter bill, and by the different type of occupied ranges, which rarely overlap. *Adults:* Glossy black; upperparts (except hind neck) with a violet sheen; underparts faintly glossed bluish; neck feathers white at base.

Although White-necked Ravens are predatory to a limited extent, taking some

young, as well as eggs, of ground nesting birds, their economic value as consumers of grasshoppers, moths, and other destructive insects compensates in part for their bad traits. Few birds seem to express greater enjoyment in action or manifest stronger attachments. At nesting time a pair may be seen sitting side by side fondling bills or apparently expressing their emotions by bowing and elevating wings in a unique manner, or engaging in intimate conversation. During hot summer days they seem to revel in their aerial acrobatic stunts, such as plunging into the spiraling funnels of "curling devils" (whirlwinds), common over the desert lands on calm summer days—and riding them to dazzling heights, then pitching out into normal atmosphere, and leisurely winding or diving back to earth. While they are not scavengers in the same sense as Vultures, they are adept at locating food, such as scraps thrown out along highways and from railroad dining cars. They also

YOUNG WHITE-NECKED RAVENS AND NESTS IN MESQUITE. *Photograph by the Author.*

have learned that campers often leave bits of food, and a pair of these birds will patiently wait at a safe distance until camp is broken, to pick up all edible leavings. This adaptation as scavenger no doubt accounts for the fact that many of the birds remain in the state throughout the winter.

DISTRIBUTION. In summer the White-necked Ravens are the most common of the larger birds found in the eastern and southeastern sections of the state. In the southwest portion they range north to Glenwood and Silver City; in the Rio Grande Valley to Socorro; and in the Tularosa Valley northward to Carrizozo. In the Pecos Valley they are common to Santa Rosa, while they cover the eastern high plains as far north as Clayton and beyond. The semidesert Jornada del Muerto from Las Cruces to and beyond Engle is a good example of preferred summer range. Here, the Ravens seem to find ample food in the abundance of grasshoppers and other insects in season, while the mesquite and tree yuccas provide ample nesting places. While there is some southward drift in the fall, many winter across the entire southern section of the state, particularly about Lovington, Hobbs, Carlsbad, Las Cruces, and Deming, where they frequent garbage dumping grounds, and feed on rabbits and smaller rodents killed on highways. At this season they usually congregate in considerable numbers and spend much time winging their way about in search of whatever food their keen eyes may discover.

NESTING. The White-necked Raven usually begins nest building in late April or early May. On May 29 many nests were examined in the Lovington area, around 4,000 feet elevation. Some had well-feathered young; others had four to six well-incubated eggs, while a few had incomplete clutches. In the Engle section, fresh eggs were noted on May 2; in the Clayton area: "Nests in limited number; known to nest on windmill towers on occasion" (Kreh-

biel). It is of interest to note that while they "jump" the broken wooded section of the Dry Cimarron in the extreme northeast corner of the state, they occur again and nest in southeast Colorado and southwest Kansas. Because of lack of suitable nesting places over much of their arid-land range, a variety of sites are chosen: abandoned, or even utilized windmill towers, insulator bars on telephone lines, crossbars on power lines, or gate posts. On one occasion, near Tatum, a bird incubated on a windmill tower platform, with the wheel spinning much of the time only a foot or two above. However, on the eastern high plains, nests are more often placed in mesquite bushes, or in native chinaberry or hackberry trees sometimes found in valleys or basins. In the southwest section of the state the "tree" yucca (*Yucca elata*), which grows 10 to 15 feet tall, often in extended "forests," provides safe nesting sites, which sometimes are shared with Scott's Orioles. The White-necked Raven also takes advantage of bushes or trees growing about abandoned homesteads or stock-watering wells. *Nest:* Base made of sticks; bowl deep and padded, lined with wool, rabbit fur, rags, and almost always cow hair. The unique nesting material, in some instances, is hay baling wire or other pieces of wire; a few nests have been found in which the entire structure except lining consisted of such wire. *Eggs:* 4 to 7; greenish, generally with streaks and hairlines or blotches of lilac, gray, and drab.

❬ COMMON CROW
Corvus brachyrhynchos
17—19″ long. Color pattern of sexes alike. (Pl. XXI)

Crows are distinctive, yet wherever White-necked Ravens occur, the latter are often referred to as Crows. The Crow is considerably smaller than the White-necked Raven. It is larger than the largest Blackbird. Also the Crow's familiar saucy "caw caw" is characteristic. Plumage black with violet sheen.

DISTRIBUTION. The summer range of the Common Crow is confined to the central and northern parts of the state, from Glenwood, Bluewater, Mountainair, and Las Vegas northward. It is usually regarded as uncommon at this season. Formerly it was rather rare south of Albuquerque, but in recent years vast numbers move down the Rio Grande Valley in winter as far south as Las Cruces, where considerable damage to winter crops is attributed to them. Although Crows allegedly rob pecan trees of their nuts, in this instance the principal thieves are probably White-necked-Ravens. The more recent southward drift has been influenced by increased agricultural activities. The Crows also at times come as far south as Mayhill in the Sacramento Mountains. During the winter of 1953-54, more than 2,000 Crows wintered about Albuquerque.

NESTING. The Common Crow nests sparingly throughout its summer range in the state. The author has recorded it nesting in the tall cottonwoods along the San Francisco River near Glenwood, the southern limit of its breeding range. In the Santa Fe area, the upper Pecos, Las Vegas, and along Cimarron Canyon, it nests regularly. It nests in the cottonwoods along the Rio Grande and tributaries, about Española. "Several pairs nesting at Lake Burford May 23 to June 19" (Wetmore). Nest: Usually in cottonwoods or other deciduous trees; made of twigs and sticks, cup rather deep; lined with bark, grass, rootlets, and hair. Eggs: 4 or 5; green to olive buff, variously spotted and blotched with browns and grays.

⟨ PINYON JAY

Gymnorhinus cyanocephala

10—11½" long. Color pattern of sexes alike. (Pl. XX)

The Pinyon Jay, resembling both the Crow and other Jays, is often called the "Blue Crow." It is a free traveler, and in the absence of mast, its presence anywhere outside its regular range is unpredictable. Unlike most other Jays, it is without predatory inclinations. It also is inclined to be more social than other members of the Jay family. Its communal tendency is especially evident at nesting time when one or several of the birds may be seen almost constantly commuting between nesting grounds and the main feeding group. Distinctive features of the Pinyon Jay are the uniform grayish-blue color and the long, heavy bill. In flight, the incessant loud whining or mewing notes of the birds as they wing over the great stretches of pinyon-oak-juniper woodlands are diagnostic. Often one is constrained to believe that these Jays have means of communication other than voice or vision, for a flock will leisurely commute over the foothills in indirect course, perhaps to be followed minutes later by another group precisely in the same flight pattern. When danger threatens, such as a cruising Falcon or Cooper's Hawk, they swing into a compact mass and, with swish of wings but silent of voice, dash headlong into some dense pine or other cover and remain completely silent until safety is assured. Wandering, as from their chosen and accustomed range, seems to be influenced by lack of a dependable source of food, such as pinyon or oak mast, rather than by set, seasonal migratory movements.

DISTRIBUTION. The regular range of the Pinyon Jay is largely coextensive with that of the pinyon pine, from which its name, because of its preference for this habitat, is derived. Its preferred summer habitat is from about 5,500 feet in the foothills to the upper edge of the Transition Zone, 7,400 feet, giving it a rather wide distribution, which is more or less constant when there is pinyon mast. In the fall, during years of scant or no mast, the birds wander far and wide in small or large flocks, many going out of the state. On January 6, 1920, a great flock of Pinyon Jays was observed on and about the many strings of freight cars in the Santa Fe Railway yards at Clovis. On several occasions migrant bunches have been seen or heard calling as they sped in compact groups over or near Carlsbad. At other times migrants have been observed in the southwest area, where evidently they were going into or coming from Mexico.

NESTING. Nesting of the Pinyon Jay is often prolonged, but unpredictable, depending on availability of food. Fresh eggs may be found from late February or early March into October. The birds' social instinct is clearly reflected in colony nesting. The author had a rare opportunity to observe their nesting conduct in early 1913, on the south slope of Black Mountain (about 7,500 feet), 60 miles north of Silver City, where at the time there was a heavy pinyon mast. On February 17, when the south slopes were half covered with snow, a colony was located with nest building already under way. Many nests were partly completed, practically all in scrubby gray live oak. There were more than 50 of the birds, noisily mingling and dispersing about the nesting grounds. On March 3, when a return pack trip was made, nests were found in almost all of the oaks of sufficient size (10 to 15 feet high) but never more than one nest to a tree. One nest, half completed, was in a juniper. Much snow had fallen since the first visit, and nests were rather damp. With the exception of one nest—which contained 5— all others examined contained 4 eggs. On this trip a second, but smaller, colony was located not far from the first. On March 28, a third colony, comprising some 50 nesting birds, was located on the southeastern slope of Black Mountain, where many nests were under construction in the live oaks. On October 7, young were just leaving nests, 25 miles southwest of Magdalena. Others were dead in nests, no doubt as result of cold rains. In northern Santa Fe County, Jensen found Pinyon Jays nesting from February to June. A colony consisting of 13 nests with large young was found March 19. *Nest:* Rather bulky, compactly made of twigs and shreds of bark and weed stems; cup deep and well lined with rootlets, weed fiber, dry grass, and usually some feathers. *Eggs:* Usually 4, rarely 5; bluish white, covered with minute brown spots; others wreathed about the large end with spots and blotches.

⟮ CLARK'S NUTCRACKER
Nucifraga columbiana
12—13" long. Color pattern of sexes alike. (Pl. XX)

The home of the Clark's Nutcracker, or Clark's Crow, as it is often called, is the Canadian Life Zone and upward to timber line. Although it belongs to the Crow-Jay family it is distinct both in appearance and conduct. It has a plump body and rather short tail. *Adults:* Nasal tufts and face white; remainder of body gray (paler and browner in summer); upper-tail coverts and central tail feathers black; others white above and below; wings glossy black, secondaries broadly tipped with white. The life of the Clark's Crow is spent largely on the wing or in forest treetops. The author has rarely seen one on the ground although it does sometimes, like the Gray (Canada) Jay, descend to the ground, particularly when seeking scraps about camps. Like most other Jays they are omnivorous, their diet including insects, fruit, pinyon nuts and meat of freshly killed animals, when this is left hanging. The skill with which they locate a source of food is astonishing. On several occasions the author has hung the carcass of a deer in the shade of some thick conifer, returning later to find two or three Clark's Crows helping themselves to a meal from the exposed flesh where the animal had been drawn. Although it is contrary to research findings, this ability to spot a feast so quickly indicates that such food might be located by scent. Since there are often Chickadees or Nuthatches about when such game kills are made, the conduct of these birds may sometimes provide clues for other birds. Or it is probable that the older leaders have learned from experience to associate the report of a gun with a possible series of meals, hence proceed to investigate. The apparent practice of watching the movements of a hunter may have been followed by their ancestors when the Indian was the only human occupant of the land, for even in Alaska the author observed that Ravens usually were on hand to partake of the remains of kills left by hunters.

This Jay is named in honor of William Clark (1770-1838), who with Meriwether Lewis commanded the famed Lewis and Clark Expedition, across the continent to the mouth of the Columbia River, 1803 to 1806.

DISTRIBUTION. Since the Clark's Crow is practically resident in the mountain forests from 8,000 feet to and above timber line, it follows that its summer range is restricted largely to such forested types. While Nutcrackers are not as common as the true Jays (except the Gray) they are often observed in loosely ranging groups or families of a half-dozen or more. When disturbed they make their presence known by loud raucous grating squawks, and other, more subdued notes, usually of a protesting nature. Often, when flying high, they deviously plunge down, with a loud swish of wings, to treetops. In summer they frequent and seem to enjoy the silent, cool summits of the highest mountains. In winter they may be observed as low as 6,500 feet.

NESTING. As the Clark's Nutcracker nests early, usually while snow still lies in the higher, more inaccessible mountains, searching for an occupied nest involves hardships, and more often disappointment. This fact accounts for the few nests recorded, although the noisy, squawking young are commonly heard and seen in mid-June with the parent birds. Even in Yellowstone Park, nest building has been known to start around the first of February, with incubation going on with temperatures below zero. Some nests found in the Colorado mountains in late March contained young birds. The author observed young as large as adults calling for food on the summit of the Black Range, southwest of Chloride, at 8,500 feet on June 25. "Three nests with young were found below Santa Fe Lake at an altitude of 12,000 feet on July 4, 1921" (Jensen). Thus it is evident that nesting may be extended over a considerable period of time. Nest: Regarding nests of the Clark's Nutcracker, Major Bendire, who had considerable experience with the nesting birds in Oregon, stated: "The outer diameter of the nest measures from 11 to 12 inches, by about 7 inches in depth, made of twigs and sticks from 8 to 12 inches long. The cup is from 4 to 5 inches wide and 3 inches deep. The quilted inner walls are fully 1½ inches thick." This provision for warmth of eggs and young during the low temperatures they must withstand is indicative of the bird's superior instinct, if not knowledge, in carrying out its parental duties. Most of the nests found were situated in south exposure of pine trees, 15 to 45 feet above ground. Eggs: 4 to 6; pale gray green; usually finely flecked, spotted and blotched with brown, gray, and lavender, generally more heavily around the larger end.

TITMICE, VERDINS, AND BUSHTITS
Family: PARIDAE

THIS FAMILY consists of a group of very active small birds with relatively long tails and small bills, indigenous to habitat of wide variation, from arid desert type to dense forests of the higher mountains. The Chickadees (popular name of the American Black-capped Titmouse), because of their friendliness and trusting ways and nature of clinging adroitly upside down or otherwise to limbs while intently searching trees for insects, are probably the best known of the group. The Titmice prefer the wooded foothills, while the Verdins cling to the Lower Sonoran desert type of terrain. All are highly beneficial as destroyers of injurious insects.

(BLACK-CAPPED CHICKADEE
Parus atricapillus

4¾—5½" long. Color pattern of sexes alike.

The three Chickadees (Black-capped, Mexican, and Mountain) occupy a similar type of habitat and their color patterns are much alike, yet there are a few fine points of distinction. The Black-capped, sometimes referred to as the Long-tailed Chickadee, is rather conspicuous in gray, white, and black dress. It has a solid black cap, while the Mountain has a white line over each eye. In the Mexican, black of throat is more extensive. *Adults:* Top of head, nape and throat glossy black; sides of head white; back pale gray, becoming buffy on rump; outer margins of wing coverts grayish; outer tail feathers edged with white; more richly colored in fall and winter than at other seasons.

DISTRIBUTION. The range of the Black-capped Chickadee is confined almost wholly to the higher, forested mountains of northern New Mexico. Ranging from about 7,500 feet to timber line, it seems to be most common in the mountains east of the Rio Grande, from Santa Fe and Pecos northward. A specimen was taken in the Capitan Mountains but this record may be considered as accidental since it was far outside of the known, established range. It was common in the Sangre de Cristo Range, on June 18 and 19, 1924. It was noted by Bailey on Pueblo Creek near Taos at 7,400 feet on July 18. In the fall, old with young seemingly move higher into the mountains. On August 15 it was noted at 10,500 feet, below Pecos Baldy. On October 18, it was found at 9,000 feet, 20 miles southwest of Cimarron. Though its most extensive distribution is in the Sangre de Cristo Range, it has been reported as quite common in the Aztec area around 5,500 feet, but these observations were made near the lofty mountains of southern Colorado.

NESTING. Although the Black-capped Chickadee is fairly common in the northern section of the state, comparatively few nests have been reported. Jensen reported a nest containing young at 9,000 feet, in Santa Fe Canyon east of Santa Fe, in a Woodpecker hole in an aspen tree. *Nest:* In holes in trees or stumps; lined with fur, hair, and feathers. *Eggs:* 6 to 8; white, sprinkled with reddish-brown dots and spots.

(MEXICAN CHICKADEE
Parus sclateri

5" long. Sexes alike in appearance.

The Mexican Chickadee is similar to its close relative, the Black-capped, but identification is no problem since their established ranges are widely separated, the Mexican being confined to the extreme southwest corner of the state, while the Black-capped is indigenous to the northern sections. In the Mexican, black of the throat is more extensive than that of the Black-capped. *Adults:* Top of head, nape, and throat jet black with a faint gloss; sides of head white; rest of upperparts plain deep olive gray; wings and tail slaty with gray edgings; median lower underparts white; sides and flanks dark gray.

DISTRIBUTION. Both Mearns and Goldman found the Mexican Chickadee rather common in the Animas and Peloncillo Mountains near the International Boundary, in southern Hidalgo County. The author has found it to be fairly common in the higher portions of the Animas Mountains.

NESTING. While there seems to be no nesting record for this species within the state, undoubtedly it does nest, since it is resident. *Nest:* In cavities of trees. *Eggs:* 6 to 8; white, sprinkled with reddish-brown spots.

❨ MOUNTAIN CHICKADEE
Parus gambeli
5–5½″ long. Color pattern of sexes alike.

The Mountain Chickadee is the most abundant and widely spread of the Chickadees which inhabit New Mexico. Since it fills the gap between the more limited ranges of the other two species—Black-capped and Mexican—its identification is simplified. The observer may expect to see the Black-capped in the north and northeastern areas and the Mexican in the extreme southwest, hence the Mountain is the dominant bird. Like most of the small birds, Mountain Chickadees are highly beneficial. They are fearless of man, and are commonly seen hanging upside down on a pine twig searching for insects. *Adults:* The Mountain Chickadee, like the Black-capped, has a black cap, but the cap is broken by a white line over the eyes; sides of head white; rest of upperparts olive gray; throat black; median under-

parts white; sides, flanks, and under-tail coverts grayish brown.

DISTRIBUTION. As the name indicates, the Mountain Chickadee is a bird of the mountains, therefore in New Mexico its chosen habitat is extensive. In summer it ranges from 7,500 feet to near timber line. In winter it may drop down to as low as 5,000 feet at Shiprock, and 5,500 feet in the Guadalupe Mountains; otherwise it may be regarded as resident. Its range overlaps that of the Black-capped in the northern section.

NESTING. The Mountain Chickadee nests from 7,000 to 12,000 feet. "A nest with eight fresh eggs was found May 14, in a Bluebird box 8 miles east of Santa Fe, and on May 30, 1921, another with 7 eggs, also in a box was found in the same locality" (Jensen). These nests were located around 11,000 feet. The author noted young out of the nest, at timber line, east side of Pecos Baldy, July 18. "It was breeding among the pines on the Pinos Altos Mountains, July 8" (A. K. Fisher). *Nest:* In natural cavities or old Woodpecker holes, or in nest boxes put up for them or for other birds not more than 15 feet above ground; generally lined with rabbit fur. *Eggs:* 4 or 5; plain white or spotted with reddish brown, chiefly around the larger end.

❨ PLAIN TITMOUSE
Parus inornatus
5½–6″ long. Color pattern of sexes alike.

The gray back and conspicuous crest readily distinguish the Titmouse. Its conduct as it searches its preferred habitat of oak and pinyon-juniper foothills for insects is fearless and animated. The Plain Titmouse has a wide range of alarm notes which alert its kind as well as other birds when danger threatens. *Adults:* The common name well describes this little busybody: unmarked, with prominent crest;

upperparts light gray; underparts whitish gray.

DISTRIBUTION. The Plain Titmouse is resident and one of the commoner small birds of the wooded foothills of the upper Sonoran Zone, east to the Guadalupe and Capitan Mountains, Montoya, and the Dry Cimarron. Its principal range is from 5,000 to 7,000 feet, elevations which conform rather closely to the upper Sonoran Life Zone.

NESTING. Being resident where found, the Plain Titmouse nests throughout its range. Jensen reports nests and eggs on May 3, 5, and 6, in nesting boxes near Santa Fe. *Nest:* In natural cavities of trees or stumps, or in bird boxes; made of soft felted materials and feathers. *Eggs:* 6 to 8; plain white.

(BRIDLED TITMOUSE
Parus wollweberi

4½–5″ long. Color pattern of sexes alike. (Pl. I)

The "bridled" face distinguishes the Bridled Titmouse from its relative, the Plain, the only other crested Titmouse in the state. *Adults:* Crown gray; crest and back of head black; sides of head white with blackish markings that complete the "bridle"; rest of upperparts plain grayish; throat black; median underparts grayish white. Bill is tiny for size of bird.

DISTRIBUTION. The restricted range of the Bridled Titmouse includes the Animas and Peloncillo Mountains, and north to Alma and the Pinos Altos Mountains, from 5,500 to 6,500 feet elevation. It is

PLAIN TITMOUSE. *L. A. Fuertes, U.S. Fish & Wildlife Service.*

resident and not uncommon within its limited range. Like the Plain Titmouse it is inclined to be social and is usually seen in groups or families.

NESTING. Although no nests have been recorded in the state, young have been seen. Several Bridled Titmice were seen on June 21, 4 miles west of Cloverdale, but no nests were located. Adults with young were noted in the Peloncillo and Animas Ranges, Hidalgo County. *Nest:* As reported in adjacent Arizona, usually in hollows of oaks; lined with soft plant material. *Eggs:* 5 to 7; plain white.

([VERDIN

Auriparus flaviceps

4–4½" long. Color pattern of sexes similar.

The dainty, spirited Verdin, formerly sometimes referred to as the Gold-tit, is resident in the arid lower Sonoran Life Zone of the southern part of the state. The Latin, *Auriparus*, "gold-tit," and *flaviceps*, "yellow-head," are definitely applicable. *Adults:* Head dull yellow, forehead usually tinged with orange brown (golden); upperparts, except head, gray; wings and tail darker with pale edgings; shoulder patch rich rufous; underparts whitish gray, median line usually tinged with yellow. The female is slightly duller in color. One marvels at the ability of so frail a little bird to survive heat, cold, drought, and winds of its desert environment. Verdins are usually to be found in or about mesquite, catclaw, blue chaparral (*Condalia*), desert willow or other low shrub or brush. Since they are rather shy their repeated, plaintive squeaky notes may be heard though the birds cannot be seen. When one is seen it will be so active (unless a pair is in the act of protesting intrusion about young or nest) that identification must be quickly made.

DISTRIBUTION. The range of the Verdin covers the southern section of the state,

extending north to Silver City, Socorro, Tularosa, and Dexter. The highest elevation at which it may be seen is around 5,500 feet. It is commonest about the brushy sand washes that drain the more barren desert hills and mountains.

NESTING. It is in nest location and building that the little Verdin shows superior architectural skill. Nests are usually located near the drooping end of a slender branch of some thorny shrub or tree, and the outside framework is almost always well fortified by thorny twigs. The nest, resembling that of the Cliff Swallow, is a completely covered, retort-shaped ball, with small, curved or slanting neck on one side, even the entrance neck or tube sometimes being safeguarded by a circular projection of the nest-framing twigs. The bird's intelligence is indicated further by its use of surplus nests for roosting and protection in stormy weather. As many as four and five birds have been routed from a nest in the late afternoon of a cold day. Swinging, as they usually do, from terminal branches of thorny brush, nests and contents are fairly free from enemies such as molest most other small nesting birds. *Nest:* Outside framework usually thorny twigs; weed stems, leaves of mesquite, desert willow or other tree, or lichens matted together, form the mid-structure, while feathers comprise the ample lining. *Eggs:* 4 or 5; greenish white, blotched, mostly around larger end, with reddish brown.

([COMMON BUSHTIT

Psaltriparus minimus

4–4½" long. Color pattern of sexes alike.

The tiny, long-tailed Common Bushtit, often referred to as the Lead-colored Bushtit, is but little larger than the Broad-tailed Hummingbird. Bushtits range in bunches (except at nesting time), probably the adults with young of the season, progressively moving from cover to cover, twittering and chattering as a means of contact as they search the pinyons, oaks or other trees for insects. No matter how engrossed they may be with their food hunting and family relations, they usually desist long enough to scold or otherwise protest the presence of any intruder before proceeding on their course, flying one, two, three, until all have passed from one tree to another. Soon all is quiet where minutes before there had been a chorus of protest and family conversation. Knowledge of these unique traits is helpful in identification. *Adults:* "Midget size, plain drab color, short bill, and long tail" pretty well describes the Bushtit. Its animated social relations, twittering notes, and adherence to the foothill oak-pinyon-juniper association are further clues to identification. Upperparts plain olive gray; wings and tail darker, with light gray edgings; sides of head brown; underparts pale gray.

DISTRIBUTION. The Common Bushtit is resident from 4,500 to 7,000 feet, and in some places higher. One was sighted by Bailey "on a local hot slope among the nut pines and junipers in the Costilla River Valley, at 9,000 feet, August 25." This record may be regarded as representing the extreme in elevation for this bird, which was no doubt accidental or of temporary occurrence.

NESTING. Like the Verdin, the Common Bushtit is a master in the art of nest

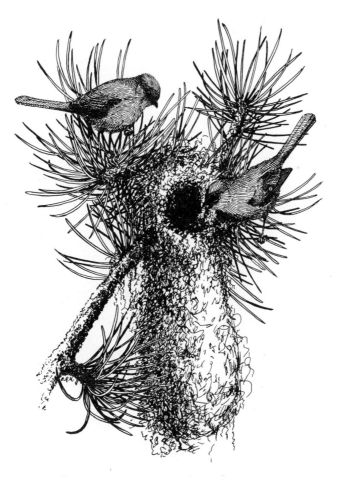

PAIR OF BUSHTITS ON NEST. *E. R. Kalmbach.*

construction. Young were observed in nest on May 22, summit of Big Hatchet Mountain, and nests were found in April at Silver City, and at Santa Rosa in June. On May 17 the author also found a nest at Chloride, 6,200 feet, containing 7 well incubated eggs. Jensen reported a nest with fresh eggs near Santa Fe, May 4, and one with 6 heavily incubated eggs, May 24. Close observation has led to the conclusion that eggs, and no doubt young birds, are subject to considerable destruction, particularly by Jays. Hence, large, successful clutches are required to offset the losses. *Nest:* Six to eight inches long, purselike, usually swung from a top, or terminal, branch of a scrub oak or pinyon, 10 to 15 feet from the ground; made of lichens, fine leaves, oak flowers, and catkins woven with web. *Eggs:* 6 to 8; white.

BLACK-EARED BUSHTIT
Psaltriparus melanotis

4–4½″ long. Color pattern of sexes alike.

Adult male: Sides of head black, top of head bluish gray, back brown, underparts whitish, sides buffy. *Adult female:* Similar to male, but sides of head brownish. Formerly listed as the Lloyd Bushtit.

DISTRIBUTION. The distribution of the Black-eared Bushtit seems to be confined to the extreme southwest corner of New Mexico. Mearns collected an adult male in the San Luis (Animas) Mountains, near the Mexican Boundary, July 10, 1892. It is quite probable that the birds are resident in limited numbers in that area. There seems to be no record of its nesting in the state.

WHITE-BREASTED NUTHATCH. *L. A. Fuertes, U.S. Fish & Wildlife Service.*

NUTHATCHES

Family: SITTIDAE

NUTHATCHES are very alert, active, tree-climbing birds, similar in some respects to the Chickadees. These little busybodies often are seen zigzagging over the bole of a tree or working downward headfirst on some large limb in pursuit of insects, pausing momentarily as if to ascertain the intent of an observer, only to resume the search. Unlike the closely related Creeper, whose tail serves as a support, the Nuthatch depends on its curved, compressed claws for clinging to the bark. Bills are strong, almost straight; tongues horny and barbed; tails short. Although largely insectivorous, they feed also on small wild fruits and seeds. The common name Nuthatch supposedly comes from their habit of chucking seeds and nuts in cracks in bark to enable them to break the shell by hammering.

⟨ WHITE-BREASTED NUTHATCH
Sitta carolinensis

5—6″ long. Color pattern of sexes similar.

The White-breasted Nuthatch, common in practically all forested areas from 7,000 to 8,000 feet, is also referred to as the Rocky Mountain Nuthatch, a subspecies. *Adult male:* Readily distinguished by the conspicuous white breast, black cap, blue-gray back, and its nature of searching tree trunks and limbs in every conceivable position, paying little attention to the interested observer. The jerky, intensive searching motion is also characteristic. *Adult female:* Similar to the male, but black of head is obscured by grayish or bluish-gray.

DISTRIBUTION. Few other species of birds are more intimately attached to the Transition Life Zone. Wherever this zone is present as a forest, the White-breasted Nuthatch may commonly be seen, winter or summer. However, a few may descend into the valleys in the fall, as at Albuquerque (5,000 feet), where the author observed them in September. They were also noted up to 10,000 feet in the Mogollon Mountains in October. Such records seem to be the exception and are probably of birds that wander from their preferred range.

NESTING. Nests usually are placed in natural cavities of oaks, pines, or other trees. On June 6 young in nest were observed near Tres Piedras at about 8,000 feet. "Several pairs nested in Santa Fe Canyon up to 7,800 feet" (Jensen). Merrill noted them in the Organ Mountains, and Goldman in the Animas Mountains in southern New Mexico. *Nest:* Mostly of hair and rabbit fur, and some fine grass. *Eggs:* Usually 5; spotted with reddish brown.

RED-BREASTED NUTHATCH
Sitta canadensis

4¼—4¾″ long. Color pattern of sexes similar.

The Red-breasted is smaller than the White-breasted, and underparts are buffy brown. *Adult male:* Top of head glossy black with faint bluish gloss; white stripe over eye and black line through eye; tail black tipped with gray, except middle feathers; wings without black or white. *Adult female:* Similar but colors duller; back of head and hind neck usually plumbeous.

DISTRIBUTION. Records indicate that the Red-breasted Nuthatch is a fall and winter resident in New Mexico, entering the state from the north usually in late August. It was noted August 17, on Sierra Grande, Union County, at 8,732 feet. Bailey recorded it in Taos Pass on September 11 at 8,700 feet, and it was noted October 3 in the Manzano Mountains. It is regarded as an uncommon bird in the state.

([PYGMY NUTHATCH
Sitta pygmaea

4—4½" long. Color pattern of sexes alike.

This Nuthatch, really a pygmy and one of the most spirited of the small birds, is in a class with the Bushtit, both in action and communal living. These little busy-bodies are strictly tree-dwellers and seem to prefer the yellow or ponderosa pine as their home. The short bill and short tail distinguish them. Their communal living —probably made up of parents with young —may be a precautionary measure against surprise attack. Squeaking, chattering, and other noisy protests serve as danger warnings. Pygmy Nuthatches apparently bear a grudge against the diurnal Pygmy Owl, which also prefers the yellow pine environment. It is amusing to observe these little balls of feathers go into action as a mob upon spotting one of the little Owls. The Owl usually tries to throw off the molesters by dashing away to other cover. On one occasion while descending Deep Creek, near Eagle Peak, with a pack outfit, the author heard quite a commotion among a family of Pygmy Nuthatches in a large pine on the side of the canyon. The cause of the disturbance was soon apparent. When a Pygmy Owl dashed out and headed for other pines across the canyon, the whole delegation of chattering Nuthatches was close behind and to the sides as if to escort their unwelcome neighbor out of their temporary retreat.

Adults: Crown and hind neck olive, usually with white spot on nape. Rest of upperparts bluish or leaden gray; middle feathers of tail like back with basal half partly white; rest of feathers black, outer pairs tipped with slate and banded with white; throat white or buffy white; rest of underparts buffy; side and flanks bluish gray.

DISTRIBUTION. These sociable little birds are found throughout all forested mountains of the state, particularly in the Transition Zone, and except at nesting time, almost always in family groups. If there is any seasonal drift or movement it is seemingly of a vertical nature—up or down mountain slopes, rather than by direct migration. They may range as high as 10,000 feet on a slope with southern exposure, but such elevation is probably about the limit, while on the other hand, in winter they may descend to the lower pine belt, around 6,000 feet. The Pygmy is common in northern Santa Fe County, from 7,500 to 10,000 feet, where Jensen found a nest in a stump on June 1, containing six fresh eggs, and other nests with young.

NESTING. In preparing a nest for occupancy, the Pygmy Nuthatch displays astonishing industry, as was witnessed on April 19, in the Black Range, northeast of Silver City. The nesting hole which was being excavated by the pair was about 35 feet up in a dead pine. Working in shifts, one of the pair was inside hammering on the partly decayed wood in the cavity, and appearing at the entrance at intervals of about three minutes to fling the chips and dust to the wind with a quick flip of the bill. After about the third or fourth clearing, it would come out to rest. Immediately the other bird would go in and resume the hammering, bringing the cuttings to the surface at intervals as its mate had done. It seemed at that time as though all the Pygmies were preparing nesting cavities. One of these cavities, examined on April 20, although lined with feathers and other soft material, was still without eggs. Nest: From 30 to 40 feet from the ground in holes in pine or other trees; also in crevices of loose, thick bark; lined with feathers, down, and hair. Eggs: 6 or 7; white with red spots, thickest about large end.

CREEPERS

Family: CERTHIIDAE

CREEPERS, as their name suggests, spend much of their time creeping up and around the trunk or large limbs of trees, intently searching for and prying out with their long, slender, decurved bills, insects or larvae hidden in crevices of the bark. In scaling trees, they are aided by their sharp, curved claws, and stiff tails which serve as a prop. After searching a tree, they fly down to the base of another to repeat the upward movement.

(BROWN CREEPER

Certhia familiaris

5–5½″ long. Color pattern of sexes similar.

The Brown Creeper, or Rocky Mountain Creeper, as the New Mexico bird is usually called, occurs in all the higher forested mountains of the state. However, the author has never found these birds abundant anywhere. Because of their creeping movements and their brown plumage which blends so perfectly with the bark, they may often go unobserved. Once their squeaking notes are known, their presence may often be determined even though the birds are not seen. *Adults:* Upperparts dusky; head and back conspicuously streaked with white; primary coverts tipped with whitish; underparts white. Their spirited activity as they scale the bark of a tree and their progressively jerky movements are characteristic and an aid in identification. Because of their incessant cruising they usually can be observed only very briefly.

DISTRIBUTION. Summer range of the Brown Creeper is largely confined to forested mountains, at elevations between 7,000 and 11,000 feet. Those that occur, rarely, in the Animas and Peloncillo Mountains near the Mexican border are sometimes referred to as the Mexican Creeper. Some birds of the typical form may drop down to a lower altitude in winter, but it is not probable that many leave the state, since they do not seem constituted for long, continuous flight.

NESTING. Nests of Brown Creepers may be placed behind loosened slabs of bark, or in cavities of stumps or dead trees. Young were observed out of the nest at 7,500 feet elevation on the north side of Mt. Taylor on June 24, and adults were feeding young in Black Canyon 30 miles southwest of Chloride, at the same altitude, on June 28. Breeding birds often display considerable caution and deception about the location of their nests, as was noted in the Black Range, where a nest was situated about 35 feet from the ground under the partly decayed shell of a yellow pine snag. There were three outlets from the inner cavity, and when the parents entered one with food for the young, they would creep out at another and scale around the tree before flying away. On returning they used the same precaution, alighting low down and creeping up the trunk to one of the nest openings. *Nest:* Made of twigs and moss, and other soft material, lined with feathers. *Eggs:* Usually 5; white, spotted with reddish brown.

DIPPERS

Family: *CINCLIDAE*

THE DIPPER or Water Ouzel, the only representative of this family, is seldom found below 6,000 feet elevation.

(DIPPER

Cinclus mexicanus

7–8″ long. Color pattern of sexes alike.

Adults in summer: Slaty gray; underparts paler; head and neck brownish; tail feathers and primaries dark brown; eye ring white. *In winter:* Primaries and underparts margined with whitish.

To one acquainted with this unique composite of land and water bird, the name Dipper or Water Ouzel recalls an intrepid mountaineer as rugged as the mountain gorge and as playfully active as the rolling white-capped water of its preferred habitat. When overjoyed by roaring cascades or boulder stream rapids, it trills its enchanting melody, from a boulder in mid-stream, and then, as if to emphasize its exultation, dives headlong into icy, turbulent water, bobbing up seconds later some distance away. Its slight Wrenlike appearance, even to the upturned tail, belies its Ducklike conduct. Although seemingly lacking the diving bird's adaptations, such as web feet, for living in water, it does have an undercoat of heavy down which is impervious to water and cold, a protection it needs in diving and swimming or in walking under water, which may at times be partly frozen, to pick up aquatic life at the bottom of a stream. Below-zero weather seems to affect it but little. When not splashing about in the water, the Dipper may be seen on the bank, seeking food among the rocks, or perched on a boulder

in mid-stream, bobbing up and down while contemplating its next venture.

Some years ago while accompanying J. T. McMullen, a government predatory-animal hunter, with a pack outfit and seven bear dogs, up the Santa Barbara River in the high Sangre de Cristo Range north of the Truchas Peaks, in pursuit of grizzly bears which had been preying on cattle, the author observed at close range the self-reliance of young Dippers in their rugged way of life. Among the bear dogs were some young ones which were unaccustomed to the high, swift water of the swollen stream. At an exceptionally bad crossing it was necessary to cut a spruce tree to span the stream as a bridge to enable the dogs to cross safely. All the while the crossing was being prepared an alarmed Dipper kept flying back and forth over the stream. The cause for its anxiety was soon apparent—a nest on a large boulder that lay in mid-stream just above the crest of the turbulent water, the spray from which constantly showered it. After the dogs had been led across the improvised bridge, an examination was made of the nest, and it was found to contain 5 smoothly feathered young, almost adult size. On being disturbed, they piled into the raging, icy torrent, disappearing some distance below where the current was thrown into a confusing mass of billows against drifts that had lodged in the stream. That any had escaped being hammered to pieces or drowning seemed improbable. However, one was observed down the stream bank calmly perched on a drift just above the foam, while below three others were standing on stones or on the bank, imitating the conduct of the adults by flitting their tails and dipping their bills, ready to hop again into the roaring, tumbling water. Although they had their introduction to the turbulent waters only a few minutes before, they obviously were able to care for themselves.

DISTRIBUTION. The distribution of the Dipper is largely restricted to clear mountain streams, from about 6,000 feet to timber line or above. It is most common along the many permanent mountain streams of the Sangre de Cristo Range, but is found as far south as the White and Mogollon Mountains. It is resident except for a more or less seasonal movement between the lower and higher altitudes. "In July it was found in Wheeler Peak amphitheater at 11,400 feet" (Bailey). One was noted at 7,800 feet near Chama on December 21, when the water of the river was frozen in all but a few places.

NESTING. Dippers nest along most of the higher mountain streams of the state, but rarely below 6,500 feet elevation. On June 19 and 20, the author found Dippers nesting on the upper Red River, Taos County, at 10,000 to 11,000 feet. "Five young in nest, Rio Hondo, north of Taos, banded, June 24, 1942" (Lena McBee).

On June 5, Jensen and the author located a nest containing 5 fresh eggs in the Rio Chiquito Canyon, 25 miles northeast of Santa Fe, at 8,000 feet. On June 1, 1935, a dozen or more Dippers were noted in the Sapillo Canyon, from the Gila River to the Sapillo Loop road, a distance of about 4 miles; and a nest containing young birds was located in a pocket in a perpendicular cliff six feet above water. On October 1, 1955, John R. Patterson, ranger, Carlsbad Caverns National Park, saw 5 Dippers in Dark Canyon, in the foothills of the Guadalupe Mountains, about 30 miles southwest of Carlsbad, elevation about 6,000 feet, the most southern record of the birds yet noted in the state. Nest: On rock ledges; on boulders in mid-stream; in cavities in cliffs above water, and behind waterfalls. More recently on undersills of bridges. Nest: Oven-shaped, made of weed stems, leaves or pine needles; lined with mud. Interior of nest made "of twigs and non-absorbent wiry grass," the entire nest is usually covered with moss or lichens, and often so situated as to be sprayed sufficiently to keep the covering green—the whole a masterpiece of bird architecture. Eggs: 4 or 5; white.

DIPPER. R. J. Sim, U.S. Fish & Wildlife Service.

WRENS
Family: TROGLODYTIDAE

BECAUSE of their similarity in action and in color pattern, identification of the Wrens is not always easy. They are mostly small brownish-gray birds, no larger than sparrows—the Cactus Wren, which is larger and more colorful, being the exception. Wrens are very active and live largely in undergrowth near the ground, or among rocks and ledges, where they find ample protection. They are excellent songsters, and all are highly beneficial as destroyers of insects. Wrens display much skill in nest construction, and they lay rather large clutches of eggs, indicating that natural mortality, particularly among the young, may be high.

◖ HOUSE WREN
Troglodytes aedon
4½—5″ long. Color pattern of sexes alike.

The little House Wren, usually referred to as the Western House Wren, is a dweller of practically all wooded foothills and forested mountains of the state up to 10,000 feet. It also inhabits man's dwelling places. *Adults:* Upperparts cinnamon brown, barred with blackish; underparts grayish with a brownish wash. Its uniform grayish or brownish color pattern with no visible white in tail distinguishes it from other Wrens. The Greek, *troglodytes*, means "cave dweller;" *aedon*, "the songstress."

DISTRIBUTION. The House Wren is fairly common in practically all sections of the state, occurring even to timber line in the Sangre de Cristo Range. Bailey recorded it above Twining, around 10,500 feet, August 6; on Pecos Baldy at 11,600 feet, August 9; at Carlsbad, September 1 to 14. Goldman found it in the Burro

Mountains at 6,500 to 7,800 feet, September 15 to 23, and in the Magdalena Mountains, 6,500 to 9,000 feet, on September 4. The author has noted House Wrens in the Mogollon, Black, and Sacramento Ranges. Most of them are out of the state by the last of September. The first arrivals appear in the southern section around mid-April.

NESTING. This Wren nests most commonly from 7,000 to 8,500 feet. "In Santa Fe at 7,000 feet it nests in bird boxes; a nest was found in Santa Fe Canyon June 22" (Jensen). The higher altitude records seem to be due to the movement of the birds, old and young, to higher elevations after nesting season. The author found it nesting around 7,000 feet in Chloride Canyon, west of Chloride, and in the Guadalupe Mountains at 6,500 feet. *Nest:* In Woodpecker holes or natural cavities, in nesting boxes or about buildings; made largely of twigs and lined with feathers. *Eggs:* 5 to 7; pinkish white, thickly spotted with reddish brown or brownish purple.

WINTER WREN
Troglodytes troglodytes
4″ long. Color pattern of sexes alike.

The few authentic records indicate that the tiny Winter Wren is a rare visitor to the state. It is smaller and darker in coloration than the House Wren, and has a shorter tail. *Adults:* Upperparts dark brown, brighter on rump and upper-tail coverts, wings, tail, and back narrowly barred with blackish, line over eye; throat and breast tawny; underparts barred with blackish. It prefers humid, forested places. It was recorded on the Mescalero Apache Indian Reservation in September, at 8,500 feet, and at Cooney on December 26.

WRENS

Top: Canyon, Rock. Right: Bewick's, House, Marsh. Left: Cactus.
Orville O. Rice, N.M. Dept. of Game & Fish

Montgomery recorded it at Roswell, November 12, 1952, and Krehbiel reports it as accidental in the Clayton area. "We have, for the El Paso area these records, between 1938 and 1942, April 17 and 25th, October 17 and November 7" (Lena McBee).

⟮ BEWICK'S WREN
Thryomanes bewickii
5–5½" long. Color pattern of sexes alike.

The Bewick's, one of the small Wrens, is readily distinguished by the white line over the eye, and whitish tips of outer-tail feathers. *Adults:* Upperparts pale brown, tinged with rufous on rump; middle-tail feathers brown barred with black; underparts whitish, lighter on throat. It takes advantage of outbuildings about farms or ranches for nesting, although not as freely as does the House Wren. The Bewick's Wren has been divided into seventeen subspecies. It is named in honor of Thomas Bewick (1753-1828), English wood engraver, and author of *History of British Birds*, 1797-1804.

DISTRIBUTION. Distribution of the Bewick's Wren is rather spotty in the state. It is fairly common in certain localities and absent from others with seemingly comparable environment. It is an inhabitant of the wooded oak, pinyon, and juniper foothills, mainly in the southern half of the state, from 4,000 to 7,000 feet elevation. It appears to be resident, particularly in the southern section, although there may be a downward movement in the fall to 4,000 feet or lower. The author has found it most common in the foothills of the Black, Mogollon, and Guadalupe Ranges, also in the southwestern section— Animas and Peloncillo Mountains. It is rather common also about Santa Rosa and Tucumcari, around 4,000 feet.

NESTING. The Bewick's Wren nests in cavities of trees and in crevices of almost any sort that provide shelter, and in nesting boxes. It was noted feeding young in the Guadalupe Mountains, August 1 to 10 and at Santa Rosa in late May. Young out of nest were observed at Tucumcari, June 15; and adults with young were seen near Cloverdale, 5,000 feet elevation, June 28. *Nest:* Made of twigs and lined with feathers. *Eggs:* 5 to 7; white or pinkish; finely marked around larger end with reddish brown and lilac.

CAROLINA WREN
Thryothorus ludovicianus
5–6" long. Color pattern of sexes alike.

The Carolina Wren, common in the eastern and southern states, is a rare visitor to New Mexico and the Southwest. *Adults:* Upperparts rufous; wings and tail barred with dusky, wing and lateral tail feathers with whitish spots, conspicuous whitish stripe over eye; underparts buffy, throat white. The Carolina is one of the largest of the Wrens.

STATE RECORDS. Records of this Wren apply only to the Pecos and Rio Grande Valleys. One was observed on July 14, 1955, on Bosque Refuge by Fleetwood, who states, "This is the fifth time the bird has been seen or heard here." Montgomery recorded it at Roswell June 6, 1951. There are no nesting records for the state.

⟮ CACTUS WREN
Campylorhynchus brunneicapillum
7–8" long. Color pattern of sexes alike.

The Cactus, the largest of the Wrens, makes its home in the cactus and other thorny shrubs of arid lands. Most descriptive is Mrs. Bailey's account of this desert dweller: "The large Cactus Wren, with his heavily spotted breast, caught sight of perhaps as he flies from a cactus or yucca to a thorny mesquite adds a grateful touch of desert life to the interesting landscape with its strange plant forms, so marvelously adapted to their conditions. His song, which he sings with abandon—head thrown back and tail hanging—seems as shorn of ornament as the cactus but, grating and monotonous as it is, harmonizes so well with the surroundings that he seems, indeed, to sing the song of the desert." *Adults:* Bill almost an inch long; top of head to neck black with white line on each side; back brown with white median stripes; tail rounded, middle feathers brown barred with black; underparts white shading into cinnamon brown posteriorly; throat and breast heavily spotted with black.

DISTRIBUTION. The Cactus Wren is a common resident of the Lower Sonoran Zone in the southern half of the state. Its distribution is confined almost wholly to the thorny cactus, mesquite, catclaw, brushland type, north to Socorro in the Rio Grande Valley; Carrizozo in the Tularosa Basin; and Hagerman in the Pecos Valley. It ranges up to 6,000 feet in the more arid foothills. The bulky grass nests are often clues to the presence of the birds even though they may skillfully keep out of sight. Favorite nesting retreats are the large clumps of cholla cactus, a familiar part of the Sonoran Life Zones. Just what renders Cactus Wrens impervious to the sharp spines of cholla cactus, so painful to man, is a mystery. The spines, however, provide effective protection against most potential enemies. The prairie racer, or coachwhip snake, sometimes succeeds in robbing the nest if in mesquite or like bushes, but always under the most vigorous protest on the part of the defending birds. On one occasion upon going to a nest in a mesquite bush, in response to distress notes of a pair of Cactus Wrens, the author was confronted by a prairie racer, which thrust its head defiantly from the domed nest. It was too late to save the

nestlings but not too late to prevent a repetition of depredation by this particular marauder.

NESTING. Like the Verdin, the Cactus Wren usually has a surplus of nests which it utilizes as roosting retreats. Judging by the great numbers of old and new nests observed in areas of normal populations, considerable time must be devoted to building new nests and repairing old ones. Nests with eggs have been recorded from late April to the middle of August, indicating that second broods might be raised. On May 28 a nest containing well developed young was noted six miles northeast of Engle. On the same date a nest containing eggs was examined in the foothills of the Cuchillo Mountains northwest of Cuchillo, 5,600 feet elevation; while previously, on April 23, a nest containing eggs was recorded at Silver City. *Nest:* In cholla cactus, yucca, Spanish dagger, mesquite, catclaw, or other thorny shrubs. Large, considering size of bird; made of grass, retort-shaped with horizontal, tunnel-like entrance; lined with assortment of feathers and other soft materials. *Eggs:* 4 to 6; buffy, ground cover hidden by reddish-brown spotting.

⟨ LONG-BILLED MARSH WREN
Telmatodytes palustris
4½—5½" long. Color pattern of sexes alike.

The Long-billed Marsh Wren is a pert, active little bird which is easily distinguished by the white line over the eye, and black and white stripes on the back. *Adults:* Top of head and foreparts are black; underparts grayish. Its habit of clinging to rushes and other aquatic vegetation of marshes, springs, or lake shores, is also helpful in identification. Suitable habitat for the Marsh Wren is greatly restricted in the arid Southwest.

DISTRIBUTION. The Long-billed Marsh

Wren is listed as "winter resident, common" at Bosque del Apache, and as "transient visitor, occasional" at Bitter Lake Refuge. In summer it is most common about the mountain lakes of the northern part of the state, particularly Burford and other lakes on the Jicarilla Apache Indian Reservation.

NESTING. The author has found the Long-billed Marsh Wren nesting at Burford Lake, and Bailey found it common at both Lakes La Jara and San Rafael, near Grants. Nest: Large and globular with entrance on the side; woven of wet tule stems, with wet grass and algae matted in, and a lining of dry algae and tule pith. Eggs: 5 to 10; thickly dotted with chocolate brown.

⟨ CANYON WREN

Catherpes mexicanus

5½—5¾" long. Color pattern of sexes alike. (Pl. I)

Few birds so enliven the dark recesses of canyon and cave as does the vivacious Canyon Wren. Its sudden clear outburst of song, high-pitched, tapering off on descending scale and usually concluding with a revived repetition of trills, never fails to bring the bird lover who hears it to rapt attention, although no bird may be in sight. The white throat and breast, body dotted with small dusky and whitish spots, the characteristic high-tailed pose, and its attachment to canyon and cave enable an observer to recognize it immediately. It seems to revel in the security and seclusion of caves, the maw of the great Carlsbad Caverns, where its amplified greeting may thrill the visitor, being no exception.

DISTRIBUTION. The Canyon Wrens inhabit practically all of the higher and more rugged mountainous sections of the state. Although some local movement from established range takes place in the fall, these Wrens do not seem to follow any

well-defined migratory pattern. Several were found in the Guadalupe Mountains, at 6,500 feet in January. Jensen reported them common in the canyons about Santa Fe. They were met with throughout the Black and Mogollon Ranges, and less frequently to the northward. Their altitudinal range extends from 5,000 to 7,500 feet, although there are lower as well as higher recordings, the exceptions depending on the ruggedness of the country. Since they live for the most part about sheltering canyon walls and caves, they probably are little affected by winter storms.

NESTING. Since it is practically a resident species, the nesting range of the Canyon Wren is coextensive with its distribution. The author found nests with eggs on May 16 and 26, at 6,000 to 6,300 feet in Chloride Canyon, west of Chloride, and on May 31, young were noted in a nest in the same canyon. Wetmore found it nesting in the canyon walls at Burford Lake. Nest: In crevices of rocks, on ledges in tunnels or caves, and sometimes about buildings; compact, made of twigs, grass, and moss; lined with feathers, and wool when available; almost always placed where completely protected from weather. Eggs: 4 or 5; these are spotted, chiefly around the large end, with reddish brown.

⟨ ROCK WREN

Salpinctes obsoletus

5—6¼" long. Color pattern of sexes alike.

In size, conduct, and preference of environment, the Rock and the Canyon Wrens are similar. Either almost always will be seen on, under, or among rocks. The coloration of the Rock Wren is a perfect simulation of its drab surroundings. Adults: Upperparts dull grayish brown, finely flecked with black and white dots;

rump light brown, tail rounded, tipped with buffy brown; underparts dull whitish (not white as in the Canyon Wren); brownish on flanks; chest usually lightly streaked.

Its notes and song are more harsh than those of the Canyon Wren. It is a friendly associate of man where his dwelling place is in keeping with its chosen habitat— rocky canyons and ledges.

DISTRIBUTION. Rock Wrens are statewide in distribution. Although they appear to be resident in the southern half of the state, there is evidence that most of the birds vacate the northern section for the winter. This conclusion is based on the fact that the birds may be seen at this time only, throughout the eastern and southeastern plains areas where there are cutbanks or sand dunes with holes and crevices which serve as substitutes for rock shelters. At such times they may be seen about buildings, or perched on a rock in characteristic bobbing fashion, while pouring out their joyous trilling notes which lend charm and animation to what might otherwise be lifeless surroundings. The Rock Wren is one of the few species adapted to all life zones of the state.

NESTING. No less extraordinary than its distribution is the individuality displayed by the Rock Wren in the building of its nest, which is usually placed in holes or crevices of stone ledges or soil banks. Unlike other Wrens, it has an intriguing way of "paving" the entrance to its nesting cavity, and often the area around the nest proper, with small flat stones. The purpose of such embellishment is open to speculation, but since the treated entrance is usually just large enough for the birds to enter, it may be assumed that the purpose is one of concealment and camouflage. Approximately a quart of such stones was removed from the entrance of a nest in the foothills of the Guadalupe Mountains. Near Santa Rosa, the Baileys found eight nests; two were on the ground under stones, the others in crevices or holes in rocks. "In two nests that we found," Mrs. Bailey states, "there were over 80 pieces of stone, varying from one-half to one-and-a-half inches in length. One contained 260 stones, and a quart of sticks and lining material. In a nest we discovered in the wall of the ruined church of Pecos Pueblo, fragments of Indian pottery were used instead of stones." Such accumulations of stones and nesting material in places which are particularly attractive to them indicate years of utilization. The method and the skill employed by these dwellers of rocky places in eradicating evidence of nest location are a marvel. The nesting period usually extends from the middle of April to late August. Young were noted in a nest August 25 near timber line on Pecos Baldy. On July 4 young were seen in a nest 8 miles northwest of Hillsboro, at 7,500 feet. Nest: Usually in crevice or hole in rock ledges, soil banks, hollow stumps, or about buildings; made of weed stems and grasses, lined with rootlets and pieces of bark. Eggs: 6 to 8; white.

MOCKINGBIRDS and THRASHERS
Family: MIMIDAE

SIX SPECIES of this interesting family nest in New Mexico: the Mockingbird and the Catbird, and the Bendire's, Curve-billed, Crissal, and Sage Thrashers. The Brown Thrasher, though rare, does occur throughout the eastern portion. Of this strictly American group, the Mockingbird is best known. With the exception of the Brown, Thrashers are by no means as rare in their preferred habitat as one might be led to believe. The favorite retreats of the desert forms, such as the Bendire's and Curve-billed, are the thorny shrub-cactus associations of the southern and south-western sections. Thrashers live on or near the ground, and are so adept in evasion that caution and patience are necessary in order to see them. Most of them are fine songsters and, as the family names implies, are largely vocal mimics. With the exception of the Sage, which is a some-what smaller form, Thrashers have long, more or less curved bills, long, wide and rounded tails, and relatively long, sturdy legs which serve them well in their Quail-like running movements on the ground, a gift they largely rely on to permit them to keep out of sight. The Catbird is some-what smaller than the Mockingbird, but like the Mocker, has a predilection for the habitation of man, especially yards and gardens that provide food and ample nearby escape cover. While its notes are less pleasing than those of some of the Thrashers, the song of the Catbird never-theless possesses a distinctive and varied quality. Unfortunately, only a limited portion of New Mexico is favored by the seasonal appearance of the Catbird.

⟨ MOCKINGBIRD
Mimus polyglottos
10—11″ long. Color pattern of sexes alike.

Its designations, *Mimus* (Latin), "a mimic" and *polyglottos* (Greek), "many-tongued," are truly descriptive of the prime characteristic of the Mockingbird. Its repertoire of mimicked songs of a host of other species sets it apart in musical rendition. Its friendliness, vivacity, and spontaneous outburst of a medley from dawn into—and at times through—the night, are unrivaled qualities which have endeared the Mocker to all who know it. Few birds have been immortalized through song and poetry as has the Mock-ingbird. It has the distinction of having been designated the State Bird in five states. In its musical vocabulary are mimicked songs of birds not to be found within its nesting orbit, indicating clearly that the Mocker has a retentive memory. At nesting time it may be heard imitating with superb accuracy the song of a King-bird or of a Bobwhite heard perhaps months previously, a hundred miles away.

This acrobat of the air has, in summer, the unique habit of vaulting upward and back to its accustomed perch, all the while giving voice to its exuberant joy. Charac-teristic also is its nature, when running about on the ground, of alternately raising and lowering its wings. The aerial display, as well as its conduct on the ground, may be designed in part as a warning to others of its kind to respect its pre-empted do-main. Woe unto any intruder who dares to violate its borders.

Adults: Upperparts grayish brown; wings and tail blackish brown, conspicuous white patches on wing; underparts white, white-tipped outer-tail feathers. Eyes, pale yellow.

DISTRIBUTION. The summer distribution of the Mockingbird is virtually statewide. While it shuns the highest, more densely forested mountains, its summer distribution extends from the lowest and most arid sections into the semi-forested mountain area of the north, up to 8,000 feet as, for example, about Burford Lake and Tres Piedras, and like elevations elsewhere. While most of the birds leave the state for the winter, some remain in and about the brushy bottom lands of the Pecos Valley (Carlsbad), the Rio Grande Valley (Las Cruces, Hatch, Socorro), and the lower Gila Valley. There are even winter records for Santa Fe (Jensen), and "Los Alamos, 7,300 feet, winter of 1954-1955" (Burton Lewis). The more northern records are exceptional and are probably of birds largely influenced by the presence of enticing food, adequate ground cover, and mild winter weather. Most of the birds are out of the state by the end of September, returning about April 15.

NESTING. The Mocker displays little of the skill usually employed by other birds of like size in camouflaging or concealing nests. Most other birds employ deceit or feign affliction to deflect intruders from nests or young, but the Mockingbird elects to meet any intruder in open aggressive combat. It seemingly enjoys terrorizing cats, dogs, Roadrunners, or any other suspected enemy that chances to venture too near its sanctum, by dashing about threateningly, all the while giving vent to its indignation in outbursts of raucous notes. So persistent are Mockers in keeping their nesting cycles going that the foundation for a new nest is frequently laid by the time the current brood are ready to leave their occupied nest. Consequently, little time is lost between broods, and two clutches of eggs a season are not unusual. Close observation often discloses heavy loss of eggs and serious mortality of nestlings as the result of storms and depredation by snakes. Normal populations, however, usually are maintained through their systematic nesting procedure. *Nest:* A bulky structure of coarse twigs, invariably lined with grass roots, evenly placed in the perfectly formed cup or bowl of the nest; in Condalia, mesquite, hackberry, native chinaberry, also in rose bushes, vines, shrubs or in the lower branches of trees about dwellings. *Eggs:* 3 or 4; pale blue or green, speckled with brown.

❪ CATBIRD
Dumetella carolinensis
8—9″ long. Color pattern of sexes alike.

Although the Catbird differs in some respects from other members of the family, its habits are similar. Like that of the Mockingbird and Thrashers, when the bird is on the ground, the tail usually is held upright. Adept at concealment in thickets, the Catbird is more often heard than seen. Besides its mewing note, which has given the bird its name, it has a varied warble-like song. *Adults:* Dark gray, appearing almost black as they dash from cover to cover; crown and tail black; undertail coverts dark mahogany.

DISTRIBUTION. The Catbird, principally a summer visitor, is rather uncommon, and its presence is unpredictable. As is true of the Bobolink, in migration the Catbird adheres to an east-west rather than the north-south pattern followed by most other migrants. Although this deviation may be influenced by the eastward drainage of both the Canadian and Dry Cimarron Rivers, that fact does not fully explain the contradiction, since the birds nest in the Upper Pecos and Rio Grande Valleys, both of which represent north-south drainage courses. The bird even crosses the Continental Divide and nests about Dulce in a canyon tributary to the San Juan River, which flows to the west. Its more recent occurrence in the southwest part of the state lends further confusion to its status. A striking example of its unpredictable presence is the observation made by Wayne Bohl on June 20, 1955, in the northern part of the Mogollon Mountains, where, he states, a singing Catbird, evidently one of a breeding pair, persistently remained in thick bushes on Willow Creek, near the Ranger Station. This location is more than a hundred miles from any other known nesting place. Montgomery recorded a Catbird in his yard at Roswell, June 6, 1951, while Durrie observed one in his yard at Albuquerque, October 8, 1956.

NESTING. An interesting thing about the Catbird's spotty occurrence is that almost invariably a nesting pair is represented, indicating that pairs might remain in close contact when migrating. On June 8, the author recorded a pair feeding young on the Pecos River just north of the town of Pecos. He also found the Catbird breeding in a canyon of the San Juan River drainage, just west of Dulce. On June 24, Jensen noted it feeding young at Santa Fe, and it was found nesting in Pueblo Canyon north of Taos. *Nest:* Usually placed near the ground in thick bottomland bushes or vines; made of twigs, bark, and rootlets. *Eggs:* 4; deep greenish blue, unspotted.

BROWN THRASHER
Toxostoma rufum

10–12″ long. Color pattern of sexes alike.

The Brown Thrasher, the only Thrasher found in the Eastern states and in the Middle West, occurs only sparingly in New Mexico. *Adults:* Upperparts rust red with a bronze luster, decidedly streaked be-

low. Its reddish back, straight bill and yellow eye are its best identification marks.

DISTRIBUTION. The Brown Thrasher has been recorded at various points in the state, from the Rio Grande Valley eastward. However, it has been observed more frequently in the northeastern section. The author has records of this bird for Carlsbad over a period of many years including October 8, 1951 and October 10, 1954. "One was observed at Alameda, February 25, 1951" (Durrie). "One or more each winter [El Paso area] prior to 1955" (Lena McBee). "On November 6, 1956 a male Brown Thrasher was found dead on the campus here at State College [Las Cruces]; apparently it was hit by a car" (Richard F. Johnston). It is listed "transient visitor, rare" at Bosque del Apache Refuge.

NESTING. There is no definite record of the Brown Thrasher nesting in the state. The author located a pair in a willow-bordered meadow northwest of Logan; although their conduct indicated that they were nesting, no nest was found. In the summer of 1955, Mr. and Mrs. Miers Johnson repeatedly saw about the shrubbery and lawn at their home on the lake shore at Carlsbad a pair which they believed were nesting. *Nest:* Usually in thorny bushes or vines; made of twigs, leaves, and rootlets. *Eggs:* 4 or 5; buffy, washed with green and spotted with reddish brown.

[BENDIRE'S THRASHER
Toxostoma bendirei

9–10″ long. Color pattern of sexes alike.

The Bendire's—whose range overlaps that of the Curve-billed and Crissal—is smaller than either. Formerly Bendire's Thrasher was believed to be a rare species in the state, probably because of its shyness. However, more recent and intensive field work disclosed it to be more common

THRASHERS
Top: Catbird, Sage Thrasher, Brown Thrasher
Middle: Bendire's Thrasher, Curve-billed Thrasher. Bottom: Crissal Thrasher
Orville O. Rice, N.M. Dept. of Game & Fish

than was supposed. It is a fine songster; its varied songs are considered by some to be superior to those of all other Thrashers, and in this respect it is a close rival to the Mockingbird. It is named in honor of Major Charles Bendire (1836-97). *Adults:* Upperparts and tail grayish brown; outer-tail feathers tipped with white; underparts buff; throat almost white with small brownish spots; flanks brown. Bill slightly decurved and shorter than that of either the Curve-billed or Crissal.

DISTRIBUTION. The Bendire's Thrasher is not uncommon in the southwest corner of the state from about Columbus west to the Arizona line and north to Steins Pass and Lordsburg. It is most common, however, in the foothills of the Animas and Peloncillo Mountains, preferring a cactus and thorn-brush environment.

NESTING. The first nest of Bendire's Thrasher recorded for the state was found by the author on June 18, 1926. It was on the border of a dry sand wash about ten miles west of Animas. Judging by the lateness of the season, the eggs may have been a second clutch. The nest was in a hackberry bush that grew in association with desert willow, catclaw, and Apacheplume (*Fallugia paradoxa*). On May 27, 1951, several adults with broods of young out of nests were located in a cholla-chittimwood (*Bumelia rigida*) thicket in Adobe (Doby) Canyon northeast of the Animas Mountains, 15 miles south of Animas. *Nest:* Rather small and compact; made of twigs, grass, and rootlets. *Eggs:* 3 or 4; greenish spotted with reddish brown.

⟨ CURVE-BILLED THRASHER

Toxostoma curvirostre

10—12″ long. Color pattern of sexes alike.

The Curve-billed, one of the larger of the Thrashers inhabiting the state, is the most common in occurrence, although because of its shyness, its presence in typical habitat often escapes notice. Its pleasing, restrained, liquid warble is somewhat like that of the Thrush, and is not confined to the nesting season. Even during calm winter days, the notes, though subdued, may be heard from some perch above a brush retreat. Like others of its kind, it lives on or close to the ground. *Adults:* Upperparts grayish brown; whitish throat; light mottled underparts; tail darker brown, long, wide, and slightly rounded; bill 1¼ inches, black, decurved, but not to the degree of the Crissal. Eyes, orange.

DISTRIBUTION. The Curve-billed is usually resident where found in the state. For the most part, this Thrasher inhabits the southern section from the Pecos Valley to the Arizona line, although tongues of its range extend north to Roswell in the Pecos Valley and to Socorro along the Rio Grande. Its distribution is practically the same as that of the Crissal. Neither species occurs in the higher, forested areas, both seemingly preferring a habitat of thorny desert shrubs, and particularly the cholla cactus. It could well be designated as the Cholla Cactus Thrasher.

NESTING. While the Curve-billed Thrasher nests in a variety of thorny and other desert shrubs, it seemingly prefers the cholla cactus. The feet and legs of the Thrashers, like those of the Cactus Wren, are apparently impervious to the sharp spines that protect the various cacti. Since the nesting period extends from early May well into late summer, it is quite probable that these Thrashers lay more than one clutch of eggs in a season. *Nest:* Usually made of thorny twigs and lined with grass roots; rather a bulky structure and almost always conspicuously in evidence, which probably accounts, in part at least, for the bird's selection of a forbidding location. *Eggs:* 4 or 5; pale bluish green, uniformly speckled with brown.

CRISSAL THRASHER

Toxostoma dorsale

11½—12½″ long. Color pattern of sexes alike.

Like the other Thrashers, the Crissal is shy, and spends most of its time on or near the ground. Its favorite habitat, unlike that of the Curve-billed, is stream-bottom borders with thick brush, such as Condalia, mesquite, and tornillo. Its long bill is well adapted for probing hard soil for insects and grubs. *Adults:* Upperparts brownish gray; wings and tail somewhat darker; under-tail feathers deep chestnut; underparts light gray. The Crissal is readily distinguished from its close relative, the Curve-billed Thrasher, which occurs over practically all of the former's range. The Crissal has a more pronounced decurved bill, 1½ inches long, and unspotted breast. Its under-tail feathers contain decidedly more chestnut red, conspicuous when the bird is in flight.

DISTRIBUTION. The Crissal Thrasher ranges in the Pecos Valley north to about Roswell, and in the Rio Grande Valley to Socorro, west to the Arizona line. It is generally resident where found.

NESTING. On May 24, the author found a nest containing 4 well-incubated eggs, near Truth or Consequences. *Nest:* Of twigs, lined with fine grass, rootlets, and particles of bark; usually in mesquite, Condalia, or other thorny shrub or cactus. *Eggs:* 2 to 4; bluish green.

SAGE THRASHER

Oreoscoptes montanus

8—9″ long. Color pattern of sexes alike.

The Sage Thrasher, the smallest of the family, somewhat resembles the Mockingbird in action. Its song also is somewhat like that of the Mockingbird, but consists more of short warbling notes, repeated in succession. It may be heard almost any season wherever it occurs, even when snow is on the ground. It also has a characteristic nasal *chuck* frequently heard during a concentrated migration movement, probably a means of continued social contact. In addition to wild fruits and berries, its diet consists of a variety of beetles, weevils, and other insects. One recording of stomach contents disclosed 62 per cent grasshoppers, indicating its high economic value. *Adults:* Upperparts grayish drab; wings blackish with white bars; tail blackish tipped with white; underparts whitish, distinctly marked with dusky stripes; bill short and straight; eyes yellow.

DISTRIBUTION. Few birds have been more appropriately named than has the Sage Thrasher. Its summer and nesting range in the state is confined almost wholly to the big or purple sage (*Artemisia tridentata*) area, distributed from the Upper Rio Grande Valley (Embudo), northward and west to the Arizona line, rarely below 7,000 feet. The bird's attachment to a sage environment is so intimate that outside of the big sage area it is usually seen in a similar vegetative type such as rabbitbrush or sand sage. While most of the Sage Thrashers are out of the state by late November, some remain in the southern part throughout the winter. The main spring northward movement begins to enter the state in mid-March. On April 4, 1953, many were observed in the Milnesand-Portales section of Roosevelt County. On May 2 and 3, 1935, the author made an observation trip in the country east and north of Tres Piedras, elevation about 7,500 feet. A few days previously, four to five inches of snow had fallen. Even so, Sage Thrashers and Sage Sparrows were everywhere in evidence.

In its southward migration it often may be seen in considerable numbers or even in flocks in the central section of the state where rabbitbrush, one-seeded juniper

(*Juniperus monosperma*) and pinyon constitute the prevailing cover. The Latin designation, *montanus*, implying that it is a mountain bird, is misleading, since it shuns the higher, heavily forested areas.

NESTING. Nesting of the Sage Thrasher in the State is almost wholly coextensive with the distribution of the big sage. However, Jensen recorded two nests in rabbit-brush near Santa Fe. The author found it nesting about Tres Piedras in late May and at Burford Lake in July. "Nest with 3 eggs, in Arroyo Hondo, north of Taos, July 12, 1942" (Lena McBee). *Nest:* Usually in sagebrush, but sometimes on the ground; bulky, made of plant stems, sage twigs and particles of bark; lined with fine roots. *Eggs:* 4; greenish blue, spotted with brown.

THRUSHES, SOLITAIRES, AND BLUEBIRDS
Family: TURDIDAE

THIS group includes some of the finest songsters, as well as some of our most attractive and beneficial American birds. Representatives of this family have relatively long legs, wings longer than tails, bills rather slender; and the young have spotted breasts. In migration, they spread far and wide. Most Thrushes, particularly the Robin, fit in well with urban and rural habitation of man, where they frequent lawns, shrubbery, and parks. Thus they offer a better opportunity for identification than do most other birds.

ROBIN
Turdus migratorius
10—11″ long. Color pattern of sexes similar. (Pl. XXII)

The Robin is among the most widely known, most beneficial, and most loved of American birds. His friendly association with man makes it possible for everyone to see the Robin at some period of the year. In conduct and plumage pattern it is so unlike any other species occurring in the state that identification can easily be made. *Adult male:* Head blackish; upperparts slaty flecked with black; chin white; throat black streaked with white; breast and underparts reddish brown; tail blackish. *Adult female:* Somewhat paler in color. Young have spotted breasts, and brownish underparts. Because it is so familiar, the Robin is often used as a standard, particularly of size, in describing other birds. At migration time it is most at home on lawns or parks, where it may often be seen running about, or cocking its head to locate the source of some faint crunching or grating sound of a lawn or garden pest, which its sensitively attuned ears detect. It is through probing for plant pests and their larvae from the soil that its economic value is most evident.

DISTRIBUTION. Summer range of the Robins is confined largely to forested mountains above 6,500 feet elevation. During fall and spring migration they may occur any place. Although most of them are out of the state during the coldest part of the winter, some remain in the southern part. A majority of these are probably migrants from further north. A dependable source of preferred food would do much to hold them year-round for it is undoubtedly the scarcity of food rather than the rigors of winter which causes them to leave. Prolific fruit-bearing shrubs, such as currants and yellow Pyracantha, the latter containing berries throughout the winter, are an attraction to Robins. They may be induced to remain about residences where feeding stations are provided for their benefit. Great fall and winter concentrations occur in the Upper

Sonoran Zone, in the central and southern sections of the state, when there is a heavy juniper (*Juniperus monosperma*) mast, a relished food of both Robins and Bluebirds. Such concentrations have been observed particularly over the juniper-pinyon divide country between Carrizozo and San Antonio, the wooded mesa country south of Laguna, and about the lower slopes of the San Mateo Mountains. When such sustained food supply is lacking, the birds may wander far and wide or vacate the state almost entirely. Like Mockingbirds, Robins may at times become locally destructive to fruits and berries, but their economic value as destroyers of insect pests usually outweighs any temporary damage they may do.

NESTING. The principal nesting range of the Robin is the forested mountains from 6,500 feet to timber line, although some may nest down to 5,000 feet (Albuquerque), 4,000 feet or even lower in urban districts where lawns and parks with evergreens are available. They require ample cover and a more humid environment than natural arid conditions provide. The nesting period extends from mid-May to mid-August. *Nest:* Usually near the ground but sometimes at considerable height, compact and rather bulky, made of twigs, weed stems, leaves and grasses plastered together with mud; lined with rootlets. *Eggs:* Usually 4; greenish blue.

❰ HERMIT THRUSH
Hylocichla guttata

7–8″ long. Color pattern of sexes alike. (Pl. I)

As its name indicates, the Hermit, the most common of the Thrushes which occur in New Mexico, lives mostly in the solitary seclusion of dense undercover, preferably near forest streams. The songs of few other birds are so refined and pleasing as those of the Thrushes. It is at nesting time that the Hermit approaches perfection as a delightful and consoling songster. The author fondly recalls a peaceful evening with the Hermit Thrush under the primitive forest conditions of Upper Diamond Creek near the summit of the Black Range. Pack and saddle animals were resting in a nearby meadow after the long upward climb by trail. The refreshing coolness of an afternoon July shower and the fragrance of damp, moss-covered soil and conifers permeated the air. From the silent depths, attuned to the wilderness calm, came the soft, blended, liquid notes of a Hermit Thrush, seemingly more ethereal than earthly, to prevail all too briefly, fading into silence with the engulfing twilight.

The Hermit can be distinguished from the Swainson's and the Veery Thrush by its tail, which is reddish, but which in the other two is a uniform brown. *Adults:* White underparts shaded with grayish olive on sides; breast tinged with buffy and marked with numerous large dusky spots.

DISTRIBUTION. In migration, the Hermit Thrush may be seen in low country wherever there is shrub or tree cover. This Thrush is most commonly heard and seen in summer in the higher, well-watered forested areas, particularly in the Sangre de Cristo, Sacramento, Mogollon Mountains, and the Black Range. While most of the birds are out of the state during the severer part of the winter, some do remain, particularly in the southern part, where there is ample cover along streams or about parks and lawns. Watering and feeding stations are incentives for them to remain throughout the winter.

NESTING. Unlike the Swainson's and the Veery, which are found only in the northern section of the state in summer, the Hermit nests throughout the forested mountains. It prefers a humid environment. Jensen recorded, June 1 to 20, nests with fresh eggs in the mountains near Santa Fe, and the author found a nest on June 25 southwest of Chloride, at about

6,800 feet, containing young, and another nest with eggs in the same area on July 6, indicating that nesting is confined largely to June and early July. *Nest:* In bushes or trees; usually from 4 to 10 feet from the ground; made almost wholly of bark and coarse grasses, covered with moss. *Eggs:* 4 or 5; light greenish blue, normally unspotted.

❲ SWAINSON'S (RUSSET-BACKED) THRUSH

Hylocichla ustulata

6¾—7½″ long. Color pattern of sexes alike.

Swainson's Thrush, sometimes listed as Olive-backed, seems to be a rather rare summer resident of the state. *Adults:* Upperparts olive brown; wings and tail darker than back; eye ring distinctly buffy; sides of head washed with tawny; throat and chest buffy; chest with triangular olive brown feathers; lower underparts white; sides pale brown. In winter, colors are similar but brighter; upperparts olive brown to russet; underparts more buffy.

DISTRIBUTION. This Thrush undoubtedly occurs more commonly in migration than the few records indicate, since it is known to summer in the northern part of the state.

NESTING. The only nesting record of the Swainson's Thrush for the state seems to be that by Fleetwood and the author: on July 15, 1951, a pair with young out of the nest was located on the Brazos River near Parkview, at 7,000 feet. The nesting location was the steep south bank of the river, overgrown with brush, vines, and trees. Field work may disclose that the bird is a regular breeder in that part of the state, since it is known to nest regularly in adjacent parts of Colorado. *Nests:* In vines or bushes in moist places, usually near water; made largely of mosses and shreds of bark. *Eggs:* 4 or 5; light greenish blue, spotted with rusty and brown.

VEERY (WILLOW) THRUSH

Hylocichla fuscescens

7—7¾″ long. Color pattern of sexes alike.

Seemingly quite rare in the state, the Veery Thrush prefers alder and willow thickets. The fact that it is quite shy and is rarely seen in the open may account, in part, for the few records for the state. There seems to be no definite account of specimens having been taken. There are two notations of sight records only: one at El Rito, 6,500 feet; the other on Pueblo Creek near Taos, at 7,000 feet. The fact that it occurs in Colorado would indicate that it should pass through New Mexico. It may be distinguished from the Swainson's and the Hermit by lack of white eye ring. *Adults:* Upperparts uniformly olive or cinnamon brown; throat buffy white; chest pale buffy, lightly spotted with triangular brown spots; median underparts white; sides washed with gray.

❲ WESTERN BLUEBIRD

Sialia mexicana

6½—7″ long. Color pattern of sexes different.

The Western Bluebird, also known as the Chestnut-backed and the Mexican Bluebird, is a relative of the more widely distributed Bluebird of the eastern United States. The Bluebirds shun undercover. Western Bluebirds are seen for the most part on the wing, in treetops, or, in migration, often on fence or telephone wires. At times, they may be seen suspending themselves on hovering wings in midair, after the manner of Sparrow Hawks, as they locate surface insects, which they snap up, then moving on to repeat the feeding process. *Adult male, in spring:* Upperparts dark purplish blue except for chestnut back and scapulars; chest band and sides chestnut, separating blue of throat from that of rest of underparts, which fades to gray on lower underparts. *Adult female, in spring:* Back dull brown; rump, tail, and wings bluish; outer-tail feathers and outer primaries edged with white; underparts grayish or brownish, sometimes tinged with blue. *Adult male in fall:* Similar to summer male, but blue of head, neck, and chest obscured by brownish feather tips; upperparts duller than in spring plumage. *Adult female in fall and winter:* Similar to summer female, but head and back decidedly bluish, and brown of underparts more chestnut.

DISTRIBUTION. Summer distribution of the Western Bluebird is confined to wooded and forested mountains, from 6,500 to 9,000 feet, usually among yellow pines. By late July, old and young begin to congregate in the high valleys, later moving into the lower foothills and onto the mesas, particularly where the one-seeded juniper is the dominant tree, the berries of which constitute a good portion of their winter diet. Great flocks of the wintering birds often may be seen over the vast spread of this juniper from Mountainair southward, and over similar wooded types west of the Rio Grande, and also about the Guadalupe Mountains. While some may fan out over the more arid country and at times even over the eastern high plains, winter concentrations are usually confined very largely to the one-seeded juniper zone. Some of these birds probably move out of the state in the fall, but a vast majority of residents—reinforced by incoming migrants from the north—account for heavy winter populations wherever there is a dependable supply of preferred food.

NESTING. The Western Bluebird breeds throughout practically all forested mountains of New Mexico. It nests commonly in the foothills and mountains about Santa Fe, fresh eggs having been found from May 20 to June 20, and in all mountains as far south as forests occur. The au-thor has found it nesting commonly in both the Black and San Mateo Ranges (7,000 to 8,000 feet) in May. Following the nesting season it commonly moves higher, to or even above timber line. *Nest:* Usually in Woodpecker holes in dead pines but also in hollows of trees or in nesting boxes. *Eggs:* 4 to 6; pale blue.

⟮ MOUNTAIN BLUEBIRD
Sialia currucoides
6½–7¾" long. Color pattern of sexes different. (Pl. I)

The Mountain Bluebird prefers a mountainous habitat and is therefore largely confined to western United States. In late fall and winter it wanders into open country, even onto the high plains. While other blue birds of similar size, such as the Blue Grosbeak, occur in New Mexico, they are of a different shade, are shyer and spend more time in concealing cover, usually about brushy watercourses, while the Mountain and Western Bluebirds live more in the open and spend much time on the wing. It is highly beneficial as a destroyer of insects.

The male Mountain Bluebird is readily recognized by its uniform cerulean or azure blue plumage with a greenish hue; underparts paler. *Adult female:* Head and back gray, sometimes faintly tinged with blue; rump, upper-tail coverts, tail, and primaries turquoise or light cerulean blue; eye ring white; underparts pale brownish gray. In winter the coloration is somewhat intensified.

DISTRIBUTION. In summer the Mountain Bluebird is widely distributed, from 7,000 feet to timber line and above. It is a familiar resident over the open ridges and in the treeless basins and valleys above timber line in the Sangre de Cristo Range, particularly about Pecos Baldy, Wheeler Peak, and Gold Hill. Following the nesting season it is often seen in association with Chipping Sparrows and Juncos. In winter it may vacate the higher areas, but it winters throughout the state, though principally in the southern half, where it may be quite common.

NESTING. The Mountain Bluebird nests throughout the forested mountains, from the southern portion of the Black and Pinos Altos Ranges northward to the Colorado line and east to the Sacramento and Capitan Mountains. "It is common in Santa Fe County; fresh eggs from May 1 to June 20" (Jensen). On May 17 a nest with five fresh eggs was found 14 miles north of Chloride, at 7,000 feet. It was situated in a crevice among rocks of a highway bridge abutment. Young were still in nest June 19 in James Canyon near Mayhill, Sacramento Mountains, at 7,500 feet. *Nest:* Made of grass and weed stems; lined with bits of bark and feathers; in old Woodpecker or Flicker holes, in crevices among rocks, or in buildings and bird houses. *Eggs:* 5 to 7; pale greenish blue.

(TOWNSEND'S SOLITAIRE
Myadestes townsendi

8—9½" long. Color pattern of sexes alike.

Although the Solitaire's outbursts of Thrushlike song may be heard even in midwinter on calm mild days, it is at nesting time that the male gives full vocal expression to his joyous spirits. As he progressively ascends from treetop or ledge, he pours out his clear charming notes, which become less audible as the songster rises higher and higher, until they no longer register on attuned ears. Upon completing his aerial rendition, he descends, and may assume his Flycatcher ways of plucking insects from the air though only momentarily, for soon, as if obsessed by song, he again wings upward for a repeat performance of his aerial delight. As with the Thrushes, the soft, warbling notes are often heard though the bird may not be seen. *Adults:* Prevailing color brownish gray; body streamlined eye ring white; outer-tail feathers white; wings with two whitish bars; bill short. The Solitaire, as a songster and in its preference for solitary living, is definitely in the Thrush class, but unlike the true Thrushes, it shuns dense cover, preferring the treetops and open spaces of woodlands or park borders. The Greek term, *myadestes*, means "a flycatcher," and such it is.

DISTRIBUTION. The summer range of the Solitaire is confined largely to the higher mountains of the state, from 8,000 feet to the dwarfed trees at timber line, or even higher, where Horned Larks, White-crowned Sparrows, and Pipits nest. Although local birds, or migrants from further north, are found throughout the winter, for the most part they occupy wooded foothills, mesas, and valleys, some even venturing out on the eastern high plains, frequenting farms and ranches where there are shade or other trees. They are more in evidence where there are fruits or berries, such as the one-seeded juniper, which is a dependable source of winter food.

NESTING. While the Townsend's Solitaire nests throughout the more extensive and higher mountain ranges of the state, it is most common in the Sangre de Cristo country, centering about timber line. Jensen and the author, however, found it nesting commonly around 9,000 feet, east of Santa Fe, most of the nests being on rock ledges or among exposed roots of trees along the steep banks of an abandoned road along the mountainside. The nests contained eggs and small young the latter part of June. The author found Townsend's Solitaires nesting in the Black Range, west of Hermosa on July 7. *Nest:* Usually made of conifer twigs, weed stems, grass, pine needles and moss; lined with fine grass. *Eggs:* 4 to 6; faint grayish blue, ground color partly obscured by brick red to lavender.

GNATCATCHERS AND KINGLETS
Family: SYLVIIDAE

FEW OTHER BIRDS are daintier or more active than the American representatives of this large Old World family—the Gnatcatchers and the Kinglets. As they are quite fearless, they generally are readily observed on their nesting grounds. Because of the diminutive size of these birds, however, the finer points of distinction require close attention. Gnatcatchers are migratory; the Kinglets only partly so. They may be seen almost any place in late fall, and some remain in the southern part of the state throughout the winter. Gnatcatchers rarely are seen above 7,000 feet, whereas Kinglets may be looked for at nesting time in the dense cool forests of the higher elevations.

(BLUE-GRAY (WESTERN) GNATCATCHER
Polioptila caerulea

4½–5″ long. Color pattern of sexes essentially alike. (Pl. I)

Of the two Gnatcatchers, both occurring in New Mexico, the Blue-gray is by far the commoner. It can be distinguished from its relative, the Black-tailed, by the U-shaped bluish-gray head markings—in the latter the entire top of head is glossy black—the narrow white eye ring, and the more conspicuous white in tail. Upperparts are bluish gray; underparts whitish, washed with bluish gray; tail long with black center and white outer feathers. The term *Polioptila* (Greek), meaning "hoary," has reference to the primaries, which are edged with whitish; and *caerulea* (Latin), "blue," suggests the color combination of this bird. This trim, dainty and vivacious feathered pygmy, in its harmonizing dress, assiduously searching for insects while uttering its charming notes of joy and contentment, truly approaches perfection among songbirds.

DISTRIBUTION. Range of the Blue-gray Gnatcatcher is largely coextensive with the brushy canyons and foothills of the southern half of the state, although it was recorded as far north as Fort Wingate by Hollister, and in Santa Fe County by Jensen. The author has found Blue-gray Gnatcatchers most common in the wooded foothills of the central and southwestern sections, around 5,000 to 6,500 feet. They are usually out of the state by late September, returning in early April.

NESTING. The nest of this Gnatcatcher is a marvel in beauty and compactness. It is made of plant down, shreds of bark and leaves, and covered with lichen. Saddled on a limb, it simulates surroundings and is all but invisible except when its location is betrayed by the birds. The Gnatcatchers are frequently duped by Cowbirds. On June 3 a nest was located in a canyon of scant desert shrubs on the west side of Big Hatchet Mountain, Hidalgo County. Situated about four feet from the ground, on the leaning limb of a squawbush, it contained five eggs, four of the Gnatcatcher and one of the Cowbird. The parent bird was reluctant to leave the incubated eggs. On June 6, another nest containing three eggs of the Gnatcatcher and one of the Cowbird was found in a dry wash about two miles to the north, some three feet above ground in a rather large squawbush. Had the Cowbird eggs been permitted to hatch, the larger and more gluttonous birds would have dominated the nest to the detriment, possibly even starvation, of the more delicate young of the Gnatcatchers. (Some years ago near Grayling, Michigan, the author found such tragedies com-

mon among the very rare Kirtland Warblers.) Jensen found Blue-gray Gnatcatchers nesting sparingly in late May and
June in the pinyon flats about Santa Fe.
On May 27 the author found a nest containing four slightly incubated eggs, two
miles west of Chloride, at 6,300 feet. *Eggs:*
4 or 5; greenish white, spotted with reddish brown and purplish around larger
end.

⟦ BLACK-TAILED (PLUMBEOUS) GNATCATCHER
Polioptila melanura

4½–5″ long. Color pattern of sexes
similar.

The Black-tailed Gnatcatcher either is
rare in the state, or the average bird observer is unable to distinguish it from the
Blue-gray. The male, in summer plumage,
may be recognized by the glossy black of
entire top of head, in contrast to the bluish gray of back; upper-tail coverts and
tail black, outer web of outside tail feathers white; wings slaty with paler edgings;
underparts white, washed with bluish
gray on sides. The Blue-gray Gnatcatcher,
which it resembles, has a bluish gray
crown, white eye ring, and more white in
tail. *Adult female:* Similar to male but
head slate gray without black; rest of upperparts brownish gray.

DISTRIBUTION. This Gnatcatcher has
been observed only in the southern and
western parts of the state. There is an old
record of one having been taken near
Hachita. "Grown young were seen July 30,
1901, at Carlsbad, and a few days later the
species was found not rare in the Guadalupe Mountains" (Bailey). In recent years
few observers have had collecting permits,
so the bird could have been seen and not
recognized, or identification may have
been questionable. It might well be on the
list of prospects for future birders.

NESTING. Bailey's record of young,
noted above, seems to be the only authen-

tic account of breeding of the Black-tailed
Gnatcatchers in the state. Nest and eggs
probably are little different from those of
the Blue-gray Gnatcatcher under similar
conditions.

⟦ GOLDEN-CROWNED KINGLET
Regulus satrapa

3½–4½″ long. Color pattern of sexes
essentially alike. (Pl. I)

The tiny Golden-crowned, usually referred to as the Western Gold-crowned
Kinglet, seems to be rarer in the state than
its relative, the Ruby-crowned. The distinguishing marks of the two species, as
their names indicate, are the crown color
patches. *Adult male, summer:* In addition
to the orange crown bordered with black,
a white line extends backward above eye,
but no eye ring. Upperparts greenish olive;
wings and tail dusky; wings with two yellowish bands; underparts pale white.
Colors brighter in fall and winter. *Adult
female:* Similar, but crown patch yellow
instead of orange.

DISTRIBUTION. Summer range of the
Golden-crowned Kinglet seems to be
confined to the northern part of the state.
Both Bailey and the author recorded it in
the higher elevations of the Sangre de
Cristo Mountains, and these mountains
seem to mark the extreme southern limit
of its range at this season. In migration
and during the winter, however, Golden-
crowned Kinglets are not uncommon elsewhere. At Bosque del Apache Refuge it is
listed as "winter visitor, rare." In the Roswell area: "Somewhat common September to December" (Montgomery). "One
observed December 14-18, 1958, on the
University of New Mexico campus, Albuquerque" (Durrie). Apparently most of
the birds leave the state for the severer
part of the winter. The northward spring
migration occurs in late April and early
May. Food consists mainly of tree-infesting insects and their larvae.

NESTING. The only nesting records of note for the state are those obtained in the Sangre de Cristo Range. Bailey saw Golden-crowned Kinglets on July 31 at 11,000 feet on Pecos Baldy, where both old and young were observed, and on August 5 to 8 at 10,700 feet elevation near Twining. The author found two nests containing small young near Lake Peak east of Santa Fe at 11,500 feet on July 4, 1927. So far as New Mexico is concerned the Golden-crowned prefers the Canadian and Hudsonian Zones, near timber line, for nesting. *Nest:* Usually 12 to 40 feet above ground in fir or spruce tree, generally near end of a limb, compact and ball-like in appearance; made of green moss and lichens, interwoven with small twigs; lined with fine bark fibers, rabbit hair, and feathers. *Eggs:* 5 to 10; creamy, reddish white, colored around larger end with reddish-brown dots.

❨ RUBY-CROWNED KINGLET
Regulus calendula

3¾—4½″ long. Color pattern of sexes similar.

The Ruby-crowned Kinglet is much more common in New Mexico than the Golden-crowned. Like its close relative, it is tiny but very active. In addition to the ruby, or scarlet, crown streak, which is sometimes barely visible, the male has a white eye ring. The Golden-crowned has no eye ring. Otherwise the olive gray of the body extends to the forehead and eye, without the black-and-white head streaking of the Golden-crowned. Wings have two white bars; underparts ashy white. *Adult female:* Similar to male but without the ruby crown stripe.

DISTRIBUTION. Summer range of the Ruby-crowned Kinglet, although more extensive than that of the Golden-crowned, is confined largely to the fir and spruce forests of the highest mountains. At this season the author has recorded it as far south as the summit of the Black Range west of Hermosa. It is most abundant, however, in the Sangre de Cristo Range, where it is found from 9,500 feet to timber line. It winters rather commonly throughout the southern half of the state. It is listed as "winter resident, common" at the Bosque del Apache Refuge. It has been recorded throughout the winter in the Guadalupe Mountains and westward, and occasionally at Carlsbad.

NESTING. Like the Golden-crowned, the Ruby-crowned confines its nesting to the high forests, mostly in the northern section, although the author found two pairs feeding young on the summit of the Black Range, 28 miles southwest of Chloride, at 8,000 feet, on June 28. Most other records, however, are for the Sangre de Cristo Range, centering around 11,000 feet. "It is one of the commonest birds at 11,000 to 11,600 feet below Pecos Baldy from July 21, 1903, when young were in the nest, to August 17, when they were fully fledged. The next year it was common, July 26, on Wheeler Peak at 11,400 feet, while still feeding young August 17, at 11,000 feet on Lost Trail Creek in the Culebra Mountains west of Costilla Pass" (Bailey). *Nest:* From 8 to 30 feet above ground in spruce, fir, or pine; semi-pensile (hanging) in form, thick-walled, made of green moss, shreds of bark and feathers; lined with hair and feathers. *Eggs:* 5 to 11; whitish or pale buffy, faintly marked with pale brown, mostly around larger end.

PIPITS
Family: MOTACILLIDAE

IN SOME RESPECTS the Pipit bears a superficial resemblance to the Thrush. The Pipit, however, is terrestrial. It shuns dense cover, preferring open ground. Of the two species occurring in the United States—the Water (American) and the Sprague—the former is the Pipit commonly found in New Mexico. The Sprague Pipit occurs on the plains of Montana and Wyoming, east of the Rockies, and migrates over the Texas Panhandle. The only record for the state is that by Krehbiel in the Clayton area, where, he states, it is "accidental transient." The two species are so much alike that one easily could be mistaken for the other, on sight alone. The term "pipit" probably came from the imitative notes or song.

❨ WATER (AMERICAN) PIPIT
Anthus spinoletta
6 to 7″ long. Color pattern of sexes alike. (Pl. I)

This rather plain brown and striped bird is seen by the average observer in migration or in winter only, since its summer range is above timber line of the highest peaks. Several features separate the Water Pipit from other birds of similar size and markings. It is a ground- rather than a tree-dweller, preferring mud flats, barren lake and marsh shores, where it may be seen walking about, its tail pulsating, as it seeks insects. On rising, it flies erratically, circling and dipping up and down, so that the white of the outer-tail feathers, a distinguishing mark, is plainly visible. Its "pip" or "pit" is somewhat like that of a Horned Lark. *Adults in spring and summer:* Upperparts grayish tinged with olive or brown, indistinctly streaked; tail blackish, outside feathers largely white; wing blackish brown with two buffy bars and light edgings; underparts buffy; chest, sides and flanks streaked with dusky. *Adults in winter:* Upperparts are more olivaceous; underparts paler and more heavily streaked.

DISTRIBUTION. During the summer period Water Pipits in the state are confined almost, if not wholly, to the barren ridges and ledges above timber line in the northern section. During the fall and early spring they are widely distributed, occurring singly, in small groups, or in considerable flocks. While most of them normally are out of the state by late December, winter records are not unusual. Migrants usually return by mid-March.

NESTING. In June 1924, Pipits were found nesting commonly above 11,500 feet elevation, in the Sangre de Cristo Range, particularly on Pecos Baldy, Tierra Amarilla, Truchas and Wheeler Peaks, and Gold Hill. Several nests were located, some right at the lower edge of snowbanks. The birds were observed feeding young on Pecos Baldy on July 12. At the height of the nest-building activities and laying season the males are very active. To the accompaniment of a charming song, they rise into the air, sometimes 50 feet or more, and float away as they complete the rendition. Dropping back silently to some prominent stone or boulder, which may be projecting above a snowbank, they sit quietly for a short interval before repeating the performance. "In 1904 it was common about and on Wheeler Peak from 12,000 feet to the summit" (Bailey). *Nest:* On the surface, usually on a steep slope at edge of a stone or bunch of grass; compact, made of grass and mosses; lined with feathers. *Eggs:* 4 to 6; almost uniformly brown from the dense spotting.

WAXWINGS
Family: BOMBYCILLIDAE

THE TWO American representatives of the Waxwing family—named from the red waxlike appendages on tips of wings—occur in the state. Few other birds are so distinctly and exquisitely marked. The head is conspicuously crested, and the fawn-colored plumage is smooth and silky. Plumage patterns of the two, the Bohemian and Cedar Waxwings, are very similar, but the Cedar Waxwing is considerably smaller.

BOHEMIAN WAXWING
Bombycilla garrula

7½—8½" long. Color pattern of sexes similar.

Until very recently, the sight of one of these artistically adorned, velvety plumaged visitors to the higher altitudes of the state was a noteworthy occasion. *Adults:* Body, including the conspicuous crest, soft, silky, fawn colored; black stripe around forehead continuing past eye; chin velvety black; tail tipped with yellow; primaries tipped with yellow, sometimes white; middle of secondaries with a small white zone ornamented by red waxlike appendage. The Bohemian Waxwing is larger, more highly colored than the Cedar.

STATE RECORDS. Prior to April 1959, there were but three authentic records of the Bohemian Waxwing in New Mexico. On November 18, 1926, the author observed several of the birds on Gold Hill, near Red River village, at 11,500 feet, and secured one. None were again recorded until December 28, 1958, at which time 26 were observed during the Española Christmas Count. (See *Audubon Field Notes*, Vol. 13, No. 2, 1959.) On March 27, 1959, Dexter Dunlap of the State Game Department observed a single bird in Cimarron Canyon, west of Cimarron.

These few records were climaxed by an unparalleled incident of bird invasion in the Southwest, when in early April 1959, an estimated 10,000 descended on the City of Santa Fe. Jens K. Jensen states: "I first noticed the birds April 5, when some small and some large flocks flew over the City of Santa Fe." He concludes: "I have seen none of the birds since May 12." This mass invasion so far south in New Mexico seems to be one instance in a century; for the hundred years that bird observations have been recorded, no like phenomenon appears. Lack of suitable food farther north may account for this amazing invasion. There seems to be no nesting record for the state.

CEDAR WAXWING
Bombycilla cedrorus

6½—7½" long. Color pattern of sexes alike.

Except during the nesting season, the Cedar Waxwing is a wanderer and its presence is unpredictable. A compact flock may suddenly appear, squeaking and lisping, and alight in some treetop. If such food as fruit or berries is not available, they may leave just as suddenly. *Adults:* Body, including high silky crest, mainly fawn color; forehead and streak through eye velvety black, narrowly bordered with white; wings blackish, primaries tipped with grayish, secondaries tipped with red, waxlike appendages; underparts yellowish; tail blackish tipped with yellow. *Young:* Duller, streaked with whitish, and crest smaller. The principal food of Waxwings consists of wild cherries, currants, juniper and other such berries, and a variety of insects.

DISTRIBUTION. The Cedar Waxwing occurs rather sparingly as a fall, winter, and spring dweller, but there are some summer records. A number of the birds were noted, August 12, on the Hondo north of Taos, and in February about Corona. The author has observed them at other points throughout the state, including a small number at Carlsbad, April 14.

NESTING. There seems to be no record for the state of actual finding of nests with eggs or young. On June 20, 1954 Jensen wrote: "I may have a nesting record for your book. Late June 1954 I got a nest from an old apple tree in a Santa Cruz orchard. The nest was empty, but a typical nest of Cedar Waxwing. A dead Waxwing was hanging in a long horse hair, part of the nest." In absence of definite record of eggs or small young, however, it is not listed as a breeder. Nest: In bush or low tree; a rather deep, bulky structure made of twigs and weed stems, grasses and vegetable fibers; lined with leaves and fine rootlets. Eggs: 4 to 6; pale bluish to purplish gray, sharply and usually heavily spotted with black and paler, or lilac, shell spots, more thickly around larger end.

SILKY FLYCATCHERS
Family: PTILOGONATIDAE

DARK glossy plumage and fan-shaped crest and tail distinguish the streamlined Phainopepla from any other American perching birds. When not in erratic flight, this elusive aerial dweller is usually seen perched in tops of trees.

([PHAINOPEPLA
Phainopepla nitens
7–7½" long. Color pattern of sexes different.

The Phainopepla, a slim, rather shy bird, is the only one of the Silky Flycatchers found in the United States. Bird observers are apt to feel that a simpler common name could have been chosen for the species. However, Phainopepla (Greek), meaning "shining robe," seems most appropriate. Adult male: Glossy black (less so on wings and tail); a conspicuous fan-shaped crest and tail; white patches on wings. Adult female: Plain dark gray; longest feathers of crest black, edged with gray; wings and tail dusky, faintly glossed with greenish; under-tail coverts tipped with gray or white; little or no white on wing patches, which in the male are very conspicuous in flight; bill short and slender.

DISTRIBUTION. Range of the Phainopepla is confined largely to the south-central and southwestern parts of the state, although in the Rio Grande Valley it ranges northward to Socorro, rarely farther. It is usually resident where found, but is unstable in distribution. Its presence, in winter, seems to depend very largely upon the availability of mistletoe berries, its principal food at this season. It is most common in the Rio Grande Valley, north to Truth or Consequences. The eastern limit of its range seems to be southeast slope of the Guadalupe Mountains, in Big Canyon, just north of the Texas line. "All-year resident, Las Cruces" (Williams).

NESTING. Nest containing two fresh eggs was located by the author on the Rio Grande, just below Las Cruces, May 29, 1949. Nests of the Phainopepla are small, shallow, and very compact, usually saddled on limbs of tornillo, cottonwood, or oak trees, 8 to 20 feet from the ground; made of tips of plant twigs, blossoms, plant fibers, down, and bits of soft dead grass. Where sheep range the nest may be made almost wholly of wool. Eggs: 2 or 3; grayish or greenish white, thickly spotted with brown, blackish, or faint lilac.

SHRIKES
Family: LANIIDAE

DISTINCTIVE in their black-and-white garb, Shrikes should not be confused with the Mockingbird, which is almost wholly gray, with white wing patch and somewhat wider and longer tail. The Shrike is the only bird of prey—if such it can be called—with the gift of song, a soft musical warble with pauses between notes.

NORTHERN SHRIKE
Lanius excubitor

9—10½" long. Color pattern of sexes alike.

The Northern Shrike is an uncommon winter visitor in the northern section of New Mexico. Its larger size distinguishes it from its relative, the Loggerhead. *Adults:* Underparts white; chest and sides with grayish, wavy barring. Otherwise, general plumage pattern is practically the same as that of the Loggerhead. It is usually seen perched atop bush or tree, and in flight it takes a beeline course, near the ground, rising gracefully to its next chosen lookout perch. It was noted by Kalmbach at Koehler Junction (Colfax County) October 23, and by Jensen near Santa Fe on December 18, and there is a November 7, 1902, record for Tularosa by Gaut. There is no nesting record for the state.

⦗ LOGGERHEAD SHRIKE
Lanius ludovicianus

9—9½" long. Color pattern of sexes alike.

The Loggerhead is the common Shrike in the state, usually seen singly, sitting on a wire or top of bush or tree, often motionless for a time as it watches for a clue to the whereabouts of a grasshopper or beetle. When one is located the Shrike

sails down, picks up the insect and flies back to the perch, where the victim is eaten or impaled on a convenient thorn, in crotches of bushes, or possibly on the barb of a fence wire. This habit has earned it the name "Butcher Bird." The purpose of such impaling seems to be two-fold—to enable the Shrike to tear its food to pieces for eating, and probably to provide food for a subsequent meal. When the Loggerhead leaves its perch, it usually drops down to near the surface of the ground, and in undulating flight goes straight away, rising abruptly and alighting on some other convenient lookout point. Its large head, rather large, straight, hooked bill, and gray, black, and white markings are distinctive. *Adults:* Upperparts light gray; rump white; black streak from bill extending to neck; tail and wings black; underparts white. The conduct of this Shrike is not in reality as bad as its reputation would indicate. In the great open spaces of the Southwest, the small birds usually succeed in evading it. One or two are usually present in winter at the author's bird farm at Carlsbad, where they prey on House Sparrows that become confused in the wire netting pens. In Colfax County, from July to October, Kalmbach found that 89 percent of the diet of the Loggerhead Shrike consisted of grasshoppers. So, generally speaking, they are far more beneficial than harmful.

DISTRIBUTION. The Loggerhead—or White-rumped, as the common Shrike is often called—is for the most part resident and statewide in distribution, being found from the lowest elevations up to 7,000 feet in the mountain foothills. It seems to shun the forested areas, although in the fall it may be seen around 8,000 feet on mesas or in open valleys.

NESTING. The Shrike usually nests early,

but nesting may be prolonged, indicating that more than one brood may be raised in a season. In the Carlsbad and Las Cruces areas, nesting usually starts in early March. On April 12, 4 fresh eggs were found near Milnesand; on March 30, 1 fresh egg in a nest at Carlsbad. Jensen reports fresh eggs in the Santa Fe area (7,000 to 7,500 feet) April 20 to June 1. "Eggs in nest July 4, 1951, east of Roswell" (Montgomery).

Nest: Usually in small thick bushes, such as squawbush, catclaw, mesquite, or other thorny shrub. It also nests commonly in plum bushes and orchard trees in the eastern plains country. Nest is rather bulky, like that of the Mockingbird; made of sticks and twigs; lined with soft material, such as grass, cotton, or wool if available. *Eggs:* 4 to 6; grayish or yellowish white, spotted with brown and lilac.

STARLINGS
Family: *STURNIDAE*

STARLINGS somewhat resemble Blackbirds in appearance and conduct. Like the latter, in the Southwest, they are most apt to be seen in flocks about towns and fields in the fall and winter, when their greenish metallic summer plumage has assumed a heavy grayish mottled or spotted pattern.

(STARLING
Sturnus vulgaris

7½–8½" long. Color pattern of sexes alike.

The winter plumage, in which the Starling is normally seen in New Mexico, is dark brown, heavily spotted with light dots. This bird's rather large black bill becomes yellow with the approach of the breeding season. The tail appears short for the plump body. Although the European Starling, like the House Sparrow, is an exotic in America, it is now so well established as to be considered a resident bird. The first Starlings were brought to this country by Eugene Schiefflin, who also imported one of the early shipments of House (or English) Sparrows. Sixty Starlings were released in Central Park, New York City, in 1890, and 40 more in 1891. Now millions of these pests are scattered over most of the United States, and their numbers still are increasing. In time they

may become an even greater nuisance than the House Sparrow. Although Starlings usually occur in large flocks, and walk as do Blackbirds, they can be distinguished by their much swifter and more direct flight. Blackbirds fly in a more irregular, undulating pattern. In spring the Starling's bill changes to yellow; back retains some of the dotting, but head and underparts become black, or greenish, decidedly glossed.

DISTRIBUTION. In winter Starlings are becoming more common and more widely spread in New Mexico, but as yet they are rare in summer. They are most abundant in the eastern farming section and in the Pecos and Rio Grande Valleys, where great flocks may occasionally be observed. Fleetwood reported approximately 10,000 Starlings on December 10, 1952, two miles south of San Antonio. The first record of the bird by the author, in the Carlsbad area, was for November 1935.

NESTING. Prior to 1954, there seems to have been no record of Starlings nesting in New Mexico. In a letter dated September 12, 1955, however, Krehbiel states: "As to Starlings, Mr. Cook and I are quite well satisfied that a few of these birds nest here. We saw them in 1954 as follows: March 28; April 10 and 25; May 30; June 5 and 19; July 10. In 1955 the birds were regularly seen and we kept more careful record.

We each saw immature Starlings this summer in company with mature birds." *Nest:* Made of twigs and grass; placed in crevices in buildings, or in hollow trees. *Eggs:* 4 to 7; pale bluish or bluish white. Since the Starling, like the House Sparrow, lives about habitation of man, and nests in protected places, vast populations can be expected unless effective control measures are devised.

VIREOS
Family: *VIREONIDAE*

THE VIREOS are rather small, greenish- or olive-sided birds of woodland and forest; hence, like the small Flycatchers and Sparrows, are not easily identified even by the advanced bird student who finds it difficult to differentiate on sight alone between species of these uniformly marked little birds. Knowing where they may be found in summer somewhat simplifies identification. Their slow movements, while searching leaf and branch in quest of insects, set Vireos apart from the more active Warblers, which for the most part also have distinctive color patterns. Fortunately, all of the Vireos do not occupy similar habitat at nesting time. Five species have been listed as occurring in New Mexico: Hutton's, Bell's (Least), Gray, Solitary (Plumbeous), and Warbling. The different species have been subdivided, but such divisions do not interest the average bird student.

rump; wings and tail brownish gray; wings with two white bars; underparts creamy white and buff.

DISTRIBUTION. The Hutton's is very restricted in distribution. The most dependable records are those by Goldman, who found it from July 30 to August 6, 1908, from 5,800 feet in Indian Creek, to 8,100 feet near the top of the Animas Mountains. At Cloverdale in Hidalgo County on June 22, the author collected a male which was obviously a breeding bird.

NESTING. Stephens recorded taking eggs of Hutton's Vireo at Ft. Bayard in 1876, which seems to be the only definite account of this Vireo nesting in the state, although it is reasonable to assume that it does nest in the Animas Mountains as well as in the Silver City area. *Nest:* Hung from limb of oak or other tree; made of fine grass and oak blossoms. *Eggs:* 4; white, spotted with brown.

([HUTTON'S VIREO
Vireo huttoni
4½–5" long. Color pattern of sexes alike.

The Hutton's, also known as the Stephens Vireo, is of rare occurrence in the state. It can best be identified by its diminutive size and the notes of the male, which are not unlike the mewing of a kitten. Like other members of its family, it is fearless of man and therefore not difficult to observe. *Adults:* Upperparts, dark olive gray blending into olive green on

BELL'S (LEAST) VIREO
Vireo bellii
4½–5" long. Color pattern of sexes similar.

Like the Hutton's, the Bell's, also listed as Least Vireo, is very rare and is found in the southwestern corner of the state only. *Adults:* Head, hind neck, back and shoulders, brownish gray; lores and eye ring white; two faint wing bars; underparts white; sides faintly washed with grayish olive green. An aid to identification is its preference for brushy streams and canyons of the lower country. Monson took a specimen near San Antonio, May 4, 1942, and observed two others at Bosque del Apache Refuge. Stephens secured a specimen on the Gila River, May 20, 1876. It has been recorded at Fort Bowie, just over the line in Arizona, and it should be found about the San Simon Marshes on the New Mexico side. It is another of the extremely rare species that constitute a challenge to the enthusiastic bird hunter.

(GRAY VIREO
Vireo vicinior

5½–5¾" long. Color pattern of sexes alike.

Although the range of the Gray Vireo in the state seems to be limited, the bird is rather common where found. *Adults:* Upperparts and cheeks dull gray, faintly tinged with olive green on rump; tail and wings dusky with light edgings; outside tail feathers white; underparts washed with grayish; throat and chest tinged with olive; one faint wing bar; lores and eye ring gray. Its preference for wooded foothills and canyons is a clue as to where it may be found in summer.

DISTRIBUTION. An interesting thing about this Vireo's occurrence is its spotty or "island" summer distribution. Anthony reported seeing it in summer at Apache, near Hachita. But finding it in considerable numbers in the eastern section of the state came as a surprise. "A breeding colony of the Gray Vireo was found, and one bird taken, on June 14, 1903 on Pajarito Creek near Montoya at 4,300 feet. There is no other nesting place known within 300 miles in any direction, and its presence there is unexplained" (Bailey).

NESTING. In addition to the above-noted Bailey nesting records, Fisher reported the Gray Vireo nesting June 28 and early July 1904 in the Silver City area. *Nest:* Usually placed 4 to 6 feet from the ground in small trees or thorny bushes.

"Made of mesquite bark and loosely woven coarse grass, lined with fine grass, but also made of plant fiber, spider web and cocoon, lined with long, vegetable fibers and decorated with leaves" (Bailey). *Eggs:* 3 or 4; white, sparsely marked with minute dark brown dots, chiefly around larger end.

(SOLITARY (PLUMBEOUS) VIREO
Vireo solitarius

5½–6" long. Color pattern of sexes alike.

So imbued with song is the Solitary Vireo that no summer day seems long enough for rendering his sweet rich notes. Singing seems to dominate all of his activities, be it gleaning insects among leaves and branches, or building or occupying a nest. Wetmore tells of a Solitary Vireo carrying a bit of nesting material about with him and singing at the same time. As though inviting intimacy, this friendly little songster comes close and eyes the intruder curiously, seldom pausing in his joyous singing. The male of a pair that had a nest in a large box elder near the author's cabin, at Chloride, spent most of his time singing while his mate was on the nest or as he followed her about as she searched for insects. But tragedy struck suddenly at a time when the nest contained 3 eggs. On the morning of May 14 when the notes of the Cowbirds were heard, investigation revealed three of these robbers—two males and a female—on the ground picking at the remains of 2 of the Vireo eggs which they had thrown from the nest, presumably to make room for their own eggs. *Adults:* Upperparts slate gray in sharp contrast to white eye ring; white patch in front of eye; two conspicuous whitish wing bars; throat white; rump tinged with olive green; tail and wings slate black; outer webs of outer tail feathers white; underparts white; sides and flanks broadly but indistinctly striped with grayish olive and pale yellow.

NESTING. Jensen recorded fresh eggs near Santa Fe, at 7,500 feet elevation, on May 31. Wetmore noted the Solitary Vireo commonly about Burford Lake at nesting time, and it is a regular breeder in the Black Range and Mogollon Mountains. It was seen feeding young in the nest on August 1 at 6,000 feet in the Guadalupe Mountains. *Nest:* From 5 to 20 feet above ground, usually in walnut trees where available, but also sometimes in box elder, maple, ash, or pine; almost always swinging from forks of branches. Made of inner bark and vegetable fibers, lined with grass and plant down, sometimes decorated with pieces of white cocoon. *Eggs:* 4; white, lightly spotted around larger end with brown and black.

⟨ WARBLING VIREO
Vireo gilvus

5–5½″ long. Color pattern of sexes alike.

This Vireo, usually listed as the Western Warbling, is, like the Solitary, a common, widely spread summer resident. *Adults:* The principal distinguishing feature is a long gray stripe over eye; head indistinctly striped; no wing bars; upperparts grayish olive; tail and wings brownish gray with pale edgings; underparts white; sides washed with yellowish.

DISTRIBUTION. The summer range of this Vireo includes all of the forested mountains of the state from 6,000 to 9,000 feet, but occasionally it may be found even higher or lower. Few other ornithologists know the Warbling Vireo as intimately as did Henshaw, as indicated by his interesting account of its habits and distribution: "Often finds its home in the gardens or streets of towns, thus exhibiting the same traits of confiding familiarity which attached to it in the East; it is equally numerous in the wild, uncultivated districts where man has not yet penetrated. It frequents, for the most part, the deciduous trees, especially the cottonwoods, and ranges from the valleys to high up in the mountains. Its habits are everywhere the same, and the sweet, half meditative notes of its beautiful song have the same power to charm the ear in the solitude of its wild home as when heard under the more familiar conditions of civilization."

NESTING. Because of its trusting nature and almost incessant warbling at nesting time, the Warbling Vireo is readily located and easily observed. The author observed a pair of Warbling Vireos with young in nest near Chama, at 8,500 feet, July 12, 1951. *Nest:* Hung from forked branch of deciduous tree or bush; cup-shaped and compact, a model of dainty, artistic construction. Made of vegetable fibers and bleached grasses, bound together with spider web and lined with soft grass. *Eggs:* 4 or 5; white, spotted around larger end with reddish, dark brown, or lilac.

WOOD WARBLERS
Family: *PARULIDAE*

WITH THE EXCEPTION of the Finch and Sparrow group, the Wood Warblers, so named to distinguish them from Old World Warblers, *Sylviidae*, constitute the largest family of North American birds. Twenty-eight species have been recorded —13 as nesting—in New Mexico. The other 15 species are transient migrants and strays or of rare occurrence.

While the Warblers as a group, particularly the females and immature birds, are not easily identified, most of the adults have distinctive color patterns. By disregarding the subspecies, classification of which is scarcely justified within a single state or region, identification becomes less difficult. The usual flow of fall migrants with young of the year and with adults in modified plumage, further adds to confusion, so the bird student will do well to concentrate on spring and summer identification. At this time even the females can be more readily recognized, although they may be in sharp contrast to the conspicuous males. Although the Warblers as a group cannot compete with the Thrushes and Thrashers as songsters, many of them have pleasing songs. Since their food consists almost wholly of injurious insects, they are of enormous value in farm and forest economy.

Their tightly compressed plumage does not afford adequate protection from intense cold, hence most of them are highly migratory. They are largely arboreal, although some prefer marshes or brushy, arid lands, contradictory to the "Wood" Warbler designation. Paintings, drawings, and photographs are of much benefit in identifying these birds.

❨ ORANGE-CROWNED WARBLER
Vermivora celata
4½–5" long. Color pattern of sexes similar. (Pl. XXIII)

The Orange-crowned is one of the few modestly dressed Warblers, a feature which may cause some difficulty in identification, especially since the Orange-crowned male resembles the females of some other species. *Adult male:* Crown with partially concealed orange-brown patch; upperparts yellowish olive green, brighter on rump; wings and tail brownish gray, edged with yellowish; underparts yellow washed with olive. *Adult female:* Crown patch duller or indistinct.

DISTRIBUTION. The Orange-crowned is rather common and widely distributed in forested mountains throughout the state in migration, but it is confined largely to the northern section, from 7,500 feet to timber line, in summer. It is usually out of the state by mid-October, returning in late April or early May.

NESTING. Nesting records include the Burford Lake area and the higher portions of the Sangre de Cristo Range. "It was found breeding August 6, at 10,700 feet near Twining, and at 12,300 feet on the Culebra Mountains on August 20" (Bailey). *Nest:* On or near the ground, made largely of leaves and fine grasses. *Eggs:* 4 or 5; white with brown specks, more numerous at larger end.

᚛ VIRGINIA'S WARBLER

Vermivora virginiae

4½" long. Color pattern of sexes similar. (Pl. XXIII)

The Virginia's, like the Lucy's, is one of the smallest and daintiest of all Warblers. It is regarded as a close relative of the Nashville Warbler of the eastern United States. Also, in several respects, it resembles the Lucy's, but the yellow of tail coverts is distinctive. The breeding range of the Lucy's occupies the lower and extreme southwestern part of the state, whereas the Virginia's summers in the higher forested mountains. The type specimen of this Warbler was taken by Dr. W. W. Anderson in 1858; in describing it, Prof. Spencer F. Baird named it after Dr. Anderson's wife. *Adult male, in breeding plumage:* Crown with chestnut patch; upperparts gray except for greenish-yellow rump; eye ring white, rather conspicuous; underparts dull white with chest patch and throat (usually) yellow. *Fall and winter plumage:* Similar, but upperparts and flanks tinged with brown; yellow of chest duller; crown patch concealed by grayish tips to feathers. *Adult female in spring and summer:* Like male in summer, but duller, especially on rump and uppertail coverts; crown patch restricted; back browner.

DISTRIBUTION. For the most part the summer range of the Virginia's Warbler is confined to the mountains of the northern half of the state, from 7,000 to 8,000 feet elevation. On June 29, 1928, the author found it rather common in the Sandia Mountains east of Albuquerque around 7,500 feet. It also has been found in August in the Animas Mountains near the southwestern corner of the state. The Virginia's Warbler, therefore, may be more widely spread than records indicate. It is usually out of the state by late September, returning in late April.

NESTING. At nesting time the male often resorts to some treetop to pour out his beautiful melody. "At Lake Burford it was common May 23 to June 19, an incubating female taken June 16" (Wetmore). The author found it nesting in the Sandia Mountains at 7,500 feet on June 29. *Nest:* On the ground under a bush or by some concealing plant; made of rootlets, weed stems, and fibers. *Eggs:* 4 or 5; white ground color, lightly wreathed around larger end with spots of reddish and purplish brown, scattered spots over remainder of surface.

᚛ LUCY'S WARBLER

Vermivora luciae

4" long. Color pattern of sexes alike. (Pl. XXIII)

This little Warbler, like the Virginia's, is trim and dainty. *Adults:* Crest and rump rich brown maroon; remainder of upperparts gray; underparts light gray to whitish, tinged with buff. A good means of separating this Warbler from the Virginia's in summer is the character of their habitats.

It was named in honor of Miss Lucy Baird, daughter of Prof. Spencer Fullerton Baird, Assistant Director of the Smithsonian Institution, by C. G. Cooper, in 1862.

DISTRIBUTION. As is true of many other rare birds that occur in New Mexico, distribution of the Lucy's Warbler is confined, while in the state, to the lower Sonoran Life Zone of the southwest corner. It is most common along the Gila River, from the Arizona line to the vicinity of Cliff. It leaves the state in early fall, returning in early June. Bohl recorded it at San Simon marshes on June 25, 1955.

NESTING. The bottomlands of the Gila River seem to be the principal nesting place of this Warbler. On May 4, 1928, the author found a nest containing 4 heavily incubated eggs, just below Red Rock, in an old Woodpecker hole, 6 feet up in a half-decayed willow limb. On May 4, 1953, a breeding pair was located on the Gila 2 miles below Cliff. *Nest:* 5 to 15 feet above ground, in Woodpecker holes, crevices, or behind bark of trees; made of fine twigs, leaves, hair, and feathers. *Eggs:* 4; white or creamy, finely specked with reddish brown in ring around larger end.

OLIVE WARBLER
Peucedramus taeniatus

4½–5″ long. Color pattern of sexes different.

The male Olive Warbler differs from any other member of this big family of birds. It is the only Warbler with orange brown head and chest and black cheek patch. Remainder of upperparts mainly gray; tail and wings dull blackish, with light edgings; wings with two conspicuous white bars; median underparts dull white; sides gray. *Adult female:* Yellowish where male is brown; eye patch dusky. White wing bars narrower than in adult male.

DISTRIBUTION. The few state records of this interesting Warbler indicate that it is rare and its distribution is confined, in summer, to the southwestern section. However, since it seems to dwell mostly about the tops of pines and other conifers, it might easily be overlooked. A male was taken at Reserve on September 17, 1927 (Phillips, *Condor,* Vol. 49, May-June 1947). In October 1906, Bergtold saw a number of Warblers which he identified as the Olive, in McKnight Canyon, upper Mimbres River. This is an authentic record, since he was familiar with the bird in Chihuahua and Durango, Mexico. "One was seen Aug. 14-17, 1954, 8 miles south of Thoreau" (F. R. Gehlbach). This is far north of other observations.

NESTING. There seems to be no nesting record for the state, although it safely may be assumed that the Olive Warbler does nest in the mountains bordering the San Francisco River in the Reserve area. *Nest:* In fork of conifer tree 30 to 50 feet above ground; made of bits of lichen, moss, and spider web, lined with rootlets. *Eggs:* 3 or 4; olive gray or sage green, with black markings sometimes almost obscuring the ground color.

⟪ YELLOW WARBLER
Dendroica petechia

5–5½″ long. Color pattern of sexes similar. (Pl. XXIII)

The Yellow Warbler, widely known as the Wild Canary, has been separated into several subspecies, but the fine points which form the basis of division mean little to the average observer. It is a common summer dweller and its almost pure yellow coat is a mark of distinction, since no other Warbler is so dominantly yellow. *Adult male:* Breast and sides conspicuous brick-red streaking over yellow base; upperparts yellowish olive green; wing feathers broadly tipped with yellow. *Adult female:* Duller, breast and sides sometimes streaked.

DISTRIBUTION. The principal summer range of the Yellow Warbler extends from the lower altitudes of the state, 3,100 feet, up to 7,000 feet. Favorite haunts are the willows and cottonwoods of watercourses, and except for the more arid plains and mesas, distribution is statewide. "Common in April and May [Roswell area] sometimes in September and October" (Montgomery). Yellow Warblers begin to arrive in the southern section in mid-April and generally are out of the state by mid-September.

NESTING. This Warbler nests throughout New Mexico wherever there is stream and forest cover. Unfortunately, it is often a dupe of the Cowbird, which shifts the responsibility of nest building and raising of young onto other species. So resourceful are these Warblers that they sometimes build a second story to their nest and the female lays a second clutch of eggs in an effort to defeat duping by the parasitic Cowbirds. Jensen reported fresh eggs June 1 to 15 in the Santa Fe area, and the author found the birds nesting on the Brazos River, near Parkview, at 7,000 feet, in mid-June. *Nest:* In bushes or trees; cup-shaped and compact, made largely of plant fibers, lined with down and usually a few feathers. *Eggs:* Normally 4; greenish or grayish, heavily marked with brown, tending to wreathe about larger end.

BLACK-THROATED BLUE WARBLER
Dendroica caerulescens
5–5½″ long. Color pattern of sexes different.

All records of this Warbler in the state are comparatively recent, indicating that it is becoming a regular visitor. The male is so conspicuous in his blue, black, and white dress that it seems unlikely that the competent early-day ornithologists would have overlooked it. *Adult male:* Upperparts dark blue; throat and sides black; white patch at base of primaries; underparts white. *Adult female:* Plain of dress, brown on back; light line extending from bill back over eye; underparts yellowish white; white spot on wing.

DISTRIBUTION. Although there are records for this Warbler from various parts of the state, it has been observed most frequently in the Las Cruces area, where it is known to winter. "It was noted here [Las Cruces] January 20 and 28, and February 21, 1953" (Williams.) "A male was observed September 20, 1953, at Alameda" (Fitzsimmons and Durrie). Allan Phillips recorded one near Anthony in December 1953. Montgomery reported seeing it at Roswell, May 7, 1954. "A male was observed October 9, 1938, on Milk Ranch Creek, near Gallup" (Monson). On October 23, 1956, one was seen near Peña Blanca" (Mary Belle Keefer).

There seems to be no nesting record for the state although more careful observation may disclose this Warbler as a breeder.

MYRTLE WARBLER
Dendroica coronata
5½–6″ long. Color pattern of sexes essentially alike.

The Myrtle and the Audubon's Warblers are so similar when in full plumage that care must be exercised in order to tell them apart. The Myrtle, however, is distinctive in that it has a white throat and two white wing bars, whereas the Audubon's has a yellow throat and large white wing patch. In a few publications the Myrtle is listed as the Hoover Warbler, supposedly a subspecies of the Myrtle. *Adult male in spring and summer:* Crown, rump, and sides of breast with yellow patches; upperparts bluish gray; back streaked with black; wings with two white bars; throat white; breast black streaked and tipped with white; center of underparts white; flanks streaked. *Adult female in summer:* Similar to summer male but color patches restricted and duller; upperparts tinged with brown.

DISTRIBUTION. The Myrtle Warbler is no doubt a far more common summer dweller than the few authentic records indicate. Because of their similarity, it has probably often been mistaken for the Audubon's. Surber reported it fairly common in migration about Rinconada, north of Española, and he took specimens from April 16 to May 2. "Eight were seen, including one male taken, in the Bosque Refuge, April 8, 1942" (Monson). It is listed as occasional winter visitor at this refuge, and as transient visitor, occasional, at Bitter Lake Refuge. There evidently is need for more intensive field work to determine its status in the state.

NESTING. There is little doubt that this Warbler breeds in New Mexico, but in the absence of definite records it is not listed as a nesting species.

❨ AUDUBON'S WARBLER
Dendroica auduboni

5—5⅔" long. Color pattern of sexes similar. (Pl. I)

The Audubon's is one of the most abundant Warblers in the state during the nesting period. Larger than most other Warblers, it can be distinguished from the Myrtle, which it resembles, by the yellow throat—white in the Myrtle—and white wing patch instead of white wing bars. *Adult male in summer:* Crown, rump, throat and sides of chest yellow; upperparts bluish gray mottled with black; tail and wings dark brown; outer-tail feathers white near tips; wings with large white patch; underparts with black of chest separating yellow of throat and sides from white of lower underparts. *Adult female:* Similar to summer male but duller, with color patches restricted. Fall and winter plumage of both male and female is less conspicuous, being toned with brown.

DISTRIBUTION. Summer range of the Audubon's Warbler includes forests of all the higher mountains of the state, but it is most common at this season in the northern section, where it ranges from 7,000 to 11,000 feet. It is uncommon in the mountains of the southern section. While most Audubon's Warblers leave the state, some may be seen in midwinter as far north as Socorro or Roswell.

NESTING. At Burford Lake Wetmore found the Audubon's nesting "in fair numbers in yellow pine areas surrounding the lake." On Mt. Taylor it was seen feeding young out of the nest July 25, and on June 28 young were observed out of the nest 30 miles southwest of Chloride on the summit of the Black Range at about 8,000 feet. Jensen and the author recorded a nest containing 4 fresh eggs on May 28, 8 miles east of Santa Fe, at 8,700 feet. This nest was situated on a shelf of a steep bank of an old mining road alongside the mountain, in soil threaded with roots of a leaning aspen. It was made of twigs, grass, and web, and lined with fine grass and feathers, including one of a Steller's Jay. Jensen states: "Their nests always contain blue feathers." Nests may be well above ground in various kinds of trees, but usually where aspens constitute a part of the forest growth. The breeding birds resort to various ruses, fluttering and falling about in an attempt to lead an intruder away from nest or young. *Eggs:* Out of 14 nests recorded by Jensen, June 7 to 23, 1924 to 1929, 6 contained 4 eggs each, and 8 contained 5 eggs. Eggs are dull or bluish white, spotted with olive brown, lilac, and lavender, more or less wreathed around larger end.

❨ BLACK-THROATED GRAY WARBLER
Dendroica nigrescens

5" long. Color pattern of sexes similar. (Pl. XXIII)

So conspicuous is this Warbler in its gray, black, and white dress that there should be little difficulty in identifying it. *Adult male in summer:* Head, throat, and chest black except two white lines on side of head and yellow spot in front of eye. The lower white line extends from lower mandible and ends in white spot at shoulder; back dark gray streaked with black; wings with two white bars; breast and underparts white; sides streaked with black. In fall plumage it is similar, but black markings are concealed and sides are washed with brown. *Adult female in summer:* Similar to male in summer, but as a rule with less black on head; back browner and less heavily streaked.

DISTRIBUTION. The Black-throated Gray Warbler is widely distributed throughout the wooded and forested mountains in summer, but it is most numerous in the southern section, where it ranges down to 6,000 feet. In late May and late June 1955 it was quite common in the Animas and Peloncillo Mountains. It also has been observed in the Capitan Mountains and at Fort Wingate in July. There are summer records for both Shiprock and the Chuska Mountains, yet the southwestern section seems to be the preferred range, as the many records indicate.

NESTING. There is need for observers to fill in gaps in nesting records of this common Warbler. Numerous records indicate that it is a regular summer breeder. Jensen found nests May 22, 1920 and June 11, 1922 near Arroyo Hondo, about 6 miles southeast of Santa Fe. *Nest:* In low scrub oaks, or high in pines; compact, deeply cup-shaped, made of grass, weed stems and feathers, lined with feathers or rabbit fur. *Eggs:* Usually 4; white to pale greenish white, delicately spotted with reddish brown.

TOWNSEND'S WARBLER
Dendroica townsendi
4¾—5″ long. Color pattern of sexes similar.

The black and yellow head markings and yellow breast with black side barring are outstanding identification features of the Townsend's Warbler. *Adult male in spring and summer:* Crown, throat, and cheeks black, with black of cheek set in yellow that conspicuously covers side of head; back and rump bright olive green with black arrow-shaped dotting. Wings and tail dark brown edged with gray; wings with two conspicuous white bars. It is in spring migration that the males will be seen in full plumage. A beautiful male was taken by the author at this season in the Animas Mountains. Fall plumage is similar, but black of head is obscured by olive green. *Adult female in summer:* Similar to male, but crown is olive green spotted with black; cheeks olive, and black and

white marking restricted; throat and breast obscurely marked with black.

DISTRIBUTION. This handsome Warbler is in the state as a spring and fall migrant only, but is common and widely spread. It begins to enter the state from the south in early April and may be observed well into May. It was seen at Carlsbad on April 23, and in the Animas Mountains on May 8. In the southward migration it begins coming into the northern section in early August and is usually out of the state by mid-October. Although there are no nesting records for New Mexico, it is quite probable that the Townsend's nests in the Canadian and Hudsonian Zones in the northern part of the state, but has been overlooked.

(GRACE'S WARBLER
Dendroica graciae
4½—5″ long. Color pattern of sexes similar. (Pl. XXIII)

The Grace's Warbler is related to the Yellow-throated Warbler of the Mississippi Valley. Principal distinguishing spring and summer marks of the male are gray head and back, yellow throat, and yellow line over eye. It resembles the Audubon's, but has no black on throat. Crown and back narrowly streaked with black; wings with two white bands; underparts white streaked with black. *Adult female in spring and summer:* Similar to male, but black streaks indistinct; wing bars narrower; yellow and white duller. Winter plumage of sexes alike. It was discovered by Dr. Elliott Coues, on Whipple's Pass, Arizona, in 1864, and named for his sister Grace in 1865, by Spencer F. Baird, assistant director of the Smithsonian Institution.

DISTRIBUTION. The Grace's Warbler is common in summer and widely distributed over the forested mountains, but does not range as high as do some other species, seemingly preferring elevations from 7,000 to 8,000 feet. Goldman, however, record-ed it at 9,000 feet June 16 in the Zuñi Mountains. It was noted at 8,000 feet in the Pinos Altos Mountains north of Silver City in July. Bailey reported it common June 25 on Mesa Yegua, 30 miles north of Santa Rosa at 7,400 feet. On June 12, 1944, Gabrielson and the author found it common in the Sacramento Mountains near Mayhill at 7,800 feet. It has been ob-served during fall migration as late as Oc-tober 6 at Albuquerque. It returns to the state around mid-April.

NESTING. There are but few actual nest-ing records for the state, although the many summer records, occurring even as far south as the Pinos Altos Range, are convincing evidence that it is a regular breeder. Bailey indicates that it breeds commonly on Mesa Yegua and elsewhere. *Nest:* Usually 50 to 60 feet from the ground in pine or fir; made compactly of vegetable fiber, hair, and oak catkins; well lined with hair and feathers. *Eggs:* 3 or 4; white, lightly spotted with reddish brown.

NORTHERN (GRINNELL) WATERTHRUSH

Seiurus noveboracensis
6″ long. Color pattern of sexes alike.

Although classed with the Warblers, the Northern Waterthrush in some re-spects is more like the true Thrush. It is more often seen near or on the ground, about stream banks or ponds where there is concealing vegetation. *Adults:* The long white or yellowish stripe over the eye from bill to neck, and brown stripe through the eye, are distinguishing marks; upperparts olive green; underparts usually white; throat finely, and breast broadly, streaked with black.

DISTRIBUTION. Most records of this Waterthrush date back to the early part of the century: 1903-08. However, it is a regular spring and fall migrant through-out the state. It was observed both at

Carlsbad and in the Playas Valley, Hidal-go County, in September. "In the spring of 1928, two of these delightful birds stopped over for about three weeks in Mr. Jensen's garden, in the heart of Santa Fe, where the stream banks afforded them congenial hunting grounds" (Florence Bailey). "Two were noted at Bosque del Apache Refuge September 15 and one on August 19, at the San Andres Refuge" (Fleetwood). Montgomery reports it: "Regular visitors in April and May" in the Roswell area. In the Clayton area: "Noted August 28" (Krehbiel). They are present in the state until early summer, having been reported at "Lake Burford May 25" (Wetmore), and "June 15, Santa Fe" (Jen-sen), but there seems to be no nesting record.

⟨ MacGILLIVRAY'S WARBLER
Oporornis tolmiei
4½–5½″ long. Color pattern of sexes similar. (Pl. XXIII)

In its summer plumage, with olive green upperparts and yellow underparts, this Warbler is quite distinctive. *Adult male, spring and summer:* Head and neck bluish slate, darkening to black on lores and to blackish on throat and chest, where the feathers are broadly tipped with grayish white; eye ring white; back, wings, and tail plain olive green, without any white; lower underparts lemon yellow, darker on sides. *Adult male, fall and winter:* Like summer male, but feathers of crown and hind neck tipped with brownish; throat tipped with grayish. *Adult female, spring and summer:* Like summer male but feath-ers of head and back tipped with brown.

DISTRIBUTION. Judging by the num-ber of late spring and summer records, MacGillivray's Warbler is evidently widely distributed at this season but either it is uncommon or because of its shyness, it may escape notice. It seems to prefer the luxuriant undergrowth of moist places.

It was noted on the West Fork of the Gila River, Mogollon Mountains, in August. Montgomery reports it as common April and May and "one in September" in the Roswell area. The southward migration is under way by late August and the birds are usually out of the state by early October.

NESTING. While MacGillivray's Warbler has been recorded throughout most of the forested mountains in summer, most nesting records are from the northern section. "A nest containing young was found in Pueblo Canyon near Taos, at 8,000 feet on July 17, 1904 and on August 10 a young one, out of the nest but still being fed by the parent birds was taken in Hondo Canyon, at 8,200 feet" (Bailey). "Nest containing young in Arroyo Seco, near Taos, July 2," and "young in nest at a spring in Rio Hondo, June 18, 1942, banded" (Lena McBee). Nest: Near ground in vines or bushes; made of bits of dried weeds, bark, and grass; lined with fine grasses, rootlets and sometimes hair. Eggs: Usually 4; white or buffy, spotted on larger end with dark brown and lilac gray, with a few pen lines.

(YELLOWTHROAT
Geothlypis trichas
5½" long. Color pattern of sexes different. (Pl. XXIII)

The Yellowthroat, often referred to as "Maryland Yellowthroat," is a bird of marshes and pond borders with thick rushes and cattails. The adult male is easily distinguished by the black mask around forehead, and by the repeated "rickety-rickety-rickety" song which it sings even while under cover of marsh vegetation. Adult male: Forehead and sides of head, black, bordered above with white band; remainder of upperparts olive green; wings and tail without any white markings; underparts mainly bright orange yellow. Adult female: Head without black or white; upperparts yellowish brown.

DISTRIBUTION. The Yellowthroat is a common summer dweller. Altitude seems to be no barrier so long as rank rushes or other aquatic vegetation are present in marshes, ponds, or lakes. It occurs from the lowest parts of the Rio Grande and Pecos Valleys up to 8,000 feet in the northern mountains. It was established in late spring at the ponds of the Dexter Fish Culture Station, and in marshes about Las Cruces, as well as at Burford, Horse, and Dulce Lakes on the Jicarilla Indian Reservation. It arrives in the southern section in early April and is usually out of the state by the first of October.

NESTING. The Yellowthroat nests throughout its summer range, from 3,100 feet in the lowest part of the state, to 8,000 feet or higher in the northern mountains. Wetmore estimated that 15 pairs nested at Burford Lake from May 23 to June 19, and the author found it nesting near Albuquerque on June 16. For the Roswell area, Montgomery states: "Common nester in cattails; July 1, 1951, young in nest." Nest: Usually on ground at base of some plant, or in bunch of grass; deeply cupped; made of grass, sometimes lined with hair. Eggs: Normally 4; white, finely spotted on larger end with dark brown or black.

(YELLOW-BREASTED (LONG-TAILED) CHAT
Icteria virens
6½—7½" long. Color pattern of sexes similar. (Pl. XXIII)

The Chat is well named, for on the breeding grounds it is a real chatterbox, and a mimic and clown as well. Its noisy courtship and acrobatic antics as it flits on thumping wings above some dense willow thicket are distinctly characteristic. The varied whistling notes tied in with harsh clucks and mimic outbursts quickly catch the ear, although the bird, being shy and adept at concealment, may not be seen unless extreme caution is employed. Although so classified, the Chat scarcely seems to belong to the Warbler family. Much larger than most Warblers, in contour it somewhat resembles a Thrush. Bill is stout and rather curved; wings rounded; long tail also rounded. *Adult male:* Upperparts, including wings and tail, olive green; white line above eye; underparts and wing linings bright yellow. *Adult female:* Similar to male but duller.

DISTRIBUTION. On its arrival in spring the Yellow-breasted Chat is more often heard than seen. Widely distributed in summer, it is found from the lowest elevations to as high as 8,000 feet, but preferred habitat consists of the thick, brushy, moist valleys, particularly where willow, cottonwoods, and other deciduous shrubs and trees provide dense cover. The Rio Grande bottomlands from Las Cruces to Española constitute the most suitable habitat, and are where the birds seem to be most common. They are usually out of the state by September, returning to the southern section by the end of April.

NESTING. Jensen found fresh eggs June 10 to July 1 in the brushy watercourses about Santa Fe. Williams reports it as a common breeder about Las Cruces. The author found it nesting in willows about Albuquerque from early May to early June. *Nest:* In bushes and briers, 2 to 4 feet above ground; made largely of dry leaves and grasses; lined with fine grass. *Eggs:* 4; white or pinkish, spotted over entire surface and wreathed around larger end with brown and spots of lavender.

⟨ RED-FACED WARBLER
Cardellina rubrifrons
5¼" long. Color pattern of sexes alike. (Pl. XXIII)

So descriptive of the bird is its name, and so different from all other Warblers is the Red-faced, it is easily distinguished. Adults of both sexes are almost identical

in color, with forehead, throat, and chest bright red; crown and cheeks glossy black with white neck patch; upperparts gray and whitish, more or less tinged with pink; underparts tinged with pink.

DISTRIBUTION. Summer range of the Red-faced Warbler is confined to the Transition Zone of the mountains of the southwest and central western sections of the state. It is fairly common in the Pinos Altos, Black Range, and Mogollon Mountains, less so in the San Mateo Range and the Magdalena Mountains. It seems to prefer a rather dense forest locale, usually along streams or shaded canyon beds around 6,500 to 7,500 feet. Water Canyon, Magdalena Mountains, records represent the extreme north and northeast extension of its range. Henshaw found it common in the Graham Mountains of Arizona, where "In August they were in flocks of 10 to 15, among the pines and spruces." "A small flock of Red-faced Warblers was observed north of El Paso, Aug. 1, 1956" (Lena McBee). The birds leave the state about the first of September, and return from their winter haunts about mid-April.

NESTING. On June 27 the author located a nest 25 miles southwest of Chloride, in the Black Range, at 7,800 feet, which contained four heavily incubated eggs. It was situated near a half-decayed log among alder bushes in a canyon bed. The nest was made of twigs, rootlets, bark, and leaves. *Eggs:* 4; white, spotted with reddish brown.

⟨ WILSON'S (PILEOLATED) WARBLER
Wilsonia pusilla
4¼–5" long. Color pattern of sexes essentially alike. (Pl. XXIII)

In action the Wilson's (Pileolated), as it hurriedly moves through the foliage flitting its tail while seeking insects, is a composite of Vireo, Flycatcher, and Warbler. This active little bird seems never too engrossed to pause momentarily to gaze curiously at an intruder, but is soon off with a flit of the tail to resume its incessant search. In its striking garb of yellow, topped with a black cap, it is easily identified. It is named for Alexander Wilson (1766-1813), author of *American Ornithology*, in which he originally described the species. *Adults:* Rather uniformly yellow, with a black cap; forehead orange; rest of upperparts bright yellowish olive green; wings and tail without white markings; underparts vivid yellow. *Adults, fall and winter:* Similar, but black cap tipped with olive. *Female:* Almost identical to male in color pattern, but black cap may be less sharply defined and the yellow duller.

DISTRIBUTION. In summer this Warbler's distribution seems to be confined almost wholly to the higher mountains of the northern section of the state, particularly in the Sangre de Cristo Range. It is rather common in migration. In the Roswell area: "Numerous April and May, less numerous August, September, and October" (Montgomery). It is recorded as "transient visitor, common" at Bosque del Apache Refuge, and "common migrant" in the Clayton area (Krehbiel). It is present in the state until late October, but departs before stormy weather, reappearing in the southern section in late April.

NESTING. The nesting range of the Wilson's Warbler seems to be confined largely to the higher elevations of the northern mountains. "On July 23 it was found feeding young at 11,000 feet, below Pecos Baldy" (Bailey). "In Santa Fe Canyon, near Monument Rock, on June 5, 1921 a nest with five fresh eggs was found near a stream" (Jensen). *Nest:* On or near ground, often in willow thickets; made of willow leaves, weed twigs, and grasses. *Eggs:* 4 or 5; white or creamy, spotted with reddish brown and lavender, wreathed around larger end.

AMERICAN REDSTART
Setophaga ruticilla

4½–5" long. Color pattern of sexes different.

Adult male: Black, glossed with bluish; sides of breast, patch on wing, and wide band on tail rich salmon; underparts white. *Adult female:* Wing patch and tail band pale yellow; crown gray; back olive brown; underparts white.

DISTRIBUTION. The American Redstart is uncommon in the state. There are records, however, from widely separated sections. It is listed as "transient visitor, rare" at Bosque del Apache Refuge. "One female, Roswell, September 4, 1952" (Montgomery). James W. (Jimmy) Peckumn recorded it near Las Cruces April 5, 1956. One was seen August 28, 1957, at Rattlesnake Spring, 30 miles southwest of Carlsbad, by Paul F. Spangle, Carlsbad Caverns National Park naturalist. "We have 29 records; some years we miss it. 1953 was a banner Warbler year, and for that year I have these New Mexico dates: May 6, 7, and 10, female or immature at Durling's [near Canutillo], October 13 one at Durling's. In El Paso we had an adult male October 22, and a female October 25. May 8, 1955 a female at Durling's. We have only three adult males thus far" (Lena McBee). Durrie and Fitzsimmons have observed it at Albuquerque and Caballo Lake September 3, 1955. "Observed at University of New Mexico campus, Albuquerque, September 10, 1955" (Fitzsimmons). There seem to be no nesting records for the state.

(PAINTED REDSTART
Setophaga picta

5" long. Color pattern of sexes alike. (Pl. I)

The Painted Redstart, one of the most highly colored of the Warbler family, is an active, restless bird as it flits about in the foliage or perches on branches of trees alternately half opening and closing its wings. The designation, *Setophaga* (Greek), "insect-eater" and *picta* (Latin), "painted" is most applicable. *Adults:* Black; underparts deep red, white patch on wing, and outer-tail feathers white.

DISTRIBUTION. The mountains of the southwestern portion of the state constitute the main summer range of the Painted Redstart. It is fairly common as far north as Reserve and the northern tip of the Black Range, west of Chloride. There is one record for the Zuñi Mountains, but the bird recorded there must have been a wanderer, far out of its normal range. The Redstart prefers humid conditions, and is partial to waterfalls at elevations of from 5,500 to 8,000 feet. It is usually out of New Mexico by late Sep-

tember, returning here in late March or early April.

NESTING. Preferred nesting site of the Painted Redstart is beneath projecting rocks or by grass or weed hummocks on ledges of canyons, usually near water or waterfalls. On May 11 the author located a nest containing 3 fresh eggs, at the head of Bear Canyon, east slope of the Animas Mountains, 7,500 feet. The nest was situated by a small waterfall, under the edge of an overhanging bunch of grass growing in the crevice of a rock halfway up a sloping, rocky ledge, and was exposed to the morning sun only. *Nest:* Made of weed stems and "rock" moss, lined with soft grass, the whole set in dry leaves bedded beneath the bunch of grass. *Eggs:* 3 or 4; white, wreathed around larger end with reddish brown.

WEAVER FINCHES
Family: PLOCEIDAE

ONLY A SINGLE representative of the Weaver Finches occurs in America—the exotic House, or English, Sparrow. Unlike most other members of this European and Asiatic group of birds, known for their skill in the construction of elaborate, dome-shaped nests by interlacing fine grasses, House Sparrows generally build crude, bulky nests.

❪ HOUSE SPARROW
Passer domesticus

5½–6¼″ long. Color pattern of sexes different.

The so-called English or House Sparrow is an exotic species which is now nationally established. About all that can be said in favor of this unwelcome resident is that

it feeds on injurious insects to the extent of compensating, in part, for its undesirable traits. It is not a Sparrow but is a relative of the European Weaver Finches. *Adult male:* The gray crown and black throat and chest distinguish the adult male from other Sparrows. Cheeks white; patch from eye to nape bright chestnut; upperparts brown streaked with black; underparts dull gray. *Adult female:* Crown and hind neck grayish brown or olive; remainder of upperparts like male but lighter brown; underparts brownish white.

According to Chapman: "This pest was introduced to the United States at Brooklyn, New York, in 1851 and 1852. As late as 1870 it was largely confined to the [Eastern] cities." It is now resident, or semi-migratory, throughout most if not all of the western hemisphere, from Canada to Argentina. Probably no other bird has ever attained such phenomenal spread, adjusted itself to so varied climatic conditions, nor reached such enormous population. It is abundant about villages, cities, and rural settlements throughout the Southwest. Fortunately, it is semidomestic and as yet has not resorted to populating rural America, hence is not in serious conflict with valuable native species, except in localized ways. In many cities of the Southwest, where there are shade trees, particularly about public buildings, winter concentrations become a serious nuisance. In Roswell and Carlsbad, for example, some of the most attractive trees have been sacrificed, only to induce the roosting, noisy hordes to move to other nearby trees. The problem persists but the beautiful, sorely-needed shade trees are gone. In their respective categories, the status of the House Sparrow corresponds to that of the house mouse and rat among mammals. Alike they pose the most difficult problems in control. Any control measures against the Sparrow, be it gun,

trap, or poison, must be carefully applied to avoid sacrificing valuable native species. These undesirable aliens soon learn to avoid almost every kind of trap or other means of control, yet only through wholesale destruction can their ranks be materially reduced. Systematic destruction of nests containing eggs or young seems to be the most effective means of reducing excessive populations.

NESTING. The large, unsightly, loosely-made nests which clutter up the branches of all sorts of trees in towns, cities, and about rural homes, are in keeping with the many other undesirable traits of these birds. The nesting season in the milder climates is spread over a good part of the year, and so persistent in nesting are they that if a nest is torn out, another will be made and contain eggs within an amazingly short time. Furthermore, young, with the inherent pugnacity of the adult birds, are able to care for themselves soon after leaving the nest. These factors are conducive to vast, sustained populations. Eggs: 5 to 7; spotted with brown and purple.

MEADOWLARKS, BLACKBIRDS, AND ORIOLES
Family: ICTERIDAE

THE STUDENT may ponder the inclusion of such a diversified group of birds in the same family. Close comparison, however, reveals that certain characters are common to all: the rather large, conical, sharp-pointed bill fitted with cutting edges, and—if one wishes to go into the finer points of demarcation—the features which are described by Wetmore as "peculiar palates adapted to their food habits," and possessing "only nine developed primaries, a combination of characters which distinguish them from all other North American families." Their greater size, conspicuous coloration, and preference for living in the open are clues to identification. All are migratory but in the case of Blackbirds, only partially so.

(BOBOLINK

Dolichonyx oryzivorus

6½—7½" long. Color pattern of sexes different.

The Bobolink, a rare visitor in New Mexico, is one of the unpredictable birds which enter and leave the north half of the state crosswise rather than in a north-south direction. *Adult male:* So striking in plumage is the male Bobolink during his stay here that he is readily identified. The only other bird with which he might be confused is the male Lark Bunting in his black and white summer coat. The Bunting, however, has conspicuous white on wings only, while practically all of the underparts of the male Bobolink are white. Remainder of body is largely black except for the large, buffy neck patch back of the black crown, which is a distinguishing mark. *Adult female:* Upperparts olive buff streaked with black; crown blackish with buffy median stripe; underparts yellowish or buffy white. *Young:* Similar to female but buffier.

DISTRIBUTION. There are many summer-flowering marshes and meadows in the northern half of the state which seem ideal as breeding areas, yet careful observation has disclosed that extremely few of them are ever occupied by Bobolinks. Records seem to refer almost entirely to accidental occurrences or to wandering individuals. In the author's many years of observation he has seen only one, a male, in the Carlsbad area (May 1933). "Rarely seen in migration, two pairs having been identified definitely May 14, 1950, when seen in Clayton. Males were singing" (Krehbiel).

NESTING. The only definite Bobolink nesting record for New Mexico is one by Fleetwood and the author, July 15, 1951, in the extensive meadows at the Parkview Fish Hatchery, Chama River Valley, below Parkview, 7,000 feet. Although no nest was located, a singing male was ob-served and while the meadow was being searched, a female was flushed; but she was immediately forced down into the meadow growth by the male. Their conduct was such as to leave no doubt that they were a breeding pair. *Nest:* A depression in the ground; lined with weed stems and grass. *Eggs:* 5 to 7; gray or reddish brown, spotted and blotched with brown and purple.

(EASTERN (RIO GRANDE) MEADOWLARK

Sturnella magna

8½—10½" long. Color pattern of sexes essentially alike.

The Eastern is far less common in the state than the Western Meadowlark. The two constitute one of the most difficult problems in sight identification, wherever they range together. The radical difference in song is the chief means of separating them, and this advantage is of little consequence except in spring and summer when both species are in full song. The finer points of distinction are in the shades and extent of breast and head coloration. In the Eastern, the yellow of the throat is not as extensive as in the Western, but the crescent is wider, and the yellow a deeper shade.

DISTRIBUTION. The principal range of the Eastern Meadowlark includes approximately the southern half of the state. If purity of song is a dependable distinguishing feature, there has been little hybridization. This is surprising in view of the fact that ranges of the two species overlap. The Eastern is nowhere common. The author has recorded it, however, in the rank grass, shinnery oak type of the eastern plains (Roosevelt County); the Rio Grande Valley; Mt. Taylor Mesa, and southward. "It occurs in April, May and June in the Roswell area" (Montgomery). Goldman found it in the Animas and the Playas Valleys, Hidalgo County, July 16 to August 15. Whether any number remain in the state during the colder part of the winter is yet to be determined.

NESTING. Two nests containing eggs of the Eastern Meadowlark were found in May 1909, on the grassy slopes of the San Andres Mountains east of Engle, where the birds were fairly common. Young were noted at the San Simon Marshes, Hidalgo County, May 10. *Nest:* On the ground; made of dried grass with dome-shaped cover. *Eggs:* 4 to 6; white, entire surface speckled with brown or purple.

⟨ WESTERN MEADOWLARK
Sturnella neglecta
9—10½″ long. Color pattern of sexes essentially alike. (Pl. XXIV)

The Western is the common Meadowlark found throughout New Mexico. Its popularity is best attested by the fact that it has been named State Bird by at least six states: Kansas, Montana, Nebraska, Oregon, South Dakota, and Wyoming. Its rather plump, large body, brown and white striped crown, and yellow underparts with black crescent are unmistakable identification marks. In flight the flashing of the white-bordered tail is characteristic. The female is a little smaller than the male, paler, and with yellow and black more limited. Conduct and general color pattern of the Western and the Eastern are almost identical, but the songs differ; that of the Western being loud and varied while that of the Eastern is soft and rippling or wavy. Both, however, are among our most gifted and pleasing songsters and are highly beneficial as consumers of insects.

DISTRIBUTION. In summer the Western Meadowlark is found practically statewide. Whether a majority of these summer residents leave the state for the colder part of the winter is questionable. If they do, other waves from the north flow down over the state with the coming of severe weather. So hardy and resourceful are they that they survive the severest winter storms, even where their habitat is impaired, as it now often is, by resorting to feed-lots about farms and ranches.

NESTING. Western Meadowlarks nest on open plain, mesa, or meadowland—where there is concealing grass cover. During periods of drought, when upland grass is scant, many resort to the saltgrass of the Pecos and Rio Grande Valleys for nesting. Altitude seems to have little bearing on summer distribution where there are meadows or upland grasslands, since these birds occur and nest from the lower levels up to 8,000 feet. On April 29 a nest containing 4 fresh eggs was found in heavy grass on a sloping ridge at the Dexter Fish Culture Station. At Burford Lake (7,800 feet), "Nest with four eggs and two newly hatched young was found on June 11" (Wetmore). *Nest:* A hooded bower in concealing grass, made of soft dry grass. *Eggs:* 4 to 6; white or sometimes light green, entire surface speckled with brown and purple, usually heaviest around larger end.

⟨ YELLOW-HEADED BLACKBIRD
Xanthocephalus xanthocephalus
8—10½″ long. Color pattern of sexes different. (Pl. XXV)

So striking is the male Yellow-headed Blackbird in full summer dress that in comparison, the much smaller female, with brown head, appears unrelated to him. *Adult male:* Yellow head and breast and black body with conspicuous white wing patch are distinctive marks. The black markings about the bill serve as attractive trimming for the yellow adornment of head and neck. Winter plumage is similar to summer, but yellow of crown and neck is obscured by dusky tips of feathers. *Adult female:* Much smaller; upperparts dark brown, without white on wings; line over eye, cheek, chin, and throat dull whitish, changing to yellow on chest; breast streaked with white. Size of male distinguishes him even in winter, but the smaller female might be confused with the female Redwinged Blackbird, although the yellow of chest remains as a determining feature.

DISTRIBUTION. The summer range of this Blackbird is confined largely to the northern section of the state, for the most part above 6, 500 feet where, locally, it is common. It is at this season that the loud, rasping, and fascinating notes of the male are heard. In migration Yellow-headed Blackbirds occur statewide, although not as abundantly as the Brewer's or the Redwinged. Some usually remain in the southern section of the state during winter, particularly about livestock feeding pens in the Carlsbad and Las Cruces areas. They are also listed as "winter residents, common" at Bosque del Apache Refuge. Their favorite haunts are marshes and lake shores which have a liberal growth of rank rushes or other aquatic vegetation.

NESTING. The lakes (Burford, Stone, Horse, and others) along the Continental Divide in Rio Arriba County are the principal Yellow-headed Blackbird nesting retreats in the state. In 1918 Wetmore estimated that there were 210 pairs of these Blackbirds at Burford Lake, and "By May 28, nest building was going on everywhere." "They were found nesting in willows along the river near the Santa Fe Indian School June 18, 1924" (Jensen). There is an old record of a nesting colony near Las Cruces, but there are no recent records of the species breeding in the Rio Grande Valley or elsewhere under 6,000 feet. *Nest:* A rather thick-walled basket-like structure, made of marsh grasses woven together and hung between stalks of rushes or other vegetation, well above water. *Eggs:* Usually 4; grayish or greenish white, blotched, speckled and lined with

brown over the entire surface but heaviest about larger end.

⟨ REDWINGED BLACKBIRD

Agelaius phoeniceus

7½–9½" long. Color pattern of sexes different. (Pl. XXV)

At nesting time the male Redwinged Blackbird is a handsome and highly animated resident of marshes and lake and pond shores where rushes and other aquatic vegetation predominate. He often has two mates whom he guards jealously, especially when other males of his kind intrude. At such times should his mates take wing, he attempts to force them down into concealing cover. Males of few birds are more aggressive in defending nesting grounds. The male is usually established on pre-empted nesting places well in advance of the arrival of females and young males of the previous season. The black coat and scarlet wing patch clearly distinguish the adult male. The dazzling wing patch he displays to best advantage by spreading his tail and puffing out his wings. *Female:* Smaller and radically different in color pattern: upperparts brown, streaked with buff; crown with median line and stripe over eye; shoulders buffy, faintly washed with red; underparts streaked with brown; throat and breast streaked with whitish, more or less suffused with pinkish buff. In fall and winter when different species of Blackbirds assemble in great flocks, females of the Redwinged and Yellow-headed may be confused. The Redwinged has been divided into many subspecies. Three are listed as occurring in New Mexico: the Nevada, the Thick-billed, and the Sonora. However, most observers recognize the Redwinged as a species only.

DISTRIBUTION. Although Redwinged Blackbirds may not be permanent residents any place, they are common throughout much of the state year-round. They may be found at nesting time about marshes, lakes, or ponds bordered with rushes or other aquatic vegetation, from the lowest elevation to 8,000 feet or more. In winter they congregate in great flocks and are quite common in agricultural districts of the Rio Grande and Pecos Valleys, especially from Albuquerque and Santa Rosa southward. At roosting time (March 22, 1949) there were over 3,000 in and about the rank rushes at Lake No. 4 at the Dexter Fish Culture Station. The 1952 Christmas bird census for the Socorro–Bosque del Apache Refuge area showed an estimated 75,000 Redwinged Blackbirds. The 1953 census for Bosque del Apache alone included an estimated 35,600. Considering the wide distribution of the Redwinged Blackbird and its persistence in nesting activities, it is not surprising that heavy populations of the species are maintained.

NESTING. Nesting of the Redwinged Blackbird seems to be limited only by lack of acceptable nesting places. Quite often a breeding trio (male and two females) may be noted about a small marsh or pond, clearly indicating that the species is polygamous. Fledglings are often out of the nest by early June, while small young may be seen in nests as late as mid-August, indicating that two broods are often raised in a season. Nest: Made of blades of rushes or other marsh grasses, woven into a deep, rather compact cup and laced to the upright stalks of rushes or other plants, almost always over water. This type of nest building sometimes leads to tragedy, as when one side of the nest is supported by green or growing stalks, and the other by dead or slower growing ones, causing the nest to become tilted to such extent that eggs or young birds fall into the water. Nests of very few other birds are subject to such fate. Eggs: Usually 4; bluish green, heavily blotched and lined with brown.

ORIOLES

ALTHOUGH classified with the Meadowlarks and the Blackbirds, Orioles are in certain respects quite different. They are arboreal, rarely being seen on the ground, while their distant relatives are largely terrestrial. Though they are not gifted songsters, their beauty and economic value compensate for what they lack as vocalists. With the exception of the Scott's, they are commonly observed about human habitation, particularly where trees are a feature of the domestic landscape. New Mexico has four species—the Orchard, Hooded, Scott's, and Bullock's—as summer residents.

⟨ ORCHARD ORIOLE
Icterus spurius
6½–7½" long. Color pattern of sexes different.

The Orchard, the smallest of the Orioles, is an uncommon and unpredictable summer resident in the state. In its striking black and chestnut plumage it quickly attracts attention as it dashes from tree to tree, or briefly tarries on a wire or limb. At nesting time it has a pleasing way of flitting between trees, all the while rendering a joyous whistling and warbling medley, thereby often betraying its presence. *Adult male:* Where other Orioles show yellow in flight, the Orchard exhibits rich chestnut, and appears black when seen through heavy foliage. Except for the dark chestnut of underparts, shoulders, and rump, and the white wing barring, the plumage is black. *Adult female:* Upperparts yellowish olive green, more yellowish on upper-tail coverts and tail, wings with two whitish bars and white edgings; underparts pale yellow.

DISTRIBUTION. Although uncommon, the Orchard Oriole does occur regularly only in the southeastern corner of the state. The author has observed it most frequently about trees at Carlsbad, and he has one record for Hagerman. The earliest record for Carlsbad is May 4.

NESTING. Orchard Orioles nest occasionally, if not regularly, where there are suitable trees, in the Carlsbad and adjacent areas south and east to the Texas line. In 1954, a pair nested in a large American elm on the Lawrence Rayroux farm, three miles north of Carlsbad, and in June 1958, and again in 1959, a pair raised a brood at the author's place, three miles northwest of Carlsbad. Normal reproduction of this Oriole, as with many other small birds, is inhibited as result of the birds being victimized by the parasitic Cowbird laying in their nests. This intrusion may account in part at least for its rarity in the state. One of the author's earliest and most cherished recollections pertains to his introduction to a pair of Orchard Orioles in an umbrella chinaberry tree at his birthplace near Austin, Texas. The enchanting sight of the vividly colored male at the symmetrically constructed yellow grass nest diffusing a fragrance of newmown hay, created a vivid impression the richness of which has not been dimmed by the passing of the years. *Nest:* Usually swung from the fork of a terminal limb; cup-shaped, made of fine grass blades that, when cured, give the nest an attractive yellowish or golden color; lined with down or cotton. *Eggs:* 4 to 6; pale bluish white, sometimes overlaid with grayish, blotched and lined, mostly around larger end, with browns and purples.

(HOODED ORIOLE
Icterus cucullatus
7½–8½″ long. Color pattern of sexes different. (Pl. XXVI)

The Hooded Oriole, named from its yellow "hood," or forespot, is a handsome streamlined bird with distinctive song and coloration. *Adult male:* Color pattern almost wholly yellow and black; head, neck, and rump, entire underparts, except black throat patch, yellow; tail black; wing with white patch and white border to wing coverts. *Female:* Upperparts olive green, grayish on back; wings brownish with two white bands; underparts pale yellow, black throat patch usually lacking.

DISTRIBUTION. The Hooded Oriole is confined in summer to the southwestern part of the state; north to the Gila River and Silver City and east (rarely) to the Rio Grande (Las Cruces). It is most common in and about the Animas and Peloncillo Mountains, preferring the large sycamore trees common along streams and canyons of that section. However, it may be found in the more desert types where there are clusters of other trees, particularly cottonwoods, about basins, wells, or stock-watering tanks. It may also be seen about groves of Emory oak, at and near the Cloverdale picnic grounds where many other birds may also be observed.

NESTING. A nest with three fresh eggs was located by the author and Wayne Bohl twelve feet above ground, on a terminal branch of a large hackberry on the east slope of the Animas Mountains, June 27, 1955. *Nest:* A well-woven cup, unlike the pendant nest of the Bullock's Oriole; made of fine, long grass stems and fibers from other plants; all having a clean, cured yellowish shade; lined with soft particles of grass. *Eggs:* 3 to 5; bluish white, spotted and lined with brown, mostly on larger end.

(SCOTT'S ORIOLE
Icterus parisorum
7½–8½″ long. Color pattern of sexes different. (Pl. XXVI)

The Scott's Oriole of the arid and desert lands is one of the most beautiful and most interesting of Southwestern birds. The flash of its black and lemon plumage over a bleak, rugged canyon or cactus and stone-covered mountain slope seems strangely out of place as the bird restlessly moves from place to place. Its bright color, fascinating ways, and far-carrying clear whistling song provide a thrill. Although suggesting that of the Meadowlark, the song of the Scott's Oriole is more repetitious, has more volume, and can be heard at a greater distance. *Adult male:* The Scott's, like the male of most other Orioles, is dominantly colored black and yellow; however, the black is pronounced and the yellow of a distinctive lemon shade, which with the two white wing bars make a pleasing combination. All of the head to middle back, breast, middle tail feathers, and all of outer half of tail are jet black; bright lemon dominates the wing shoulders, connecting with yellow of the underparts when the bird is at rest; the lemon of underparts extends back to middle of tail, which also includes the rump and basic part of tail feathers; wings with two white zones. *Adult female:* Somewhat smaller than male; upperparts olive gray, top of head and back with dark streaking, wings crossed by two white bars; underparts greenish yellow, median portion brighter yellow; chin and throat usually washed with black.

DISTRIBUTION. The Scott's Oriole has a rather extensive summer range, but is confined almost wholly to the Lower and Upper Sonoran Zones. It ranges up the Rio Grande Valley, rarely to Albuquerque, and in the Pecos Valley to about Santa Rosa. It shuns the more humid, forested mountains, nor does it occur on the high plains of the eastern side. It is most common on and adjacent to the desert foothills and mountains of the southern and southwestern portions of the state, particularly in southern Hidalgo County. The Scott's is not generally regarded as common, although the author has found it so locally, particularly on and adjacent to the Big Hatchet Mountain. Jensen observed it along the western slope of the Sandia

Mountains east of Albuquerque, and Bailey recorded it at Santa Rosa and eastward to Montoya; both records seem to represent the extreme northernmost limit of its range.

NESTING. Height of the nesting season occurs in late May or early June. The tall yuccas or soapweed (*Yucca elata*), a familiar part of the landscape in Doña Ana, Sierra, Luna, and Hidalgo Counties, where they sometimes attain a height of 20 feet or more, in groups of a few stately sentinels, or in extensive "forests," are preferred nesting retreats of the Scott's Oriole. *Nest:* Usually placed in the dead, drooping blades of yuccas beneath the live crown, which provide ample protection from both the weather and potential enemies. Few other bird nests are more secure. Nests are sometimes found in scrub pinyon and other trees, but by far the greatest number are in yuccas. Made mainly of fiber obtained from the border of yucca blades, woven into a neat, attractive yellowish cup, laced to the dead blades. The nest is not only a model of artful construction but is so securely laced to the tough blades that it may remain intact for several years. *Eggs:* 3 or 4; pale blue, scrolled and spotted with black, brown, and purple.

BULLOCK'S ORIOLE
Icterus bullockii
7½–8½″ long. Color pattern of sexes different. (Pl. XXVII)

Few other birds adjust so readily to man-made habitat—shade trees, orchards, and cultivated fields—as does Bullock's Oriole. Its striking orange and black plumage flashing here and there from the green foliage of a tree or from a cultivated plant, as it diligently searches for caterpillars, moths, and worms, is a reminder of its economic value. Few other birds are more beneficial than the Bullock's in cornfields where it intently searches stalks of corn and the silk of ears for insects and worms.

It is usually among the first birds to spot an enemy, especially a snake, when its raucous upbraiding chatter alerts other birds to imminent danger. *Adult male:* Line over eye, sides of head and neck, posterior upperparts and underparts yellow or orange; crown, back, line through eye, and narrow throat patch, black; tip of tail and middle tail feathers mainly black; wings black with large white patch and white edging. *Female:* Head and hind neck yellowish olive; back and rump grayish; wings with one broad white band and white edging; throat usually with some black; underparts lemon yellow, gray posteriorly.

DISTRIBUTION. The Bullock's is the most common and most widely distributed of the Orioles in the state, its summer range consisting of practically all areas from the lowest elevation up to 7,000 feet. Bullock's Orioles are most common in the irrigated sections of the Rio Grande and Pecos Valleys, preferring verdant cottonwood bottomlands. Populations are more stable than is true of many other birds, since the Bullock's prefer trees of yards and parks for nesting—a more dependable habitat than would otherwise be available to them. The Bullock's is out of the state by early October and begins to return in mid-April. Williams and White have a March 16, 1953, Las Cruces record, which is unusually early.

NESTING. The Bullock's Oriole nests in greatest numbers in the Rio Grande and Pecos Valleys, particularly about Las Cruces and Carlsbad. It may occur at higher elevations after the nesting season. *Nest:* Usually in cottonwood trees, sometimes in clusters of mistletoe, 20 to 40 feet from the ground, purse-shaped and pensile; made of weed stems, strings, hair, or fur, tightly woven together into a neatly secure whole, lined with down and soft grasses. The finished nest, laced to a branch, sometimes in the forks of a limb, usually swings clear. *Eggs:* 4 or 5; grayish or bluish white, or pale buffy; scrawled and lined with black, mostly around large end.

◖ BREWER'S BLACKBIRD
Euphagus cyanocephalus
8½—10″ long. Color pattern of sexes different.

The Brewer's is strictly a western Blackbird. It is a relative of the Rusty Blackbird, which occurs rarely in the eastern part of the state. The birds are rather clannish, usually remaining to themselves. In fall and winter, when they often congregate in considerable bunches, they frequent farms and feed lots, even feeding on lawns or in gardens, boldly walking about, perhaps with drooping wings and elevated tail. At such times, when resting on fences or in trees, they usually participate in a rather harsh, chattering song session. The bird was named for Thomas Mayo Brewer, American ornithologist, 1814-80. *Adult male:* Black glossed with bluish green, which, in winter, is intensified. Head and neck glossed with violet; white eye is a distinguishing mark. *Adult female:* Head, neck, and underparts dark brownish gray, faintly glossed with violet on head and neck; upperparts darker, wings and tail more highly glossed with bluish green.

DISTRIBUTION. In summer, Brewer's Blackbirds are widely scattered over the northern half of the state, usually localized at 6,500 to 7,500 feet. They prefer grassy meadows with sparse wooded borders. They winter commonly in the state, particularly in the Rio Grande and Pecos Valleys south of Albuquerque and Roswell.

NESTING. The Brewer's Blackbird nests most commonly along the Continental Divide in the northern section of the state, but only about lakes and marshes, or in valleys with streams and meadows. It seems to prefer these places to the heavy tule borders of lakes, which are the favorite nesting places of Redwinged and Yellow-headed Blackbirds. From May 1 to 10,

1918, nests with eggs were found in meadow grass in the marshes of upper Beaver Creek (now known as Beaverhead), at about 7,000 feet, the southernmost point at which this bird was known to nest. Excessive use of the area by livestock caused the birds in later years to abandon these meadows as a nesting place. "In northern Santa Fe County, a few pairs nest occasionally along the river, and nests were found June 3 and 10" (Jensen). They often nest in colonies. *Nest:* Generally in trees but also in bunches of meadow grass near the ground; rather bulky, made of twigs and weed stems; inner cup of rootlets and grass cemented with mud; heavily lined with grass and sometimes feathers. *Eggs:* 4 to 6; grayish or greenish white, spotted and lined with browns and lavenders.

(BOAT-TAILED (GREAT-TAILED) GRACKLE

Cassidix mexicanus

12—17″ long. Color pattern of sexes different.

So conspicuous is the Boat-tailed Grackle with its long, rudder-like tail, that it immediately attracts attention. It is the common Grackle of the state. In south Texas, where Boat-tailed Grackles are very common, they are generally known as "Jackdaws." The male is the dominating figure, being considerably larger than his more modestly garbed mate. Like the Common, the Boat-tailed displays plumage in variegated shades of green and purple, with colors scintillating according to the slant of sunlight in which they are seen. Iris of eye is pale yellow. *Female:* Smaller and of a prevailing brown shade, head darker; back blackish, glossed with green and purple; underparts more buffy.

DISTRIBUTION. The presence of this Grackle in summer is spotty and unpredictable. It usually occurs throughout the southern half of the state, particularly in the Pecos and Rio Grande Valleys, but also more sparingly in the southwestern portion (Lordsburg). Although it is reported as far north as the San Juan Valley, about Aztec, this is far outside its former normal range. The Boat-tailed prefers to live about water or marshes at nesting time. Scarcity of water, therefore, may have a direct influence on its presence or absence. It is listed as "permanent resident, common" at Bosque del Apache Refuge. Montgomery notes it as "increasingly common; nests; no record October, November" for the Roswell area. Krehbiel and Cook collected a male Boat-tailed Grackle at Clayton, April 24, 1958. This record, and those for Aztec definitely indicate that the species is extending its range. They are more numerous in winter than formerly, especially about livestock feeding pens. Thirty-two were seen at Socorro on December 20, 1954. Boat-tailed Grackles are now common year-round in the Las Cruces area, where Williams and the Whites advise that they commit severe depredation on other birds' eggs and young. The increase in population of this species probably is due to agricultural development which has taken place, particularly in the Rio Grande and Pecos Valleys. Twenty-five years ago they were rare here.

NESTING. The first nesting of the Boat-tailed observed by the author was on July 21, 1924, when a small colony was found with young on Cass Draw, 8 miles south of Carlsbad. Since that time, breeding colonies have become more numerous. On April 26, 1950, a nesting colony of 10 or more pairs was observed in the large mulberry trees surrounding an irrigation reservoir on the Stephenson farm four miles southwest of Carlsbad. They have continued to nest there as well as at other points in the area. In recent years they have been found nesting as far north as Albuquerque. Bohl reported Boat-tailed Grackles nesting in trees in Lordsburg in the spring of 1955. They nest also in considerable numbers at Bosque del Apache Refuge. *Nest:*

In small or large trees, a bulky structure, made mostly of grass stabilized inside with mud. *Eggs:* 4 or 5; varying in base shade from bluish, greenish, olive, or purplish gray; heavily scrawled with brown or black spots and lines.

⟨ COMMON (BRONZED) GRACKLE
Quiscalus quiscula

12—13″ long. Color pattern of sexes similar.

The Common Grackle is included in the New Mexico list of breeding birds as result of the author's discovery of a nesting colony on the Dry Cimarron, in the extreme northeast corner of the state. *Adult male:* Body mainly bronze; head iridescent bluish green; eyes yellowish white; wings and tail glossy purple; tail long. *Adult female:* Somewhat smaller with a shorter tail; plumage similar, though more brownish.

DISTRIBUTION. No doubt this Grackle occurs in the northeastern corner of the state more frequently than might be assumed from this one record.

NESTING. On June 15, 1951, the author located a nesting colony of about 12 pairs 50 miles east of Folsom, one-half mile from the New Mexico–Oklahoma line. The nests were placed on sleepers beneath the floor of a long bridge on State Highway 325. Nests examined were rather bulky, made of sticks, and contained well incubated eggs and young. *Eggs:* 4 to 7; pale green or greenish blue, spotted and lined with brown and black.

⟨ BROWN-HEADED COWBIRD
Molothrus ater

7—8″ long. Color pattern of sexes similar.

The Cowbirds, smallest of our Blackbirds, are often seen in summer walking about in the shadow of cattle or horses, catching insects disturbed by their movements, or riding contentedly on their backs with apparent mutual consent. *Adult male:* Head, neck and breast purplish brown; back and underparts steel blue to greenish; wings and tail black, glossed with bluish green; lesser wing coverts steel blue. *Adult female:* Upperparts dusky brown; head dark brown; back glossed with green and purple; underparts brownish; chin and throat pale. It is the only Blackbird with a brown head. Despite their vivacious and beguiling ways, Cowbirds, Brown-headed as well as the Bronzed, possess some very obnoxious traits. The scientific designation, *Molothrus* (Greek), means "tramp," "vagabond," "parasite," all of which they definitely are. They neither build their own nests nor care for their young, leaving these family duties entirely to foster parents, which may be any of the smaller species in whose nests they deposit their eggs. Unfortunately the young Cowbirds are so hardy and have such gluttonous appetites that in a short time they dominate the nest and may actually cause the rightful members of the family to starve. Unfortunately, too, Cowbirds are common and widespread, hence this imposition is a serious limiting factor in the populations of smaller birds, and one which they are all but helpless to resist. The Cowbirds have been divided into several forms in New Mexico, including "Dwarf," and "Sagebrush," but the average observer regards it as the Brown-headed Cowbird. Its smaller size readily distinguishes it from the other Blackbirds. When Cowbirds congregate in large bunches in the fall they often do considerable damage to unharvested head grains. Their bad traits more than outweigh any benefits they may render as destroyers of insects. They do not merit legal protection.

DISTRIBUTION. In summer, Brown-headed Cowbirds are found statewide, from the lowest sections to as high as

8,000 feet. For the most part they are seen wandering in pairs or in trios. In the fall they gather in great flocks, particularly in the Rio Grande and Pecos Valley agricultural districts. Most of them leave the state for the winter, but some may be present in the Carlsbad and Las Cruces areas at this season. Spring migrants begin to arrive in mid-April.

NESTING. No nest constructed. *Eggs:* Deposited in nests of other birds; whitish, surface covered with brown specks and blotches, heaviest about larger end. Cowbirds may even throw out the eggs of other nesting birds in order to make room for their own.

⟮ BRONZED COWBIRD
Tangavius aeneus
7½—8½″ long. Color pattern of sexes similar.

The occurrence of the Bronzed, also known as the Red-eyed, Cowbird is of considerable interest. Its nature, including the habit of depositing eggs in nests of other birds, differs little from that of its relatives. Allan R. Phillips reported taking a specimen of this Cowbird in Guadalupe Canyon, New Mexico, near the Mexican boundary, in July 1947, thus verifying former reports of its occurrence in the state. *Adult male:* Larger than the common or Brown-headed Cowbird. The Bronzed has red eyes; bronzy black body; feathers of the neck have appearance of a ruff; wing coverts glossy purplish. *Adult female:* Duller, but darker than female of the common form.

NESTING. The breeding range of the Bronzed Cowbird is confined to extreme southwestern New Mexico. On June 28, 1957, Wayne Bohl collected a pair in breeding condition on the east side of the Animas Mountains, thirty miles south of Animas. "Breeds in southwestern New Mexico (Guadalupe Canyon)" (A.O.U. *Check-list*). *Eggs:* Deposited in nests of other birds, usually 2 or 3; bluish green, unspotted.

TANAGERS
Family: *THRAUPIDAE*

THE TANAGERS are highly colored birds, mostly of tropical origin. Of the four species that occur in the United States, three are summer residents of New Mexico. Tanagers are almost the size of Orioles but the males, in particular, have a distinctive color pattern and their bills are deeper and not so keenly pointed as those of Orioles. Their songs are pleasing, but not comparable to those of the more gifted singers. They are migratory and wholly beneficial. The sexes differ so greatly in coloration that it will be well for the novice to study them on the nesting grounds at a time when the male and female are together.

⟮ WESTERN TANAGER
Piranga ludoviciana
6—7″ long. Color pattern of sexes different. (Pl. XXVIII)

The Western formerly was referred to as the Louisiana Tanager. The male of these handsome birds is largely black and yellow. The red head clearly sets him apart from other black and yellow birds. *Adult male:* Head crimson; neck, rump, and underparts yellow: back, wings, and tail black; wing coverts with a broad yellow patch and whitish bar. *Adult female:* Forehead sometimes washed with red; upperparts olive green; rump and upper-tail coverts yellowish; wings and tail grayish brown with olive green edgings; wings with two distinct yellowish, or one yellow and one white band; underparts mainly dull yellowish. The black and yellow plumage of the male is conspicuous in flight.

DISTRIBUTION. In summer the Western Tanager is widely distributed throughout mountain forests, mainly from 7,500 to 10,000 feet. It prefers a pine, fir, and spruce environment at this season. Although not abundant, it is fairly common throughout practically all of the high forested country. Normally it leaves for the south by late September, returning in late April.

NESTING. The Douglas fir seems to be the preferred nesting tree of this Tanager. The author found three nests with eggs, all in fir trees, on June 28, at 7,000 to 7,500 feet elevation, in Black Canyon northeast of Silver City. In the Sangre de Cristo Range, Jensen reported 12 nests, all in Douglas firs. "It was noted feeding young August 4 in the Hondo area near Twining, at about 10,000 feet" (Lena McBee). Nest: Usually on horizontal branch of a Douglas fir, 10 to 30 feet above ground; a frail structure made of twigs and weed stems and lined with fine rootlets. Eggs: 3 or 4; pale bluish green, lightly spotted with browns and purples.

⟨ HEPATIC TANAGER
Piranga flava
7—8" long. Color pattern of sexes different. (Pl. XXVIII)

Because of their similarity, some difficulty may be experienced in distinguishing the Hepatic from the Summer Tanager. However, the male Summer Tanager is more uniformly red. The somewhat larger size of the Hepatic and its preferred habitat are aids in identification. In summer the Hepatic ranges in the higher forested areas while the Summer Tanager is more likely to be found in the lower valleys and along watercourses. Adult male: Upper-

parts deep red; crown lighter; cheeks grayish; tail and wings reddish brown; underparts bright red. Adult female: Above, grayish olive; crown and tail greenish; underparts pale yellowish.

DISTRIBUTION. The summer range of the Hepatic is largely centered in the Transition Zone, above the 7,500-foot level, but the bird may occur as low as 6,500 feet. It seems to be most common in the southern half of the state, although it is statewide wherever the Transition Zone prevails. It occurs less commonly in the Sangre de Cristo and other more northern mountains. The southward migration starts rather early, and most of the birds are out of the state by September 15. Arrival in the spring may be as late as early May.

NESTING: Young were noted at the head of the Mimbres River in the Black Range, 7,000 feet, June 27, and in August in the Guadalupe Mountains at 6,700 feet. Nest: Usually in walnut or oak trees, on horizontal branches 10 to 15 feet above ground; rather frail, made of dry twigs and coarse rootlets; lined with softer materials. Eggs: 3 or 4; pale bluish green, lightly spotted with brown and purple, mostly around larger end.

⟨ SUMMER (COOPER) TANAGER
Piranga rubra
6¾—7½" long. Color pattern of sexes different.

The male Summer Tanager may be confused with the Hepatic male, although the Summer is slightly smaller and its entire body is a bright rose red. Its preference for deciduous trees in lower valleys and watercourses is an aid in identification. Adult female: Upperparts plain olive grayish tinged with yellowish on back and scapulars; underparts dull yellow.

DISTRIBUTION. The Summer Tanager ranges north to Albuquerque in the Rio Grande Valley and to Santa Rosa in the

Pecos Valley. It was noted at Roswell and Fort Sumner on September 19 and 22. It is rather common in the cottonwoods about Carlsbad. Regarding this Tanager, Dayton Eugene Merrill states in a letter: "This Tanager comes to Mesilla Park (Las Cruces area) from the middle of April to the first of May; nests in June and leaves in September. It is a shy bird, the female being rarely seen and the male seldom, considering his conspicuous color. The pairs seem to prefer isolated trees for nest-ing although nests in groves are common." The latest fall migrating record is October 1, at Las Cruces.

NESTING. The Summer Tanager seems to prefer cottonwoods of the lower valleys for nesting. However, the author found a nest near the top of a walnut tree in Chloride Canyon, west of Chloride, at 6,200 feet. Incidentally, this nest was de-stroyed by Scrub Jays. *Nest:* Made of weed stems, grass, and catkins. *Eggs:* 3 or 4; green, spotted with brown.

GROSBEAKS, FINCHES, SPARROWS, AND BUNTINGS
Family: *FRINGILLIDAE*

COLOR PATTERNS of members of this large and important family of song, insec-tivorous, and seed-eating birds vary re-markably, depending largely on the type of habitat they occupy. The more colorful arboreal species—for example, Grosbeaks, Finches, and small Buntings—live where there is protective foliage of shrubs and trees. The terrestrial representatives, par-ticularly the Sparrows, are generally of plain coloration, which simulates the ground cover of their habitat. All have esthetic and high economic value.

⟨ CARDINAL
Richmondena cardinalis

8—9″ long. Color pattern of sexes dif-ferent. (Pl. XXIX)

The adult male Cardinal is the only completely red bird with a large, conspicu-ous crest. It has a black chin and black around base of bill. *Adult female:* Wings and tail dull red, crest partly so; tail feath-ers edged with olive; underparts clay color, under-wing coverts rose. The Cardinal, or Redbird, as it is generally called, is so con-spicuous and well known that it needs lit-tle introduction. The term *Cardinalis* (French and Latin) has various meanings, but here seems to refer to the ecclesiastical application, i.e., wearing the vestments of a cardinal. The status of the Cardinal in the Southwest is of unusual interest to the ornithologist, particularly because of its broken distribution. It occurs on each side of the state, with a wide intervening space between the two ranges, a range contradic-tion rarely noted among birds.

DISTRIBUTION. In the southwestern part of the state, distribution of the Cardinal is restricted almost entirely to the Gila River Valley from the Arizona line upward to about Cliff, where it is resident and fair-ly common. It is very rare in the eastern part of the state, but does occur in the ex-treme southeast corner (San Simon Ranch and Jal). One was recorded during the 1954 Christmas Bird Count, at the Bitter Lake Refuge.

NESTING. The Cardinal is resident in the Gila River Valley and it nests there. There seem to be no nesting records for the southeastern section of the state. *Nest:* In vines or thick bushes, usually near the ground; made of weed stems, leaves, and strips of bark. *Eggs:* 3 or 4; spotted with brown and dark chocolate.

ℂ PYRRHULOXIA

Pyrrhuloxia sinuata

7½–8″ long. Color pattern of sexes similar. (Pl. XXX)

In the arid lands, the cheery song of the Pyrrhuloxia heralds the arrival of spring. It is resident and content with its habitat of mesquite, catclaw, cactus, and little rain. Few other arid-land birds are more attractive in plumage or more pleasing in song. *Adult male:* Body mainly grayish brown; crest, large and prominent, upper portion red; face, throat, median underparts, and underside of wings rose red; wings and tail dull red; bill yellowish in summer, horn-colored in winter. *Adult female:* Similar to male but red of face and underparts lacking or only partially evident; underparts buffy brown.

DISTRIBUTION. Range of this resident Grosbeak is confined to the Lower Sonoran Zone in the southern part of the state. In the Rio Grande Valley it ranges north to Socorro, in the Tularosa Basin to Tularosa, and in the Pecos Valley to about Hagerman. Distribution rather closely coincides with that of mesquite bushes, although this shrub extends beyond the northern limit of the birds' range. "January 23, 1954, there were 7 or 8 at the Andrus Ranch under the Caprock, 65 miles southeast of Roswell. Larry Andrus said that they had been there through November and December" (Montgomery). This location would put them at about the same latitude as Hagerman. The Pyrrhuloxia is rather common throughout most of its range where there are extensive thickets of thorny shrubs.

NESTING. Since the bird is resident, it nests wherever found. On July 19, 1954 a nest five feet up in a small Siberian elm, containing 4 fresh eggs, was observed at the author's game farm, three miles northwest of Carlsbad. On July 27, another nest with 4 small young was located in an Osage orange bush. *Eggs:* 3 or 4; white, covered with purplish brown spots.

ℂ BLACK-HEADED GROSBEAK

Pheucticus melanocephalus

6½–8″ long. Color pattern of sexes different. (Pl. XXIX)

Conspicuous with their contrasting plumage and heavy beaks, Black-headed Grosbeaks are readily identified. Few birds excel them as songsters. *Adult male:* Largely black and white above; underparts buffy brown; top and sides of head black; three white patches on wings. *Adult female:* Upperparts brownish or olive-streaked on head and back; tail and wings grayish brown; under-wing coverts lemon yellow; underparts dull buffy with median yellowish patch; sides and flanks streaked; line of white spots on wings and white line over eye.

DISTRIBUTION. This Grosbeak is a summer resident throughout the forested mountains in the state, normally ranging from 5,500 to 8,000 feet, although it is occasionally found even as high as 10,000 feet, as on the slopes of Pecos Baldy. No other Grosbeak so thoroughly covers all of the mountainous sections. Generally the birds migrate early, and are absent from the state by late September, usually returning early in May. However, Williams states in a letter: "A Black-headed Grosbeak spent the winter of 1952-53 about my home in Las Cruces."

NESTING. Nesting usually begins about the middle of May. A nest containing 3 partly incubated eggs was found by the author on May 26 at 6,500 feet, west of Chloride. "Fresh sets are found May 20 to July 1 [in the Santa Fe area]" (Jensen). "It breeds down to 5,600 feet in the Animas Mountains" (Goldman). At nesting time the male is a persistent and pleasing vocalist. On Beaver Creek near Beaverhead investigation of the source of the melodious notes of one of these Grosbeaks issuing from a willow thicket revealed the singer to be a male on the nest. His mate soon returned, apparently quite disturbed at such rashness in disclosing the nest location. She "hustled" him off and quietly assumed command of the nest and its 4 eggs. *Nest:* Rather loosely constructed of twigs and rootlets. *Eggs:* 3 or 4; pale bluish white, thickly spotted with brown.

(BLUE GROSBEAK
Guiraca caerulea
6½–7½" long. Color pattern of sexes different. (Pl. XXIX)

The Blue is the smallest and most retiring of the Grosbeaks occurring in the state. It lives near the ground, and prefers brushy valleys and stream bottoms where there are willows, arrowweed, or berry bushes. When in plain view, the adult male is readily recognized by his purplish blue coat; depressed crest; and wings with two brownish bands. *Adult female:* Olive brown; back streaked, more or less tinged with blue; tail and wings dusky; tail with bluish edging; wings with brownish edgings and two light bands; underparts buffy or clay-colored, darkest on chest.

DISTRIBUTION. The Blue Grosbeak prefers the lower valleys although it is found up to 7,000 feet in the northern part of the state. It occurs commonly in the Gila, Rio Grande, and Pecos Valleys, particularly about irrigated districts. It is among the latest birds to arrive from the south in the spring and among the earliest to leave in late summer. The first and earliest record of the Blue Grosbeak's arrival at Carlsbad was that by the author on May 1, 1952. Merrill recorded it at Las Cruces on May 7, and he noted one as late as October 12.

NESTING. "They breed commonly in northern Santa Fe County in orchards and willows along streams. Fresh eggs are found June 15 to August 1" (Jensen). In June 1953 a pair nested and raised their brood in grapevines under the edge of the author's carport at Carlsbad, and Bailey reported a nest with eggs—"evidently a second set," at Carlsbad on July 22. *Nest:* Rather frail, made of weed stems, grass, and leaves. *Eggs:* 3 or 4; pale greenish blue, or bluish white, unspotted.

(LAZULI BUNTING
Passerina amoena
5–5½" long. Color pattern of sexes different. (Pl. XXXI)

The term, *amoena* (Latin), denoting "delightful," "charming," "dressy," is a fitting appellation for the beautiful Lazuli. *Adult male:* Upperparts bright turquoise blue, duller and darker on middle of back, where feathers are bordered with rusty shade; wings and tail blackish with blue edgings, wings with two white bars; breast brownish; rest of underparts white. *Adult female:* Upperparts brown, back usually streaked; rump tinged with greenish blue; wings and tail dusky with greenish blue edgings; two wing bars buffy; anterior underparts pale buffy, deeper on chest; lower underparts white.

DISTRIBUTION. In summer the Lazuli Bunting is widely distributed in the state, mostly at intermediate elevations—7,800 feet being about the highest point at which it has been recorded. Since it is shy and resorts to timbered watercourses and streambank cover, particularly willows, it appears less common than it actually is. It is migratory, rarely being seen in the state after September 1. It usually appears in the southern section about the first of May.

NESTING. Most nesting records of the Lazuli Bunting apply to the northern section of the state. The author found breeding birds on June 16 in the Brazos River bottoms northeast of Parkview, at 7,000 feet. On the Little Rio Grande southeast of Taos, they were noted on June 5, and evidently were nesting. "A nest with eggs was found June 13 in Santa Fe, on the river bank in willows" (Jensen). Hollister noted old feeding nearly grown young on June 29, 1905, near Fort Wingate. They were observed near Santa Rosa on May 19 and June 8, and were no doubt nesting. *Nest:* In rose bushes, willows, and other low-growing shrubs, usually near water; made of inner bark and plant fibers, lined with hair. *Eggs:* 3 or 4; plain bluish white or pale greenish blue, sometimes spotted.

⟮ PAINTED BUNTING
Passerina ciris
5—5½" long. Color pattern of sexes different. (Pl. XXXII)

The Painted Bunting is one of our most beautiful and delightful birds, in color and in song. The author has searched in vain for the Varied, or Beautiful, Bunting in the southern part of the state—a real disappointment! He predicts eventually it will be recorded. The Greek term, *ciris,* or *keiris,* is the name of the bird into which Scylla, daughter of Nisus, was supposed to have been transformed. *Adult male:* Head and back of neck violet blue in sharp contrast to yellowish or bright green of back and scapulars; rump and upper-tail coverts dull red; tail dusky reddish; wing coverts parrot green, reddish and purplish blue; eye ring and underparts orange red. *Adult female:* Color pattern entirely different from that of male; upperparts plain dull green; underparts olive yellow, brighter yellow posteriorly.

DISTRIBUTION. Summer range of the Painted Bunting is confined largely to the southern section of the state, mainly the Pecos Valley about Carlsbad, and the Rio Grande bottomlands around Las Cruces. "July 18, 1954, a male in bright color appeared in my yard at Roswell" (Montgomery). This is apparently the northernmost record for the state. It is a fairly common

summer dweller in the Carlsbad area. "A fairly common resident in the Rio Grande Valley [Las Cruces], it arrives about the first of May and departs the latter part of September" (Williams).

NESTING. The Painted Bunting has been found nesting in fruit trees, also in willows and tamarisk, in the Pecos Valley about Carlsbad. *Nest:* Usually 4 to 8 feet above ground, in orchard trees, hackberry, and other shrubs of thick bottomland cover; made of grass and leaves; lined with bits of grass and hair. *Eggs:* 4 or 5; creamy to bluish white, spotted with reddish brown.

DICKCISSEL
Spiza americana
5½—6½" long. Color pattern of sexes essentially alike.

The yellow breast and black throat patch are distinguishing marks of the Dickcissel, whose charming, repetitious, *dick-cissel-cissel-cissel* at nesting time, delivered from the top of some swaying willow tree or from a telegraph wire, evidently gave rise to the unusual name. It is about the size of a House Sparrow but is slimmer and more streamlined. *Adult male:* Head and sides of neck gray; streak over eye yellowish, back brownish streaked with black; wings with reddish brown patch; chin white; throat with black patch; balance of underparts grayish yellow; bill bluish. *Adult female:* Similar but duller, upperparts browner streaked with white; black throat patch usually absent; yellow largely limited to throat and breast.

DISTRIBUTION. The Dickcissel has been recorded in the state as a migrant only. Although there has been evidence of its breeding, particularly in the Mora Valley near Shoemaker (June 30), actual nesting has not been verified. It is not a common migrant through the state, but has been recorded at various points, among them: Silver City, Santa Fe, Las Vegas, and

Carlsbad. It is recorded as "casual" or "accidental" at the Bosque del Apache Refuge. The author has found it to be most common in the Pecos Valley, where its crackling notes are frequently heard overhead at night in fall and spring. The Dickcissel no doubt ultimately will be found breeding in the northeastern part of the state.

⟨ EVENING GROSBEAK

Hesperiphona vespertina

7½–8″ long. Color pattern of sexes similar. (Pl. XXXIII)

The Evening Grosbeak is one of the most interesting and beautifully marked perching birds. While it is often seen in large flocks in the northern section of the state, its arrival, duration of stay, and departure are unpredictable. Rather fearless and very vocal when in large groups, Evening Grosbeaks never fail to provoke interest wherever concentrations occur. In family and group relations they are very social, rarely being seen with other species. The name, Evening Grosbeak, is said to

have been applied on the unfounded assumption that the birds dwelt by day in the heavy forests, coming out in the evening to feed and sing. They do, however, often collect late in the day in fall and winter to feed on the seeds of box elder, maple, or ash. *Adult male:* Forehead and line over eye yellow; crown, wings, and tail black; wings with large white patches; upperparts graduating from olive on hind neck to yellow on sides and rump; underparts greenish yellow to lemon yellow on underwing and tail coverts. *Adult female:* Brownish to yellowish, lighter underneath; throat bordered by dusky; wings and tail black; two white patches on wings. The contrasting plumage of the male, yellow, black, and white, and the very heavy parrot-like greenish yellow bill are distinctive.

DISTRIBUTION. Evening Grosbeaks possess many individual and fascinating ways. One year they may be numerous at a given park, as in the box elder trees of the capitol grounds at Santa Fe, and the following year they may be totally absent, probably because relished foods are available elsewhere. They may accept civilization, or

NEST AND EGGS, EVENING GROSBEAK. *Photograph by J. K. Jensen.*

ignore it. Jensen writes: "In Santa Fe, in the spring of 1927 thousands of Grosbeaks were seen daily in town." Again he states: "About the middle of July 1928, pairs of the Grosbeaks were seen in Santa Fe and on August 5 it was estimated several hundred were in the city." Among the author's notes (Santa Fe, October 1926) is the following notation: "They were so numerous in the box elder trees about residences and on the capitol grounds that the hulls from the winged seeds, when the birds were actively feeding, fell like snow and covered the ground beneath the trees." At times a watch may almost be set by the regularity with which these birds appear at feeding stations. They depart as suddenly as they arrive. In some sections, particularly in northern Michigan and Minnesota, where the water is deficient in saline content, Grosbeaks seem to have a craving for salt. At a hunting lodge in northern Michigan great numbers came daily to pick up salt which was thrown out for them, or to seek bits of it about the outdoor meat blocks where salt-cured meat had been cut. It was there, on Whitefish Point, that the author obtained one of the first authentic nesting records of the Eastern form. (See "Nesting of the Evening Grosbeak in Northern Michigan" *The Auk*, Vol. XL, No. 2, Apr. 1923.)

NESTING. For many years the nesting activities of the Evening Grosbeak remained a mystery. New Mexico ornithologists were among the first to dispel the mystery, with tragic consequences, however, in one instance. The first eggs collected in New Mexico were taken in the Sangre de Cristo Mountains a mile above Willis (now Cowles) at 8,100 feet, in 1901 by Francis J. Birtwell, a graduate student at the Territorial University (University of New Mexico) and a promising ornithologist. He and his wife were honeymooning on the Upper Pecos. On June 20 and 26 he succeeded in taking two sets of the coveted eggs. Two days later, in attempting to take a third set with the use of a rope high above ground, he slipped and in some manner hanged himself in the presence of his frantic and helpless bride. On June 17, 1928, Jensen and M. W. Talbot, after much searching, found a nest containing 4 eggs in a Douglas fir sapling in Santa Fe Canyon east of the city, at about 8,300 feet. In 1930, in the same area, Jensen located another nest containing 5 eggs. He states in a letter: "The eggs are incubated very unevenly. Possibly laid with a day's interval and incubation starts when the first is laid." *Nest:* Only slightly more substantial than that of the Mourning Dove; made of twigs and rootlets; placed 35 feet or more from the ground, near end of horizontal limb, usually in fir trees. *Eggs:* 4 or 5; green blotched with pale brown; often visible from below through bottom of nest.

([CASSIN'S FINCH

Carpodacus cassinii

5½–6″ long. Color pattern of sexes different. (Pl. XXIX)

The Cassin's Finch is about the size of the common House Sparrow and rather closely resembles the House Finch, or Linnet. Its distribution is confined largely to the high, densely forested mountains, while the Linnet ranges down into the lowest altitudes. *Adult male:* Head with squarish crimson crown patch in contrast to rest of upperparts; back and scapulars dull pinkish brown, streaked with dark brown; rump dull rose pink; wings and tail dusky; wings with reddish edgings; underparts pale pink fading to unstreaked white on lower underparts. *Adult female:* Upperparts olive grayish, conspicuously streaked with dusky; underparts white or whitish, also streaked with dusky except on lower underparts.

DISTRIBUTION. The Cassin's Finch is uncommon, except locally in migration, and is confined to the denser mountainous forests up to near timber line. It may be observed, in summer, throughout the higher elevations but is most common in the northern section. Some winter in the state. In November, Henshaw saw large flocks south of Zuñi, where, he states, "The salt of lakes there doubtless added zest to their diet." James Gaut found them common in the Manzano Mountains at about 8,000 feet, in October, and Bailey observed them at 11,000 feet in the Mogollon Mountains on October 23. The fact that some descend into lower country, as at Albuquerque and Silver City, does not necessarily indicate that they leave the state.

NESTING. Definite nesting records of Cassin's Finch are rather difficult to obtain because the birds live, for the most part, high in the tops of conifers, usually in remote areas. The author recorded breeding birds on June 24 at his lake camp 20 miles southeast of Taos, at 10,000 feet. A male, in full breeding condition, was secured. *Nest:* Usually on horizontal branch of a conifer; made of weed stems and rootlets; lined with shreds of bark. *Eggs:* 4 or 5; greenish blue, marked chiefly around larger end with brown and black.

❨ HOUSE FINCH
Carpodacus mexicanus

5½–6″ long. Color pattern of sexes different. (Pl. XXIX)

With the exception of the House Sparrow, the House Finch, or Linnet, is probably the most common and widely spread of the Finch-Sparrow group in the state. Because of its preference for living about habitation of man, it is better known than most other songsters. The joyful song of the House Finch is among the earliest reminders that spring is near. *Adult male:* Forehead, line over eye; rump, rose pink or orange; rest of upperparts brownish gray; head and back often tinged with red-

dish; lower underparts sharply and closely streaked with brown (colors much deeper and brighter in summer than in winter). *Adult female:* Upperparts grayish brown, indistinctly streaked; underparts white, broadly streaked.

DISTRIBUTION. The principal habitat of the Linnet is the Lower and Upper Sonoran Life Zones; however, the birds are found also in the pine belt in summer up to 7,500 feet, or even higher. They are often abundant in irrigated valleys, where unfortunately they may become destructive at times to head grains and to berries and other small fruits; hence they are sometimes referred to as "fruit birds." Although the higher altitude summer dwellers move down for the colder period of the winter, they seem to be nonmigratory.

NESTING. The House Finch nests commonly from the lowest elevations, 3,100 feet about Carlsbad to 7,500 feet or higher in forested mountains. Few birds select a greater variety of sites for nest building. They nest in bushes or trees, behind slabs of bark, in crevices of rock ledges, in evergreens about homes or gardens, or in nesting boxes provided for them or other birds. They are among the earliest nesting Finches. No sooner is one brood out of the nest than preparations are under way for a second brood. *Nest:* A well-made compact cup woven of grass stems and fibers; also, according to location, rootlets, hair, wool, and strings. *Eggs:* 4 to 6; white or pale greenish blue, dotted, blotched and lined, chiefly about the larger end.

❨ PINE GROSBEAK
Pinicola enucleator

8–9″ long. Color pattern of sexes different. (Pl. XXIX)

The Pine is the largest, and the rarest, of the Grosbeaks occurring in New Mexico. In beauty and dignity it fully measures up to other members of the group. *Adult male:* Bill thick but short; upper mandible strongly decurved; head, rump, throat, and middle underparts rich rose, brighter on head and rump; back and posterior underparts bluish gray; tail and wings dusky to blackish; wings with light edgings, and two conspicuous white bands or patches. *Adult female:* Bluish or smoky gray, head and rump russet or tawny olive; wings and tail dark brown, wings with light or white edgings.

DISTRIBUTION. It will be a memorable day for the bird student who sees this beauty in its cool, native habitat, the high mountainous country in the extreme northern part of the state. On July 25 and August 15, 1903, the Baileys found the Pine Grosbeak below Pecos Baldy at 11,000 and 11,600 feet, and on August 14, "A family party was found at 12,000 feet near the Truchas Lakes at the head of Pecos River." It was found August 5 and 6 at 11,200 feet. The author has a beautiful male specimen in his study collection, taken November 29, 1926, at 11,000 feet on Costilla Peak near the Colorado line, in Colfax County. He has observed it on Gold Hill at 12,000 feet. It seems to be nonmigratory except for a slight vertical movement. Its heavy coat of feathers protects it against the severe winter weather of its habitat.

NESTING. Since the Pine Grosbeak nests rather early (young have been observed out of the nest in June), and in high country, ornithologists have had little opportunity to locate nests. Since it is resident, however, and has been seen, including "a family party," on the various mountain peaks in June, July, and August, the evidence is conclusive that it breeds in the state. *Nest:* 10 to 30 feet above ground in conifers; compactly made, a framework of twigs enclosing the nest proper, which is composed of coarse weeds and straws lined with a fine wiry weed. *Eggs:* Usually 3; greenish blue, irregularly spotted and blotched with brown and black with lilac, shell spots.

ROSY FINCHES, OR LEUCOSTICTES

FEW SONGSTERS have greater ornithological appeal than do the Rosy Finches, or Leucostictes, since few others live to themselves as they do or can tolerate the rigorous climate of their habitat. They rarely associate with other birds. Their chosen summer range is the highest elevations of the Rocky Mountains and northward. They descend to adjacent lower areas only during the severest part of the winter, hence are at home in arctic climates practically the year round. So far as pertains to New Mexico, the Rosy Finches live in a miniature world characterized by violent weather, a habitat shared by the Ptarmigan in the Sangre de Cristo Range and mountains to the northward.

Three species occur in the state. Although the range of the Leucosticte is restricted, the author, while conducting bird studies in northern New Mexico on November 19, 1926, encountered a bunch of approximately 300 on a mountain road 12 miles northwest of Vermejo Park, Colfax County, at 10,500 feet. Specimens of the three different species were secured from this assembly: the Gray-crowned, the Black, and the Brown-capped. The ground was frozen and partially covered with snow, and the birds were in a rather compact flock, evidently feeding on grass and weed seeds. No doubt most of them were new arrivals from the mountains of Colorado.

GRAY-CROWNED ROSY FINCH
Leucosticte tephrocotis
6–7" long. Color pattern of sexes similar.

The Gray-crowned Rosy Finch must be closely observed in order to separate it from the Brown-capped. *Adult male in summer:* Body mainly chestnut brown; forehead and part of crown black bordered by ash gray band; rest of head mainly reddish brown; feathers of rump, sides, and upper-tail coverts washed with pink; wing coverts tipped with pink. *Adult male in winter:* Similar to summer but feathers of back and scapulars with lighter brown edgings, pink markings softer. *Adult female:* Similar to male; somewhat paler.

STATE RECORDS. The author saw 3 Gray-crowned Rosy Finches and secured 1, on November 11, 1919, fifteen miles southwest of Cimarron, at 9,000 feet. James S. Findley recorded about 40 Rosy Finches, November 26, 1955, on the crest of the Sandia Mountains east of Albuquerque, which he identified as the Gray-crowned. This record places the species a hundred miles farther south than indicated by any previous record. It is a summer resident on Costilla Peak.

BLACK ROSY FINCH
Leucosticte atrata
6—6½″ long. Color pattern of sexes similar. (Pl. I)

The Black Rosy Finch is similar to the Gray-crowned. *Adults:* Forehead and part of crown black; underparts brownish black; feathers of sides, rump, and flanks washed with pink; hind neck and back dark brown. The blackish body distinguishes it from the Brown-capped and the Gray-crowned Rosy Finches. This Rosy Finch seems to occur in the state in winter only, and seems to be confined to the Sangre de Cristo Mountains. There is no nesting record for the state. The more rugged bird observers have much of interest in the possibility of adding this species to their lists. When winter gales of hurricane proportions blast the barren summits of the summer range of the Black Rosy Finches, these birds move down into ad-jacent, broken country where the leeward sides of cliffs, timber, or basins provide both shelter and food, hence unlike most other species that move to milder climates, they defy all but the most severe storms, rarely descending below 7,000 feet. On one occasion, in late November, high in the Sangre de Cristo Mountains southwest of Cimarron, the author encountered a mixed bunch of Black and Brown-capped Rosy Finches industriously feeding where the wind had swept the snow from the frozen ground.

(BROWN-CAPPED ROSY FINCH
Leucosticte australis
6—6½″ long. Color pattern of sexes similar.

This Rosy Finch is much like the Gray-crowned, but brown of body is lighter and the head is without the gray band. The term, *australis* (Latin), "southern," denotes in this case the southernmost member of the family. *Adult male in summer:* Top of head dark grayish brown; black on forehead; rest of head and foreparts of body cinnamon or russet brown, usually flecked with bright red below; feathers of rump and upper-tail coverts broadly tipped with pink; wings and tail dusky, with pinkish edging; wing coverts pink, may be scarlet in midsummer; sides, flanks and underparts carmine pink. *Adult male in winter:* Similar to summer male, but forehead and crown with grayish brown feather edgings, pink areas softer. *Adult female:* With same seasonal changes as adult male but much duller; underparts brown; upperparts grayish brown and pink markings indistinct.

DISTRIBUTION. The summer range of these Finches in New Mexico is confined to the Arctic Zone peaks above timber line, from Wheeler Peak northward. Apparently they may not be expected south of that area at this season, and the observer who locates breeding birds on one of the several peaks is fortunate. In winter, resident Brown-capped Rosy Finches, joined by Gray-crowned and Black from the north, may be observed in close-ranging bunches on adjacent mesas or in valleys rarely below 7,000 feet elevation. The first definite summer records appear to be those by Bailey, July 20 to 30, 1904: "Found them on the crest of Taos Mountains near Wheeler Peak at over 13,000 feet altitude." They are usually to be seen at this time about the deep snowbanks and drifts that have remained. The author has observed them on Gold Hill, and on Costilla Peak near the Colorado line. On February 16, 1950, Gabrielson observed about 200 Rosy Finches and collected some specimens on Highway 64 about 15 miles southwest of Taos, at 7,000 feet elevation. Like other Rosy Finches, occurrence of the Brown-capped is unpredictable.

NESTING. Nesting records of the Brown-capped Rosy Finch are scant but sufficient to classify it as a nesting species. Vernon Bailey's record of July 1904 indicates beyond reasonable doubt that the birds were nesting about Wheeler Peak. He states: "Several were seen and two collected; they presumably nested not far away." On July 4, 1955, Wayne Bohl and the author made an investigation of birds on Gold Hill (12,600 feet), south of the town of Red River. Bohl observed several Brown-capped Rosy Finches among the broken ledges on the east side of the main peak. While no nests were located, conduct of the birds indicated they had either nests or young nearby. *Nest:* Described by F. C. Lincoln (*The Auk*, XXXIII, 41-42, 1916), "In a cavity of cliff, compactly woven of dry grass and flower stems and a quantity of fine moss, lined with fine grass, a few of the bird's own feathers, and one of the White-tailed Ptarmigan." *Eggs:* 3; white.

❨ PINE SISKIN
Spinus pinus

4¼–5" long. Color pattern of sexes alike.

The forested, mountainous habitat of the Pine Siskin, a small, brownish, very active Finch, extends to timber line. *Adults:* Entire body (except posterior underparts) streaked with dusky on grayish or brownish ground, whitish below; wings and tail dusky or blackish, wings with two whitish bars; basal portion of wing and tail pale yellow. The yellow wing and tail patches show most in flight.

DISTRIBUTION. In summer the Pine Siskin is a common resident throughout all principal mountainous sections, ranging from intermediate to the highest altitude, dropping lower into adjacent foothills and valleys in winter and spring, and often collecting in large flocks. Bailey reported a hundred or more together in October on Willow Creek in the Mogollon Mountains. In the low country, Pine Siskins feed largely on weed seeds still on the plants as well as on the ground. In late summer they feed extensively on seeds of spruce cones and on a variety of insects.

NESTING. Siskins evidently are rather late nesters since they appear to be almost anywhere in April or May—at Silver City on May 10, and in the Big Hatchet Mountains May 22. Most summer records apply to the higher northern section of the state. On August 17, at 10,400 feet on Pecos Baldy, young were seen calling for food. "Nest was found June 3, 1920, on Santa Fe Indian School Campus [7,000 feet] in box elder about 12 feet from ground" (Jensen). This record is unusual since the species generally nests much higher. However, in Colorado nests have been found principally in the foothills. *Nest:* Usually in conifers; well built and compact; made of roots, grass, and leaves. *Eggs:* 3 or 4; light greenish blue, spotted and blotched brown and lavender around larger end.

GOLDFINCHES

THERE SEEMS to be uncertainty and confusion on the part of observers and reporters pertaining to the identification of Goldfinches in the state. By disregarding confusing subspecies and remembering that only three species occur in the Southwest, the bird student has fewer problems of identification. The American, also referred to as the Pale, Goldfinch, is the largest form. It occurs rarely in New Mexico. The Lesser, or Greenbacked, is the Goldfinch most frequently seen in the state. The Lawrence's, a Western species, has been recorded in the southwestern part.

AMERICAN (COMMON) GOLDFINCH
Spinus tristis
5—5½" long. Color pattern of sexes different.

The American, or Pale, Goldfinch is a little smaller than the House Sparrow but considerably larger than the Lesser (Arkansas) Goldfinch. *Adult male in summer:* Canary yellow with black forehead, tail, crown, and wings; tail coverts, wing bars and edgings, white. *Adult female in summer:* Upperparts olive grayish; tail and wings dusky; underparts grayish white, tinged with pale yellow. *Male in winter:* Similar to summer female but wings and tail darker, white markings more conspicuous. *Female in winter:* Similar to summer female but with more grayish brown; wing and tail markings tinged with buffy.

DISTRIBUTION. Strangely, there are no recent records of the American Goldfinch for the state, although it is listed in the A.O.U. *Check-list* as occurring in the adjacent states. Old records indicate this Goldfinch was observed only in the extreme northwestern section. On October 31, 1908, Birdseye saw three at Farmington and collected one. Marshall F. Gilman

reported seeing "a few" the previous year at Shiprock.

([LESSER (ARKANSAS) GOLDFINCH
Spinus psaltria
4" long. Color pattern of sexes different.

The Lesser, also known as the Arkansas, is the most common Goldfinch in the state. It does not have the bright yellow back of the American Goldfinch, which is of rare occurrence. While the Lesser may be confused with the Yellow or other Warblers, it is almost always seen in open places, on sunflower or other seed-producing plants, rather than in bushes or in foliage of trees, such as are more often frequented by Warblers. Furthermore, except at nesting time, it is usually seen feeding in groups of a half dozen or more. *Adult male:* Cap, wings, and tail black; tail feathers white basally; wings with broad white edgings; back and cheeks olive green; entire undersurface yellow. *Adult female:* Upperparts plain dull olive green; wings and tail as in male but black duller and white more restricted; underparts light greenish yellow.

DISTRIBUTION. The Lesser Goldfinch is a summer resident throughout the state, ranging from the lowest elevations about Carlsbad and Las Cruces up to 7,000 feet in mountain valleys, rarely higher. It is most common around 5,000 feet, and usually where weed seeds are available, particularly those of the wild sunflower. A few remain for the winter in the southern part of the state (Las Cruces) but most of them go south, returning the latter part of April.

NESTING. The Lesser Goldfinch nests commonly in the Rio Grande Valley. Young just out of the nest were noted on August 2 at Albuquerque, and on October 16, in James Canyon, Sacramento Mountains, at 7,000 feet. But it remained for Jensen to find the greatest nesting concentration at Santa Fe: "Twenty-two pairs nested on the campus of the Indian School in 1921, and fresh eggs from June 15 to October 1." "Adults were feeding young at Bandelier National Monument, July 21, 1945" (Lena McBee). *Nest:* Often in cottonwood, compact, cup-shaped, made of plant fibers, lined with down and other soft materials. *Eggs:* 4 or 5; bluish white, normally unmarked.

LAWRENCE'S GOLDFINCH
Spinus lawrencei
4—4½" long. Color pattern of sexes similar.

The regular range of the Lawrence's Goldfinch is far to the west of New Mexico, but it occurs periodically in the southwestern part of the state. *Adult male:* The black patch on forehead and chin and yellow wing-bars are key identification marks. Upperparts brownish gray, back sometimes washed with olive green, with yellowish olive green on rump; median underparts yellow, white posteriorly. *Adult female:* Like male but without black on head, colors duller, yellow less distinct.

STATE RECORDS. Recent winter and spring records of the Lawrence's Goldfinch indicate that it is not as rare as was formerly believed. However, records are mostly limited to the Rio Grande Valley from El Paso to Hatch. Williams reported it at Las Cruces, February 26, while Allan Phillips recorded it at Hatch, November 8, 1947. "A flock of about 30 was seen in a bosque near La Mesa March 7, 1948, and on November 12, 1950, 17 were seen at the same place feeding on white mistletoe berries" (McBee and Keefer). A more thorough investigation may reveal that it nests in this part of the Rio Grande Valley. The El Paso Audubon Society Christmas Count for December 29, 1953, included 7 Lawrence's Goldfinches. On July 9, 1959, Dale A. Zimmerman, of Silver City, advised in a letter: "Today I collected one of four Lawrence's Goldfinches, 2 miles

north of Silver City." This is approaching a breeding record, but is not sufficient to warrant nesting status.

([RED CROSSBILL
Loxia curvirostra
5½—6½" long. Color pattern of sexes similar. (Pl. XXIX)

The red plumage, chunky size, and peculiar crossing of mandibles distinguish the Red Crossbill from other Finches. Its swift, direct flight over treetops and its clear, piping notes are also distinctive. Although it is divided into subspecies—Bendire's and Mexican—to the average bird observer these are the same bird. *Adult male:* Brick red, but varying in shade seasonally, which probably accounts for some confusion in its classification; wings and tail blackish without white markings. *Adult female:* Red of male replaced by olive gray; rump and underparts yellowish. The crossed bill, with its sharp points, is well adapted for prying the seed which constitutes a good portion of the Red Crossbill's food from pine, spruce, or other cones. Like the Evening Grosbeak and the Cassin's Finch, the Crossbill seems to have a special liking for salt, which may be induced by the nature of its diet.

DISTRIBUTION. The higher mountains of the northern part of the state constitute the summer range of the Red Crossbill. In winter it ranges wherever there are forested mountains, as low as 7,000 feet, as in the Pinos Altos and Animas Mountains in the southwest section, but rarely below the conifer and spruce zones.

NESTING. The surprising scarcity of breeding records of the Red Crossbill may be due to the fact that the bird nests in the high country very early (in January in the Colorado mountains), when birding expeditions are rare. On March 7, 1888, Brewster found young just able to fly in the Chiricahua Mountains in southeastern

Arizona, near the New Mexico line. The author has observed Red Crossbills in February high in the Black and San Mateo Ranges, where they were evidently nesting, although no nests were found. "On April 13, 1941 a male was seen in the head of Red River Canyon [south of Red River village] which was engaged in feeding an immature bird in a pine" (Lena Mc-Bee). Since the birds seem to be restless wanderers, usually in small bunches, it is probable that at times they go through a season without nesting. As they are swift of flight and spend much time in concealment in tall evergreens, they probably have few natural enemies, which may account for their more or less stationary numbers even though they fail to nest regularly. Much remains to be learned about their life history. Nest: "In coniferous trees; rather flat, made externally of conifer twigs, shreds of soft bark or tree moss and grass stems; lined with fine rootlets and sometimes horsehair" (Florence Bailey). Eggs: Usually 4; greenish or bluish green, flecked with lavender, with wreath of lavender around larger end.

WHITE-WINGED CROSSBILL
Loxia leucoptera
6—6½" long. Color pattern of sexes similar.

As with the Red Crossbill, the crossing of mandibles is a dependable means of identifying the White-winged. In this species the rose pink of the adult male, and his black wings with two wide white bars, are added distinguishing marks. Adult female is olive gray with yellowish rump, and likewise has two wide white wing bars.

DISTRIBUTION. Although the White-winged Crossbill is listed as coming as far south in winter as Colorado, it is very rare or accidental in New Mexico. The only record is by Krehbiel, who found one dead in Paradise Canyon, 3 miles north of Clayton, November 4, 1954.

TOWHEES

THE TOWHEES comprise a small group of active but rather shy ground-dwelling birds. They are slightly smaller and more streamlined than Robins. Cleverly evasive, they are rarely seen, except occasionally in migration, away from protective weed or brush cover. The Brown (Canyon) Towhee, often called "Camp Bird," is an exception. Four species are indigenous to and nest in the state: Green-tailed, Rufous-sided, Brown, and Abert's. The last-named, however, has a very restricted range.

⟮ GREEN-TAILED TOWHEE
Chlorura chlorura
6—7" long. Color pattern of sexes alike.

The Green-tailed is the smallest of the Towhees found in New Mexico. The prevailing colors are various shades of green and greenish olive, capped by a rufous crown patch, a striking and softly blended effect. The sensitive crown patch pulsates in response to the mood of the bird. Adults: Except for the conspicuous rufous crown, upperparts are olive gray to olive green becoming bright greenish on wing and tail; throat with white patch; sides of head, neck and chest, gray fading to whitish on lower underparts. Its mewing note, under cover, and its habit of scooting over open ground with tail spread and held upright, are additional identification clues. If no house cats are lurking, it may appear perhaps as a flash, or for a few moments on lawn or walk adjacent to concealing cover.

DISTRIBUTION. While some Green-tailed Towhees may be observed in winter in the southern part of the state, they are confined in summer almost wholly to brushy, humid, mountain valleys and canyons, from 7,000 to as high as 11,000 feet. They are fairly common in such preferred habitat as patches of big sage (in the north), wild rose, currant or similar ground cover. Most of them leave the state the latter part of November, returning to the southern section about mid-March.

NESTING. This dignified little Towhee nests throughout most of the high, timbered mountains of the state but not, as a rule, below the Transition Zone. On June 20 it was found nesting rather commonly along the Little Rio Grande south and southeast of Taos, at 7,500 feet and higher, also about Round Mountain, above Cowles, at 9,000 feet. "It is common in northern Santa Fe County, from 7,500 to 9,000 feet, nesting in sage, rose, and other small bushes. Fresh eggs were found from May 20 to July 10" (Jensen). "At Burford Lake it was fairly common and a nest with three eggs was found June 11" (Wetmore). Very small young were recorded by the author on Mount Taylor July 25, and in the Black Range, 28 miles southwest of Chloride, June 28, at 8,000 feet. *Nest:* Near the ground in currant, wild rose, or other low-growing tangled bushes; made of weed stems and grass; lined with rootlets and, usually, some hair. *Eggs:* 4; white, pale greenish or grayish, spotted with reddish brown.

⟨ RUFOUS-SIDED (SPOTTED) TOWHEE

Pipilo erythrophthalmus

7–8" long. Color pattern of sexes different.

The Rufous-sided Towhee, known variously as the Spurred Towhee, Arctic Towhee, and Chewink, is a beautifully marked bird, widely distributed in summer throughout forested mountains of the state. Like the Green-tailed, it is shy and spends most of its time in the safety of cover. These Towhees have strong feet. Claws are stout and curved, adapted for scratching among leaves, which the birds do by jumping forward, then making a

backward rake, to expose worms, insects, or their larvae. The term *Pipilo* (Latin), means "pip," "peep," or "chirp." A male may frequently be seen on some treetop above the nesting cover, delivering his cheery song, but he is always quick to dive down and disappear at the least sign of danger. *Adult male:* Foreparts and entire upperparts black except for graying rump and white markings on wings and tail coverts; tail long, graduated; sides deep rufous; underparts white; eye red. *Female:* Black replaced by dark brown; back streaked with black.

DISTRIBUTION. In summer the Rufous-sided Towhee may be observed in all sections of the state from 6,000 feet in the southern mountains and foothills, to about 8,000 feet. Although there is a general southward movement in the fall, some of the birds remain throughout the winter in the south. Willet observed them at 7,000 feet in the Guadalupe Mountains in January, while Gaut found them in the San Andres Mountains northeast of Las Cruces in December and January.

NESTING. The Rufous-sided Towhee nests in practically all wooded sections of the state. "Eggs were found at 8,000 feet in the Guadalupe Mountains, near the Texas line as late as August 20" (Bailey). It was found nesting near Silver City, at 6,000 feet, while Goldman reported nests at 6,200 feet in the Animas Mountains. The author observed young out of the nest on Mount Taylor, on July 25. "Eggs were found July 22 (3,900 feet) at Mesilla Park" (Merrill). This seems to be the lowest altitude at which nesting has been recorded. "It is fairly common in the foothills of northern Santa Fe County; nest with fresh eggs was found May 31, two miles southeast of Santa Fe" (Jensen). *Nest:* On the ground or in bushes; made of twigs, inner bark and leaves, lined with grass. *Eggs:* 4 or 5; pale greenish or bluish, speckled with brown and lavender massed on larger end.

TOWHEES
TOP: GREEN-TAILED. MIDDLE: RUFOUS-SIDED, ABERT'S. BOTTOM: BROWN.
Orville O. Rice, N.M. Dept. of Game & Fish

⟮ BROWN (CANYON) TOWHEE
Pipilo fuscus

8½—9½" long. Color pattern of sexes alike.

The Brown is the most friendly and trusting of the Towhees. In the ranch country it is often referred to as "Camp Bird," since in the broken, brushy, canyon sections where it makes its home, a pair (they usually associate in pairs) may become a familiar part of a camp scene, picking up scraps or avidly taking crumbs thrown to them. Woodpiles about camps or cabins are favorite retreats, and the bird often becomes so tame as to enter cabins or shop buildings. It spends much time on the ground, and runs rapidly, Thrasher-like, but its shorter tail and bill readily distinguish it from the Thrashers. Pairs apparently remain mated throughout the year. The Brown Towhee is social and is frequently heard intimately "conversing" or cheerily singing from bush or treetop, when all about is calm. *Adults:* The prevailing dull grayish brown of the body, reddish-brown crest, and striped breast with dark dot or spot, are identification marks. Under-tail coverts dusky; throat pinkish buff.

DISTRIBUTION. The preferred range of this resident Towhee is the rough, brushy canyons of foothills and mountains, from 5,000 to 7,000 feet, throughout the state, except the southeastern and eastern high plains. Its intimate attachment to ranch buildings, mine sites and camps of any sort serves it well during winter storms when natural food is scarce. It is a cheerful and welcome visitor in surroundings which, without its presence, might at times be dull and lifeless.

NESTING. Nesting of the Brown Towhee usually begins in the southern section in early April. However, Jensen reported a Brown Towhee nest with newly-hatched young near Santa Fe on April 13—exceptionally early for this high (7,000 feet) northern section. The author noted fresh eggs at Chloride on May 7, and again as late as July, indicating second broods. *Nest:* Usually in scrub oak, pinyon, juniper, or sagebrush, but occasionally in cholla cactus or between the broad leaves of the Spanish bayonet; rather bulky, made of twigs and coarse grass; lined with rootlets and hair. *Eggs:* 3; bluish white or pearl gray, spotted and lined with brown and sometimes black, with purple shell markings.

⟮ ABERT'S TOWHEE
Pipilo aberti

8—9" long. Color pattern of sexes alike.

A very active, shy bird, whose distribution is restricted to the southwestern part of the state, the Abert's Towhee is readily distinguished from the Brown Towhee and the desert Thrashers by its rather plump body and uniformly dark brown upperparts; black face and chin; throat streaked with blackish; rest of underparts pinkish brown. Like the Brown Towhee, the Abert's is largely a ground dweller. It is named for James William Abert, Lieutenant, later Major, U.S. Army, 1820-97. Three of his journals were published as Congressional Documents, 1846-48.

DISTRIBUTION. The range of this handsome, resident Towhee is confined to the Gila River bottomlands from the New Mexico–Arizona line to about Cliff, upstream a distance of about 50 miles by the devious course of the river. It is rather common in the mesquite and other thick brush cover characteristic of the bottomlands, particularly in the vicinity of Red Rock, about 3,900 feet.

The type from which the bird was described and named was taken by Lieutenant Abert in New Mexico in 1846. There is some question as to the exact location. According to his journals, one is led to believe that it was taken at the old settlement of Valverde on the Rio Grande about 20 miles south of Socorro. However, there is considerable doubt as to whether the bird was taken there, because since his time there are no records of the bird's occurrence in the Rio Grande Valley despite the great amount of work that has been done by collectors and field observers from Albuquerque to Anthony.

NESTING. The Abert's nests in thick brush cover, usually in mesquite, Condalia, arrowweed, or willow. On May 15, 1928, the author located four nests containing eggs, near Red Rock in such cover. *Nest:* 3 to 5 feet above ground; made of twigs, bark, leaves, and grass; lined with soft inner bark, grass, and some hair. *Eggs:* 3 or 4; pale blue, sparsely marked with dark brown and black.

(LARK BUNTING

Calamospiza melanocorys

5½—7″ long. Color pattern of sexes essentially alike. Different in summer.

This Bunting has little in common with the dainty, beautifully colored Painted and Lazuli. It is unique in that the summer dress of the adult male is entirely different from his late fall and winter plumage. In summer he wears a conspicuous combination of black and white, which contrasts sharply with the brown garb of the female. He is black, or bluish black, except for white edgings and large white patch on wings, and white edging to tail coverts and outer-tail feathers. *Adult female in summer:* Upperparts grayish brown streaked with dusky; white wing patch smaller than in summer male, tinged with buffy; underparts white streaked with dusky. *Adult male in winter:* Like adult summer female, but chin black and feathers of underparts black beneath

the surface. *Adult female in winter:* Like summer female but less grayish brown and paler markings more buffy. The seasonal change in plumage coloration of the male Lark Bunting is not the result of a normal molt of feathers, but presumably is effected through "feather-wear,"—the black appearing on the surface as the light tips and edgings of feathers wear away. This phenomenal change takes place in late spring, and again in early fall. On April 29, in Socorro County, a bird was taken which was probably two years old or older, which had acquired complete summer plumage; and on May 12 one was taken near Roswell in the transition stage. It is probable that males of the previous year are the last to assume the full summer coat. The change back to the modest winter dress occurs after the breeding season. By the middle of August, male Lark Buntings may still show the black and white, although there is usually evidence of the change, which by early September may be complete.

DISTRIBUTION. Lark Buntings are gregarious, and their summer or winter distribution is largely unpredictable. Few other birds are more mobile or erratic in their seasonal movements. Favorable moisture conditions, particularly at nesting time, determine their presence or absence. In fall and winter they may occur at almost any place, generally in the lower altitudes, in limited numbers or in large flocks. In late summer great numbers move down into the southeastern section of the state from their more northern breeding grounds. It is at this time that they often incur the enmity of farmers because of damage to crops such as maize or hegari. Damage to grain, however, can generally be attributed to combined numbers of House Sparrows, Cowbirds, Redwinged Blackbirds, and Buntings, particularly in the irrigated sections of the Pecos Valley. The Buntings destroy vast numbers of injurious insects. Thus, benefits far exceed any crop damage for which they may be responsible. In Colfax County Kalmbach found that 78 percent of their food consisted of grasshoppers. Throughout the milder portion of their winter range they feed extensively on insects or their larvae, in addition to weed seeds.

It is on the northward spring advance that the birds, usually still in great flocks, participate in mass song festivals which are no less phenomenal than is the change in plumage coloration of the male. At such times the birds seek an area favored by winter moisture and consequent early spring vegetation and the ample insect life which such habitats provide. The colorful, animated mass moves across the flower-bedecked valley or prairie, the rear guard continuously vaulting over the advance contingent of the procession, all the while delivering blended chimes unexcelled by any other avian choir. Hundreds may make up such a mobile assembly and be so animated as to continue their chorus for extended periods during the calm of a perfect spring day. Meadowlarks and Redwinged Blackbirds also participate in spring song festivals, but never perform so charmingly as do these masters of blended song. To observe and hear one of these song sessions is a memorable occasion for any bird lover.

NESTING. Nesting of the Lark Bunting is unpredictable, depending upon seasonal moisture. Following ample moisture in the spring and early summer, when the open valleys, ridges, and plains are verdant carpets, the black-and-white males may be observed repeatedly floating overhead and singing above these parklike areas, anywhere from Lovington northward on the high plains, in the wide open valleys about Santa Rosa, and on the bleak Vaughn–Encino mesas, and northward. During periods of little or no widespread winter or spring moisture, breeders may be entirely absent from these, and from areas farther north. Another singularity as pertains to the breeding season is that late May arrivals and stragglers south of the regular breeding range appear to be nonbreeders. They may be young of the previous year. Breeders at that time are already on the chosen nesting grounds. Nests with eggs were found May 30 on the plains near Caprock, west of Tatum. On May 20 the birds were nesting commonly in the Vaughn area. From these and other records it is evident that most of the breeding pairs are established on their nesting grounds while individuals, and even large flocks, are still wandering about to the southward. It is also evident that the nesting period is brief. On July 24, 1952, Lark Buntings were concentrated, or were in loosely ranging bunches about Springer Lake, east of Cimarron, and although there was no evidence of nesting at the time, they probably had nested. In the high, open, short-grass country to the west of Santa Rosa (about 4,900 feet), during the latter part of June, male Lark Buntings were seen performing their characteristic breeding antics—rising above ground and floating away while pouring out their joyful song—an almost certain indication that they were nesting birds. Harding and Union Counties, in the northeast section, periodically constitute the most extensive breeding range in the state. Nest: A slight depression in ground, near a bunch of grass, or under a weed, small cholla cactus, or other protective growth; lined with weed stems, fine grass, rootlets, and hair. Eggs: 4 or 5; pale plain blue, sometimes lightly spotted around larger end with reddish brown.

LARK BUNTING: MALE IN WINTER AND SUMMER PLUMAGE; FEMALE IN SUMMER PLUMAGE
E. R. Kalmbach

SPARROWS

OF the thirty-six species of sparrows listed in *The A. O. U. Check-list*, 24 have been recorded in New Mexico; 14 of these have been found nesting. A few others have been denied recognition as breeders for the reason that no occupied nests have been located, even though breeding birds were present. One or more species nests from the lowest elevation, approximately 3,000 feet in the southern part, to 13,000 feet, on the summits of the highest mountains in the northern section. Interestingly, 19 of the 24 species known to occur in the state have been recorded in the Roswell–Bitter Lake section, and 12 species on the Bosque del Apache Refuge, a much more restricted area. Sparrows, with the Finches, constitute the largest group of American birds, and are in many respects so much alike that they are not always easily identified. However, descriptive literature, photographs, paintings, drawings, and especially mounted specimens or study skins are all aids in learning to separate them. In the field, binoculars are indispensable. If one concentrates on species and disregards subspecies—often of questionable distinction—less difficulty will be experienced in Sparrow identification.

⟨ SAVANNAH SPARROW

Passerculus sandwichensis

5–6″ long. Color pattern of sexes alike. (Pl. XXXIV)

The preferred summer habitat of this little Sparrow is grassy meadows about spring-fed ponds or lakes. Its small size, rather short, slightly forked tail, and the yellowish line over eye are distinguishing marks. *Adults:* Median crown stripe grayish or buffy; lateral crown stripe black-streaked on pale clay color; feathers of back with broad black central areas mar-gined with whitish; underparts white; breast lined with brownish.

DISTRIBUTION. The Savannah Sparrow is widely distributed throughout North America and has been divided into many subspecies. Such divisions are usually of little concern to the observer with a practical interest in a restricted area. The summer distribution of this Sparrow in the state is confined largely to the northern section, from 7,000 to 10,000 feet. While some Savannah Sparrows winter in the southern part, most of them leave the state by early November, returning in early April.

NESTING. Although there seem to be no positive accounts of nesting, there are many summer records under conditions which clearly indicate that Savannah Sparrows nest at various points. The author observed singing males about Burford Lake in late May and June. Bailey observed them commonly "around Taos, at 7,000 feet, July 14, where they were presumably breeding." Kalmbach states: "They were frequently seen in tall grass areas near Koehler Junction, from the time of [my] arrival, July 28, to October 24, 1913." The author found them nesting commonly about Big Lake, and other lakes, in the White Mountains in eastern Arizona, around 9,000 feet elevation. *Nest:* Usually in meadow grass, on the ground; made of grass and lined with fine grass and horsehair. *Eggs:* 4 to 6; pale brownish, varying to dull whitish or greenish white, spotted with brown.

GRASSHOPPER SPARROW

Ammodramus savannarum

4½–5″ long. Color pattern of sexes similar.

The Grasshopper Sparrow, so-named from its buzzing, grasshopper-like note, is strictly a ground- and grass-dwelling species. It resembles the Savannah Sparrow, but does not have a streaked breast and has yellow in bend of wings. *Adults:* Crown light brown, striped with black; back of neck grayish; remainder of upperparts brownish gray, streaked with black; wing bars buffy; underparts whitish, tinged with buffy on chest and sides. One of the best clues to identification is its habit of flushing almost at one's feet in the grass, dashing off Wren-like, close to the ground for a short distance, then dropping down to dart about, skillfully keeping out of sight.

DISTRIBUTION. In the fall migration this shy little Sparrow may be flushed almost any place where there is open grassland for concealment. Kalmbach collected it in Colfax County, September 27. It was taken in the Manzano Mountains in September, and near Roswell in October. Most of the Grasshopper Sparrows apparently move out of the state for the colder part of the winter, but they are fairly common at this season in the extensive rank grass—shinnery (Havard) oak sections of Roosevelt and Lea Counties. So adept are they at evasion that they may often be overlooked.

NESTING. There seems to be no authentic nesting record for this bird within the state. However, since it is known to breed in the adjacent Panhandle section of Texas and in southeastern Colorado, it is quite probable that it eventually will be found nesting in northeastern New Mexico. *Nest:* On the ground, well hidden in grass; a rather deep cup sometimes more or less arched over, made of weed stems and grass. *Eggs:* 4 or 5; white, spotted with reddish brown.

BAIRD'S SPARROW

Ammodramus bairdii

5—5½″ long. Color pattern of sexes alike.

After discovering this Sparrow in the Yellowstone country, Audubon named it for his friend, Spencer F. Baird, who later became Secretary of the Smithsonian Institution. In habits, size, and color the Baird's resembles the Savannah and Grasshopper Sparrows. The broad center stripe in the crown is a distinguishing mark. The Baird's has a light breast streaked with black; the Savannah has more extensive streaking and blotching of underparts, whereas the Grasshopper has an unstreaked buffy breast. In the Baird the tail is deeply emarginate while in the Grasshopper it is short and rounded. All three species prefer grassy, open-land habitat. *Adults:* Head yellow or buffy; crown streaked laterally with black; remainder of upperparts light brown, feathers spotted with black, edged with buffy; throat bordered with blackish streaks; underparts white or pale buffy; chest and sides streaked with black.

DISTRIBUTION. The Baird's nests far to the north and is only a seasonal visitor to the Southwest. Usually arriving in the northern section of the state in early August, it soon becomes quite common and widespread. "Taken up to 12,000 feet on Pecos Baldy, August 4" (Bailey). On August 10 it was noted as far south as the Animas Valley south of Animas. At this season it seems to disregard elevations and land types, occurring even on the eastern plains. None seem to winter in the state, although Henshaw observed the Baird's Sparrow on the Gila River as late as October 16. The only spring record for New Mexico seems to be that by Brooks and Law, who took 4 on April 28, 1913, along the Gila River near the Arizona line. This record seems to indicate that the birds return to their nesting grounds west of the state. More field work is necessary to clear up this point.

LE CONTE'S SPARROW

Passerherbulus caudacutus

5″ long. Color pattern of sexes alike.

Le Conte's is one of the rarest as well

as smallest of the Sparrows occurring in the state. *Adults:* Line over eye, throat, breast and sides rich buff; hind neck chestnut and grayish; rest of upperparts brownish black bordered with chestnut; throat, breast, and sides buffy; underparts white. Its pointed tail is also a distinguishing feature. It is most apt to be seen in marshy places.

DISTRIBUTION. Eastern New Mexico seems to be the extreme western limit of the range of the Le Conte's Sparrow. The few records are for the Pecos Valley. It is recorded as "winter resident, unusual" at the Bitter Lake Refuge. Montgomery reported it near Roswell January 28, 1953. (*Condor*, Vol. 55, No. 5, September 1953.) He recorded it again January 1955.

(VESPER SPARROW
Pooecetes gramineus
5½—6½" long. Color pattern of sexes alike. (Pl. XXXIV)

The Vesper, one of the larger members of the Sparrow group, is easily distinguished by the white outer-tail feathers, which flash rather conspicuously in flight, and by its preference for open grassland. Being a dweller of open spaces, it is more often in evidence, perched on a bush or wire fence, than are the smaller, shyer species, such as the Grasshopper, Savannah, or Baird's. *Adults in summer:* Upperparts grayish brown streaked with black and chestnut; outer-tail feathers mostly white; wings with indistinct bars; wing-bends reddish brown; underparts dull whitish; breast and sides streaked with black and chestnut. It is said that the eminent naturalist, John Burroughs, was in part responsible for the name "Vesper," given to this Sparrow because of the beauty of its evening song. Prior to the 1880's it was known as the Grass Finch. Both the Greek, *Pooecetes*, and the Latin, *gramineus*, have reference to its grass-inhabiting nature.

DISTRIBUTION. The Vesper Sparrow is widely distributed during migration, and may be seen commonly from the lower to higher elevations, but nearly always in open, grassy areas. In summer its distribution is confined largely to mesas and valleys, from 7,000 to 10,000 feet. Where there are open grasslands, elevation seems to be no factor in its summer distribution. On June 29 the author found it at 10,000 feet on Hamilton Mesa, in the Sangre de Cristo Range. "At Burford Lake it was common, and a nest with young was found June 6, 1918" (Wetmore). Hollister noted it in the Zuñi Mountains near Agua Fria, at 8,000 feet, July 16 to 24. Although most Vesper Sparrows leave the state for the winter, some remain in the southern section, particularly on the bluestem grass plains and sandhills of Roosevelt and Lea Counties.

NESTING. This fine songster nests commonly throughout the high mesa and valley country over the northern third of the state. In Santa Fe County, Jensen reported fresh eggs from May 15 to July 15. On July 25 the author found a Vesper Sparrow nest containing fairly fresh eggs on the Mt. Taylor Mesa, while at the same time young were out of nests. The southernmost point at which he has recorded it nesting was on the head of Apache Creek, north of Reserve, at about 7,500 feet elevation. *Nest:* Slight depression in ground, well made of grass, with thick walls. *Eggs:* 4 to 6; greenish or brownish white, spotted and streaked with reddish brown and lavender.

(LARK SPARROW
Chondestes grammacus
5½—6½" long. Color pattern of sexes alike. (Pl. XXXIV)

The friendly Lark Sparrow is not a surface, grass dweller to the extent that are several of the smaller Sparrows. It perches on bushes, fences, or telephone wires, or hops about in plain view. The conspicuous chestnut, white and black head striping, the black spot on chest, and the white outer-tail feathers are distinguishing features. *Adults:* Top and sides of head striped with white and chestnut, black or buffy; upperparts brownish gray; back narrowly streaked with blackish; middle-tail feathers grayish brown, tipped with white; wings with white band and a white patch at base of primaries; underparts, white with conspicuous black spot on chest.

DISTRIBUTION. The Lark Sparrow is a widely distributed summer resident, being found from the lowest southern section up to 7,800 feet, rarely higher. It is most common, however, in the eastern half of the state. Although it does occur at the higher extension of the Upper Sonoran Zone, or even in the more open sections of the Transition Zone, it usually avoids wooded or forested types. It is more tolerant of man's utilization of the land than are most other Sparrows. Its joyous song is a pleasing accompaniment to its presence. It is normally out of the state by late October, returning in late March or early April.

NESTING. The nesting range of this Sparrow extends from the lowest section, about Carlsbad, to about 7,800 feet. A nest with eggs was located at Santa Rosa, June 5. "Nests were found between May 23 and June 19, 1918 at Burford Lake, where the birds were fairly common" (Wetmore). The author noted Lark Sparrows with young in the Cuchillo Hills near Winston on August 4, and a nest containing 5 fresh eggs on June 13, 1953, in the Dry Cimarron Valley about 35 miles north of Clayton. *Nest:* Usually on ground but sometimes in bushes, particularly in the southern section, where catclaw or mesquite is usually chosen; made of weed stems, grass, and rootlets; lined with hair. *Eggs:* 4 or 5; white, speckled and lined mostly around larger end with brown and black.

⟦ RUFOUS-CROWNED SPARROW

Aimophila ruficeps

5—6″ long. Color pattern of sexes alike. (Pl. XXXIV)

Its preferred habitat—arid canyons and mountain slopes—is a clue to identification of the Rufous-crowned, sometimes listed as Scott's, Sparrow. The designation *ruficeps* (Latin), "red-headed," is descriptive. Its pleasing and distinctive song, consisting of variable notes fading out on a falling scale, directs attention to a nearby bush, where one may glimpse the reddish-crowned songster, only to have him vanish and presently be heard some distance away. *Adults:* Upperparts gray, broadly streaked with chestnut; sides of head and neck and most of underparts light brown, tinged with buffy. In winter the color of upperparts is obscured by grayish edges of the feathers.

DISTRIBUTION. The Rufous-crowned Sparrow is not to be found any distance from rugged foothills. It prefers the desert land types of rough canyon and mountain slopes, characterized by scrub oak and like brush, from 5,000 to 7,500 feet, rather than woodlands and forests. It is resident as far north as Glenwood, to the head of the Mimbres River, Salinas Peak of the San Andres Range, and on all of the rugged slopes of the Guadalupe Mountains. In the Trans-Pecos country of Texas it ranges down into much lower terrain, which is, however, of the same general character. On June 25, 1903, the Baileys took a specimen of the Rufous-crowned Sparrow at Cabra Springs, 25 miles north of Santa Rosa, at 6,000 feet—a hundred miles, airline, from where the nearest record has been obtained to the southwest. This brings up an interesting point regarding the distribution of the species. Its over-all range includes southeastern Colorado, western Oklahoma, and Texas. The Cabra Springs record indicates a westward thrust of distribution by way of the rugged canyon of the Canadian River.

NESTING. There seem to be no recorded accounts of nesting in the state, but since the Rufous-crowned is resident, there can be no doubt that it does breed wherever found. The author has been on the east slope of the. Guadalupe Mountains, as well as elsewhere, when singing males gave evidence of nesting, although no nests were located. *Nest:* Concealed under a rock, overhung with dead grass, or under blades of mescal, hence hard to find; made of grass, lined with finer grass. *Eggs:* Usually 3; pure white.

(CASSIN'S SPARROW
Aimophila cassinii
5½—5¾" long. Color pattern of sexes alike. (Pl. XXXIV)

The Cassin's is the most unpredictable of the many Sparrows that occur in the Southwest, both as to when and where it may appear, as is indicated in an article by Phillips (*Auk*, July 1944, pp. 409-12). It is named for John Cassin, American ornithologist (1813-69), author of "*Illustrations of the Birds of California, Texas, etc.*," 1856, and other works (McAtee). In New Mexico and west Texas, the nature of the season, whether dry or favored by early summer moisture, directly influences its occurrence. *Adults:* Upperparts sandy brown broadly streaked with light gray; top of head streaked with blackish; feathers of back with black cross-barring near tips and ashy margins giving a spotted effect; edge of wings yellow; underparts grayish, fading to white, tinged with brown on chest and sides. Type of summer habitat, conduct of bird, and its song, are aids in distinguishing it from other Sparrows. On the nesting grounds it is a pleasing songster, and where habitat is favorable there is a tendency toward communal living. On calm days, at all hours, male after

male may be seen flying upward from mesquite, catclaw, or other low shrubs, delivering their tremulous songs as they float away, and silently dropping down to protective cover. So persistent are Cassin's Sparrows in song that the clear, subdued notes may often be heard issuing from roosting cover on calm nights.

DISTRIBUTION. The preferred summer habitat of the Cassin's Sparrow is rank, green vegetation with a liberal sprinkling of mesquite or other semidesert shrubs. Even a small "oasis" in the form of a basin where water collects in an otherwise desert area may be inhabited by one or more pairs. The following year, should there be insufficient timely moisture, no birds may be present. Or, should moisture conditions improve by midsummer, the birds may appear and occupy their old haunts. At favored places, during years of normal rainfall, the Cassin's may be observed regularly in the Carlsbad-Roswell sections, whereas during prolonged drought probably no birds will be seen or heard. Range forage deficiency, resulting from excessive use by livestock also has a bearing on the Cassin's seasonal appearance. It is more consistent in its seasonal occurrence in Texas, to the south and southeast, where habitat conditions are more stable.

NESTING. Nesting of the Cassin's Sparrow in the state is confined almost wholly to the Lower and Upper Sonoran Zones. It breeds rather commonly locally during favorable years throughout the eastern section as far north as Clayton. On August 3, 1949, Cassin's Sparrows were found nesting in a small mesquite basin two miles southeast of Lake McMillan Dam, and on June 2, 1955, two pairs were located in a small grassy cove where there were a few bushes, one-half mile east of the Washington Ranch, thirty miles southwest of Carlsbad. *Nest:* On the ground or in low bushes or tufts of grass; deeply cupped; made of grass, weed stems, and fibers; lined with finer grass. *Eggs:* 4 or 5; pure white or bluish white.

(BLACK-THROATED (DESERT) SPARROW

Amphispiza bilineata

5—5½″ long. Color pattern of sexes alike. (Pl. I)

The little Black-throated Sparrow is one of the commonest birds of the lower and more arid regions of the Southwest. This fine songster is likewise one of the most attractive of the small Sparrows. Its trusting nature and its habit of perching atop low bushes, and its distinctive gray, white and black head markings are aids in identification. *Adults:* Upperparts deep brownish gray; tail blackish, outside feathers marked with white; lores, throat and chest patch black; underparts and line over eye white, shading into grayish on sides and flanks.

DISTRIBUTION. The range of the Black-throated Sparrow includes practically all of the Lower and Upper Sonoran Zones, elevation limit being approximately 7,000 feet. Its preferred habitat is the arid mountain slopes and adjacent semidesert land types characterized by shrubs such as mesquite, catclaw, Condalia, sage, and cactus. In the northern section, distribution is more spotty and the birds are less common. The author has observed Black-throated Sparrows on the tablelands about Santa Fe, and in the sage and scrub juniper valleys about Cuba, at 6,500 feet. Henshaw noted them at Fort Wingate, at 7,000 feet, and they were recorded at Shiprock at 5,000 feet. Bailey found them west of Tucumcari at 4,500 feet. It is probable that during severe winter weather they move down into the lower valleys where they have better protection. Significantly, these northern records are from the upper branches of the main drainage systems (Rio Grande, San Juan, and east of the mountains, the Canadian) from which the birds can readily move down into lower country for the winter.

NESTING. Nesting of the Black-throated Sparrow begins in late April in the southern section of the state, in late May in the north. Eggs were recorded on July 1 near Cutter, and young in nest at Carlsbad in mid-August, indicating that two broods may be raised in a season. *Nest:* Usually near the ground in mesquite, catclaw, or other thorny shrub, or in cactus. In the northern section, sagebrush is utilized. Made of grass and plant stems; lined with feathers or hair. *Eggs:* 4; bluish or pinkish white.

(SAGE SPARROW

Amphispiza belli

5½—6¼″ long. Color pattern of sexes alike. (Pl. XXXIV)

Like many other species of the Sparrow group, the Sage is a ground dweller. It is quite shy and darts about to keep out of sight, with tail held upright like that of a Wren. *Adults:* Upperparts light grayish brown; back usually streaked with dusky; tail and wings dull blackish, outer web of outside tail feathers white; edge of wing yellow; sides of throat with broken series of streaks; eye ring and most of underparts white; chest with black spot; sides and flanks faintly tinged with brown.

DISTRIBUTION. The summer range of the Sage Sparrow is confined to the sage valleys and mesas in the northwest corner of the state, from the Continental Divide westward. Wetmore recorded it about Burford Lake in late May and early June. The author also found it there and in the Gallina River Valley to the southward. It also inhabits the extensive big sage country northwest of Cuba and the Tres Piedras area at this season. By the first of October, migrants begin to move into the state from the north, and by the end of the month they have usually spread to the southern border. Sage Sparrows remain throughout the Lower Sonoran Zone during the winter. They are recorded as "winter resident, common" at Bosque del Apache Refuge; and in the Roswell area, "common October to April" (Montgomery). They are rather common throughout the winter in the Jornada Valley—Las Cruces to Engle—and in the southeastern section, east of the Pecos, particularly in areas where sand sage thrives.

NESTING. Nesting range of the Sage Sparrow is confined to the northwest corner of the state where the big sage (*Artemisia tridentata*) occurs, principally along and adjacent to the Continental Divide from Cuba north and northwest, at 6,500 to 7,500 feet. Young were seen by the author in late June in the Gallina Valley north of Cuba and about Burford Lake. *Nest:* On the ground or in sage or other low bushes; made largely of fine shreds of sage bark, sage stems, and grass; lined with fine grass and cow or rabbit hair. *Eggs:* 3 or 4; greenish white, speckled chiefly around larger end with reddish brown.

JUNCOS

ALTHOUGH the Juncos are frequently seen in association with Sparrows, the black or gray heads and the flash of white outer-tail feathers as they dash for cover are distinguishing features of these slaty gray-colored birds. On breeding grounds, or about lawns and parks, Juncos are tamer than most species and are therefore more readily observed. They are familiarly known as "Snow-birds," and winter weather seems to have little adverse effect on Juncos. In summer, their distribution is confined largely to the forests and mountains. Five species occur in the state; however, only two—Gray-headed and Mexican —have been recorded as nesting birds.

WHITE-WINGED JUNCO
Junco aikeni

6—6¾" long. Color pattern of sexes essentially alike.

The White-winged, one of the larger Juncos, is the only Junco with white wing bars; thus it is readily identified. *Adult male:* Entire head, breast and upperparts light slate gray; two wing bars and three outer-tail feathers white; underparts white; bill pinkish. *Adult female:* Similar but paler; upperparts tinged with brownish; wing bars less distinct.

DISTRIBUTION. The White-winged, like most other Juncos, spends its summers far to the north of New Mexico; and in winter, although not common, it is found in the northern part of the state. On November 19 and 20, 1926, the author found it fairly common about the town of Red River, and in Moreno Valley, Colfax County (9,000 to 10,000 feet). On November 24, 1933, one was banded by Jensen at Santa Fe. One was collected by Surber, January 20, on Arroyo Seco, north of Taos, at 8,000 feet. These records indicate that it does not venture far into the state, even in midwinter.

SLATE-COLORED JUNCO
Junco hyemalis

6—6½" long. Color pattern of sexes essentially alike.

The Slate-colored, one of the larger Juncos, and of rather uniform gray markings, is generally found in association with other members of this family, usually in weeds or rank grasses which provide seed, the principal winter food. *Adult male:* Head and body slate color, darker on crown; paler on rump and sides; two outer-tail feathers and underparts white; iris dark reddish brown; bill pinkish with dusky tip. *Adult female:* Similar, but slate color lighter, and outer-tail feathers dusky.

JUNCOS AND LONGSPURS
TOP: OREGON JUNCO, WHITE-WINGED JUNCO, MEXICAN JUNCO
MIDDLE: GRAY-HEADED JUNCO, SLATE-COLORED JUNCO
BOTTOM: McCOWN'S LONGSPUR, CHESTNUT-COLLARED LONGSPUR
E. R. Kalmbach, N.M. Dept. of Game & Fish

DISTRIBUTION. Like the White-winged, the Slate-colored is a winter visitor only, and its distribution is confined largely to the northern part of the state. Surber recorded it on January 4 on the Hondo near Taos, at 8,000 feet. Marshall F. Gilman recorded it at Shiprock in March, and on Willow Creek in the Mogollon Mountains, 8,500 feet, on October 26. Montgomery reports it as "occasional, January, February" in the Roswell area. It is listed as "winter visitor, uncommon" at Bosque del Apache Refuge.

OREGON (SHUFELDT) JUNCO
Junco oreganus
6" long. Color pattern of sexes similar.

The Oregon Junco, a winter resident only, is the commonest of the Juncos found in the state. The black head and reddish or rusty back of the adult male clearly set this Junco apart from others of the family; two outer-tail feathers and median underparts white; sides buffy brown. *Adult female:* Colors more subdued with rufous tinge on sides.

DISTRIBUTION. Arriving in mid-September, the Oregon becomes common throughout the state in winter. "By the first of October, 1908, it was the commonest of the Juncos noted in the Chuska Mountains north of Gallup, being present in flocks of thousands" (Birdseye). Goldman reported: "It was abundant the latter part of October 1908 in the Mogollon Mountains from 7,000 to 10,000 feet; apparently about as common as dorsalis [Red-backed], these two species together outnumbering all other birds combined." "In November 1906, the Shufeldt [Oregon] and Red-backed [Gray-headed] were the commonest Juncos seen in the Gila Valley at Cliff, 5,000 feet" (Bailey). These records indicate that Oregon Juncos are most abundant in the western half of the state. Montgomery records them, however, as "common, late September to

April" in the Roswell area. But Jensen obtained the most intimate contacts with the Oregon Junco. While these birds nest far north of New Mexico, the same banded bird returned each year for three years, not merely to the state, but to the same spot—the campus of the Indian School at Santa Fe. Banded December 1, 1922, it was retaken on its return from the north on February 14, March 15, and March 22, 1923; and after another nesting season the same bird was taken on December 13, 1923, and again on December 7, 10, 18, and 23, 1924; and finally on February 17, 1926. Another banded Oregon, as recorded by Jensen, "acquired the trap or 'easy food' habit and was even more persistent; banded on December 28, 1924, it was retaken the following day and all but six days during January. It was taken as often as six times a day."

([GRAY-HEADED JUNCO
Junco caniceps
6–6½" long. Color pattern of sexes alike. (Pl. I)

As the Gray-headed—formerly also known as the Red-backed— and the Mexican are the only nesting Juncos in New Mexico, identification at this season is simplified. Furthermore, the Mexican occurs only in the extreme southwestern part of the state, thus the possibility of confusing the two species in summer is largely eliminated. *Adults:* Slaty gray, except for the blackish lores, bright reddish back, and white median underparts; three outer-tail feathers white.

DISTRIBUTION. The Gray-headed Junco is one of the commonest of the smaller birds found in New Mexico during the nesting season. At this time the birds are present in all of the higher forested mountains from the Guadalupe, Sacramento and Black Range Mountains northward. With the arrival of fall, these Juncos spread over the foothills and valleys of the southern part of the state, wherever there are sunflowers and other seed-producing weeds, and mingle with migrant Juncos from the north. Some usually remain in the lower valleys of the southern section, but the majority move on south, returning to the state about the first of April.

NESTING. The Gray-headed Junco nests in all forested mountains of the state, from about 6,500 to 9,000 feet. Nests found by the author were all on the ground, usually rather well hidden under bunches of grass or small bushes. When approached, the bird nearly always betrays the nest location by flying away from it. *Nest:* One found on August 16 near Chloride, at 6,500 feet, was under a small pine where leaves had collected and settled, providing an excellent receptacle. It was well made of grass and rootlets; lined with fine grass. *Eggs:* 4; greenish white, marked with lilac and reddish brown around larger end.

(MEXICAN JUNCO
Junco phaeonotus
6–6½″ long. Color pattern of sexes alike.

The Mexican, also referred to as the Arizona Junco, is a relative of the Gray-headed Junco, which it closely resembles. *Adult:* Head and neck gray, chest and sides paler; back reddish brown; underparts white; outer-tail feathers white.

DISTRIBUTION. The range of the Mexican Junco is confined to the southwestern corner of the state—Big Hatchet, Animas, and Peloncillo Mountains, where it seems to be resident. Goldman found Mexican Juncos common in the Animas Mountains, from 7,000 to 8,000 feet in July. The author collected a specimen near Animas Peak on May 28.

NESTING. Nesting of the Mexican Junco is essentially the same as that of the Gray-headed. The author observed young out of nest in the Animas Mountains on May 26, 1951.

TREE SPARROW
Spizella arborea
6–6½″ long. Color pattern of sexes alike.

This rather large Sparrow breeds far to the north of New Mexico, hence is only a winter resident and a late arrival in the state. *Adults:* Conspicuous rufous crown and two white wing bars; back pale buffy streaked with black and rusty; tail with pale edgings; dusky spot on breast; underparts grayish; sides of chest brown. Winter plumage is similar but colors are duller; chestnut or rufous of crown obscured by buffy tips to feathers.

DISTRIBUTION. The Tree Sparrow is in the state for a comparatively brief time, since it does not ordinarily arrive before the middle of November and is out of the state by early March. Most of the records are for the northern half of the state. It is recorded as rare or accidental at both Bosque del Apache and Bitter Lake Refuges. It was noted at Aztec on December 9 and at Albuquerque January 11. Ernest Thompson Seton recorded, "First flock seen at Currumpa [near Clayton] January 17 and other flocks two days later."

(CHIPPING SPARROW
Spizella passerina
5–5½″ long. Color pattern of sexes alike. (Pl. XXXIV)

The Chipping is one of the smaller Sparrows that may give the novice some trouble in identification. It is largely a bird of the open spaces and bushes or trees, and since it is less shy than the grass-dwelling varieties, it is more easily observed. Its small size and its bright rufous crown are the best identification marks. *Adults:* Forehead blackish, cut by a median white line; line over eye white or grayish, and black line through eye; back brownish or pale buffy, streaked with black; rump and upper-tail coverts gray; tail dusky; wings with two restricted white bands; underparts white or grayish.

DISTRIBUTION. The Chipping Sparrow is one of the commoner breeding birds in New Mexico. It ranges practically statewide in summer, but prefers a wooded habitat; consequently at this season it is rarely observed below 4,500 feet. After the nesting season it may be observed with Bluebirds or other species, up to timber line or even higher. By the end of November it is usually out of the state, returning to the southern section early in March. In migration the Chipping Sparrow is often seen in bunches.

NESTING. Preferred nesting range of the Chipping Sparrow is from 6,000 to 8,000 feet. The lowest points at which it has been found nesting are in the pinyon-juniper country in the Tucumcari area, around 4,500 feet. At Chloride, 6,200 feet, small young were seen in nest on June 13, and fresh eggs were found two days later. On Mt. Taylor Mesa (8,000 feet) young were out of nests on July 25, and young were still being fed out of nests at 11,000 feet near Pecos Baldy in July. The Chipping Sparrow nests as far south as the Guadalupe Mountains. Nest: Usually in bushes or small trees; made of twigs and dried grass stems; lined with hair and rootlets. Eggs: 4 or 5; light greenish blue, speckled, mostly around larger end, with black and brown.

CLAY-COLORED SPARROW
Spizella pallida

5—5½" long. Color pattern of sexes alike.

The Clay-colored Sparrow is a common migrant in the state, although the comparatively few recent records indicate that some observers may have difficulty separating it from the Brewer's and other problem Sparrows. Clay-colored Sparrows generally are seen in numbers in ample grass and weed cover, a clue to identification. Adults: Crown, light brown striped with black; light stripe through center of crown; conspicuous white line over eye; ear patch buffy brown with enclosing black marks strongly contrasted; hind neck gray; back brown, broadly streaked with black; wing bars buffy; underparts whitish tinged with buffy on chest and sides. Winter plumage is similar to summer, but the crown streaks are narrower and the plumage is more tinged with buffy.

DISTRIBUTION. In the Clayton area, it is "common transient" (Krehbiel). For the Anthony area, south of Las Cruces, Lena McBee reports: "Began to notice it in numbers, 20 or more, in 1937. Best months September and April; often with Brewer's in flocks; sings in April. We usually get a few for the Christmas count." Among earlier records are those of Bailey: "It enters the State in August and was common the last few days of that month in 1903 near Las Vegas." "It was still common near Santa Rosa in early October, but was not recorded at a later date" (Gaut). In 1956, Clay-colored Sparrows were common early fall migrants in the Pecos Valley, reaching the Carlsbad area by mid-September, and by the middle of the month there were large concentrations at several places, including the author's home grounds, where matured grass and weed seeds held them until early October, at which time they moved on southward. They begin to re-enter the state on their northward migration about the first of April.

NESTING. The Clay-colored Sparrow has not been found nesting in the state, but is known to breed commonly a few miles distant in southeastern Colorado, so eventually it should be found nesting in New Mexico; hence the liberal space accorded it at this time. Nest: In bushes, made of grass; lined with hair or fur. Eggs: 4; light greenish blue, spotted with brown around larger end.

([BREWER'S SPARROW
Spizella breweri

5" long. Color pattern of sexes alike. (Pl. XXXIV)

The small and dainty brownish-gray Brewer's Sparrow, though more streamlined, resembles the Chipping and the Clay-colored. It is named for Thomas Mayo Brewer, 1814-80, the American oölogist, author of *North American Oology*, 1857. Its size, in contrast with that of most other Sparrows, is indicated by the ease with which it slips through the one-inch poultry netting enclosures at the author's bird farm near Carlsbad. This netting repels most other Sparrows which try to enter the pens. The streaked head and back distinguish the Brewer's from other Sparrows. It is readily observed since it is less shy than most Sparrows. *Adults:* Entire upperparts pale brownish gray streaked with black; underparts whitish. In fall and winter, similar but more buffy.

DISTRIBUTION. Brewer's Sparrows are among the commoner summer-dwelling Sparrows in the northern section of the state. At this season their distribution is almost coextensive with rabbit brush and the big sage, hence they occur mainly around 6,500 to 8,000 feet. They are common throughout the state during August and September migration, most of them being absent by late October. However, a few may be in evidence throughout the winter in the Carlsbad, Las Cruces, and Animas areas. Advance spring arrivals begin to appear in early March, moving northward.

NESTING. Nesting of the Brewer's Sparrow in the state is confined largely to big sage (*Artemisia tridentata*) and rabbit brush (*Chrysothamnus nauseosus*) areas. It nests commonly in rabbit brush in the Santa Fe area, around 7,000 feet. (The range of the big sage begins a little north of Santa Fe.) Fleetwood found it nesting in 1953 around 6,000 feet in the Socorro area, the farthest south it has been reported. In the Burford Lake section, where the big sage dominates the landscape, "May 23-June 19, 1918, it was found to be one of the most common breeding birds and a number of nests found—one on June 4 with 3 eggs, and one June 17 with 3 newly-hatched young" (Wetmore). It is a common breeder throughout the vast sage-dominated portion of northwestern New Mexico. *Nest:* In sage, small juniper or other low-growing shrub; made compactly of twigs and shredded sage bark, fine grass stems and leaves; lined with rootlets, and usually some horsehair or rabbit fur. *Eggs:* 3 or 4; greenish with a wreath of reddish brown spots around larger end.

WORTHEN'S SPARROW
Spizella wortheni

5–5½" long. Color pattern of sexes alike.

New Mexico has the distinction of having contributed the type specimen of the Worthen's, the rarest of the Sparrows occurring in the state. The bird was taken at Silver City, evidently on its nesting ground, on June 16, 1844, by Charles H. Marsh, an early-day bird collector. Ornithologists have been on the alert ever since, hoping that others of the species would appear from their regular range in Mexico. None has been taken, nor has it been reported since the type specimen was obtained. It may still occur locally, and offers a challenge to observers of the future. The Worthen's so strikingly resembles the Chipping Sparrow that it could be mistaken for the latter. The Worthen's is more streamlined, however, and has a conspicuous white eye ring, and lacks the black eye streak. *Adults:* Crown dull cinnamon brownish, indistinctly streaked; rest of head ashy; underparts whitish, shaded with buffy grayish on sides. It is regarded as resident, or semi-migratory, and should be looked for in desert or semi-desert, scrub brush type.

⟨ BLACK-CHINNED SPARROW
Spizella atrogularis
5—5½″ long. Color pattern of sexes similar. (Pl. XXXIV)

The Black-chinned is a rather common summer dweller with range restricted to the central and southwest portions of the state. Its habitat, semidesert type, and the black chin are identification clues. It is a rather shy bird, and its pleasing repetitious song delivered from tree or bush is distinctive. *Adult male:* Black chin patch; neck and underparts gray, fading to white on lower underparts; back rusty brown or cinnamon, narrowly streaked with blackish; wing coverts broadly streaked with brownish. *Adult female:* Similar to male but usually with black of chin restricted or entirely lacking.

DISTRIBUTION. The principal range of the Black-chinned Sparrow is the Lower and Upper Sonoran Zones, north to Silver City, Cuchillo, west of the Rio Grande, the San Andres, and the Capitan Mountains. It seems to prefer the brushy, rugged mountains and ridges, shunning forested areas. Both the author and Goldman found it in the Big Hatchet Mountains, and it has been recorded along the west slopes of the San Andres Mountains to 6,000 feet and in the brushy valley west of Tularosa. The Capitan Mountains seem to be the northeastern extremity of its range, where Bailey found it "not rare" in June, in the chaparral around 7,000 feet, at the upper edge of the juniper belt. Black-chinned Sparrows have been observed as late as November 24, and some remain in the southern area throughout the winter.

NESTING. Goldman found it "a common breeder June 1913 near Cuchillo, at 5,000 feet." The author noted young being fed out of the nest on June 25, on Big Hatchet Mountain. *Nest:* In low bushes, well concealed; made of grass and usually lined with hair. *Eggs:* 4 or 5; light greenish blue, sometimes sparsely spotted with brown around larger end.

HARRIS' SPARROW
Zonotrichia querula
7—7½″ long. Color pattern of sexes alike.

The Harris' is one of the largest as well as most distinctive of the Sparrows. *Adults in summer:* Crown, face, throat, and V-shaped breast patch black; underparts mainly white; back broadly streaked with blackish; wings with two white or buffy white bars. *Adults in winter:* Throat spotted with white; crown grayish.

DISTRIBUTION. There seems to be no account of this handsome Sparrow having been observed in the state by early-day ornithologists. Since it is a migrant, seemingly limited to the eastern section, it could have gone unobserved, as few of the pioneer collectors operated in this area in winter. One was taken by the author in Carlsbad on December 5, 1945. It is recorded as "winter visitor, rare" at Bitter Lake Refuge. Krehbiel reports it as "an occasional transient" in the Clayton area.

⟨ WHITE-CROWNED SPARROW
Zonotrichia leucophrys
6—7″ long. Color pattern of sexes essentially alike. (Pl. I)

The White-crowned may be regarded as the dominant type of the three closely related Sparrows: White-crowned, Golden-crowned, and White-throated. Although very similar in appearance and conduct, the slightly different head markings, as suggested by their popular names, enable the close observer to separate them.

The White-crowned is an abundant winter resident in the state. It is a fine songster, both on its nesting grounds and at times during warm, calm days in winter, particularly as spring approaches. While camped at the foot of Pecos Baldy (11,500 feet) in late June, the author was awakened at daybreak by the joyous songs of the White-crowns. Unlike the many Sparrows which are ground- and grass-dwellers and often difficult to see except for an instant, the White-crowned prefers being above ground, in bushes or small trees. The conspicuous white crown and the bird's friendly and trusting nature simplify identification. *Adult male:* Head striped black and white; lores black; hind neck gray; back gray broadly striped with brown; wings with two white bars; underparts gray, darkest on chest; sides and flanks pale buffy brown; bill cinnamon brown, tip dusky. *Adult female:* Sometimes indistinguishable from male, but usually with crown stripes brown and buffy instead of black and white; underparts more or less buffy. Birds of the year are similar to the adult females.

DISTRIBUTION. The summer distribution of the White-crowned Sparrow is limited almost entirely to the dwarfed-shrub timber-line zone in the northern part of the state. During migration White-crowned Sparrows occur statewide, and many winter in the southern section. Interestingly, these seasonal visitors remain in numbers, even in the southernmost part of the state, until early May, apparently aware that their nesting grounds at mountain timber line, or far to the north, will not be favorable for nesting until early summer. Migrants return to the state by late September, reaching the southern portion by early October. They arrive at Carlsbad usually about October 5. Those remaining in the northern perimeter of their wintering zone, about Socorro and Roswell, or even farther north when a suitable supply of food is available, are probably more northern migrants. This does not mean, however, that great numbers do not move on south for the winter.

NESTING. Nesting of the White-crowned is restricted to a dozen or more peaks of the Sangre de Cristo and Culebra Ranges, where limited arctic climates prevail above timber line, Pecos Baldy apparently being the southern limit. They usually nest in the stunted wind-bombarded fox-tail pines or in willows that mark the limit of tree growth. The Baileys noted young at Pecos Baldy (11,500 feet) on July 27. The author found a nest containing 2 fresh eggs, June 19, on the southeastern slope of Wheeler Peak, at 12,500 feet. Several other nests were located on the timber-line rims of Pecos Baldy and the Truchas Peaks. As the season is short at such altitudes, nesting must begin on time if it is to be successfully completed; but nature seems to dictate such details. *Nest:* May be placed on the ground, but usually is built in bushes about sub-alpine meadows, often near streamlets that gush from snowbanks; made of twigs, rootlets, and grass. *Eggs:* 4 or 5; pale greenish blue, varying to brownish, spotted with reddish brown.

GOLDEN-CROWNED SPARROW
Zonotrichia atricapilla

6–7″ long. Color pattern of sexes similar.

The Golden-crowned, one of the extremely rare Sparrows that occur in the state, in some respects is little more than a duplicate of the White-crowned. The fact that it closely resembles the White-crowned could lead to confusion in identification. However, it has a golden rather than a white stripe through center of crown. *Adults:* Crown enclosed by black stripes; upperparts streaked with blackish brown; wing with two white bands.

STATE RECORDS. The only authentic records of the Golden-crowned Sparrow are those by Lena McBee and her bird-observing associate, Miss Keefer, at Canutillo, on the Rio Grande near the New Mexico–Texas line. Mrs. McBee states in a letter: "An adult male was seen January 6, 11, and 17, 1954, at close range, and associated with Gambel Sparrows [White-crowned] at water pan, or feeding with quail. Central head-stripe of sulphur-yellow fading on nape gave the head a high effect, as sides of head were black."

WHITE-THROATED SPARROW
Zonotrichia albicollis
6—7" long. Color pattern of sexes alike.

The White-throated Sparrow, another relative of the White-crowned, according to the few authentic records is rare in the state. The white throat patch is the principal means of distinguishing it from the White-crowned and the Golden-crowned. *Adults in summer:* Head is striped with black and white, but median white stripe is narrow; yellow from bill to above eye; back and scapulars rusty brown streaked with black; wings with two white bands and pale yellow edging; throat patch white, conspicuous against adjoining gray; median underparts white; sides brownish. *Immature and adults in winter:* Crown stripes brown and buffy instead of black and white; yellow duller; throat patch less sharply defined, and in some immature specimens indistinct.

STATE RECORDS. The White-throated Sparrow was noted by Willett November 23 to December 9, 1916, about the Rio Grande Reserve (Elephant Butte). Lena McBee has recorded it at Canutillo, just over the state line in Texas. In the Roswell area Montgomery records it as "uncommon to rare, observed in December 1953 and January 1954. I had never observed them before." It is recorded as "winter visitor, rare" at Bitter Lake Refuge. On December 28, 1955, W. W. Hill stated in a letter: "The following is the information on the White-throated Sparrow. Mr. John Durrie and Dr. Paul Fitzsimmons have the following two sight records: November 22, 1952, in the vicinity of Alameda Bridge along the river near Alameda, and February 22, 1953, in the vicinity of La Joya along the river. I collected a specimen of the species in the vicinity of Isleta Pueblo, November 28, 1955." On October 31, 1956, Krehbiel advised in a letter: "Positive identification of another species, the White-throated Sparrow, has been made. Mr. Cook and I saw two October 13, three miles west of town [Clayton] on Perico Creek. Then in our back yard I saw one bird on the following days: October 21, 22, 23, 24, 26 and 27." One was observed February 9, 1957, at Carlsbad.

FOX SPARROW
Passerella iliaca
6½—7" long. Color pattern of sexes alike.

The Fox Sparrow, one of the larger members of the Sparrow group, is a shy, active bird of thicket and brush, under which it spends much time scratching for food by jumping forward and raking back with both feet at the same time, after the manner of Towhees, thereby turning over and over fallen leaves and chaff in search of tiny insects and seeds in the soil. This evasive songster is a rare winter visitor in the state, and only in recent years has it been recorded. Although there are reportedly 15 subspecies of the Fox Sparrow, the distinction lies mainly in the color and size of bill. *Adults:* Heavily streaked underparts on dark brown or gray are distinguishing marks; upperparts mixed with contrasting slate gray and reddish brown, with brown brightest on wings, rump, and tail. Wings with two white bars; sides of throat and chest spotted and blotched with reddish brown; flanks streaked with rufous.

STATE RECORDS. In the Clayton area, Krehbiel regards it as "occasional winter resident." It is listed as "accidental" at Bosque del Apache Refuge. In the El Paso area, including extreme southern New Mexico, Lena McBee lists it as "rare transient."

([LINCOLN'S SPARROW

Melospiza lincolnii

5—6″ long. Color pattern of sexes alike. (Pl. XXXIV)

The Lincoln's, like the Song Sparrow, is an excellent songster at nesting-time, and prefers the same type of habitat— willow- or alder-bordered meadows or brushy, mountain stream banks that provide concealment. In such habitat the male spends much time in the swaying branches of treetops pouring out his melodious song. Plumage of the Lincoln's Sparrow is rather dark with streaking that simulates surroundings. The slightly smaller size and shorter tail distinguish it from the Song Sparrow of similar summer habitat. It is named for Thomas Lincoln, 1812-83, who, at the age of 21, accompanied Audubon to Labrador, where he collected this new species of Sparrow. *Adults:* Top of head brown streaked with black, and olive grayish median stripe; upperparts light olive or buffy olive with black streaks widest on back; wings marked with rusty brown and black; underparts with broad buffy chest band, finely streaked with black, buffy extending over sides of body; neck and under-tail coverts white.

DISTRIBUTION. Summer range of the Lincoln's Sparrow in the state is confined almost entirely to the higher portions of the Sangre de Cristo and San Juan Ranges of northern New Mexico, for the most part around 11,000 feet, where it is fairly common. Elsewhere it is a migrant, widely distributed over the higher sections of the state by the middle of September. Bailey noted it on the Continental Divide about Burford, Stone, and other lakes, as late as October 2. Some Lincoln's Sparrows remain throughout the winter as far north as Socorro and Roswell, where there are marshes and ponds with rushes and other aquatic vegetation. It is recorded as "winter visitor, unusual" at Bosque del Apache and "regular visitor, January to April in the Roswell area" (Montgomery). It winters about marshy and brushy bottomlands in the Carlsbad and Las Cruces sections, where it has been recorded as late as the first of May.

NESTING. Nesting of the Lincoln's Sparrow is confined largely to willow- and alder-bordered meadows and streams of the San Juan and Sangre de Cristo Ranges, from 9,500 to 11,600 feet. The Baileys found it nesting on Jack's Creek near Pecos Baldy in July. The author found nests as low as 9,500 feet on Pot Creek southeast of Taos in late June, and it was noted near the head of the Santa Barbara River, at 11,500 feet, on June 29. *Nest:* On the ground; made of grasses; usually lined with hair. *Eggs:* 4 or 5; varying from greenish white to brownish white, heavily wreathed, chiefly around larger end, with chestnut brown and lavender.

SWAMP SPARROW

Melospiza georgiana

5½—6″ long. Color pattern of sexes alike.

Althoug the Swamp Sparrow is a regular winter visitor to the state, only the patient observer is apt to glimpse it as it moves stealthily over rushes and other aquatic vegetation, seeking seeds and insects. Like its relative, the Song Sparrow, it is a persistent songster at nesting time.

The Swamp Sparrow is rather shy and unless closely observed may be mistaken for the Song; however, the Swamp lacks the breast streaking of the Song. Because of limited suitable habitat, the Swamp Sparrow's occurrence is localized in the state. *Adults:* Forehead black with gray median line; upperparts rusty brown; crown chestnut; neck gray; back streaked grayish, blackish, and buff; underparts grayish white. A whitish line over eye extending back to the upper neck is also a distinguishing mark.

DISTRIBUTION. Most records of the Swamp Sparrow in the state are of comparatively recent date, and are confined to marshy places of the Rio Grande and Pecos River Valleys. Fleetwood recorded it December 27, 1950, at Bitter Lake Refuge, and Montgomery reports it as "regular visitor January and February" in that area. It is listed as "winter visitor" at Bosque del Apache Refuge, and the author has observed it wintering in the rushes about Wade Lake, above McMillan Reservoir. No nesting records for the state.

(SONG SPARROW

Melospiza melodia

5½—6½" inches long. Color pattern of sexes alike. (Pl. XXXIV)

As its name indicates, the Song Sparrow is best known for its vocal renditions. As with the Lincoln's Sparrow, the heavily streaked breast is outstanding as an identification mark. The Song Sparrow is somewhat larger than the Lincoln's, and usually ranges at lower elevations, for the most part, 7,000 to 8,000 feet. *Adults:* Crown brown narrowly streaked with black; grayish line over eye; upperparts umber brown with grayish margins to feathers; back streaked with blackish brown; wings with brown coverts and graying edging; underparts white; chest and sides streaked with blackish brown, more or less centered on breast. The whole color

pattern is unusually dark for an inland Sparrow.

DISTRIBUTION. Like that of the Lincoln's, the summer range of the Song Sparrow is confined to the northern mountains, but embraces a wider zone. It is fairly common about willow- and alder-bordered meadows and streams of the Sangre de Cristo Range, but seems to be most common on and adjacent to the Continental Divide, west of the upper Rio Grande. Fall migrants are usually widespread by late September.

NESTING. Although the summer range of the Song Sparrow is centered around 8,000 feet, nesting begins exceptionally early for such elevations. At Burford Lake, near the 8,000-foot level, Wetmore found young common on June 4. He estimated 35 pairs were nesting around the lake. "On June 19, 1921, a nest was found with four fresh eggs, above Santa Fe, at about 7,200 feet" (Jensen). The author found Song Sparrows nesting in fair numbers along the willow-bordered streams above Taos, around 7,500 feet, on June 21. *Nest:* In low bushes or on the ground, often near water; made of grass and usually lined with hair. *Eggs:* 4 or 5; dull greenish white, spotted with reddish brown.

LONGSPURS

IN SOME RESPECTS, the Longspurs are Sparrow-like birds, but they differ, particularly in that they run rather than hop as do most Sparrows. They are birds of open, grassy plains, mesas, and valleys where there is ample cover, which they use to advantage in scurrying about in order to keep out of sight; hence they are more often seen on wing than on the ground.

Two species—McCown's and Chestnut-collared—occur in the state as migrants; another, the Lapland Longspur, is recorded as a stray (see Stray Birds). Within the last few decades there has been a noticeable decline in numbers, of both species, in the state. The decline in populations may be due, in part, to land-use practices which have resulted in disruption of some of their breeding grounds. Migratory movements and general conduct of these two species are similar, as are size and winter plumage. By the time they begin to move out of the state in April, the males have begun to assume their attractive summer dress.

McCOWN'S LONGSPUR
Rhynchophanes mccownii

5—6" long. Color pattern of sexes similar in winter.

Unfortunately, the bird observer in the Southwest usually sees the male Longspur in its modest winter plumage. Occasionally, however, it may be observed in its striking breeding plumage in the spring, just before it departs for its northern breeding ground. Usually occurring in bunches of a few to considerable numbers, Longspurs are rarely seen with other birds. When disturbed, one after another pops up from cover, until all are united in a rather compact bunch, and circle about in undulating flight, all the while engaged in squeaky chatter, often returning to point of departure. Probably because of their dry seed diet in winter, they can often be seen plummeting down to a pool or lake to take a few hurried dips and then, as if pressed for time, noisily taking wing in their familiar squeaking, dashing manner. This Longspur is named for Capt. John P. McCown, of the U. S. Army, who discovered it in western Texas in 1851. *Adult male in summer:* Crown jet black, bordered by white; back and scapulars brown, broadly streaked with dusky; ends of tail feathers black, remainder of tail white, flashing conspicuously in flight; wings with light edgings, chestnut patch on coverts; chest patch black; rest of underparts white. In winter black areas are partly concealed;

black of head replaced by brown and by buffy on chest. *Adult female:* Upperparts light buffy brown, streaked with blackish; wings dusky with buffy brown edgings; tail as in male; underparts buffy to white posteriorly.

DISTRIBUTION. McCown's Longspurs winter most commonly on the high plains from Portales south and in southern Hidalgo County, particularly in the upper Animas Valley. During the spring and fall movement they may be observed almost any place where there are open grasslands, up to 7,000 feet. Seton reported that on October 22, 1893, "there were hundreds of Skylarks [Horned Larks] and thousands of White-tailed Longspurs [McCown's] about Clayton." A week later he wrote from Clapham, about 25 miles southwest of Clayton: "As I take my daily ride, I see countless multitudes of these Longspurs." Yet Krehbiel in his observations submitted in 1955 refers to this bird in the Clayton area, as "occasional winter resident." In recent years the author has observed far fewer of the birds than formerly, both in New Mexico and in western Texas. They begin to enter the state in late September and are usually absent by the last of April. There are no nesting records for the state.

CHESTNUT-COLLARED LONGSPUR
Calcarius ornatus

5½—6½" long. Color pattern of sexes similar in winter.

Adult male in summer: Underparts black; side of head with white and black stripes; throat white; hind neck chestnut rufous; rest of upperparts streaked; shoulder patch black; tail feathers, except middle pair, white at base, two or three lateral feathers entirely white. *Adult male in winter:* Similar, but black and chestnut of head and underparts obscured or concealed by brownish or buffy tips to feathers. *Adult female in summer:* Grayish buffy brown, streaked above and sometimes below. *Adult female in winter:* Colors less distinct and more blended. Since these birds almost invariably range apart from other species of birds, sex identification is simplified.

DISTRIBUTION. Formerly, the author found the Chestnut-collared Longspur quite common and widely distributed throughout the state in migration and in the southern part throughout the winter. It appears to be far less numerous in recent years. Its winter range, for the most part, is below 7,000 feet. Like the McCown's, the Chestnut-collared is an open grassland dweller. It arrives in late September and is out of the state by late April. In fact, movements and winter range of the two species coincide rather closely. There are no nesting records for the state.

SNOW BUNTING
Plectrophenax nivalis

6—7″ long. Color pattern of sexes similar.

These hardy little birds are often referred to as "Snowflakes" in the northeastern and midwestern states, where great flocks may be seen in winter, swirling like snow flurries over snow-covered ground. Although in flight Snow Buntings appear almost white, by midwinter the white breeding plumage has become largely tinged with chestnut or grayish. In early spring these vivacious birds leisurely head for their arctic summer range, breeding farther north than most other land-dwelling birds. *Adult male in winter:* Bill yellow with dusky tip; upperparts, crown, neck, and sides of head masked with chestnut; back rusty and black; outer-wing coverts white; underparts white except rusty breast band. *Adult female in winter:* Similar to male, but crown blackish; back tinged with rusty or grayish.

DISTRIBUTION. Although occurring in Kansas and Colorado, Snow Buntings are only casual winter visitors in New Mexico. Krehbiel has a record for Clayton, and it is recorded: "North central New Mexico (Las Vegas)," *A.O.U. Check-list.* Other observers in the northeastern part of the state occasionally may have opportunity to add this distinguished visitor to their lists.

APPENDIXES

RARE and STRAY BIRDS

THE FOLLOWING LIST consists of 35 very rare or stray birds which have been recorded—without nesting records—in the state up to June 1958, but not in sufficient numbers to justify inclusion in the general text. However, some are listed in the Flyway Records and in Christmas Counts. The main object in listing these "strays" is to encourage observers to watch for them. More intensive field work no doubt eventually will result in others being added to the list.

SPECIES	LOCATION	OBSERVER	DATE
Red-throated Loon	Bitter Lake	Vester Montgomery	Nov. 23, 1957
Red-necked Grebe	" "	" "	Dec. 19, 1952
" "	" "	" "	Feb. 12, 1955
Magnificent Frigate Bird (Formerly Man-o'-War Bird)	" "	Refuge Personnel	Oct. 4, 1955
Little Blue Heron	Bosque Refuge	Raymond J. Fleetwood	Apr. 19, 1954
" " "	" "	" " "	July 6, 1955
" " "	Bitter Lake	Vester Montgomery	Sept., 1955
Louisiana Heron	Bosque Refuge	Raymond J. Fleetwood	Apr., 1955
" "	Bitter Lake	Vester Montgomery	June, 1955
" "	" "	" "	Sept., 1955
Yellow-crowned Night Heron	Near Clayton	A. J. Krehbiel & W. W. Cook	Aug. 10, 1953
Trumpeter Swan	Mesilla Park	D. E. Merrill	Nov., 1931
European Widgeon	Near Clayton	A. J. Krehbiel & W. W. Cook	Apr. 10, 1954
Barrow's Goldeneye	Bitter Lake	Christmas Count	Dec. 22, 1956
" "	Near Clayton	Krehbiel, Cook, & Snoeberger	Feb. 23, 1957
Surf Scoter	Los Lunas	William S. Huey	Oct. 31, 1959
Purple Gallinule	Near Caprock	Sam Tanner	June 12, 1953
" "	Roswell	W. S. Ricker & V. Montgomery	May 10, 1958
Knot	Near Clayton	A. J. Krehbiel & W. W. Cook	Aug. 12, 1954
Buff-breasted Sandpiper	" "	" " "	May 19, 1957
Long-tailed Jaeger	Bosque Refuge	Sam Turner & Charles R. Hays	Sept. 24, 1957
Laughing Gull	Old Ft. Wingate	Elliott Coues	June, 1864
Heermann's Gull	Pinos Altos	R. T. Kellogg	May 20, 1919

SPECIES	LOCATION	OBSERVER	DATE
Sabine's Gull	Albuquerque	F. J. Birtwell	Oct. 7, 1900
" "	Lake McMillan	Bruce Harris	Nov. 11, 1957
Ridgway's Whip-poor-will	Guadalupe Canyon,		
	Hidalgo County	R. F. Johnston & J. W. Hardy	June 22, 1958
Chimney Swift	Bosque Refuge	Raymond J. Fleetwood	Apr. 20, 1952
Pileated Woodpecker	" "	Thomas L. Davis	Apr. 30, 1954
" "	S.W. New Mexico	A.O.U. Check-list, 5th Ed.	
Prothonotary Warbler	Bosque Refuge	Raymond J. Fleetwood	Sept. 9, 1953
" "	Anthony	Lena McBee & Mary Belle Keefer	May 6, 1953
Worm-eating Warbler	Las Cruces	R. F. Johnston	Sept. 14, 1956
Nashville Warbler	Anthony	Lena McBee & Mary Belle Keefer	Sept. 9, 1948
" "	"	" " " " " "	Sept. 3, 1953
" "	Roswell	Vester Montgomery	Feb., 1956
Black-throated Green Warbler	Anthony	A. R. Phillips	Nov. 1, 1954
" " " "	Roswell	Vester Montgomery	Oct. 21, 1956
" " " "	Bernardo	John N. Durrie	Oct., 1958
Hermit Warbler	Animas Mts.	E. A. Goldman	Aug. 3, 1908
" "	Reserve	Peet Collection	Sept. 13, 1927
" "	Roswell	Vester Montgomery	May 8, 1955
Blackburnian Warbler	Ft. Bayard	F. Stephens	Sept., 1886
Blackpoll Warbler	Clayton	A. J. Krehbiel	Oct. 3, 1954
" "	Roswell	Vester Montgomery	May, 1954
" "	Ft. Webster	A.O.U. Check-list, 5th Ed.	
Palm Warbler	White Sands		
	Nat'l Mon.	A. E. Borell	1935
" "	Bosque Refuge	Raymond J. Fleetwood	May 16, 1953
Ovenbird	Roswell	Vester Montgomery	Aug. 31, 1956
"	"	" "	Sept. 9, 1956
Kentucky Warbler	Carlsbad Caverns	Paul Spangler	Apr. 10, 1957
Hooded Warbler	Roswell	Vester Montgomery	Apr. 6, 1953
" "	"	" "	Apr. 11, 1953
Rusty Blackbird	"	" "	Nov. 10, 1956
Rose-breasted Grosbeak	Las Cruces	K. Valentine	June 4, 1941
" " "	Faywood	R. T. Kellogg	May 2, 1923
" " "	Silver City	C. L. Snyder	July 4, 1951
" " "	Socorro	Raymond J. Fleetwood	May 18, 1958
Indigo Bunting	Anthony	Lena McBee	May 10, 1953
" "	Silver City	C. L. Snyder	May 18, 1955
" "	Carlsbad	J. Stokley Ligon	May 23, 1957
" "	Los Alamos	Leslie G. Hawkins	May 18, 1958
Lapland Longspur	New Mexico	A.O.U. Check-list, 5th Ed.	

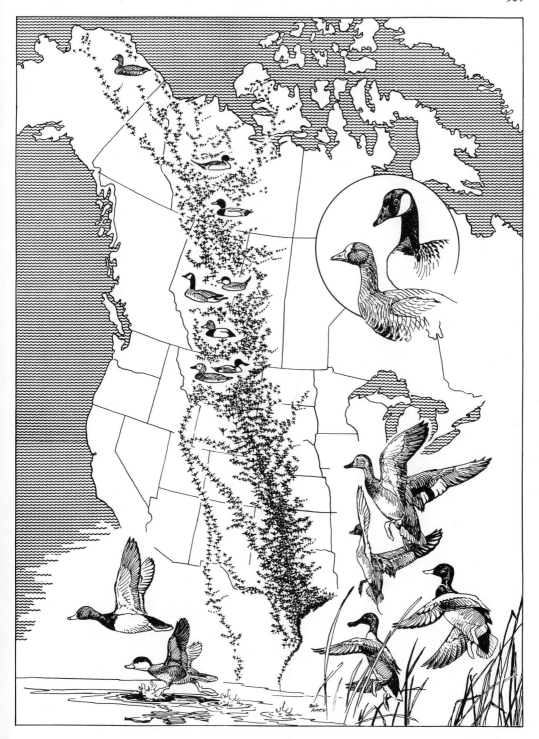

CENTRAL FLYWAY
Courtesy of U.S. Fish & Wildlife Service

FLYWAY RECORDS

NEW MEXICO is favored by three rather distinctive migratory bird passways, two of which, the Rio Grande and the Pecos Valleys, serve as offshoots of the main Central Flyway which sweeps across the northeast corner of the state. The north-south courses of the Rio Grande and the Pecos Rivers constitute a favorable route utilized by great numbers of migrants into and through the state, as well as suitable habitat for resident and summer dwellers.

Records for the Bosque del Apache National Wildlife Refuge, near Socorro, in the Rio Grande Valley, and those for the Roswell–Bitter Lake area in the Pecos Valley, and the Clayton area, which taps the main Central Flyway in the northeastern part of the state are here given for ready reference. The records cited for each area are the result of reporting by competent observers of the United States Fish and Wildlife Service and of individuals and cooperating teams over a period of years. Some additions were made by the author, while in some instances because of insufficient proof or errors in identification a few species were deleted from the lists. In view of the intensive field work which has been done, it may be assumed that these and other records, including Christmas Counts, recorded at key areas in the state (see Bird Watching) cover practically every species that is resident or that occurs in the state. This conclusion, however, does not rule out the possibility that others may in time be added as strays or even as breeders. Since the status of the different species is given in the general text, no reference is made to scarcity or abundance in the sub-flyway lists. However, names of species known to nest in these areas are preceded by an asterisk. Fortunately, the three sub-flyway observation points are easily accessible to those wishing to take advantage of them.

RIO GRANDE VALLEY
SUB-FLYWAY

The Rio Grande Valley is an important highway for great numbers as well as many species of birds. As a migratory bird sub-flyway it functions as a complement to the main Central Migratory Bird Flyway which bypasses New Mexico to the eastward. (See Flyway map.) The Bosque del Apache Refuge occupies a strategic place in the valley, not only for migrants of many kinds, but as a breeding place for a great number. The area, with its favorable natural setting plus a vast amount of development work conducted under the able administration of the United States Fish and Wildlife Service, has become one of the most important bird sanctuaries in the entire Southwest. As time passes and drainage developments eliminate more and more wetlands, marshes, and ponds, its value will be even greater. The following information relative to the refuge and the bird recordings is taken from the official records of the Fish and Wildlife Service. The list contains 264 species, the greatest number yet recorded at a single station in the state.

"The Bosque del Apache (woods of the Apaches) National Wildlife Refuge, established in 1937, is located on the Rio Grande in central New Mexico approximately 20 miles south of the city of Socorro. It contains about 57,000 acres, of which 13,500 acres are river bottom lands originally covered with saltcedar, cottonwood, willow and native shrubs. Extending from the bottomlands and up to the mountainous terrain on either side, the mesas are covered with creosote bush, sand sage, and tornillo. Several arroyos dissect the west mesa, and in the larger ones are found Apache-plume, Mormon-tea, brickell-bush, squawbrush, four-winged salt-bush, small-leaved sumac, burrobrush and juniper. This area, the only development of its kind on the entire river, administered by the Fish and Wildlife Service, U.S. Department of the Interior, is one unit in the chain of refuges of the Central Flyway extending from Canada to Mexico.

"Between the river and U.S. Highway 85, in an otherwise dry river bottom, approximately 5,500 acres of impoundments and ponds have been developed. This included the construction of dikes, canals, and water-control structures, and the removal of obnoxious trees and shrubs. Several of the impoundment units will be used for the production of cultivated crops which are utilized by ducks, geese and cranes. Ten miles of the Rio Grande lie within the refuge and are the source of water used on the area for wildlife management purposes.

"The following bird list contains 264 species which represent observations made by the refuge staff during the period 1940 through November 1957. This list, using species names, generally is in accord with the Fifth A.O.U. Check-List. When new names are sufficiently different, the former name is added in parentheses."

BOSQUE DEL APACHE

NATIONAL WILDLIFE REFUGE

CHECK-LIST OF BIRDS

(Names of birds known to nest
preceded by an asterisk)

Common Loon
Horned Grebe
Eared Grebe
Western Grebe
*Pied-billed Grebe
White Pelican
*Double-crested
  Cormorant
Great Blue Heron
*Common Egret
*Snowy Egret
Louisiana Heron
Little Blue Heron
*Green Heron
*Black-crowned
  Night Heron
*American Bittern
*Least Bittern
Wood Ibis
White-faced Ibis
Whistling Swan
Canada Goose
White-fronted Goose
Snow Goose
Blue Goose
*Mallard
*Mexican Duck
Black Duck

*Gadwall
Pintail
*Green-winged Teal
*Blue-winged Teal
*Cinnamon Teal
*American Widgeon
  (Baldpate)
*Shoveler
Wood Duck
*Redhead
Ring-necked Duck
*Canvasback
Lesser Scaup
Common Goldeneye
Bufflehead
White-winged Scoter
*Ruddy Duck
Hooded Merganser
Common Merganser
Red-breasted Merganser
Turkey Vulture
Mississippi Kite
Goshawk
Sharp-shinned Hawk
Cooper's Hawk
Red-tailed Hawk
*Swainson's Hawk
Rough-legged Hawk

Ferruginous Hawk
Golden Eagle
Bald Eagle
*Marsh Hawk
Osprey
Prairie Falcon
Peregrine Falcon
Pigeon Hawk
*Sparrow Hawk
*Scaled Quail
*Gambel's Quail
*Ring-necked Pheasant
Sandhill Crane
*Virginia Rail
*Sora
*Common Gallinule
*American Coot
*Snowy Plover
Ringed Plover
Upland Plover
Mountain Plover
*Killdeer
American Golden Plover
Black-bellied Plover
Common Snipe
Long-billed Curlew
Whimbrel
*Spotted Sandpiper
Solitary Sandpiper
Willet
Greater Yellowlegs
Lesser Yellowlegs
Pectoral Sandpiper
White-rumped
  Sandpiper
Baird's Sandpiper
Least Sandpiper
Dowitcher
Western Sandpiper
Marbled Godwit
*American Avocet
*Black-necked Stilt
Wilson's Phalarope
Northern Phalarope
Long-tailed Jaeger
Ring-billed Gull
Franklin's Gull
Herring Gull
Bonaparte's Gull
Forster's Tern
Common Tern
Least Tern
Black Tern
Band-tailed Pigeon
*Mourning Dove
White-winged Dove

Ground Dove
Inca Dove
*Yellow-billed Cuckoo
*Roadrunner
Barn Owl
*Screech Owl
*Great Horned Owl
*Burrowing Owl
Long-eared Owl
Short-eared Owl
Poor-will
Common Nighthawk
*Lesser Nighthawk
Chimney Swift
White-throated Swift
Black-chinned
  Hummingbird
Broad-tailed
  Hummingbird
Rufous Hummingbird
Belted Kingfisher
Yellow-shafted Flicker
*Red-shafted Flicker
Pileated Woodpecker
Red-headed Woodpecker
Yellow-bellied Sapsucker
*Hairy Woodpecker
Williamson's Sapsucker
*Ladder-backed
  Woodpecker
Eastern Kingbird
*Western Kingbird
Cassin's Kingbird
Scissor-tailed Flycatcher
*Ash-throated Flycatcher
Eastern Phoebe
*Black Phoebe
*Say's Phoebe
Traill's Flycatcher
Dusky Flycatcher
Gray Flycatcher
Western Flycatcher
Olive-sided Flycatcher
*Western Wood Pewee
*Vermilion Flycatcher
*Horned Lark
Violet-green Swallow
*Tree Swallow
*Bank Swallow
Rough-winged Swallow
*Barn Swallow
*Cliff Swallow
Purple Martin
Steller's Jay
Scrub Jay
Black-billed Magpie

Common Raven
Common Crow
Pinyon Jay
Mountain Chickadee
Plain Titmouse
*Verdin
Bushtit
White-breasted
    Nuthatch
Red-breasted Nuthatch
Brown Creeper
House Wren
Winter Wren
Bewick's Wren
Carolina Wren
*Cactus Wren
Long-billed Marsh Wren
*Canyon Wren
*Rock Wren
*Mockingbird
Brown Thrasher
*Crissal Thrasher
Sage Thrasher
*Robin
Hermit Thrush
Veery
*Western Bluebird
Mountain Bluebird
Townsend's Solitaire
Blue-gray Gnatcatcher
Black-tailed Gnatcatcher
Golden-crowned Kinglet
Ruby-crowned Kinglet
Water Pipit
*Phainopepla
Cedar Waxwing
*Loggerhead Shrike
Starling
*Bell's Vireo
*Solitary Vireo
Warbling Vireo
Prothonotary Warbler
Orange-crowned Warbler
Virginia's Warbler
*Lucy's Warbler
*Yellow Warbler
Myrtle Warbler
Palm Warbler
Audubon's Warbler
Black-throated Gray
    Warbler
Northern Waterthrush
MacGillivray's Warbler
*Yellowthroat

*Yellow-breasted Chat
Wilson's Warbler
American Redstart
*House Sparrow
Eastern Meadowlark
    (Rio Grande)
*Western Meadowlark
Yellow-headed Blackbird
*Redwinged Blackbird
*Bullock's Oriole
Brewer's Blackbird
*Boat-tailed Grackle
*Brown-headed Cowbird
*Western Tanager
Bobolink
Summer Tanager
Hepatic Tanager
Pyrrhuloxia
*Black-headed Grosbeak
*Blue Grosbeak
Lazuli Bunting
Dickcissel
Evening Grosbeak
*House Finch
Pine Siskin
American Goldfinch
*Lesser Goldfinch
Lawrence's Goldfinch
Green-tailed Towhee
*Rufous-sided Towhee
*Brown Towhee
Lark Bunting
Savannah Sparrow
Vesper Sparrow
*Lark Sparrow
Rufous-crowned Sparrow
*Black-throated Sparrow
Sage Sparrow
Oregon Junco
Slate-colored Junco
Gray-headed Junco
Mexican Junco
    (Red-backed)
*Chipping Sparrow
Brewer's Sparrow
White-crowned Sparrow
Tree Sparrow
Lincoln's Sparrow
Fox Sparrow
Swamp Sparrow
Song Sparrow
McCown's Longspur
Chestnut-collared
    Longspur

BOSQUE DEL APACHE
NATIONAL WILDLIFE REFUGE
CHRISTMAS BIRD COUNT
DECEMBER 26, 1953

Count area, refuge and adjacent bottom lands. 6 A.M. to 5 P.M. Clear with overcast sky in p.m. Temperature 10 to 51°; ponds frozen but some drainage ditches open. Total party hours 21 (6 on foot, 15 by car). Total party miles 67 (5 on foot, 62 by car). Elevation about 4,550 feet. (See *Audubon Field Notes*, April 1954, p. 203.)

Pied-billed Grebe	3
Great Blue Heron	36
Black-crowned Night Heron	14
Canada Goose	975
Snow Goose	300
Blue Goose	4
Mallard	10,585
Gadwall	125
American Widgeon	24
Pintail	8,658
Green-winged Teal	288
Shoveler	165
Redhead	6
Ring-necked Duck	12
Common Goldeneye	1
Bufflehead	9
Hooded Merganser	5
Common Merganser	628
Cooper's Hawk	5
Red-tailed Hawk	5
Rough-legged Hawk	3
Golden Eagle	10
Bald Eagle	2
Marsh Hawk	20
Sparrow Hawk	10
Gambel's Quail (5 coveys)	224
Ring-necked Pheasant	2
Sandhill Crane	6
Virginia Rail	2
Sora	1
American Coot	48
Killdeer	2
Common Snipe	1
Least Sandpiper	4
Mourning Dove	56
Roadrunner	3
Barn Owl	1
Great Horned Owl	3
Belted Kingfisher	1
Red-shafted Flicker	38
Hairy Woodpecker	1
Ladder-backed Woodpecker	14

Say's Phoebe	9
Scrub Jay	1
Black-billed Magpie	5
Mountain Chickadee	2
White-breasted Nuthatch	2
House Wren	1
Bewick's Wren	3
Long-billed Marsh Wren	1
Crissal Thrasher	3
Western Bluebird	17
Ruby-crowned Kinglet	2
Water Pipit	4
Loggerhead Shrike	15
Starling	420
Audubon's Warbler	7
House Sparrow	25
Western Meadowlark	34
Yellow-headed Blackbird	30
Redwinged Blackbird	35,680
Brewer's Blackbird	1,250
Boat-tailed Grackle	18
House Finch	32
Pine Siskin	17
American Goldfinch	39
Green-tailed Towhee	1
Rufous-sided Towhee	4
Brown Towhee (Canyon)	2
Savannah Sparrow	8
Vesper Sparrow	97
Sage Sparrow	5
Oregon Junco	165
White-crowned Sparrow (Gambel's)	386
Swamp Sparrow	2
Song Sparrow	149

Total 76 species, about 60,736 individuals. Raymond J. Fleetwood (Compiler), Homer S. Musgrave, F. J. Freeman.

PECOS VALLEY SUB-FLYWAY

The Pecos Valley, like the Rio Grande Valley, is not only an important migratory bird thoroughfare, but it, too, has a liberal share of breeding species, both resident and summer dwellers. For the following list of 240 species, through 1957, the author is indebted to Vester Montgomery and James H. Sikes, of Roswell. The observation area is centered about Roswell, and includes a segment of the Pecos River, flanked by salt cedar (tamarisk) bottomland jungles, and the Bitter Lake National Wildlife Refuge with its extensive lakes, ponds, and marshes. (See Bitter Lake Refuge Bird Watching Section.) The adjacent uplands are, for the most part, open mesa and hill lands.

ROSWELL—BITTER LAKE AREA
CHECK-LIST OF BIRDS

(Names of birds known to nest
preceded by an asterisk)

Common Loon	*Turkey Vulture
Red-necked Grebe	Sharp-shinned Hawk
Horned Grebe	Cooper's Hawk
Eared Grebe	*Red-tailed Hawk
Western Grebe	*Swainson's Hawk
*Pied-billed Grebe	Rough-legged Hawk
White Pelican	Ferruginous Hawk
*Double-crested	Harris' Hawk
Cormorant	Golden Eagle
Magnificent Frigate Bird	Bald Eagle
(Formerly Man-o'-War)	*Marsh Hawk
*Great Blue Heron	Osprey
*Common Egret	Prairie Falcon
*Snowy Egret	Peregrine Falcon
Louisiana Heron	Pigeon Hawk
Little Blue Heron	*Sparrow Hawk
*Green Heron	Lesser Prairie Chicken
*Black-crowned Night Heron	*Bobwhite Quail
*American Bittern	*Scaled Quail
*Least Bittern	*Ring-necked Pheasant
White-faced Ibis	Sandhill Crane
Whistling Swan	*Virginia Rail
Canada Goose	Sora
White-fronted Goose	Common Gallinule
Snow Goose	*American Coot
Blue Goose	*Snowy Plover
*Mallard	Semipalmated Plover
*Mexican Duck	*Mountain Plover
Gadwall	Upland Plover
American Widgeon	American Golden Plover
*Pintail	Black-bellied Plover
Green-winged Teal	Common Snipe
*Blue-winged Teal	Long-billed Curlew
*Cinnamon Teal	Whimbrel
*Shoveler	Spotted Sandpiper
Wood Duck	Solitary Sandpiper
Redhead	Willet
Ring-necked Duck	Greater Yellowlegs
Canvasback	Lesser Yellowlegs
Lesser Scaup	Pectoral Sandpiper
Common Goldeneye	White-rumped Sandpiper
Bufflehead	Baird's Sandpiper
White-winged Scoter	Least Sandpiper
*Ruddy Duck	Long-billed Dowitcher
Hooded Merganser	Stilt Sandpiper
Common Merganser	Western Sandpiper
Red-breasted Merganser	Marbled Godwit

Sanderling
*American Avocet
*Black-necked Stilt
Wilson's Phalarope
Ring-billed Gull
Franklin's Gull
Sabine's Gull
Forster's Tern
*Least Tern
Black Tern
*Mourning Dove
*Yellow-billed Cuckoo
*Roadrunner
*Barn Owl
*Screech Owl
Flammulated Owl
*Great Horned Owl
*Burrowing Owl
Long-eared Owl
Short-eared Owl
Saw-whet Owl
Common Nighthawk
*Lesser Nighthawk
*Black-chinned
    Hummingbird
Broad-tailed
    Hummingbird
Rufous Hummingbird
Belted Kingfisher
*Red-shafted Flicker
Red-headed Woodpecker
Yellow-bellied Sapsucker
Hairy Woodpecker
*Ladder-backed (Cactus)
    Woodpecker
*Western Kingbird
Cassin's Kingbird
*Scissor-tailed Flycatcher
*Ash-throated Flycatcher
*Black Phoebe
*Say's Phoebe
Western Flycatcher
Western Wood Pewee
Olive-sided Flycatcher
*Vermilion Flycatcher
Tree Swallow
Bank Swallow
Rough-winged Swallow
*Barn Swallow
*Cliff Swallow
Purple Martin
*Horned Lark
Blue Jay
Steller's Jay
Scrub Jay
*White-necked Raven
Pinyon Jay
Mountain Chickadee

Red-breasted Nuthatch
Brown Creeper
House Wren
Winter Wren
Bewick's Wren
Cactus Wren
Long-billed Marsh Wren
*Rock Wren
Carolina Wren
*Mockingbird
Catbird
*Curve-billed Thrasher
Sage Thrasher
Robin
Hermit Thrush
Western Bluebird
Mountain Bluebird
Townsend's Solitaire
Blue-gray Gnatcatcher
Golden-crowned Kinglet
Ruby-crowned Kinglet
Water Pipit
Cedar Waxwing
Northern Shrike
*Loggerhead Shrike
Starling
Gray Vireo
Solitary Vireo
Warbling Vireo
Orange-crowned Warbler
Virginia's Warbler
*Yellow Warbler
Black-throated Blue
    Warbler
Myrtle Warbler
Audubon's Warbler
Black-throated Gray
    Warbler
Townsend's Warbler
Hermit Warbler
Northern Waterthrush
MacGillivray's Warbler
*Yellowthroat
Yellow-breasted Chat
Wilson's Warbler
American Redstart
Hooded Warbler
*House Sparrow
Eastern Meadowlark
*Western Meadowlark
Yellow-headed Blackbird
*Redwinged Blackbird
*Bullock's Oriole
Brewer's Blackbird
*Boat-tailed Grackle
*Brown-headed Cowbird
Western Tanager
Hepatic Tanager

*Summer Tanager
Scarlet Tanager
Black-headed Grosbeak
*Blue Grosbeak
Rose-breasted Grosbeak
Cassin's Finch
*House Finch
Pine Siskin
Common Goldfinch
*Lesser Goldfinch
Green-tailed Towhee
Rufous-sided Towhee
Brown (Canyon) Towhee
Lark Bunting
Savannah Sparrow
Grasshopper Sparrow
Baird's Sparrow
Vesper Sparrow

LeConte's Sparrow
*Lark Sparrow
*Cassin's Sparrow
Sage Sparrow
Slate-colored Junco
Oregon Junco
Gray-headed Junco
Tree Sparrow
Chipping Sparrow
Clay-colored Sparrow
Brewer's Sparrow
White-crowned Sparrow
White-throated Sparrow
Lincoln's Sparrow
Swamp Sparrow
Song Sparrow
Chestnut-collared
    Longspur

ROSWELL—BITTER LAKE AREA

CHRISTMAS BIRD COUNT

JANUARY 3, 1954

6 A.M. to 6:30 P.M. Clear. Temperature 18 to 60°; impoundments and ponds mostly frozen. Total party hours 82. Total party miles 92 (10 on foot, 82 by car). Elevation around 3,600 feet. (See *Audubon Field Notes*, April 1954, p. 203.)

Pied-billed Grebe	8
Great Blue Heron	20
American Egret	1
Black-crowned Night Heron	13
American Bittern	3
Whistling Swan	1
Canada Goose	105
Snow Goose	3
Mallard	3,406
Gadwall	154
American Widgeon	14,115
Pintail	6,523
Green-winged Teal	25
Shoveler	797
Redhead	50
Ring-necked Duck	308
Lesser Scaup	29
Common Goldeneye	26
Bufflehead	37
Ruddy Duck	97
Hooded Merganser	4
Common Merganser	154
Red-breasted Merganser	2
Cooper's Hawk	2

Red-tailed Hawk	3
Swainson's Hawk	1
Rough-legged Hawk	4
Ferruginous Hawk	4
Golden Eagle	2
Marsh Hawk	17
Pigeon Hawk	2
Sparrow Hawk	3
Scaled Quail	48
Sandhill Crane	6,763
Coot	1,855
Killdeer	6
Common Snipe	3
Greater Yellowlegs	16
Least Sandpiper	12
Herring Gull	1
Ring-billed Gull	200
Mourning Dove	4
Roadrunner	2
Horned Owl	2
Burrowing Owl	1
Short-eared Owl	2
Belted Kingfisher	2
Red-shafted Flicker	35
Red-headed Woodpecker	2
Yellow-bellied Sapsucker	1
Say's Phoebe	5
Horned Lark	13
Scrub Jay	4
Red-breasted Nuthatch	2
Bewick's Wren	2
Long-billed Marsh Wren	10
Sage Thrasher	1
Robin	1
Ruby-crowned Kinglet	1
Water Pipit	307
Loggerhead Shrike	11
Starling	27
Audubon's Warbler	1
House Sparrow (estimate)	1,500
Western Meadowlark	35
Redwinged Blackbird	22
Brewer's Blackbird (estimate)	30,000
Brown-headed Cowbird	120
Cardinal (at feeding station)	1
House Finch	3
American Goldfinch	28
Savannah Sparrow	9
LeConte's Sparrow	10
Sage Sparrow	52
Slate-colored Junco	1
Oregon Junco (Pink-sided 34)	101
White-crowned Sparrow (Gambel's)	380
White-throated Sparrow	1
Lincoln's Sparrow	9
Swamp Sparrow	3
Song Sparrow	109

Total 81 species (2 additional subspecies), about 67,645 individuals. Raymond J. Fleetwood (Compiler); Ray H. Hunter, Fish and Wildlife Service; Roe E. Meyer, Fish and Wildlife Service; Mr. and Mrs. F. J. Freeman, Allen E. Anderson, Marion Embrey, Vester Montgomery, James E. Sikes, D. L. Boggs, R. A. Garrett, Sam E. Tanner.

HIGH PLAINS SUB-FLYWAY

Clayton, elevation 5,050 feet, in the extreme northeastern part of the state, represents the hub from which the following list of birds has been recorded. The author is indebted to Adolf J. Krehbiel and W. W. Cook, of Clayton, for this list. The records up to and through 1957 represent recordings over a period of several years, in the stream, canyon, plain, and mesa country adjacent to Clayton and are also applicable to adjacent portions of southeastern Colorado, western Oklahoma, and the Texas Panhandle. The Clayton observation area is of special interest because of the fact that some migrants enter from and return to the east while the main movement is south and to the southeast over the high plains. (See Flyway Map.) A total of 238 species has been recorded. Names of breeding birds listed, are preceded by an asterisk.

CLAYTON AREA
CHECK-LIST OF BIRDS

Common Loon	*Mallard
Red-throated Loon	*Gadwall
Horned Grebe	European Widgeon
Eared Grebe	American Widgeon
Western Grebe	Pintail
Pied-billed Grebe	Green-winged Teal
White Pelican	*Cinnamon Teal
Double-crested Cormorant	*Blue-winged Teal
*Great Blue Heron	*Shoveler
Little Blue Heron	Wood Duck
Green Heron	Redhead
Snowy Egret	Ring-necked Duck
Black-crowned Night Heron	Canvasback
Yellow-crowned Night Heron	Greater Scaup
Whistling Swan	Lesser Scaup
Canada Goose	Common Goldeneye
Snow Goose	Barrow's Goldeneye

Buffllehead
White-winged Scoter
Common Scoter
*Ruddy Duck
Common Merganser
*Turkey Vulture
Mississippi Kite
Sharp-shinned Hawk
Cooper's Hawk
*Red-tailed Hawk
*Swainson's Hawk
Rough-legged Hawk
*Ferruginous Hawk
*Golden Eagle
Bald Eagle
*Marsh Hawk
Osprey
Prairie Falcon
Peregrine Falcon
Pigeon Hawk
*Sparrow Hawk
*Bobwhite
*Scaled Quail
Sandhill Crane
*American Coot
Semipalmated Plover
*Mountain Plover
*Killdeer
Black-bellied Plover
*Common Snipe
*Long-billed Curlew
Upland Plover
*Spotted Sandpiper
Solitary Sandpiper
Knot
Willet
White-rumped Sandpiper
Greater Yellowlegs
Lesser Yellowlegs
Pectoral Sandpiper
Baird's Sandpiper
Least Sandpiper
Long-billed Dowitcher
Stilt Sandpiper
Semipalmated Sandpiper
Western Sandpiper
Buff-breasted Sandpiper
Marbled Godwit
Sanderling
*American Avocet
*Black-necked Stilt
Wilson's Phalarope
Northern Phalarope
Western Gull
Herring Gull
Ring-billed Gull
Franklin's Gull
Black Tern

*Mourning Dove
*Rock Dove
*Yellow-billed Cuckoo
*Roadrunner
Barn Owl
*Horned Owl
*Burrowing Owl
Spotted Owl
Short-eared Owl
Saw-whet Owl
*Common Nighthawk
Black-chinned
   Hummingbird
Broad-tailed
   Hummingbird
Rufous Hummingbird
*Belted Kingfisher
Yellow-shafted Flicker
*Red-shafted Flicker
*Red-headed Woodpecker
*Lewis' Woodpecker
Yellow-bellied Sapsucker
Williamson's Sapsucker
Hairy Woodpecker
Downy Woodpecker
*Ladder-backed
   Woodpecker
*Eastern Kingbird
*Western Kingbird
Cassin's Kingbird
Scissor-tailed Flycatcher
*Great Crested Flycatcher
Ash-throated Flycatcher
Eastern Phoebe
*Say's Phoebe
Traill's Flycatcher
Least Flycatcher
Western Flycatcher
Western Wood Peewee
Hammond's Flycatcher
Olive-sided Flycatcher
Vermilion Flycatcher
*Horned Lark
Rough-winged Swallow
*Barn Swallow
*Cliff Swallow
*Scrub Jay
*Magpie
*Common Raven
*White-necked Raven
*Common Crow
Clark's Nutcracker
Black-capped Chickadee
Mountain Chickadee
*Common Bushtit
Red-breasted Nuthatch
Pygmy Nuthatch
Brown Creeper

House Wren
Winter Wren
Bewick's Wren
Canyon Wren
*Rock Wren
*Mockingbird
Catbird
Brown Thrasher
Sage Thrasher
*Robin
Hermit Thrush
Swainson's Thrush
Eastern Bluebird
Western Bluebird
Mountain Bluebird
Townsend's Solitaire
Blue-gray Gnatcatcher
Ruby-crowned Kinglet
Golden-crowned Kinglet
Water Pipit
Sprague's Pipit
Northern Shrike
*Loggerhead Shrike
*Starling
Solitary Vireo
Warbling Vireo
Black-and-white Warbler
Prothonotary Warbler
Orange-crowned Warbler
Virginia's Warbler
Yellow Warbler
Audubon's Warbler
Black-throated Gray
   Warbler
Townsend's Warbler
Hermit Warbler
Grace's Warbler
Blackpoll Warbler
Northern Waterthrush
MacGillivray's Warbler
Yellowthroat
Yellow-breasted Chat
Wilson's Warbler
American Redstart
Bobolink
*Western Meadowlark

Yellow-headed Blackbird
*Redwinged Blackbird
*Bullock's Oriole
Brewer's Blackbird
Boat-tailed Grackle
*Common Grackle
*Brown-headed Cowbird
Western Tanager
Summer Tanager
Black-headed Grosbeak
*Blue Grosbeak
Indigo Bunting
*Lazuli Bunting
Dickcissel
Cassin's Finch
*House Finch
Pine Siskin
American Goldfinch
Lesser Goldfinch
White-winged Crossbill
*Green-tailed Towhee
*Rufous-sided Towhee
*Canyon Towhee
*Lark Bunting
Savannah Sparrow
Grasshopper Sparrow
Baird's Sparrow
*Vesper Sparrow
*Lark Sparrow
Rufous-crowned Sparrow
*Cassin's Sparrow
White-winged Junco
Slate-colored Junco
Gray-headed Junco
Tree Sparrow
Chipping Sparrow
Clay-colored Sparrow
Brewer's Sparrow
Harris' Sparrow
White-crowned Sparrow
Fox Sparrow
Lincoln's Sparrow
Song Sparrow
McCown's Longspur
Chestnut-collared Longspur
Snow Bunting

CLAYTON AREA

CHRISTMAS BIRD COUNT

DECEMBER 24, 1955

9:30 A.M. to 5:30 P.M. Clear. Temperature 55 to 77°. Total party hours, 11. Total party miles, 67 (7 on foot, 60 by car). Elevation 5,050 feet.

Mallard	26
Red-tailed Hawk	1
Rough-legged Hawk	1
Ferruginous Hawk	1
Golden Eagle	1
Bald Eagle	1
Marsh Hawk	2
Prairie Falcon	3
Sparrow Hawk	3
Scaled Quail	282
Ring-necked Pheasant	2
Killdeer	2
Mourning Dove	24
Yellow-shafted Flicker	1
Red-shafted Flicker	6
Ladder-backed Woodpecker	9
Horned Lark	260
Black-billed Magpie	41
Brown Creeper	1
Mockingbird	2
Robin	51
Townsend's Solitaire	8
Loggerhead Shrike	5
Starling	121
House Sparrow	200
Western Meadowlark	51
Redwinged Blackbird	159
Brown-headed Cowbird	40
Pine Siskin	40
Rufous-sided Towhee	1
Brown Towhee	2
Slate-colored Junco	4
Oregon Junco	64
Tree Sparrow	26
Harris' Sparrow	22
White-crowned Sparrow	180
Fox Sparrow	7
Song Sparrow	21

Total 38 species, about 1,671 individuals. (Seen count period: Canada Goose, Bufflehead Duck, Horned Owl, Red-headed Woodpecker, Downy Woodpecker, Canyon Wren, Brown Thrasher, Chestnut-collared Longspur.) W. W. Cook, A. J. Krehbiel (Compiler), P. W. Shoeberger.

THE ENTRANCE TO CARLSBAD CAVERNS, FREQUENTED BY CANYON AND ROCK WRENS
Photograph by Herman Hemler.

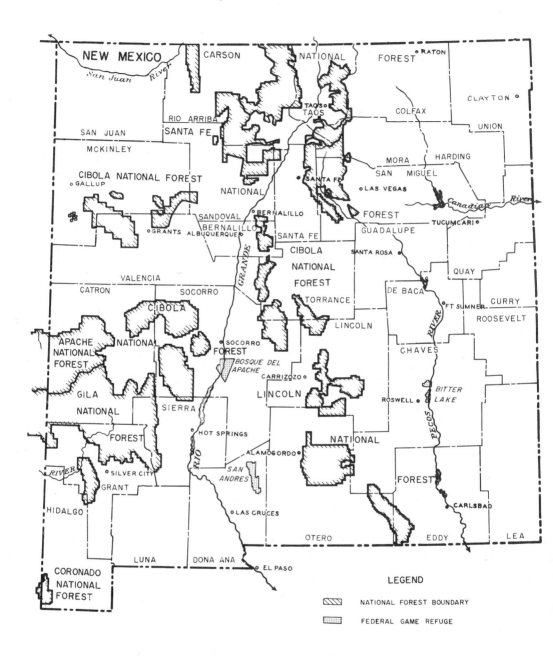

NATIONAL FORESTS IN NEW MEXICO
Courtesy of U.S. Forest Service

BIRD WATCHING

IN RECENT YEARS bird finding and watching have become national pursuits.* The growing popularity of this wholesome outdoor recreation is due largely to activities of various organizations, particularly the National Audubon Society, whose educational campaigns through the media of screen tours and lectures, and in the focusing of attention on Christmas Bird Counts, have resulted in giving impetus everywhere to bird observation, study and protection. Several colleges and universities now offer courses in bird watching. Featuring live birds in their natural environment as a national asset and as a subject of interest and beauty is a fitting sequence to the former need for collecting large series of birds for identification and classification. Few other hobbies are so adaptable to outdoor recreation or offer greater enjoyment to so many people irrespective of age. None offers more opportunities for indulgence regardless of season or vantage point, be it lawn, park, desert, forest, mountain, stream, lake, or seashore.

The most favorable time for bird observation and identification is the period just preceding and during nesting time, when most birds are at their best in plumage, song, and action, and when all nature is usually at the peak of perfection. In diversified topography and scenic beauty, few states excel New Mexico. The main north-south watercourses and the variation in altitude and land types—deserts, mesas, plains, and mountains—provide as varied range in habitat for birds as occurs in any inland state. New Mexico is one of four states richly favored with distinctive species that enter locally from Mexico. Its many forested mountainous areas are now accessible

* For a general account of bird watching, see A Guide to Bird Finding West of the Mississippi, by Olin Sewall Pettingill, Jr., Oxford University Press, 1953.

by automobiles, or by horseback. Wilderness areas can be reached by foot or horseback only. Camping in summer provides pleasant outings and the best opportunities for relaxation and study of the rarer and more wary birds. At this season, trout fishing is usually good, particularly in the northern part of the state. In winter, snow-shoeing and skiing in national forests near Albuquerque, Santa Fe, Cloudcroft, and at other points, may be combined to lend even greater enjoyment to bird finding.

By day, birds may be seen at almost any time and place; and notes of many others contribute to the interest and enjoyment of nights spent under the stars. Privileges obtained in bird finding and watching depend very largely on the attitude of the observer toward the rights and welfare of the landowner, whether an individual, a state, or the National Government. Discourtesy and vandalism by a few who go afield usually result in restricted privileges of all others. It is well for those going afield to remember the precepts of the Golden Rule. Fortunately the bird watcher is usually motivated only by an appreciation of the beauties of nature, with no intent to harm anyone or to destroy innocent life. With the rapidly growing interest in birds and bird watching, both within and outside the state, a stranger will benefit by contacting informed citizens to ascertain the most likely places for seeing the species of most interest. Especially are refuge managers and officials of bird clubs and biology instructors in high schools and colleges in position to help the visitor. Officials stationed at national parks and monuments as well as field men attached to the State Game Department, the U.S. Fish and Wildlife Service and the U.S. Forest Service, are likewise in position to assist and advise regarding bird life.

CHRISTMAS BIRD COUNTS

The National Audubon Society Christmas Bird Counts which may be conducted on, or just preceding or following Christmas Day—depending on weather conditions or the convenience of the participants—are limited to one day. As an example of the keen competitive spirit these Counts have fostered in bird watching and recording: in 1955, 498 reporting teams representing more than 6,500 bird watchers from throughout the United States and Canada, with a few even from the Hawaiian Islands, participated in the annual Count. In this Count*—the 56th consecutive—with participants from every state in the Union except Nevada—the greatest number of species, viz.: 184, and approximately 77,894 birds, were recorded by the Cocoa, Florida, team consisting of 42 participants. In second place was the San Diego, California, team consisting of 36 observers, with 168 species and 38,456 birds, and in third place, Laguna Atascosa National Wildlife Refuge, near the delta of the Rio Grande, in Texas, with a total of 164 species, and approximately 285,608 individuals, as recorded by 23 participants. As is to be expected, the greatest number of species is generally recorded along seacoasts where water birds provide the advantage. Yet some inland stations produce surprisingly long lists, both in species and numbers of individuals. New Mexico had six stations reporting: Española, Santa Fe, Socorro, Bosque del Apache Refuge, Roswell, and Clayton, in addition to El Paso, which includes portions of both New Mexico and Texas. Of the New Mexico stations, the Bosque del Apache Refuge led in 1955 with 77 species and 89,423 individuals, but with only three participants.

These annual bird counts reveal some amazing figures and contrasts. For example, at the Muleshoe National Wildlife Refuge, situated on the Texas high plains just east of New Mexico, about 662,397 birds were recorded for the 1955 count, but with a total of only 38 species. Of those listed, 30,000 were Sandhill Cranes, 380,000 Mallards, 120,000 Widgeons, 120,000 Pintails, and 10,000 Green-winged Teals. In reflecting on these amazing figures, two important facts emerge:

* See *Audubon Field Notes,* April 1956.

first, the vast numbers of migratory birds that fly the Central Flyway; and second, the frequent scarcity of resting ponds and lakes—as in 1955-1956—over much of the high plains country, resulting in concentrations. However, the unpredictable occurrence of such mass concentrations is indicated by the Roswell—Bitter Lake December 22, 1956 Count, when it was estimated there were 35,000 Sandhill Cranes, where previous counts indicated less than half that number, and for the same period the Muleshoe Refuge Count climbed from 30,000 to 41,000. Nature of winter weather, availability of food as well as water, seem to be factors in the seasonal numbers of species present.

Christmas Bird Counts are of importance not only because of the widespread interest manifested in them, but also because of the information obtained therefrom regarding different species of birds that may be seen in winter throughout the country.

However, bird recording is by no means confined to seasonal or group reporting. There is a growing rivalry among some ornithologists throughout the country in their efforts to tally the greatest number of species within a calendar year. Guy Emerson, New York business executive and former president of the National Audubon Society, held a 13-year record—from 1939 to 1952. Probably no other individual has so methodically covered the states, timing his field trips to breast the tide of seasonal migrations at key points from coast to coast as has this outstanding field ornithologist. His highest record was established in 1939, during which year he listed 497 species (no subspecies included) out of approximately 650 regularly occurring in the Continental United States. This amazing record remained unchallenged until 1953, when the combined records of two of the leading ornithologists of our time—Roger Tory Peterson, of America, and James Fisher, of England, upon completing a hundred-day, 30,000 mile trip from eastern Canada, around the United States, and ending in Alaska, exceeded the Emerson count by a few birds. Competitive bird finding and watching regardless of scope is a challenge to interest, skill, knowledge, and perseverance of participants everywhere.

Bird finding is not a new diversion. The immortal John James Audubon recorded long lists of birds at various points while traveling over the country. In seeking relaxation from the staggering load of presidential duties, Theodore Roosevelt, our greatest conservation-minded President, occasionally slipped away with friends of kindred minds to some secluded retreat to observe the birds. Among those who frequently accompanied him on his nature studies and bird finding rambles was John Burroughs, dean of American naturalists of his time, who in a fitting account* recalls a day afield with his departed friend:

"When we went birding together it was ostensibly as teacher and pupil, but it often turned out that the teacher got as many lessons as he gave.

"Early in May, during the last term of his presidency, he asked me to go with him to his retreat in the woods of Virginia, called 'Pine Knot,' and help him name his birds. Together we identified more than seventy-five species of birds and wild fowl. He knew them all but two, and I knew them all but two. He taught me Bewick's wren and one of the rarer warblers, and I taught him the swamp sparrow and the pine warbler. A few days before he had seen Lincoln's sparrow in an old weedy field. On Sunday after church, he took me there and we loitered around for an hour, but the sparrow did not appear. Had he found this bird again, he would have been one ahead of me. The one subject I do know, and ought to know is birds. It has been one of the main studies of a long life. He knew the subject as well as I did, while he knew with the same thoroughness scores of other subjects of which I am entirely ignorant.

"He was a naturalist on the broadest grounds, uniting much technical knowledge of the daily lives and habits of all forms of wildlife. He probably knew tenfold more natural history than all the presidents who had preceded him, and I think one is safe in saying, more human history also."

Theodore Roosevelt may well be regarded as the founder of the vast bird refuge system so vital to bird protection and conservation in

* *Natural History*, Vol. XIX, January 1919.

America today. During his administration (1901-09), 51 National Bird Reservations, distributed in 17 states and territories, from Puerto Rico to Alaska, were established by executive order.

BIRD WATCHING REGIONS

In order to facilitate the finding of particular birds of interest, the state has been divided into four general regions. Under the heading for each region will be found information pertaining to accessibility, representative birds to be seen near accommodations, and points of special or historic interest.

Region 1 constitutes the southwestern part of the state; Region 2, the southeastern; Region 3, the northeastern; and Region 4, the northwestern. Each possesses special interest in bird and plant life, topography, and climate. While it would be impracticable to endeavor to include all strictly migratory, non-breeding species for each locality featured in a region, all such birds of record, including resident and summer dwellers, are given for the three key areas in their relation to the principal sub-flyways; i.e., Bosque del Apache National Wildlife Refuge for the Rio Grande Valley; the Bitter Lake—Roswell area for the Pecos Valley; and the Clayton area for the northeastern high plains which tap the main central flyway. In addition, Christmas Bird Counts for representative areas are recorded.

REGION 1—SOUTHWESTERN

In certain respects the Southwestern is the most interesting of the four bird study regions. Here may be found many resident and summer visitors from Mexico that do not occur elsewhere in the state. Most of these rare kinds are limited to a hundred-mile-wide zone lying north of the International Boundary and extending from the Arizona—New Mexico line eastward to the Rio Grande Valley. Just over the Boundary from the upper Animas Valley are Cajon Bonito, a clear-running wooded stream (the extreme northern source of the Yaqui River of Mexico) and Diablo (Devil's) Canyon, where regular seasonal dwellers include such exciting species as Thick-billed Parrot, Green Kingfisher, Sulphur-bellied and Olivaceous Flycatchers, and many others indigenous to the southern Republic. Some of these have been recorded in New Mexico, and it is not improbable that others ultimately will be found north of the International Boundary.

GUADALUPE CANYON. From the standpoint of extremely rare Mexican birds, Guadalupe Canyon, situated in the extreme southwestern corner of the state, adjacent to Mexico, merits first place in the Bird Watching section. The only record of the Coppery-tailed Trogon in the state is from this canyon, while so far as is known, it is the only place the Violet-crowned Hummingbird, the Wied's Crested Flycatcher, and the Thick-billed Kingbird have been found nesting. Bronzed Cowbirds and Black (Mexican) Hawks also nest here, and there is strong possibility that such rarities as the Rose-breasted Becard, Sulphur-bellied Flycatcher, and the Varied Bunting, as well as other rare Hummers, will be recorded as breeders during seasons when rainfall is sufficient to provide continuous running water in the canyon. A vacant Becard nest was found in the canyon (See Becard in main text), while Varied Buntings have been recorded nearby in Arizona.

The source of the main canyon is in the Peloncillo Mountains. It drains to the southwest approximately seven miles, thence shears the extreme southeastern corner of Arizona, before entering Mexico. The canyon contains running water during years of normal moisture. Graced by fine cottonwoods, sycamores and other trees, and various shrubs, it is an attractive northward lure for Mexican birds. Guadalupe Canyon with its several short tributaries, is the only drainage with so many attractive features which directly enters Mexico from New Mexico, thus making it unique as a "port of entry"—actually and potentially—for rarities in Mexican birds. It should be so dedicated, with rigid protective measures instituted which would prohibit the excessive collecting of the rare species, in order to sustain its intrinsic value.

CLOVERDALE—ANIMAS MOUNTAIN AREA. As is true of Guadalupe Canyon, this border locality has magnetic appeal for bird hunters because of its proximity to Mexico. Cloverdale, a term now generally applied to the recreation and camping ground of giant live oaks, lies in the southeastern part of the Peloncillo Mountains, a segment of the Coronado National Forest. The Animas Mountains, also wooded and forested, lie across the wide, open Animas Valley or basin to the eastward. These mountains, however, are no longer a part of the national forest. Elevation ranges from about 5,000 feet in the valleys to more than 8,500 feet on the summit of Animas Peak. Such resident and summer-dwelling species as Aplomado Falcon, Harlequin (Mearns) Quail, Mexican Turkey, Band-tailed Pigeon, White-winged Dove, Elf Owl, Costa's, Rivoli's and Blue-throated Hummingbirds, Arizona Woodpecker, Vermilion and Beardless Flycatchers, Mexican Jay, Bridled Titmouse, Brown Creeper, Bendire's Thrasher, Phainopepla, Hutton's Vireo, Black-and-white Warbler, Hooded and Scott's Orioles, Bronzed Cowbird, Black-chinned Sparrow may be seen here. Many of the more common species, such as Swainson's Hawk, Golden Eagle, Roadrunner, and Black-throated Sparrow occur in the foothills and on semidesert plains that characterize the zone between the Animas Mountains–Peloncillo Ranges and the Mogollon—Black Range mountain country to the north. The Big Hatchet Mountain, rising 8,366 feet, to the east of the Animas Mountains is a conspicuous scantily-wooded landmark, of interest not only because of its birds and botanical life but also because of the Mexican bighorn sheep that inhabit it. Deming and Lordsburg are convenient points from which to visit the borderland country.

SAN SIMON MARSHES. These marshes, situated on the Arizona—New Mexico line north of Rodeo, constitute the only area of this type in the southwestern part of the state. The rare Mexican (New Mexican) Duck, as well as Blue-winged Teal and common Mallard, nest here. Lesser (Texas) Nighthawks make their summer home on the extensive creosote bush (Covillea tridentata) slopes to the east, and swarm over the marshes and ponds at evening time. Marsh Hawks usually nest in the rushes of these marshes—the farthest south the species has been found breeding. The State Game Department has concessions at San Simon Marshes, and giant cottonwood trees provide shade for the visitor during warm summer days.

GILA RIVER VALLEY. The Gila River Valley, from the Arizona line upstream well into the Mogollon Mountains, is of special interest, summer or winter. The bottomlands contain some of the most magnificent cottonwood trees to be found in the entire country, and the climate is mild and sunshiny throughout the year. The valley proper, flanked as it is by wooded canyons, provides sanctuary for such resident species as the Gila Woodpecker, Cardinal, Pyrrhuloxia, and Abert's Towhee. Summer residents include Black Hawk; White-winged and Inca Doves; Screech and Elf Owls; Gila Woodpecker; Black Phoebe; Vermilion Flycatcher; Lucy's Warbler, and many of the more common species. The ambitious observer may be so fortunate as to find the Gray and Zone-tailed Hawks nesting in the river valley cottonwoods or in such groves common in some of the tributary watercourses. This section contains some of the best Gambel's Quail habitat in the state. The upper portion of the valley is conveniently reached from Silver City, while that segment below "the box," from Red Rock to the Arizona line, can best be covered from Lordsburg.

GLENWOOD—RESERVE AREA. The forested mountainous country lying north of the Gila River, bisected by the San Francisco River, much of which is within national forests, provides a pleasing transition from semidesert to heavy forests and mountain streams, with a consequent change in bird life. Highway No. 260 enters the San Francisco River Valley near Glenwood and continues up the valley through imposing forest and mountain scenery, to the point where it enters Arizona, near Luna, New Mexico. Glenwood, Reserve, Luna, and intermediate service stations and tourist courts and cabins provide necessary accommodations. Camp grounds are also provided in the forests. Fair roads provide access to the west portion of the Mogollon Mountains and the Eagle Peak, Negrito, and Apache Creek sections. This area has a rich background of Indian and outlaw lore, and is especially attractive for both bird watching and summer outings. Such breeding birds as Blue Grouse; Harlequin Quail; Flammulated, Pygmy and Spotted Owls; Poor-wills, Cassin's Kingbirds; Coues' and Buff-breasted Flycatchers; Violet-green Swallows; Steller's, Scrub, and Pinyon Jays; Common Ravens; Common Crows; Hutton's and Bell's Vireos; Olive Warblers; Summer Tanagers; Black-headed Grosbeaks; Lazuli Buntings, and Red Crossbills may be observed.

SILVER CITY—BLACK RANGE AREA. The rugged, forested Black Range—Mogollon Mountain section of Region 1 is quite a contrast to the semidesert border zone lying to the southward. Silver City is a convenient gateway to this wonderland, which includes the Gila Wilderness and the Gila Cliff Dwellings National Monument. The Sapillo Loop drive from Silver City to Santa Rita, where the great open-pit copper mines are located, thence up the Mimbres River, down Sapillo Canyon, and back to Silver City by way of Big Cherry Canyon, provides an opportunity to see a variety of interesting birds. Much of this drive is in the Gila National Forest, with suitable camping places available. Such birds as Merriam's Turkey, Harlequin Quail, Band-tailed Pigeon, Cassin's Kingbird, Black and Say's Phoebes, and Western Bluebird may be seen on the Loop; and the presence of Dippers may be revealed by a hike into the Sapillo box canyon, below the road—one of the southernmost points at which these birds nest in the state. Big Cherry Canyon may prove to be the highlight of the trip. The Forest Service maintains an attractive campground in the Canyon. Also in Big Cherry and tributary canyons may be seen such nesting species as Spotted and Pygmy Owls, Whip-poor-wills, Poor-wills, Blue-throated Hummingbirds, Coues' and Western Flycatchers, Steller's Jay, White-breasted and Pygmy Nuthatches, Robin, Hermit Thrush, Painted Redstart, Redfaced Warbler, Western and Summer Tanagers, Black-headed Grosbeak and Gray-headed Junco.

Two other drives from Silver City—Black Canyon—Beaverhead to the north, and the Black Range Scenic Drive over the Black Range to Hillsboro—provide opportunities to see many resident and summer-dwelling birds in surroundings of inspiring mountain scenery.

GILA WILDERNESS AREA. The Gila Wilderness Area comprises much of the wild Mogollon Mountains. The Wilderness embraces approximately 439,000 acres of canyons, forest and mountain scenery. Its highest point is Whitewater Baldy, 10,892 feet. The Gila Cliff Dwellings National Monument is within the area, on the West Fork of the Gila River, which heads among the higher peaks of the mountains. Roads are prohibited in the Wilderness. It is therefore accessible only by saddle and pack animals, or by hiking. The establishment of this Wilderness Area, the first of the present long chain of such primitive places in the nation, was the crowning achievement of Aldo Leopold, one of the greatest conservationists of all time. The rugged grandeur of the area is unsurpassed. The area may be reached from the State Game Department's Gila Wilderness Habitat Area (formerly Heart Bar Ranch), from Silver City by way of Copperas Canyon; or from Willow Creek on the northeast border; or from a road (closed in winter) which skirts the area over the mountains on the north. Those who are fortunate enough to make the Wilderness trip may observe such nesting birds as Golden and Bald Eagles; Osprey; Blue Grouse; Harlequin Quail; Merriam's Turkey; Great Horned, Pygmy and Spotted Owls; Acorn, Hairy, Downy and Northern Three-toed Woodpeckers; Yellow-bellied and Williamson's Sapsuckers; Steller's Jay; Common Raven; Clark's Nutcracker; White-breasted and Pygmy Nuthatches; Brown Creeper; Dipper; Robin; Hermit Thrush; Western Tanager; Western Bluebird; Red-faced Warbler, and Gray-headed Junco.

MAGDALENA — SAN MATEO MOUNTAIN AREA. The northeastern section of Region 1, west of the Rio Grande, is dominated by plain, mesa and mountains—the Magdalena and San Mateo—within the Cibola National Forest. The Datil Range, in the extreme northern part of the region (also within this forest) is accessible by U.S. Highway 60, and is of interest mainly because of the nesting of the Common Raven, Peregrine and Prairie Falcons, and Golden Eagle. The extensive San Augustin Plains, a high inland basin lying west of Magdalena, is a nesting ground for Mountain Plover, while Ferruginous Hawks nest in the pine and juniper rims that surround the Plains. Horned Larks also are abundant on the Plains, and occasionally a pair of Burrowing Owls may be seen. The San Mateo Mountains, extending from the east end of the San Augustin Plain southward to Monticello, constitute the most extensive forested section of this portion of the Region. The many picturesque canyons of these mountains are accessible by usually passable roads, by saddle horse and pack animals, or by foot trails. Golden Eagle, Harlequin Quail, Merriam's Turkey, Pygmy and Spotted Owls, Acorn Woodpecker; Steller's, Scrub and Pinyon Jays, Red Crossbill, and many smaller species may be found here. Blue Mountain, highest in the range, was the final retreat of the Apache Kid, outlaw Mescalero Apache Indian.

The Magdalena Mountains, South Baldy, 10,787 feet elevation, southwest of Socorro, are of limited extent but of interest for short bird-watching expeditions. Water Canyon, the principal drainage system, is accessible by car. Band-tailed Pigeon, Pygmy Owl, Red-faced Warbler (most northern range extension), Western Tanager, among others nest in these mountains.

This portion of Region 1 may well be tied in with observations on and about nearby Bosque del Apache Refuge, in the Rio Grande Valley.

RIO GRANDE VALLEY. The Rio Grande Valley, radically different from the remainder of Region 1, is dominated, from Socorro to the Texas line, by alluvial bottomlands overgrown by cottonwoods, willows, tamarisks, and other trees and shrubs, with a liberal sprinkling of irrigated farmlands. This segment of the Valley, approximately 200 miles long, ranges in altitude from 4,600 feet at Socorro to approximately 3,698 feet at El Paso. It is one of the principal sub-flyways in the Southwest, although drainage has seriously curtailed water-, marsh-, and shore-bird habitats. The valley has an excellent and equitable year-round climate and is easily accessible.

BOSQUE DEL APACHE NATIONAL WILDLIFE REFUGE. The Bosque del Apache Refuge is strategically located in the central portion of the Rio Grande Valley, south of San Antonio. Of its 57,000-acre area, 13,500 acres are river valley, much of which is maintained in a high state of development by the U.S. Fish and Wildlife Service. For an account of this refuge, see Bosque del Apache National Wildlife Refuge under Flyway Bird Records.

ELEPHANT BUTTE RESERVOIR AREA. Elephant Butte Reservoir, situated in the central Rio Grande Valley between Albuquerque and Las Cruces, constitutes the principal water storage for the vast Rio Grande Valley reclamation project in New Mexico and Western Texas. While the lake is a resting place for a great variety of migratory waterfowl, it is of minor benefit as a feeding and breeding place for such birds because of the fluctuating rocky shorelines. Both Elephant Butte and Kettletop Butte, the latter also in the lake, a few miles above the dam, are of interest to the bird finder because of the nesting Golden Eagles that usually occupy them.

In winter Mergansers often become so numerous on the lake as to require control measures because of fish depredation. Various other kinds of Ducks, Whistling Swans, Snow Geese, Western Grebes, Double-crested Cormorants, and Gulls and Terns are usually in evidence in winter, while in summer great numbers of Cliff Swallows nest beneath the eaves of the dam. Black Phoebes may be seen about the water outlets at the foot of the massive dam.

Caballo Lake, a few miles below Elephant Butte Lake, and a link in the Rio Grande irrigation system, is also of interest to the bird student. Here, as on Elephant Butte Lake, boating and fishing may be combined with bird study, usually the same species being in evidence. Both Caballo and Elephant Butte Lakes are easily accessible from Truth or Consequences.

LAS CRUCES—EL PASO AREA. The Las Cruces—El Paso segment of the Rio Grande Valley is one of the most important and popular bird watching sections of the Southwest. The mild climate makes outdoor life generally as inviting and pleasant in winter as in summer. A few marshy places have escaped drainage while the Rio Grande and the many drainage canals provide added year-round habitat for many marsh and water birds. The wide, alluvial valley with its abundance of native trees and shrubs and the many exotic kinds about residences and farms, with irrigated cultivated fields, provide suitable habitat for a great variety of land species. The network of roads leads to many points of interest as pertains to both resident and migrant birds.

The cities of Las Cruces and El Paso, being strategically located, are especially attractive as bird watching centers because of their proximity to points of interest, and to New Mexico State University and Texas Western College, El Paso, thus affording students, local residents, and visitors points of centralized contact in nature study including ornithology. Fortunately, too, many of the citizens are actively interested in bird study and in the protection of birds. Although El Paso proper is in Texas, a suburb—on the west side of the Rio Grande—is in New Mexico. Furthermore, New Mexico is the main recreational outlet for the city. While most of the breeding records are for New Mexico, a few are for adjacent points about El Paso, and all listed for the area may be found in both states.

For the following list of breeding birds, the author is largely indebted to the observation teams of Harry Williams and Mr. and Mrs. Gordon White, of Las Cruces, and Mrs. Lena McBee and Miss Mary Belle Keefer, of El Paso.

U.S. DEPARTMENT OF THE INTERIOR
FISH AND WILDLIFE SERVICE

ENTERING
BOSQUE DEL APACHE
NATIONAL WILDLIFE REFUGE

BREEDING BIRDS OF THE LAS CRUCES AREA

Pied-billed Grebe	Western Kingbird
Snowy Egret	Ash-throated
Black-crowned Night	Flycatcher
Heron	Black Phoebe
Least Bittern	Say's Phoebe
American Bittern	Vermilion Flycatcher
Mallard	Bank Swallow
Mexican Duck	Rough-winged Swallow
Blue-winged Teal	Barn Swallow
Cinnamon Teal	Cliff Swallow
Red-tailed Hawk	White-necked Raven
Swainson's Hawk	Verdin
Sparrow Hawk	Bushtit
Scaled Quail	Cactus Wren
Gambel's Quail	Rock Wren
Virginia Rail	Mockingbird
Sora	Curve-billed Thrasher
Common Gallinule	Crissal Thrasher
American Coot	Phainopepla
Killdeer	Loggerhead Shrike
Black-necked Stilt	Lucy's Warbler
Mourning Dove	Yellow Warbler
White-winged Dove	Yellowthroat
Ground Dove	Yellow-breasted Chat
Inca Dove	House Sparrow
Yellow-billed Cuckoo	Redwinged Blackbird
Barn Owl	Bullock's Oriole
Screech Owl	Boat-tailed Grackle
Great Horned Owl	Brown-headed
Burrowing Owl	Cowbird
Long-eared Owl	Summer Tanager
Lesser Nighthawk	Pyrrhuloxia
Black-chinned	Blue Grosbeak
Hummingbird	Painted Bunting
Broad-tailed	House Finch
Hummingbird	Lesser Goldfinch
Red-shafted Flicker	Lark Sparrow
Ladder-backed	Black-throated
Woodpecker	Sparrow

The Fulvous Tree Duck, and Black and Zone-tailed Hawks have been observed in the valley, but there seem to be no nesting records. This segment of the Rio Grande Valley is also the most likely place for seeing the Caracara and Black Vulture.

Lying just east of Las Cruces, the rugged Organ Mountains (Organ Peak, 8,870 feet) provide opportunity for an interesting bird observation trip. The mountains are characterized by a fusion of the Lower and Upper Sonoran and Transition Zones, which with their characteristic botanical life, from desert mesquite, creosote, and cacti to yellow pine and Douglas fir on the higher north slopes are in vivid contrast to the rich agricultural Rio Grande Valley. Since the Organ Mountains are fairly close to Mexico, and radically different from other mountains of the region, there is always a possibility of finding rare summer visitors, such as Blue-throated and other Hummers. Vernon Bailey observed great numbers of Hummingbirds while on a brief trip into these mountains. Bushtits, Canyon Wrens, Scott's Orioles, Brown Towhees, Rufous-crowned and Black-chinned Sparrows may be found nesting in or about the mountains.

EL PASO CHRISTMAS BIRD COUNT
DECEMBER 31, 1955

7½-mile radius about El Paso, exclusive of adjacent Mexico. 7 A.M. to 4:45 P.M. Cloudy to 10 A.M. Temperature 44 to 55°. Total party hours 28. Total party miles 107 (19 on foot, 88 by car). (See *Audubon Field Notes*, April 1956, p. 194.)

Pied-billed Grebe	9
Great Blue Heron	1
Green Heron	1
Mallard	39
Gadwall	43
American Widgeon	172
Pintail	2
Green-winged Teal	24
Shoveler	2
Canvasback	50
Common Merganser	1
Turkey Vulture	1
Cooper's Hawk	2
Red-tailed Hawk	4
Marsh Hawk	1
Sparrow Hawk	15
Scaled Quail	19
Gambel's Quail	157
Common Gallinule	4
American Coot	226
Common Snipe	1
Mourning Dove	40
Roadrunner	3
Belted Kingfisher	2
Red-shafted Flicker	31
Black Phoebe	1
Say's Phoebe	4
Scrub Jay	8
Plain Titmouse	1
Red-breasted Nuthatch	2
Pygmy Nuthatch	11

House Wren	2
Cactus Wren	1
Rock Wren	8
Mockingbird	3
Crissal Thrasher	2
Robin	7
Hermit Thrush	1
Western Bluebird	50
Ruby-crowned Kinglet	6
Water Pipit	1
Cedar Waxwing	50
Phainopepla	1
Loggerhead Shrike	12
Starling	31
Audubon's Warbler	4
House Sparrow	111
Western Meadowlark	1
Yellow-headed Blackbird	765
Redwinged Blackbird	1,040
Bullock's Oriole	1
Brewer's Blackbird	614
Boat-tailed Grackle	530
Brown-headed Cowbird	6
House Finch	66
American Goldfinch	1
Lesser Goldfinch	10
Red Crossbill	4
Green-tailed Towhee	3
Rufous-sided Towhee	11
Lark Bunting	200
Savannah Sparrow	2
Baird's Sparrow	15
Lark Sparrow	1
Black-throated Sparrow	13
Sage Sparrow	2
Oregon Junco (2 races)	120
Gray-headed Junco	34
Chipping Sparrow	13
White-crowned Sparrow	549
Song Sparrow	4

Total 71 species, about 5,171 individuals. Mrs. J. Owen Allen, Roy Allen, Mr. and Mrs. D. I. Johnson, Mary Belle Keefer, Mrs. Lena McBee, Ethel Nobel, Chester Stewart, R. Jack Stewart, El Paso Audubon Society.

SAN ANDRES NATIONAL WILDLIFE REFUGE. The San Andres Refuge, consisting of a segment of the desert mountain range of the same name, lying east of the Rio Grande, was established primarily for the conservation of the now rare Mexican bighorn sheep. The official bird list of 113 species is imposing. Unlike Bosque del Apache Refuge, the San Andres comprising 57,215 acres, is scantily watered by springs and small surface tanks dependent on wells or seasonal rains. Consequently the area is of little benefit for water, marsh, or shore birds. Practically all migrant birds that have been recorded here appear also in the Bosque del Apache Refuge list. However, such resident species or summer dwellers as the Golden Eagle, Scaled Quail, Roadrunner, White-throated Swift, Ash-throated Flycatcher, Verdin, Brown Towhee, Rufous-crowned, Black-throated, and Black-chinned Sparrows may be found nesting. En route to the Refuge, in the yucca-mesquite studded Jornada Valley, such common nesting species as Swainson's Hawks, White-necked Ravens, and Horned Larks may be met with, while if the visitor is fortunate he may see a pair of Aplomado Falcons.

The heart of the refuge at Rope Spring is accessible from Las Cruces by a fair country road by way of the federally-administered Jornada Experimental Range. Like Bosque del Apache, San Andres Refuge is under jurisdiction of the U.S. Fish and Wildlife Service, hence those who contemplate a visit to the refuge should contact the official in charge, at Las Cruces, whose assistance will insure maximum benefits from a trip to the refuge.

WHITE SANDS NATIONAL MONUMENT. Lying between the San Andres and the Sacramento Mountains in the landlocked Tularosa Basin, is the White Sands National Monument. The Monument, a huge spread of glaring white "sand" (gypsum) dunes, covers an area of 140,247 acres. Bird life of the monument proper, because of its prevailing barren surface, is very limited. However, on or about the shallow, aquatic vegetation-bordered lake to the east of the Monument Headquarters, may be seen a variety of migrants, chiefly water and shore birds, some of which usually remain to nest. Among the more interesting species that have been recorded here, mainly migrants, are Rough-legged Hawk; Peregrine and Prairie Falcons; Snowy Plover; Solitary and Least Sandpipers; Willet; Greater Yellowlegs; Long-billed Dowitcher; American Avocet; Black-necked Stilt; Short-eared Owl; Tree and Bank Swallows; Sage Thrasher; Savannah, Baird's, Sage, Clay-colored, Brewer's and Lincoln's Sparrows. Most of the Ducks that occur in the Rio Grande Valley have also been recorded here. Visitors who wish to include bird watching in their visit to the Monument should make their wishes known to officials in charge. Here, as at some other monument and national park headquarters, museum specimens of many of the birds occurring in the area may be seen.

REGION 2—SOUTHEASTERN

The topography of Region 2 is in some respects quite different from that of Region 1. Although the western portion, consisting of the Guadalupe, Sacramento, White, and Capitan Mountains, is rugged and forested, with elevations up to 12,000 feet, the eastern section, exclusive of the Pecos Valley, consists for the most part of mesas, sandhills, and high plains, the last-named adjacent to the Texas line. Elevations of this portion of the region range from about 3,100 feet at Carlsbad to around 4,000 on the plains, and 5,500 feet on the extensive mesa country about Vaughn. Changes that have taken place in the landscape in the past 50 years, particularly in the Pecos Valley and eastward, have had a profound influence on most resident and migratory birds. The growing of trees where previously there were none, and the irrigation of croplands have favored many kinds, while periodic devastation of rangelands by live-

stock has had adverse effects on many others.

Although Region 2 is not favored by many rare species, such as are found in Region 1 (Southwestern), some resident and summer visitors are no less interesting. For example, the sandhill shinnery-oak *(Quercus havardii)* section along the eastern side of the Region constitutes the principal restricted habitat of the Lesser Prairie Chicken in the state. In Region 2 also are found the heart of the Scaled Quail distribution, and remnants of the Burrowing Owl, which were abundant and widespread prior to the almost total extermination of the Black-tailed Prairie Dog, whose surplus burrows this little Owl appropriated as living quarters.

One of the amazing changes that have taken place in the Region is the complete replacement of mesquite and other native shrubs and salt grass of the Pecos River Valley and its floodlands during comparatively recent times, by the exotic salt cedar, or tamarisk *(Tamarix gallica)*. When the cedars are in full summer leaf the valley is in most places a wide ribbon of dark green marking the course of the stream. Many species of birds now take advantage of the protection provided and remain, whereas previously they were transients only. In this regard the McMillan Reservoir delta above Carlsbad is of unusual interest to the bird student and naturalist. For many years the valley above the reservoir accumulated silt, which formed barrier dykes resulting in marshes and lakes,

WADE LAKE, McMILLAN LAKE DELTA. *Photograph by the Author.*

while the entire delta spread of approximately 14,000 acres, exclusive of water and marsh, has become a salt cedar jungle. Prior to formation of this delta with its lakes and marshes, few water and marsh birds found suitable nesting environment here. During the past few years great numbers of Snowy and Common Egrets, Great Blue Herons, Green Herons, Black-crowned Night Herons, Virginia Rails, and Redwinged Blackbirds have been nesting in the delta. The more mature cedars provide nesting places for Mockingbirds, Bullock's Orioles, Blue Grosbeaks, and great numbers of Mourning Doves.

For a complete list of migrants that enter and pass through the Pecos Valley Sub-flyway the reader is referred to the Bitter Lake–Roswell area.

CARLSBAD AREA. The city and adjacent valley lands are of special interest not only because of the arboreal and agriculturally created bird habitats, but also because of their strategic location on the heavily used Pecos Valley Sub-flyway. McMillan and Avalon Reservoirs to the north, the two-mile-long city, tree-bordered lake, and Willow Lake to the south, provide resting places for a great variety of migrant and wintering water, marsh, and shore birds such as Common Loons, Eared and Pied-billed Grebes, White Pelicans, Snow Geese, and rafts of Ducks which may be sighted on the lakes and reservoirs. In fall and spring, flocks of cruising Sandhill Cranes announce their passing, and often thrill a spectator as they feed in irrigated fields.

The shores of Lake McMillan are especially attractive to migrant shore birds of many kinds. Yellow-headed, Redwinged and Brewer's Blackbirds; Lark Buntings, and White-crowned Sparrows are the most common winter residents. However, the many city lawns and parks, with food-producing shrubs and feeding stations now induce Robins, Mockingbirds, Thrushes, Cedar Waxwings, Juncos, and others to tarry or even remain for the entire winter. Steller's and Scrub Jays often venture down in winter when there is a scarcity of mast in their mountain retreats, while noisy groups of Pinyon Jays may pause in their passing. The many trees in and about

the city have attracted increasing numbers of nesting birds, including Cuckoos, Black-chinned and Broad-tailed Hummingbirds, Western Kingbirds, Boat-tailed Grackles, Bullock's Orioles, Summer Tanagers, Blue Grosbeaks, House Finches, and Goldfinches. The author knows of no other locality in the Southwest where there is so great a resident population of Pyrrhuloxias, nor where nest so many Painted Buntings, as in the valley between Carlsbad and the Texas line—a distance of 40 miles as the river flows.

A drive east of Carlsbad and beyond provides opportunity to see such nesting species as Swainson's and Harris' Hawks, Great Horned Owls, Roadrunners, Scissor-tailed Flycatchers, and Black-throated Sparrows. The State Game Bird Farm, 3 miles northwest of Carlsbad, is a popular public attraction.

CARLSBAD CAVERNS NATIONAL PARK. The famous Caverns are 27 miles southwest of the city of Carlsbad, and 7 miles from White City. Bird life at and in the vicinity of the Caverns, though not as varied as at some other points, is nevertheless highly interesting. Assembled visitors are frequently greeted by the spontaneous outburst of song of the sociable Canyon and Rock Wrens, amplified by the spacious maw of the great cave. Other breeding birds that may be observed at or adjacent to the Caverns include: Turkey Vulture, Red-tailed, Swainson's and Harris' Hawks, Golden Eagle, Sparrow Hawk, Scaled Quail, Roadrunner, Mourning Dove, Great Horned and Barn Owls, Poor-will, Lesser Nighthawk, White-throated Swift, Ladder-backed (Cactus) Woodpecker, Western Kingbird, Ash-throated Flycatcher, Say's Phoebe, Verdin, Bushtit, Mockingbird, Curve-billed Thrasher, Loggerhead Shrike, Scott's Oriole, Blue Grosbeak, Brown Towhee, Rufous-crowned Sparrow, and Black-throated Sparrow.

The Carlsbad Caverns National Park has the distinction of providing the only known nesting places of the Cave Swallow in New Mexico (See Cave Swallow). Elsewhere in the United States it is known to breed only in caves of the Rocksprings-Kerrville sections of Texas.

WASHINGTON RANCH: Washington Ranch, situated on Black River, 30 miles southwest of Carlsbad, is the nucleus of what was formerly a widespread cattle ranch. Its esthetic, recreational, and wildlife values are greatly enhanced by many giant cottonwood and poplar trees, while the imposing Guadalupe Mountains—the extreme southeastern extension of the Rockies—to the west, lend an inspiring background to the peaceful setting. A trip to Washington Ranch can readily be combined with one to the Carlsbad Caverns. In addition to the birds listed for the Carlsbad Caverns, such species as Yellow-billed Cuckoo, Screech and Flammulated Owls, Scissor-tailed and Vermilion Flycatchers, Bullock's Oriole, Summer Tanager, Pyrrhuloxia, Painted Bunting, and Cassin's Sparrow may be found nesting. However, Washington Ranch is of special interest because of the great numbers of Mourning Doves, Red-winged Blackbirds, and White-crowned and other Sparrows that take advantage of the ample cover and abundance of feed in winter. Wintering waterfowl include most species of Ducks, Geese and Sandhill Cranes. Scaled Quail may be observed about the headquarters buildings. Bird life here varies sharply with the seasons.

SITTING BULL FALLS AND GUADALUPE MOUNTAINS. Sitting Bull Falls, in the foothills of the Guadalupe Mountains, about 40 miles west of Carlsbad, is a popular scenic and recreation attraction. Although a variety of birds will not be seen about the falls in summer, there is always a possibility of seeing Golden Eagles, White-throated Swifts, Verdins, Bushtits, Cactus, Canyon and Rock Wrens. However, the real birding opportunity comes by extending the trip into the Guadalupe Division of the Lincoln National Forest, where the elevation ranges from 7,000 to 8,000 feet and where the fauna and flora of the Upper Sonoran and Transition Zones are of absorbing interest. The most interesting, as well as the highest part of the range and the habitat of the greatest variety of birds, is adjacent to the Texas line. In order to derive the greatest benefits from this trip, one should be prepared for camping and hiking. Here, summer birds may include:

Zone-tailed Hawk	Western Flycatcher
Harlequin Quail	Violet-green Swallow
Merriam's Turkey	Steller's Jay
Band-tailed Pigeon	Mountain Chickadee
Pygmy Owl	White-breasted
Spotted Owl	Nuthatch
Whip-poor-will	Pygmy Nuthatch
Poor-will	Hermit Thrush
White-throated Swift	Warbling Vireo
Red-shafted Flicker	Audubon's Warbler
Acorn Woodpecker	Grace's Warbler
Hairy Woodpecker	Western Tanager
Cassin's Kingbird	Gray-headed Junco

ARTESIA—CLOUDCROFT AREA. As is true of the Carlsbad segment of the Pecos Valley, an exotic environment of salt cedars as well as shade trees and shrubs about residences and farmlands in the Artesia section accounts for a great increase in nesting birds over former times. The extensive bog and marsh lands, with intermittent ponds and lakes, largely dependent on local rainfall or mood of the river at times of floods, lie a few miles southeast of Artesia. The area, overgrown with aquatic vegetation, now constitutes the principal nesting grounds of the Common and Snowy Egrets in the Pecos Valley. Green and Black-crowned Night Herons, Mallards, Blue-winged Teals, Virginia Rails, Black-necked Stilts, and Redwinged Blackbirds also find favorable nesting environment.

The breeding birds for the immediate Artesia area are not herein listed, since such a listing would be largely a duplication of those recorded for the Carlsbad area.

Since Artesia is the eastern gateway to the Sacramento Mountain country, lying to the westward, it is becoming increasingly popular from the standpoint of bird finding. These heavily forested mountains, most of which are within the Lincoln National Forest, are the logical recreational outlet for a rapidly growing population of the far-flung tributary valley and plains country lying to the east and southeast. The delightfully cool summer climate, and winter sports of skiing and snowshoeing, contribute to its popularity as a public playground and as a mecca for the bird lover.

The transition from 3,500 feet elevation, semidesert type around Artesia, to 9,000 feet and coniferous forests on the summit of the mountains, 90 miles to the west, is no less enchanting than the variation of birds that may be encountered in the varied topography. The summer list may include Swainson's Hawk, Scaled Quail, Roadrunner, Western Kingbird, Scissor-tailed Flycatcher, Horned Lark, White-necked Raven and Curve-billed Thrasher. As one enters the Peñasco River Canyon, below Elk, the change in bird life and topography becomes perceptible. At the National Forest boundary, 65 miles west of Artesia, may be seen some of the largest nesting colonies of Cliff Swallows to be found in the Southwest. For a distance of approximately a half mile, colonies of 100 to 200 Cliff Swallows build their retort-shaped nests beneath overhanging limestone palisades that wall the roadway.

From Elk or Mayhill several different routes may be taken in order to reach the higher portions of the Mountains. Regardless of the route chosen, every mile unfolds a changing panorama, terminating in the Canadian Zone about the summit of the mountains, where giant Douglas fir and Englemann spruce are interspersed by aspen parks bedecked with brilliant alpine flowers. Such birds as Harlequin Quail, Merriam's Turkey, Band-tailed Pigeon, Flammulated Owl, Pygmy Owl, Violet-green Swallow, Purple Martin, Steller's Jay, Common Raven, Audubon's Warbler, and Western Tanager may be seen. By careful searching of the more densely shaded canyons, the ambitious bird student may be rewarded by the sight of a pair of Spotted Owls, Whip-poor-will, or Western Flycatcher. Good accommodations are always available at Cloudcroft and other nearby points. However, those who are prepared to camp will find it most enjoyable and rewarding.

Ruidoso—White Mountain Area. This area is situated mainly in the Lincoln National Forest, with the White Mountains (Sierra Blanca Peak, 12,003 feet elevation) as a background. Breeding birds that may be seen here are, for the most part, indigenous to both the Sacramento and Capitan Ranges. The Ruidoso area, with an elevation of 7,000

LINCOLN NATIONAL FOREST, NEAR CLOUDCROFT, BIRDWATCHERS' RETREAT
Photograph by the Author

feet, is one of the most popular resort and recreation centers in the state, where delightful climate in summer and popular sports in winter may be enjoyed along with bird observation and study.

Although the Rufous and Calliope Hummingbirds do not nest in the area, great numbers arrive in late July and early August to animate the many flower-bedecked meadows and mountain slopes. They are especially abundant about the summit of the White Mountains where flowers bloom in great profusion. But these visitors soon resume their southward movement. Goshawks may be observed in winter, and there is some evidence that they breed here. Common Crows and even Magpies may also occasionally occur in winter. The Mescalero Apache Indian Reservation is adjacent on the south and west.

BREEDING BIRDS THAT MAY BE SEEN
IN THE RUIDOSO—WHITE MOUNTAIN AREA

Turkey Vulture	Purple Martin
Red-tailed Hawk	Steller's Jay
Zone-tailed Hawk	Common Raven
Golden Eagle	Mountain Chickadee
Harlequin Quail	Plain Titmouse
Merriam's Turkey	White-breasted
Flammulated Owl	Nuthatch
Great Horned Owl	Pygmy Nuthatch
Pygmy Owl	Brown Creeper
Spotted Owl	Dipper
Saw-whet Owl	Robin
Whip-poor-will	Hermit Thrush
Black-chinned	Western Bluebird
Hummingbird	Solitary Vireo
Broad-tailed	Warbling Vireo
Hummingbird	Yellow Warbler
Acorn Woodpecker	Audubon's Warbler
Yellow-bellied Sapsucker	Western Tanager
Hairy Woodpecker	Hepatic Tanager
Cassin's Kingbird	Black-headed Grosbeak
Western Wood Pewee	Pine Siskin
Violet-green Swallow	Green-tailed Towhee

PORTALES—TATUM AREA. The bluestem sage-grass shinnery-oak sandhill country lying between Portales and Tatum represents the principal occupied range of the Lesser Prairie Chicken in the state at the present time (1957). The Chicken range from south to north is practically bisected by State Highway 18. A visit to southern Roosevelt County,

particularly the Milnesand area, the center of the thrilling nuptial performances of the Chickens from early April to mid-May, may prove to be the highlight of a sojourn in this section. The courtship, or "drumming" grounds, as they are locally called, are accessible, and performances may be observed and photographed from automobiles.

The hard land, short-grass "islands" scattered throughout the sandhills between Portales and Lovington, and from the state line west to "the Cap Rock" and Kenna, constitute the most extensive nesting range of the Mountain Plover in the state, if not in the entire Southwest. The area also designates the southern limit of Lark Bunting and Long-billed Curlew breeding ranges. Burrowing Owls are still to be found in considerable numbers, particularly where the few prairie dogs, or their burrows, remain. Swainson's Hawks and White-necked Ravens nest commonly, while the Ferruginous Hawk sometimes manages to survive a season with a nest on some remote sand dune.

BITTER LAKE NATIONAL WILDLIFE REFUGE. As a wintering place for water, marsh, and shore birds, the Bitter Lake Refuge rivals the Bosque del Apache Refuge in the Rio Grande Valley. Here, for example, occurs seasonally one of the greatest winter concentrations of Sandhill Cranes in the Southwest. The records for the refuge are excelled only by the vast concentrations that occur at the Muleshoe National Wildlife Refuge to the eastward in the Texas Panhandle. The little Snowy Plover finds its most favorable summer habitat within the Bitter Lake Refuge; and this is the only place the Least Tern has been found nesting in the state.

This refuge is strategically located on the heavily utilized Pecos Valley waterfowl Subflyway. As result of a vast development program and intensive management by the U.S. Fish and Wildlife Service, the Bitter Lake Refuge is now not only a very important resting and feeding ground for vast numbers of water, marsh, and shore birds, but it has also become an important nesting area as result of the transition. The mild winter climate and availability of food, both within the refuge and on adjacent irrigated valley lands, are incentives for more birds to winter on and about this area which formerly consisted of a few all-but-sterile alkali lakes.

For a complete list of all birds that have been recorded see Roswell—Bitter Lake Area, Christmas Bird Count and Flyway Bird Records.

REGION 3—NORTHEASTERN

In grandeur and inspiring beauty the forested mountains of northern New Mexico equal any similar section of the Rocky Mountain region. Climaxing the charm of this enchanted land is the awe-inspiring Sangre de Cristo Range of typical Rocky Mountain pattern, extending from near Santa Fe to the Colorado line. However, not all of Region 3 is mountainous. The vast spread of country lying east and southeast of the Sangre de Cristo Range is characterized by great stretches of mesa and plain, interspersed by isolated peaks and buttes, or cut by rugged canyons flanked by barren or wooded ridges, but for the most part with elevations ranging below the yellow pine belt, the usual limit of which is 6,200 to 6,500 feet. The lowest point in the Region is about 3,800 feet, where the South Canadian River enters the Texas Panhandle east of Logan.

SANGRE DE CRISTO MOUNTAINS. The Sangre de Cristo Range is featured over other areas not only because it conspicuously dominates the northern skyline of Region 3, but also because of the great number of resident and summer resident birds to be observed from such interesting and historic places as Santa Fe, Taos, the town of Pecos, and Cimarron. While many of the more common species occur adjacent to, and even on the slopes of this mountain mass, the bird observer generally will be most interested in the mountain-dwelling species, from 7,000 feet to and above timber line. The arctic climate which dominates the crest of the Sangre de Cristo Range of Region 3 is in sharp contrast to that of the southwestern section of the state (Region 1), where the lower-altitude birds may be observed in a semidesert type. Yet Region 3 is favored with some of the rarest species to be found in the Southwest. Most of the Sangre de Cristo range is within national forest, and is therefore open to public enjoyment. Here, in summer, around Santa Fe and Taos, at an elevation of about 7,000 feet, may be seen the more common species, with rarer kinds progressively encountered in the ascent from life zone to life zone to timber line, or higher, where the barren ridges and crags are animated by Pipits and White-crowned Sparrows, and where one may possibly see Ptarmigan or Rosy Finches, along with coneys and whistling marmots. Wheeler Peak, elevation 13,160 feet, is the highest peak in the range.* Throughout the length of the range there are seven other peaks which reach above timber line, approximately 12,000 feet elevation. These additional peaks, listed from south northward, are: Lake Peak, 12,408 feet; Santa Fe Baldy, 12,629 feet; Pecos Baldy, 12,623 feet; North Truchas (Trout) Peak, 13,024 feet; Gold Hill, 12,660 feet; Latir (Baldy) Peak 12,043 feet; Costilla Peak, 12,583 feet. In addition, the range is peppered with peaks and ridges of only slightly lesser elevations. Here, in a distance of only a few ascending miles may be traversed five of the seven life zones, an elevation or zonal phenomenon.

Among the resident and summer-dwelling birds which may be observed in the various life zones of the Sangre de Cristo Range are:

UPPER SONORAN ZONE
(around 7,000 feet elevation)

Scrub Jay	Lazuli Bunting
Common Crow	Summer Tanager
Pinyon Jay	House Finch
Plain Titmouse	Sage Sparrow
Bullock's Oriole	Chipping Sparrow
Black-headed Grosbeak	Brewer's Sparrow
Blue Grosbeak	

TRANSITION ZONE
(Centering around 8,000 feet)

Sharp-shinned Hawk	Black-chinned
Cooper's Hawk	Hummingbird
Merriam's Turkey	Broad-tailed
Spotted Sandpiper	Hummingbird

---

* Wheeler Peak is also the highest in the entire Southwest. Humphrey's Peak, 12,611, in the San Francisco Range, is the highest in Arizona. Guadalupe Peak, 8,751 feet, in the Guadalupe Mountains is Texas' highest.

Acorn Woodpecker
Hairy Woodpecker
Dusky Flycatcher
Western Flycatcher
Steller's Jay
Black-billed Magpie
Common Raven
Black-capped Chickadee
Canyon Wren
Rock Wren

Virginia's Warbler
Audubon's Warbler
Grace's Warbler
Western Tanager
Hepatic Tanager
Green-tailed Towhee
Rufous-sided Towhee
Gray-headed Junco
Song Sparrow

CANADIAN ZONE
(8,500 to 10,000 feet)

Goshawk
Blue Grouse
Band-tailed Pigeon
Spotted Owl
Yellow-bellied Sapsucker
Williamson's Sapsucker
Olive-sided Flycatcher
Violet-green Swallow
Purple Martin
Clark's Nutcracker
Red-breasted Nuthatch
Brown Creeper
Dipper

Robin
Hermit Thrush
Western Bluebird
Townsend's Solitaire
Golden-crowned Kinglet
Ruby-crowned Kinglet
Black-headed Grosbeak
Evening Grosbeak
Orange-crowned Warbler
Cassin's Finch
Pine Siskin
Red Crossbill
Lincoln's Sparrow

HUDSONIAN ZONE
(10,000 to 12,000 feet)

Northern Three-toed Woodpecker
Gray Jay
Pine Grosbeak
Gray-headed Junco

ARCTIC ALPINE ZONE
(12,000 to 13,000 feet)

White-tailed Ptarmigan
Horned Lark
Water Pipit
Brown-capped Rosy Finch
White-crowned Sparrow

While some species may be observed, even at nesting time, within two or more zones, others cling rather closely to distinctive zonal conditions. In winter, most resident species are apt to move to the lower levels. The more hardy and adventurous bird student who reaches the higher elevations in winter may even have the thrill of seeing other Rosy Finches than the Brown-capped and possibly Bohemian Waxwings, and there is always the possibility for first records of unrecorded winter visitors.

TAOS. Elevation 7,000 feet. Summer and fall are the favored visiting periods in this area for the climate of the adjacent high country is severe and the few roads are often impassable in the winter. Most birds listed for the Sangre de Cristo Range may be observed by making field excursions from Taos, such as the over-mountain drive to Moreno Valley and the high Eagle Nest Reservoir, where fishing and bird-watching can be combined. This trip, which takes one near Wheeler Peak, may be continued down the Cimarron

ABOVE TIMBER LINE, WHEELER PEAK AMPHITHEATER
Photograph, July 4, 1955, by the Author

Canyon, a segment of which is owned by the State Game Department. Or from Moreno Valley the observer may swing northwest, over the Divide, into Red River Canyon, and back to Taos, by way of State Road 3. Accommodations are available at many points.

A drive northwest of Taos to the Rio Hondo or beyond the Rio Grande Gorge to the Tres Piedras section, through fragrant big sage *(Artemisia tridentata)*, usually affords an opportunity to see Sage Grouse, a species confined to the big sage type of the high northern section of the state. North of Taos in the scenic Hondo Canyon may be found Spotted Sandpiper, Violet-green Swallow, Black-capped Chickadee, Hermit Thrush, Dipper, Red Crossbill, among others. Continuing up the Canyon to Twining, elevation 9,000 feet, one may proceed by foot to the habitat of such rare species as the Northern Three-toed Woodpecker, Gray Jay, Evening and Pine Grosbeaks. The more hardy may wish to continue to timber line, where such nesting species as the Horned Lark, Water Pipit, White-crowned Sparrow, and, if one is fortunate, Ptarmigan and Rosy Finches may be seen.

Of comparable interest also is a drive southeast of Taos, along the Little Rio Grande, and over the mountains on State Road 3 to Tres Ritos. On this drive one is most apt to find Wild Turkey, Blue Grouse, and Band-tailed Pigeons. There are many other canyons accessible in the Taos section where a great variety of birds may be enjoyed amid mountain grandeur. Horseback travel is the most satisfactory means of reaching remote jeweled alpine lakes and timber-line rarities in birdlife. The open big sage mesas about Taos provide nesting grounds for Sage Grouse, Sage Thrashers, and Vesper and Brewer's Sparrows. The many irrigated fields, with weed- and willow-bordered canals are the summer retreats of Catbirds, Blackbirds, Yellowthroats, Lazuli Buntings, and many other species.

SANTA FE. While the city, elevation 7,000 feet, lies at the foot of the Sangre de Cristo Range, so precipitous are the adjacent slopes that few roads penetrate the heights, leaving the bird observer the choice of hiking or horseback riding to reach the higher elevations where birds of greatest interest are to be found. Santa Fe Canyon, lying east of the city, heading at the base of Lake Peak, (12,408 feet), is accessible for several miles by car, and rivals the Upper Pecos country, just over the range to the east, as a bird enthusiast's retreat. However, the canyon is a restricted watershed, being the source of the city's water supply, and only under most stringent restrictions are visitors permitted there. Fortunately, many species of interest, listed under Sangre de Cristo Range Birds, may be seen in the foothills about the city. The mesa rims adjacent to the Rio Grande Gorge to the west and northwest of Santa Fe provide nesting retreats for Turkey Vultures, Golden Eagles, Prairie Falcons and Common Ravens.

Since headquarters of the State Game and Fish Department is situated here, those not familiar with the Santa Fe area, or other sections of the state, can obtain from officials information as to where different species of birds may be seen, with instructions as to how to reach such places.

PECOS—COWLES AREA. The Upper Pecos River Canyon and watershed are of such outstanding importance to the recreation seeker and bird observer as to justify special consideration. Pecos, just off U.S. Highway 85, is the gateway to the canyon which, likewise, is the gateway into the vitals of the southern portion of the Sangre de Cristo Range, cleaving the range as it does into two lofty arms, thrusting southward to each side. Holy Ghost Camp Ground, 13 miles above Pecos, and the resort village of Cowles represent the limit of regular automobile travel up the canyon. Beyond these terminal points, one enters what is now the Pecos Wilderness Area (approximately 165,000 acres) accessible by hiking or horseback travel only, into dense forests of pine, fir, spruce, and aspen, mountain parks, lakes, and finally Pecos Baldy and the Truchas Peaks, with their crowns well above timber line. Within the sweep of this enchanting watershed, most of the birds recorded under the Sangre de Cristo Range list may be observed about the road's end or in the higher country. The Water Ouzel, or Dipper, is here conspicuous along the dashing, boulder-studded streams, and friendly Evening Grosbeaks thrill visitors about cabins and campgrounds. Trout fishing may be featured with bird watching. Accommodations for those not equipped for camping are locally available. In late summer one should be prepared for frequent thunderstorms and chilling rains. No other area is more favorably situated for combining bird study and peaceful recreation.

THE LAS VEGAS AREA. Las Vegas, elevation 6,435 feet, is the most convenient point from which to reach the southeastern portion of the Sangre de Cristo Mountains. There are several canyon approaches into the mountains, with access roads. Most birds listed for the Transition and Canadian Zones may be seen through the Las Vegas approach, although hiking or use of saddle horses must be relied upon in order to reach the higher elevations.

The Mora River Canyon, north and northeast of Las Vegas, particularly in the Watrous locality, where there are marshes and one artificial lake (Shoemaker), provides opportunity for observing marsh and water birds, both summer and winter. Magpies, Crows and Redwinged Blackbirds are to be found in abundance here, while the many mesas are the home of great numbers of Horned Larks.

CIMARRON—PHILMONT RANCH AREA. Cimarron, elevation 6,430 feet, is the gateway to the Sangre de Cristos from the northeast. The town is located at the entrance of the famous Cimarron Canyon. The canyon proper terminates at Eagle Nest Reservoir near Wheeler Peak. Fortunately for bird seeker and touring public, a 7½-mile segment of this canyon is within the Cimarron Canyon Wildlife Area of some 33,320 acres of Game Department-owned land. The canyon portion of the refuge, which has been developed and is maintained in the interest of recreation, is accessible by U.S. Highway 64. It is favored by a perennial clear stream which is the home of the Dipper, and where this most charming bird may be observed readily. Most of the birds listed for the Sangre de Cristo Range may be seen in the canyons or forests

and mountains which flank the canyon on either side.

South of Cimarron Canyon is Philmont Scout Ranch, consisting of approximately 127,000 acres of scenic grandeur: forests, canyon water courses, mountains, and wildlife. The varied topography, with elevations from 6,600 to almost 12,000 feet, provides one of the most widely diversified wildlife areas, in almost primitive state, in the entire country. More than a hundred species of birds have been recorded on the ranch, including practically all of the Sangre de Cristo Range breeding list, while about the headquarters of the ranch (elevation 6,600 feet) such summer dwellers as Barn Swallows, Say's Phoebes, Catbirds, Eastern Kingbirds, Western Kingbirds, Western Wood Pewees, Bullock's Orioles, Yellow-breasted Chats and Lesser Goldfinches may be seen. Minerals, trees, mammals, and birds are listed in the Ranch Field Guides provided for the benefit of the Scouts.

TUCUMCARI AREA. The Tucumcari section has much of interest for the bird hunter, both summer and winter. Conchas Reservoir, 31 miles northwest of the city, and source of water for the local U.S. Reclamation irrigation project, provides a popular recreation center where boating and fishing can be enjoyed along with bird watching. Winter concentrations of Bald Eagles are of special interest; at no other point in the Southwest have so many been recorded. There are as yet no nesting records, but in time they may breed on some of the many ledges that border the lake. The Eagles, as scavengers, seem to find ample subsistence in the form of dead fish, dead or crippled waterfowl, and remains of dead mammals of various sorts in the surrounding country. The Golden Eagle also occurs commonly in winter, and some nest in the vicinity of the lake. The lake attracts great numbers of Ducks during migration, while Herons, Whistling Swans, Geese, Gulls, and Terns can usually be seen at this time. Red-tailed Hawks, Prairie Falcons and Common Ravens nest in the cliffs and beneath overhanging ledges which border the lake, and Cliff Swallows nest in abundance, easily observed from boats on the lake. The rare Peregrine Falcon is often in evidence and no doubt it too will in time be recorded as a breeder. The section of the region, from Tucumcari north to the Colorado line, constitutes the principal range of the Rio Grande Turkey in the state.

An extensive sandhill belt, continuation of the Lesser Prairie Chicken range type to the south in Region 2, lies to the east and north of Tucumcari. This portion of the region contains the best Bobwhite habitat in the state. It is also one of the most highly favored Scaled Quail ranges to be found in the Southwest. The Agricultural Experiment Station, 3 miles northeast of Tucumcari, is an excellent place to see winter concentrations of the birds. The Swainson's Hawk breeds commonly, and Burrowing Owls have survived in greater numbers than in most other sections. North of the sand zone, typical high plains spread east and north from Rosebud, with some basins that are transformed into lakes during years of normal moisture. This section, treeless, except along the few watercourses, draining to the eastward, is a breeding ground for the Long-billed Curlew, Lark Bunting, and Cassin's Sparrow, while American Avocets and Black-necked Stilts can be found breeding about the lakes.

WAGON MOUND — SPRINGER AREA. The Wagon Mound—Springer section, elevation ranging around 6,000 feet, is, for the most part plain, mesa, and valley land favored by a rather liberal precipitation, both rain and snow. Springs and many natural lakes provide suitable habitat for water and shore birds. The State Game Department's Wagon Mound Waterfowl Area (740 acres, spring-fed) lying just north of Wagon Mound, is especially suitable for migrant shore birds of many species. It is also heavily utilized by Ducks, some of which remain to breed. Charette Lake Wildlife Area (830 acres) to the northwest, also Game Department owned, is visited by many migrating birds.

Favored by numerous other lakes and by grain fields, particularly in the Springer irrigated section, this portion of the region usually provides some of the best Goose and Duck hunting in the state. The agricultural section also provides fair Pheasant habitat.

CLAYTON—DRY CIMARRON SECTION. Clay-ton, as is indicated by the long bird list contributed by the Krehbiel-Cook team, is strategically located at a heavily utilized flyway junction. Many fall migrants continue southward striking the Pecos Valley while others swerve over the Texas Panhandle plains. Also of unusual interest is the west-east movement of certain song and insectivorous birds that follow this contradictory pattern, especially along the Dry Cimarron River, which drains to the eastward. This lateral movement includes such species as Yellow-shafted Flicker, Eastern Kingbird, Great Crested Flycatcher, Catbird, Brown Thrasher, Bobolink, and Common Grackle, few of which ever occur to the southward.

The wooded streams and valleys, with their marshes and meadowlands, west of Clayton, provide favorable nesting environment for a variety of species. The State Game Department's water impoundment, Clayton Lake, a few miles north of the city, fulfills an urgent need for migrating water and shore birds. The high, open country between Clayton and Des Moines is a regularly used nesting ground of the Mountain Plover. (For breeding birds of the Clayton area, see High Plains Sub-flyway list.)

The Upper Dry Cimarron drainage about and below Folsom, with its cottonwood-willow bottomlands and forested slopes and tablelands, is in sharp contrast to the remainder of the Clayton section. The topography is climaxed by Capulin Mountain National Monument, a conspicuous black cinder volcanic cone a few miles southwest of Folsom. Breeding birds in the Folsom area include Merriam's Turkeys, Redheaded and Lewis' Woodpeckers, Scrub Jays, Black-billed Magpies, Common Ravens, Pinyon Jays, Robins, and Yellow-breasted Chats. An "island" of Sharp-tailed Grouse precariously survives on Johnson Mesa and its wooded rims, between Folsom and Raton, the only place this bird is found south of Colorado.

REGION 4—NORTHWESTERN

Region 4 has a widely diversified topography from semidesert to high, well forested mesas and mountains. The San Juan Mountains lying between the Upper Rio Grande and the Chama River, adjacent to the Colorado line, contain much of the Canadian Zone type, including birds found at comparable elevations in the Sangre de Cristo Range. The area is of special interest to the bird observer, because of its affinity to the Colorado Rockies. The Chama River constitutes an important arm of the Rio Grande Watershed, while the San Juan and Zuñi Rivers, west of the Continental Divide, drain west to the Colorado. The Jemez Mountains, with elevations of more than 11,000 feet, dominate the eastern portion of the region.

Region 4 also includes a portion of the Rio Grande Valley, the topography of which is in sharp contrast to the surrounding mountains, with resident and summer-dwelling birds in keeping with the checkerboard habitat pattern.

ALBUQUERQUE AREA. Albuquerque (elevation approximately 5,000 feet) the metropolis of the state, is centrally located on the Rio Grande Sub-flyway, and is an important hub from which bird students and observers can operate. Not only are the heavily wooded bottomlands above and below the city easily accessible, but excursions can be made into the nearby forested mountains, for the most part within national forests, which are open for public enjoyment. Trips of a day or more may be made, over good roads, to the Sandia, Manzano, and Jemez Mountains. Many of the rarer breeding birds listed for the Sangre de Cristo Range may be seen in these mountains, while in the Rio Grande Valley lower-altitude species are common.

The most scenic trip and one that provides opportunity to make the acquaintance of a variety of birds, summer or winter, is the Sandia Mountain Loop Drive. The summit of the Sandias, elevation 10,678 feet, is reached by a good automobile road through a dense forest.

The Jemez Mountains, some 60 miles north and northwest of Albuquerque, are readily accessible by automobile roads; here trout fishing and bird study may well be combined. Motorists traveling in the more remote places in the Jemez country, however, should carry tire chains, as summer rains are frequent and unsurfaced roads are at times impassable without chains.

Less than 100 miles from Albuquerque, down the Rio Grande over U.S. Highway 85, is the Bosque del Apache Refuge (See Bosque del Apache Refuge List, Region 1), where great numbers of summer-dwelling and migrant birds may be seen, in season, within a short time and on a limited area. Here, as at other federal wildlife refuges, the refuge personnel can be of much assistance to the bird observer. The lakes in the Estancia Valley, southeast of Albuquerque, provide opportunity to see a great variety of shore birds, both breeders and migrants.

Since the University of New Mexico is located at Albuquerque, the visiting bird hunter and watcher can usually obtain dependable information from members of the Biology Department faculty as to when and where different kinds of birds may be observed to best advantage. The Regional Office of the U.S. Fish and Wildlife Service is also located in the city. Personnel of this service can be of much help to both local and visiting bird enthusiasts.

The following list contains species that can be found nesting in the Albuquerque section, embracing the Rio Grande Valley, Jemez and Sandia Mountains, and the Estancia Valley. The author is indebted to W. W. Hill and John N. Durrie of the University of New Mexico for their co-operation in compiling the list. (For a list of migrants, see Bosque del Apache Refuge.)

BREEDING BIRDS OF THE ALBUQUERQUE AREA

Snowy Egret	Sora
Least Bittern	American Coot
American Bittern	Snowy Plover
Mallard	Mountain Plover
Mexican Duck	Killdeer
Blue-winged Teal	Spotted Sandpiper
Turkey Vulture	Avocet
Goshawk	Black-necked Stilt
Cooper's Hawk	Band-tailed Pigeon
Red-tailed Hawk	Mourning Dove
Swainson's Hawk	Yellow-billed Cuckoo
Ferruginous Hawk	Roadrunner
Golden Eagle	Barn Owl
Sparrow Hawk	Screech Owl
Scaled Quail	Flammulated Owl
Gambel's Quail	Great Horned Owl
Virginia Rail	Pygmy Owl

Burrowing Owl
Spotted Owl
Long-eared Owl
Poor-will
Common Nighthawk
Broad-tailed
    Hummingbird
Red-shafted Flicker
Red-headed Woodpecker
Lewis' Woodpecker
Ladder-backed
    Woodpecker
Eastern Kingbird
Western Kingbird
Cassin's Kingbird
Ash-throated Flycatcher
Black Phoebe
Say's Phoebe
Western Flycatcher
Western Wood Pewee
Horned Lark
Barn Swallow
Cliff Swallow
Steller's Jay
Scrub Jay
Common Raven
Common Crow
Pinyon Jay
Mountain Chickadee
Common Bushtit
White-breasted Nuthatch
Pygmy Nuthatch
Brown Creeper
House Wren

Canyon Wren
Rock Wren
Mockingbird
Curve-billed Thrasher
Robin
Hermit Thrush
Western Bluebird
Blue-gray Gnatcatcher
Loggerhead Shrike
Virginia's Warbler
Yellow Warbler
Audubon's Warbler
Yellowthroat
Yellow-breasted Chat
Eastern Meadowlark
Western Meadowlark
Redwinged Blackbird
Scott's Oriole
Bullock's Oriole
Boat-tailed Grackle
Brown-headed Cowbird
Western Tanager
Summer Tanager
Black-headed Grosbeak
Blue Grosbeak
Lazuli Bunting
House Finch
Lesser Goldfinch
Rufous-sided Towhee
Brown Towhee
Black-throated Sparrow
Chipping Sparrow
Brewer's Sparrow
Song Sparrow

LOS ALAMOS—ESPAÑOLA AREA. Los Alamos, America's atomic research center, is situated in the east side of the Jemez Mountains, elevation 7,300 feet. This area is of unusual interest because of the varied types of bird habitats over a comparatively limited district, from about 5,660 feet in the Rio Grande Valley, to 11,252 feet (Redondo Peak) a few miles west of Los Alamos. The Christmas Bird Count for Española is also of interest in that it includes some species rarely noted as far north at this season.

ESPAÑOLA CHRISTMAS BIRD COUNT

JANUARY 2, 1955

Made in a 7½-mile radius centering on the Rio Grande Bridge at Española, 7:30 A.M. to 5 P.M. Mostly cloudy. Temperature 20 to 42°. Snow on ground at higher elevations. Total party hours 42. Total party miles 118 (30 on foot, 88 by car). (See *Audubon Field Notes,* April 1955.)

Great Blue Heron	1
Mallard	7
Common Goldeneye	13
Bufflehead	2
Common Merganser	2
Sharp-shinned Hawk	2
Cooper's Hawk	1
Red-tailed Hawk	2
Marsh Hawk	3
Sparrow Hawk	8
Scaled Quail	7
Ring-necked Pheasant	3
Killdeer	5
Common Snipe	5
Western Sandpiper	1
Mourning Dove	14
Belted Kingfisher	7
Red-shafted Flicker	34
Lewis' Woodpecker	45
Hairy Woodpecker	1
Say's Phoebe	3
Steller's Jay	1
Scrub Jay	2
Black-billed Magpie	76
Common Raven	9
Common Crow	8
Black-capped Chickadee	5
Mountain Chickadee	8
White-breasted Nuthatch	2
Brown Creeper	1
Bewick's Wren	4
Sage Thrasher	2
Robin	473
Western Bluebird	25
Mountain Bluebird	161
Townsend's Solitaire	15
Ruby-crowned Kinglet	1
Cedar Waxwing	2
Loggerhead Shrike	2
Starling	21
Myrtle Warbler	1
Audubon's Warbler	1
House Sparrow	241
Western Meadowlark	59
Redwinged Blackbird	70
Brewer's Blackbird	16
Evening Grosbeak	20
Cassin's Finch	2
House Finch	19
Pine Siskin	80
Lesser Goldfinch	71
Rufous-sided Towhee	2
Oregon Junco (Pink-sided 19)	205
Gray-headed Junco	156
White-crowned Sparrow	87

| White-throated Sparrow | 1 |
| Song Sparrow | 25 |

Total 57 species (1 additional sub-species); about 2,040 individuals. (Seen during week, Canada Goose, 20.) Carl W. Bjorklund, Marilyn Bjorklund, Marion Gibbs, Leslie F. Hawkins, W. Burton Lewis, M. Vincent Mowbray, Joseph D. Pickard, John Ruth, Carl E. Snider, Patricia R. Snider (Compiler). Los Alamos Bird Club.

THE CHAMA-PARKVIEW SECTION. Chama (7,860 feet) is located near the head of the Chama River and is widely known as a summer recreational center, with much of interest to the birding public. Ten-thousand-foot Cumbres Pass, on the Colorado line, a few miles northeast of Chama, known for deep winter snow packs, is the source of many trout streams. The adjacent slopes are of interest to the summer bird observer because of the abundance of Rufous, Broad-tailed, and Calliope Hummingbirds that congregate there when the mountain slopes and meadows are ablaze with brilliant flowers. Dippers are common along the streams. Such species as Goshawk, Northern Three-toed Woodpecker, Gray Jay and Clark's Nutcracker may be seen any time. This section constitutes one of the most important Blue Grouse ranges in the state. The numerous small lakes near Canjilon are especially favorable breeding retreats for Ducks and marsh birds, while Spotted Sandpipers, Williamson's Sapsuckers, Lewis', Downy, and Hairy Woodpeckers, Hermit Thrushes, Mountain Bluebirds, Townsend's Solitaires, Warbling Vireos, Red Crossbills, Gray-headed Juncos, Lincoln's and Song Sparrows nest commonly.

Parkview is a preferred bird-watching station. One of the State Game Department's most important fish cultural stations, with its extensive meadowlands, is located a mile below the village. Yellow-headed, Redwinged and Brewer's Blackbirds, and Savannah Sparrows animate the meadows in summer and it is the only place where Bobolinks have been found nesting in the state. Among the willows that border the meadows Catbirds, Yellow-breasted Chats and Lazuli Buntings can be seen at nesting time.

The alpine lakes, lying in the lap of the Continental Divide, west of Parkview—Burford, Stone, Horse, and La Jara—are among the most important water and marsh bird nesting lakes in the state. Burford Lake, with its several arms, bays, and a shoreline of approximately 14 miles, is situated on the Jicarilla Apache Indian Reservation and is under joint administration of the U.S. Indian Service and the U.S. Fish and Wildlife Service. Because of its high elevation, approximately 8,000 feet, the lake provides suitable nesting environment, such as is found at lower altitudes much farther north, for both a variety and an abundance of water and marsh birds. It is one of the few places where the Redhead and Canvasback nest in the state. Great numbers of Mallard, Gadwall, Teal, and Ruddy Ducks breed here, while the Mexican Duck nests sparingly. Eared and Pied-billed Grebes and Coots also nest in great numbers. Breeding marsh birds include Black-crowned Night Heron, American Bittern, Virginia Rail, Sora, Long-billed Marsh Wren, Yellowthroat, Yellow-headed, Redwinged and Brewer's Blackbirds. In the meadows and surrounding big sage ridges may be found Sage Grouse, Sage Thrashers, Meadowlarks, Savannah, Sage and Vesper Sparrows, while on the wooded slopes and in adjacent forests Merriam's Turkeys, Lewis' Woodpeckers, Common Ravens, Black-billed Magpies, Violet-green Swallows and Purple Martins may be seen. Both Peregrine and Prairie Falcons nest sparingly in the great sandstone cliffs east of the lake.

AZTEC—FARMINGTON AREA. The fertile San Juan and Animas River Valleys of extreme northwestern New Mexico constitute one of the garden spots of the state. Farmington, 5,300-feet elevation, county seat of San Juan County, is the principal town. The timbered valleys, orchards, marshes, ponds, and lakes provide varied habitats for a variety of breeding birds including:

Black-crowned	Robin
Night Heron	Yellowthroat
American Bittern	Yellow-breasted Chat
Barn Swallow	Redwinged Blackbird
Cassin's Kingbird	Bullock's Oriole
Magpie	Brewer's Blackbird
Common Crow	Boat-tailed Grackle

Bewick's Wren	Lazuli Bunting
Rock Wren	Sage Sparrow
Mockingbird	Brewer's Sparrow

GALLUP AREA. Gallup, elevation 6,500 feet, situated near the Arizona line on transcontinental U.S. Highway 66, is the principal town of this section. Except during migration, both species and numbers of birds are limited in the immediate vicinity of Gallup, but in the nearby forests and mountains many birds of interest may be found, and the summer climate is delightful for the enjoyment of field trips.

The Chuska Mountains, approximately 30 miles long and 8 to 10 miles wide, lying north of Gallup, within the Navajo Indian Reservation, with a rather uniform elevation of about 9,000 feet, constitute an "island" of Transition and Canadian Life Zones in vivid contrast to surounding mesa and valley sage lands. This heavily forested wonderland, with its springs and many lakes, formerly provided favorable habitat for a great variety of birds, including waterfowl. Although the potential value for birds and other wildlife is still high, long and excessive use by livestock has been disastrous to ground cover and hence to all wildlife.

Breeding birds of the Chuska Mountains include: Goshawk, Sharp-shinned Hawk; Lewis', Hairy and Northern Three-toed Woodpeckers; Western Flycatcher; Violet-green Swallow, Purple Martin; Clark's Nutcracker; Brown Creeper; Hermit Thrush; Mountain Bluebird; Ruby-crowned Kinglet, Pine Siskin, and Gray-headed Junco.

The Merriam's Turkey, which had become extirpated from the Chuska Mountains, has been restored through transplanted stock by the State Game Department.

The Zuñi Mountains, more in the nature of heavily forested tableland than the typical rugged Rocky Mountain type, lie south and southeast of Gallup. This range is a segment of the Cibola National Forest and is of special interest to bird observers because here a few species, including Buff-breasted and Coues' Flycatchers, Olive Warbler and Painted Redstart, reach the most northern

extension of their breeding ranges. Other species that may be found in the western part of the mountains include Lewis' and Hairy Woodpeckers, Yellow-bellied Sapsucker, Western Wood Pewee, White-breasted and Pygmy Nuthatches, Western Tanager, Black-headed Grosbeak, Green-tailed and Rufous-sided Towhees.

GRANTS AREA. Grants, 6,460 feet elevation, is located on Bluewater Creek and U.S. Highway 66, about halfway between Albuquerque and the New Mexico—Arizona line. Grants is also conveniently situated between two divisions of the Cibola National Forest, Mount Taylor to the northeast and the Zuñi to the west and southwest. The bird observer may also include points of historical interest in his trips afield. One of the most extensive lava beds in the Southwest lies south of Grants. Within this rugged spread of black lava, or malpais, are the famous Ice Caves. A few miles west of the Ice Caves is Inscription Rock (El Morro) National Monument. Boating, fishing and birding may be enjoyed at Bluewater Lake, a few miles northwest of Grants.

Mount Taylor, 11,389 feet, the highest in the western half of the state, northeast of Grants, dominates the skyline from all directions. On the extensive 9,000-foot mesa, lying north of the peak, Horned Larks, Eastern Meadowlarks, and Vesper Sparrows nest commonly. On and about the peak such breeding birds as Merriam's Turkey; Band-tailed Pigeon; Great Horned and Long-eared Owls; Acorn, Lewis' and Hairy Woodpeckers; Yellow-bellied and Williamson's Sapsuckers; Violet-green Swallow; Purple Martin; Common Raven, and Western Bluebird may be seen.

Along the east rim of the lava beds are honeycombed sandstone ledges and walled canyons where the Golden Eagle, Prairie Falcon, Common Raven, Say's Phoebe and the Rock Wren find preferred nesting places. Bailey reported Long-billed Marsh Wrens in considerable numbers at the San Rafael spring and marshes, south of Grants, under conditions that indicated they had nested.

GLOSSARY

ADULT: A bird which has acquired complete adult plumage.

AERIE: The nest of a bird of prey, such as a Falcon or an Eagle.

A. O. U. CHECK-LIST: *Check-list of North American Birds*, prepared by a committee of the American Ornithologists' Union.

AQUATIC: Pertaining to or living in water.

ARBOREAL: Pertaining to or living in trees.

AXILLARIES: Fan-shaped tufts of feathers, usually soft and elongated, growing from the "armpit" or axilla.

BARS: Transverse lines across the body (see STRIPES).

BEND OF THE WING: The front projection of the folded wing.

CERE: The soft, swollen area of naked skin, in which the nostrils open, as in pigeons.

COVERTS: The feathers covering the bases of flight feathers of the wings and tail of a bird.

CREST: A more or less lengthened, erectile, or permanently erect tuft of feathers on top of the head.

CRISSUM: The feathers between the lower tail-coverts and the anal region.

CROWN: The top part of the head.

DECURVED: Curved downward.

DISC, OR DISK: A set of radiating feathers, surrounding the eye, as in the Owls.

DORSAL: Pertaining to the back.

EAR-TUFTS: Erectile tufts of elongated feathers on each side of the crown, giving the appearance of external ears, as in Owls.

EDGE OF THE WING: The anterior border of the wing.

FERRUGINOUS: Rust colored.

FLANKS: The hindmost parts of the sides of the body.

FRONTAL: Pertaining to the forehead.

GAPE: The opening of the mouth.

GENUS: As pertaining to ornithology, a group of birds within a family or subfamily (Plural: GENERA).

GORGET: An ornamental throat-patch, as the gorget of a Hummingbird.

HOODED: Having the head conspicuously different in color from the rest of the plumage.

HYBRID: The offspring of parents of different species.

IMMACULATE: Without spots or markings.

IMMATURE: Before having acquired complete adult plumage.

INSECTIVOROUS: Feeding upon insects.

INTERSCAPULARS: The feathers between the scapulars, on the back.

IRIDESCENT: With changeable colors which vary according to the light.

IRIS: The colored circle surrounding the pupil of the eye.

JUVENILE: In plumage, that following the nestling down.

LANCEOLATE: Lance-shaped, tapering gradually to a point.

LATERAL: At or towards the side.

LOBATE, LOBED: With membranous flaps, as the toes of a coot.

LORES: The area between the eye and bill.

MANDIBLES: The two members forming the bill, the upper and the lower mandible.

MASKED: Having the anterior part of the head colored differently from the adjoining plumage.

MELANISTIC: A state of coloration in plumage resulting from excess of black or dark pigment in which the normal colors are replaced by black or dusky, as in some Hawks.

METALLIC: Applied to colors having a brilliant appearance, like burnished metal.

MIGRATION: Periodic, spring and fall, usually north or south movements.

MOLT: The periodic shedding or casting of the feathers.

MONOGAMOUS: Birds which pair, or have a single mate in a season.

MOUSTACHE: Any conspicuous stripe on the side of the head beneath the eye.

NAPE: The upper part of the hind-neck just below the base of the skull.

NOSTRIL: The opening in the upper part of the bill.

NUCHAL: Pertaining to the nape.

NUPTIAL PLUMAGE: Ornamental feathers acquired at the approach of the breeding season and lost at its close.

OCCIPITAL: Pertaining to the hind-neck or occiput, the back part of the skull.

OLIVACEOUS: Of an olive-green color.

ORBITAL RING: A border of color encircling the eye.

PASSERINE: Relating to an order of land birds including the most highly developed species.

PECTORAL: Relating to the breast.

POLYGAMOUS: Mating with many females.

POSTNUPTIAL: Occurring after the breeding season.

PRIMARIES: The principal feathers or quills on the distal joint of a bird's wing.

QUILL: One of the primaries.

RECURVED: Curved upward.

RUFOUS: Brownish-red.

SCAPULARS: The group of feathers on either side of the back, above the wing.

SECONDARIES: A series of feathers attached to the second joint of the wing, adjacent to the primaries, that, with the primaries, constitute the main flight feathers.

SERRATE: Toothed like a saw.

SPATULATE: Shaped like a spatula or spoon.

SPECIES: Related individuals with differences that distinguish them from others.

SPECULUM: A mirrorlike or brightly colored band, usually across the secondaries, on the wings of certain ducks.

STRIPES: Lines running vertically (lengthwise) instead of horizontally across the body of the bird (see BARS).

SUBSPECIES: A division of a species.

SUPERCILIARY: A streak of color over the eye.

TAIL COVERTS: The feathers which cover the bases of the tail feathers.

UNDER-TAIL COVERTS: The coverts of the under surface of the tail, or tail linings.

UPPER-TAIL COVERTS: The feathers covering the bases of the tail feathers.

UPPER-WING COVERTS: The feathers covering the bases of the flight feathers.

VERMICULATED: Marked with irregular fine lines, like the tracks of small worms.

VINACEOUS: Wine-colored.

WASHED: Thinly overlaid with a different color.

NOTE: A diagram of the external topography of the Meadowlark is given on page 15.

COLOR PLATES

III

Left: Snowy Egret. *Right:* Common Egret.

IV

Green-winged Teal, female *(above)* and male.

V

Cinnamon Teal, male *(above)* and female.

VI

Ruddy Duck, female (*above*), male, and ducklings.

VII

Top row: Sparrow Hawk, immature; Sparrow Hawk; Swainson's Hawk.
Middle: Red-tailed Hawk. *Bottom:* Ferruginous Hawk.

VIII

Above: Golden Eagle in flight, immature; Golden Eagle.
Below: Bald Eagle, immature; Bald Eagle.

IX

Peregrine in flight; Peregrine.

X

Blue Grouse, two females and male.

XI

Scaled Quail, male (*above*) and female.

XII

Gambel's Quail, male (*above*), and female with downy young.

XIII

Ring-necked Pheasant, male (*above*) and female.

XIV

Merriam's Wild Turkey, male and female.

XV

Band-tailed Pigeon, female (*left*) and male.

XVI

Top row: Broad-tailed Hummingbird; Rufous Hummingbird. *Middle:* Calliope Hummingbird; Black-chinned Hummingbird. *Bottom:* Rivoli's Hummingbird.

XVII

Top row: Downy Woodpecker; Lewis' W.; Northern Three-toed W.
2nd row: Hairy W.; Acorn W. *Middle:* Red-shafted Flicker.
3rd row: Arizona W.; Ladder-backed W. *Bottom:* Red-headed W.;
Williamson's Sapsucker; Yellow-bellied S. *(Females left, males right.)*

XVIII
Scissor-tailed Flycatcher, male (*above*) and female.

XIX

Vermilion Flycatcher, male *(above)* and female.

XX

Above: Gray Jay; Clark's Nutcracker; Steller's Jay.
Below: Scrub Jay; Pinyon Jay.

XXI
Common Crow *(above)*; White-necked Raven *(left)*; Common Raven.

XXII

Robin, male, and female in nest.

XXIII

Top row: Wilson's Warbler; Yellowthroat; Yellow W. *2nd row:* Grace's W.; Yellow-breasted Chat; Virginia's W. *3rd row:* MacGillivray's W.; Black-throated Gray W. *Bottom:* Red-faced W.; Orange-crowned W.; Lucy's W. *(Females left, males right.)*

XXIV
Western Meadowlark.

XXV

Above: Yellow-headed Blackbird, female and male.
Below: Redwinged Blackbird, female and male.

XXVI

From top down: Hooded Oriole, female and male;
Scott's Oriole, female and male.

XXVII

Bullock's Oriole, female (*above*), male, and nest with young.

XXVIII

From top down: Western Tanager, female and male;
Hepatic Tanager, male and female.

XXIX

Top row: Pine Grosbeak; Red Crossbill. *Middle left:* Cardinal.
Middle right above: Blue Grosbeak. *Middle right below:* Cassin's Finch.
Bottom: Black-headed Grosbeak; House Finch.
(Males in foreground, except Black-headed Grosbeak.)

XXX

Pyrrhuloxia, male (*above*) and female.

XXXI
Lazuli Bunting, male (*above*) and female.

XXXII

Painted Bunting, female *(left)*, male, and nest with young.

XXXIII
Evening Grosbeak, male *(above)* and female.

XXXIV

Top row: Brewer's Sparrow; Cassin's S.; Lincoln's S.; Black-chinned S.
2nd row: Chipping S.; Savannah S.; Rufous-crowned S.; Sage S.
Bottom row: Vesper S.; Song S.; Lark S.

INDEX

INDEX